Advanced Functions

Advanced Functions

Series Authors and Senior Consultants
Chris Kirkpatrick • Marian Small

Authors
Barbara Alldred • Crystal Chilvers • Beverly Farahani • Kristina Farentino

Angelo Lillo • Ian Macpherson • John Rodger • Susanne Trew

NELSON EDUCATION

NELSON EDUCATION

Advanced Functions

Series Authors and Senior Consultants
Chris Kirkpatrick, Marian Small

Authors
Barbara Alldred,
Crystal Chilvers, Beverly Farahani,
Kristina Farentino, Angelo Lillo,
Ian Macpherson, John Rodger,
Susanne Trew

Contributing Authors
Tom Gamblin, Peter Thompson

Director of Publishing
Kevin Martindale

General Manager, Mathematics, Science, and Technology
Lenore Brooks

Publisher, Mathematics
Colin Garnham

Associate Publisher, Mathematics
Sandra McTavish

Managing Editor, Development
David Spiegel

Product Manager
Linda Krepinsky

Project Manager
Alisa Yampolsky

Contributing Editor
Dave Wright

Assistant Editor
Caroline Winter

Editorial Assistant
Kelly Schultz

Executive Director, Content and Media Production
Renate McCloy

Director, Content and Media Production
Sujata Singh

Senior Content Production Editor
Debbie Davies-Wright

Copy Editor
Paula Pettitt-Townsend

Proofreaders
Christine Hobberlin
Montgomery Kersell

Indexer
Andrew Little

Production Manager
Helen Jager-Locsin

Design Director
Ken Phipps

Interior Design
Peter Papayanakis

Cover Design
Bill Smith Studio

Cover Image
Copyright Veer

Production Services
Pre-Press PMG

Director, Asset Management Services
Vicki Gould

Photo/Permissions Researcher
Julie Pratt

Printer
Transcontinental Printing Ltd.

Reviewers and Advisory Panel

Table of Contents

Functions: Characteristics and Properties

▶ GOALS

You will be able to

- Review and consolidate your knowledge of the properties and characteristics of functions and their inverses

- Review and consolidate your knowledge of graphing functions using transformations

- Investigate the characteristics of piecewise functions

? What type of function can be used to model the height of a golf ball during its flight, and what information about the relationship between height and time can be found using this function?

Study Aid

- For help, see the Review of Essential Skills found at the Nelson Advanced Functions website.

Question	Appendix
2	R-3
3	R-8, R-12

SKILLS AND CONCEPTS *You Need*

1. Evaluate $f(x) = x^2 + 3x - 4$ for each of the following values.

   a) $f(2)$ b) $f(-1)$ c) $f\left(\dfrac{1}{4}\right)$ d) $f(a + 1)$

2. Factor each of the following expressions.

   a) $x^2 + 2xy + y^2$ c) $(x + y)^2 - 64$
   b) $5x^2 - 16x + 3$ d) $ax + bx - ay - by$

3. State the **transformations** that are applied to each **parent function**, resulting in the given transformed function. Sketch the graphs of the parent function and transformed function.

   a) $f(x) = x^2,\ y = f(x - 3) + 2$ c) $g(x) = \sin x,\ y = -2g(0.5x)$
   b) $f(x) = 2^x,\ y = f(x - 1) + 2$ d) $g(x) = \sqrt{x},\ y = -2g(2x)$

4. State the **domain** and **range** of each function.

   a)
   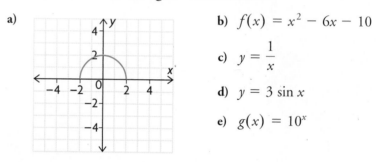

   b) $f(x) = x^2 - 6x - 10$

   c) $y = \dfrac{1}{x}$

   d) $y = 3 \sin x$

   e) $g(x) = 10^x$

5. Which of the following represent functions? Explain.

   a)
   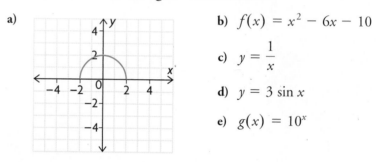

   b) $y = 2(x - 1)^2 + 3$

   c) $y = \pm\sqrt{x} - 4$

   d) $y = 2^x - 4$

   e) $y = \cos\left(2(x - 30°)\right) + 1$

6. Consider the **relation** $y = x^3$.
   a) If $(2, n)$ is a point on its graph, determine the value of n.
   b) If $(m, 20)$ is a point on its graph, determine m correct to two decimal places.

7. A function can be described or defined in many ways. List these different ways, and explain how each can be used to determine whether a relation is a function.

APPLYING *What You Know*

Modelling the Height of a Football

During a football game, a football is thrown by a quarterback who is 2 m tall. The football travels through the air for 4 s before it is caught by the wide receiver.

? What function can be used to model the height of the football above the ground over time?

A. Explain why the variables time, t, in seconds and height, $h(t)$, in metres are good choices to model this situation.

B. What is $h(0)$? What does it mean in the context of this situation?

C. What happens at $t = 2$ s?

D. What happens at $t = 4$ s?

E. Explain why each of the following functions is *not* a good model for this situation. Support your claim with reasons and a well-labelled sketch.

   i) $h(t) = -5t(t - 4)$
   ii) $h(t) = -5(t - 4)^2 + 2$
   iii) $h(t) = 5t^2 + 4t - 3$

F. Determine a model that can be used to represent the height of the football, given this additional information:
  • The ball reached a maximum height of 22 m.
  • The wide receiver who caught the ball is also 2 m tall.

G. Use your model from part F to graph the height of the football over the duration of its flight.

YOU WILL NEED

- graph paper
- graphing calculator (optional)

Represent and describe functions and their characteristics.

LEARN ABOUT the Math

Jonathan and Tina are building an outdoor skating rink. They have enough materials to make a rectangular rink with an area of about 1800 m², and they do not want to purchase any additional materials. They know, from past experience, that a good rink must be approximately 30 m longer than it is wide.

? What dimensions should they use to make their rink?

EXAMPLE 1	**Representing a situation using a mathematical model**

Determine the dimensions that Jonathan and Tina should use to make their rink.

Solution A: Using an algebraic model

Let x represent the length. Let y represent the width.

$$A = xy$$
$$1800 = xy$$
$$\frac{1800}{x} = y$$

We know the area must be 1800 m², so if we let the width be the **independent variable**, we can write an expression for the length.

The width, in terms of x, is $\frac{1800}{x}$.

Let $f(x)$ represent the difference between the length and the width.

$$f(x) = x - \frac{1800}{x},$$

where $f(x) = 30$.

$$x - \frac{1800}{x} = 30$$

Using **function notation**, write an equation for the difference in length and width. The relation is a **function** because each input produces a unique output. In this case the difference or value of the function must be 30.

$$x(x) - x\left(\frac{1800}{x}\right) = x(30)$$

> To solve the equation, multiply all the terms in the equation by the lowest common denominator, x, to eliminate any rational expressions.

$$x^2 - 1800 = 30x$$
$$x^2 - 30x - 1800 = 0$$
$$(x - 60)(x + 30) = 0$$

> This results in a quadratic equation. Rearrange the equation so that it is in the form $ax^2 + bx + c = 0$. Factor the left side.

$$x - 60 = 0 \text{ or } x + 30 = 0$$
$$x = 60 \text{ or } x = -30$$

> Solve for each factor. $x = -30$ is outside the domain of the function, since length cannot be negative. This is an inadmissible solution.

The length is 60 m.

$$y = \frac{1800}{60} = 30$$

> Calculate the width.

The width is 30 m.

The dimensions that are 30 m apart and will produce an area of 1800 m^2 are 60 m $\times$ 30 m.

Solution B: Using a numerical model

Let l represent the length. Let w represent the width.

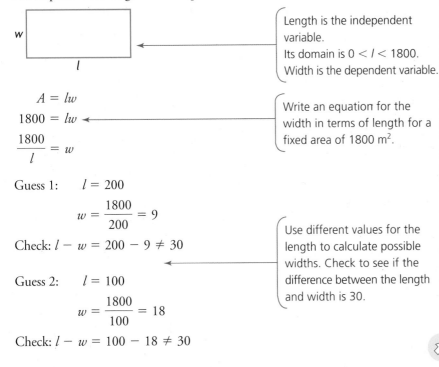

> Length is the independent variable.
> Its domain is $0 < l < 1800$.
> Width is the dependent variable.

$$A = lw$$
$$1800 = lw$$
$$\frac{1800}{l} = w$$

> Write an equation for the width in terms of length for a fixed area of 1800 m^2.

Guess 1: $\quad l = 200$

$$w = \frac{1800}{200} = 9$$

Check: $l - w = 200 - 9 \neq 30$

Guess 2: $\quad l = 100$

$$w = \frac{1800}{100} = 18$$

Check: $l - w = 100 - 18 \neq 30$

> Use different values for the length to calculate possible widths. Check to see if the difference between the length and width is 30.

Area (m²)	Length (m)	Width (m)	Length – Width
1800	100	18	82
1800	90	20	70
1800	80	22.5	57.5
1800	70	25.71	44.29
1800	60	30	30
1800	50	36	14
1800	40	45	−5
1800	30	60	−30
1800	20	90	−70

Create a table of values to investigate the difference between the length and the width for a variety of lengths.

The dimensions that are 30 m apart and produce an area of 1800 m² are 60 m × 30 m.

A function can also be represented with a graph. A graph provides a visual display of how the variables in the function are related.

Solution C: Using a graphical model

Let x represent the length. Let y represent the width.

$$A = xy$$
$$1800 = xy$$
$$\frac{1800}{x} = y$$

Using length (x) as the independent variable, write an expression for width (y).

The width, in terms of x, is $\frac{1800}{x}$.

Let $f(x)$ represent the difference between the dimensions.

$$f(x) = x - \frac{1800}{x}$$

Determine the appropriate window settings to graph $f(x)$ on a graphing calculator.

The value for x (length of rink) will be positive but surely less than 75 m, so we use Xmin = 0 and Xmax = 75.

We use the same settings for the range of f(x), for simplicity.

```
WINDOW
Xmin=0
Xmax=75
Xscl=10
Ymin=0
Ymax=75
Yscl=10
Xres=1
```

Graph the difference function.

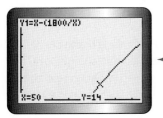

Use the TRACE feature on the graph to investigate points with the ordered pairs (length, length − width) on $f(x)$.

A length of 50 m gives a 14 m difference between the length and the width.

Determine the length that exceeds the width by 30 m.

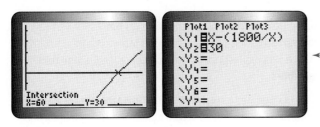

To determine the length that is 30 m longer than the width, graph $g(x) = 30$ in Y_2 and locate the point of intersection for $g(x)$ and $f(x)$.

The dimensions that are 30 m apart and produce an area of 1800 m² are 60 m × 30 m.

Reflecting

A. Would the function change if width was used as the independent variable instead of length? Explain.

B. Is it necessary to restrict the domain and range in this problem? Explain.

C. Why was it useful to think of the relationship between the length and the width as a function to solve this problem?

APPLY the Math

EXAMPLE 2 | Using reasoning to decide whether a relation is a function

Decide whether each of the following relations is a function. State the domain and range.

a)

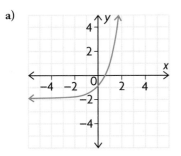

b) $y = \dfrac{1}{x^2}$

c)

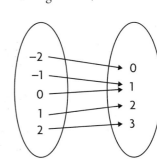

Solution

a)

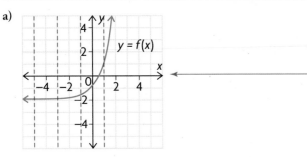

Apply the **vertical line test**. Any vertical line drawn on the graph of a function passes through, at most, a single point. This indicates that each number in the domain corresponds to only one number in the range, which is the condition for the relation to be a function.

The graph represents an **exponential function**.

$$D = \{x \in \mathbf{R}\}$$
$$R = \{y \in \mathbf{R}\,|\,y > -2\}$$

Since the graph of this function has no breaks, or vertical **asymptotes**, and continues indefinitely in both the positive and negative direction, its domain consists of all the **real numbers**.

The function has a **horizontal asymptote** defined by the equation $y = -2$. All its values lie above this horizontal line.

b)

x	-3	-2	-1	0	1	2	3
f(x)	$\frac{1}{9}$	$\frac{1}{4}$	1	undefined	1	$\frac{1}{4}$	$\frac{1}{9}$

Create a table of values.

The table indicates that each number in the domain corresponds to only one number in the range.

$f(x) = \frac{1}{x^2}$ is a function.

$$D = \{x \in \mathbf{R}\,|\,x \neq 0\}$$
$$R = \{y \in \mathbf{R}\,|\,y > 0\}$$

$f(x) = \frac{1}{x^2}$ has a **vertical asymptote** defined by $x = 0$. Its domain consists of all the real numbers, except 0. It has a horizontal asymptote defined by the equation $y = 0$. All its values are positive, since x is squared, so they lie above this horizontal line.

c)

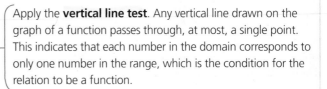

The mapping diagram indicates that each number in the domain corresponds to only one number in the range.

A function can have converging arrows but cannot have diverging arrows in a mapping diagram.

This is a function.

$$D = \{-2, -1, 0, 1, 2\}$$
$$R = \{0, 1, 2, 3\}$$

The first oval represents the elements found in the domain. The second oval represents the elements found in the range.

EXAMPLE 3 Using reasoning to determine the domain and range of a function

Naill rides a Ferris wheel that has a diameter of 6 m. The axle of the Ferris wheel is 4 m above the ground. The Ferris wheel takes 90 s to make one complete rotation, and Naill rides for 10 rotations. What are the domain and range of the function that models Naill's height above the ground, in terms of time, while he rides the Ferris wheel?

Solution

$h(t) = a \sin \left[k(t - d) \right] + c$

or

$h(t) = a \cos \left[k(t - d) \right] + c$

This situation involves circular motion, which can be modelled by a sine or cosine function.

Examine the conditions on the independent variable time to determine the domain. Time cannot be negative, so the lower boundary is 0. The wheel rotates once every 90 s, and Naill rides for 10 complete rotations.

$90 \times 10 = 900$

The upper boundary is 900 s.

$D = \{ t \in \mathbf{R} \mid 0 \le t \le 900 \}$

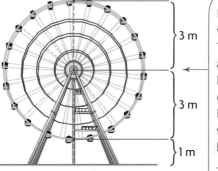

3 m

3 m

1 m

Examine the conditions on the dependent variable height to determine the range. The radius of the wheel is 3 m. Since the axle is located 4 m above the ground, the lowest height that Naill can be above the ground is the difference between the height of the axle and the radius of the wheel: $4 - 3 = 1$ m. This is the lower boundary of the range.

The greatest height he reaches is the sum of the height of the axle and the radius of the wheel: $4 + 3 = 7$ m. This is the upper boundary of the range.

$R = \{ h(t) \in \mathbf{R} \mid 1 \le h(t) \le 7 \}$

In Summary

Key Ideas

- A function is a relation in which there is a unique output for each input. This means that each value of the independent variable (the domain) must correspond to one, and only one, value of the dependent variable (the range).
- Functions can be represented graphically, numerically, or algebraically.

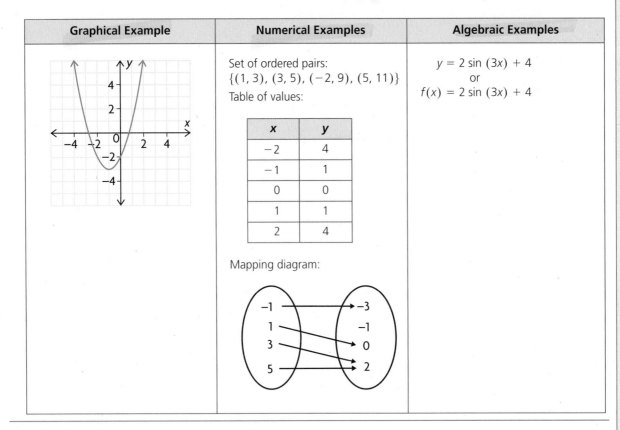

Graphical Example	Numerical Examples	Algebraic Examples

Numerical Examples

Set of ordered pairs:
$\{(1, 3), (3, 5), (-2, 9), (5, 11)\}$
Table of values:

x	y
-2	4
-1	1
0	0
1	1
2	4

Mapping diagram:

Algebraic Examples

$$y = 2 \sin (3x) + 4$$
or
$$f(x) = 2 \sin (3x) + 4$$

Need to Know

- Function notation, $f(x)$, is used to represent the values of the dependent variable in a function, so $y = f(x)$.
- You can use the vertical line test to check whether a graph represents a function. A graph represents a function if every vertical line intersects the graph in, at most, one point. This shows that there is only one element in the range for each element in the domain.
- The domain and range of a function depend on the type of function.
- The domain and range of a function that models a particular situation may need to be restricted, based on the situation. For example, negative values may not have meaning when dealing with variables such as time.

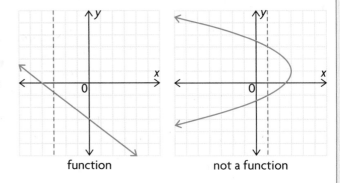

function   not a function

CHECK *Your Understanding*

1. State the domain and range of each relation. Then determine whether the relation is a function, and justify your answer.

a)
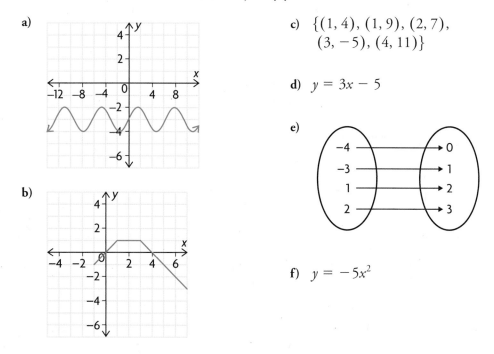

c) $\{(1, 4), (1, 9), (2, 7), (3, -5), (4, 11)\}$

d) $y = 3x - 5$

e)
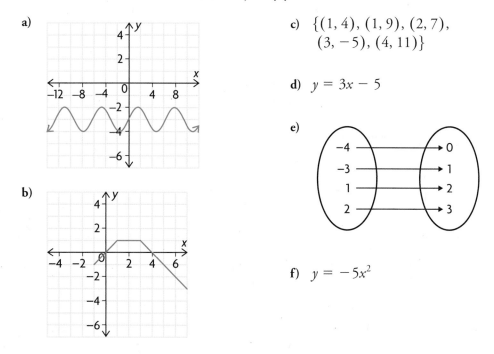

b)

f) $y = -5x^2$

2. State the domain and range of each relation. Then determine whether the relation is a function, and justify your answer.

a) $y = -2(x + 1)^2 - 3$ c) $y = 2^{-x}$ e) $x^2 + y^2 = 9$

b) $y = \dfrac{1}{x + 3}$ d) $y = \cos x + 1$ f) $y = 2 \sin x$

PRACTISING

3. Determine whether each relation is a function, and state its domain and range.

a)
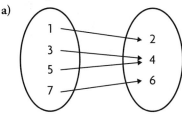

c)
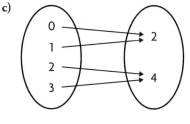

e)
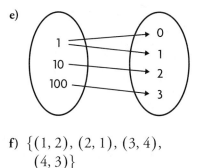

b) $\{(2, 3), (1, 3), (5, 6), (0, -1)\}$

d) $\{(2, 5), (6, 1), (2, 7), (8, 3)\}$

f) $\{(1, 2), (2, 1), (3, 4), (4, 3)\}$

4. Determine whether each relation is a function, and state its domain
K and range.

a)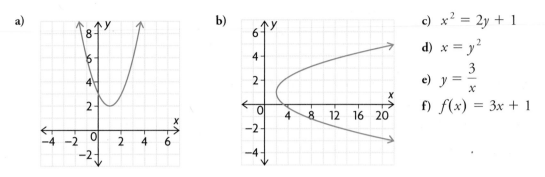

b)

c) $x^2 = 2y + 1$

d) $x = y^2$

e) $y = \dfrac{3}{x}$

f) $f(x) = 3x + 1$

5. Determine the equations that describe the following function rules:
  a) The input is 3 less than the output.
  b) The output is 5 less than the input multiplied by 2.
  c) Subtract 2 from the input and then multiply by 3 to find the output.
  d) The sum of the input and output is 5.

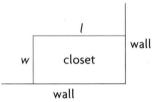

6. Martin wants to build an additional closet in a corner of his bedroom.
Because the closet will be in a corner, only two new walls need to be
built. The total length of the two new walls must be 12 m. Martin wants
the length of the closet to be twice as long as the width, as shown in the
diagram.
  a) Explain why $l = 2w$.
  b) Let the function $f(l)$ be the sum of the length and the width. Find
     the equation for $f(l)$.
  c) Graph $y = f(l)$.
  d) Find the desired length and width.

7. The following table gives Tina's height above the ground while riding a
A Ferris wheel, in relation to the time she was riding it.

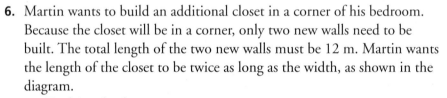

Time (s)	0	20	40	60	80	100	120	140	160	180	200	220	240
Height (m)	5	10	5	0	5	10	5	0	5	10	5	0	5

  a) Draw a graph of the relation, using time as the independent variable
     and height as the dependent variable.
  b) What is the domain?
  c) What is the range?
  d) Is this relation a function? Justify your answer.
  e) Another student sketched a graph, but used height as the independent
     variable. What does this graph look like?
  f) Is the relation in part e) a function? Justify your answer.

8. Consider what happens to a relation when the coordinates of all its ordered pairs are switched.
   a) Give an example of a function that is still a function when its coordinates are switched.
   b) Give an example of a function that is no longer a function when its coordinates are switched.
   c) Give an example of a relation that is not a function, but becomes a function when its coordinates are switched.

9. Explain why a relation that fails the vertical line test is not a function.

10. Consider the relation between x and y that consists of all points (x, y) such that the distance from (x, y) to the origin is 5.
    a) Is $(4, 3)$ in the relation? Explain.
    b) Is $(1, 5)$ in the relation? Explain.
    c) Is the relation a function? Explain.

11. The table below lists all the ordered pairs that belong to the function $g(x)$.

x	0	1	2	3	4	5
$g(x)$	3	4	7	12	19	28

   a) Determine an equation for $g(x)$.
   b) Does $g(3) - g(2) = g(3 - 2)$? Explain.

12. The factors of 4 are 1, 2, and 4. The sum of the factors is
    T $1 + 2 + 4 = 7$. The sum of the factors is called the sigma function. Therefore, $f(4) = 7$.
    a) Find $f(6), f(7)$, and $f(8)$.
    c) Is $f(12) = f(3) \times f(4)$?
    b) Is $f(15) = f(3) \times f(5)$?
    d) Are there others that will work?

13. Make a concept map to show what you have learned about functions.
    C Put "FUNCTION" in the centre of your concept map, and include the following words:

algebraic model	graphical model	numerical model
dependent variable	independent variable	range
domain	mapping model	vertical line test
function notation		

> **Communication | Tip**
>
> A concept map is a type of web diagram used for exploring knowledge and gathering and sharing information. A concept map consists of cells that contain a concept, item, or question and links. The links are labelled and denote direction with an arrow symbol. The labelled links explain the relationship between the cells. The arrow describes the direction of the relationship and reads like a sentence.

Extending

14. Consider the relations $x^2 + y^2 = 25$ and $y = \sqrt{25 - x^2}$. Draw the graphs of these relations, and determine whether each relation is a function. State the domain and range of each relation.

15. You already know that y is a function of x if and only if the graph passes the vertical line test. When is x a function of y? Explain.

YOU WILL NEED

- graph paper
- graphing calculator

GOAL

Discover the properties of the absolute value function.

EXPLORE the Math

An average person's blood pressure is dependent on their age and gender. For example, the average systolic blood pressure, P_n, for a 17-year-old girl is about 127 mm Hg. (The symbol mm Hg stands for millimetres of mercury, which is a unit of measure for blood pressure.) The average systolic blood pressure for a 17-year-old boy is about 134 mm Hg.

When doctors measure blood pressure, they compare the blood pressure to the average blood pressure for people in the same age and gender group. This comparison, P_d, is calculated using the formula $P_d = |P - P_n|$, where P is the blood pressure reading and P_n is the average reading for people in the same age and gender group.

Tech | Support

To use the **absolute value** command on a graphing calculator, press MATH and scroll right to NUM. Then press ENTER.

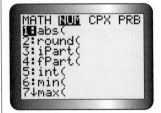

? How can the blood pressure readings of a group of people be compared?

A. Jim is a 17-year-old boy whose most recent blood pressure reading was 142 mm Hg. Calculate P_d for Jim.

B. Joe is a 17-year-old boy whose most recent blood pressure reading was 126 mm Hg. Calculate P_d for Joe.

C. Compare the values of $P - P_n$ and $|P - P_n|$ that were used to determine P_d for each boy. What do you notice?

D. Complete the following table by calculating the values of P_d for the given blood pressure readings for 17-year-old boys.

Blood Pressure Reading, P	95	100	105	110	115	120	125	130	135	140	145	150	155	160
P_d														

E. Draw a **scatter plot** of P_d as a function of blood pressure, P.

F. Describe these characteristics of your graph:

    i) domain

    ii) range

    iii) zeros

    iv) existence of any asymptotes

    v) shape of the graph

    vi) intervals of the domain in which the values of the function P_d are increasing and decreasing.

    vii) behaviour of the values of the function P_d as P becomes larger and smaller

Reflecting

G. Why might you predict the range of your graph to be greater than or equal to zero?

H. What other function with domain greater than P_n could you have used to plot the right side of your graph? Why does this make sense?

I. What other function with domain less than P_n could you have used to plot the left side of your graph? Why does this make sense?

J. How will the graph of $y = |x|$ compare with the graph of $P_d = |P - P_n|$, if P_d is the y-coordinate and P is the x-coordinate? Use the characteristics you listed in part F to make your comparison.

In Summary

Key Idea

$|-3| = 3 \quad |3| = 3$

- $f(x) = |x|$ is the absolute value function. On a number line, this function describes the distance, $f(x)$, of any number x from the origin.

Need to Know

$f(x) = -x, x < 0 \qquad f(x) = x, x \geq 0$

- For the function $f(x) = |x|$,
  - there is one zero located at the origin
  - the graph is comprised of two linear functions and is defined as follows:
  $$f(x) = \begin{cases} x, & \text{if } x \geq 0 \\ -x, & \text{if } x < 0 \end{cases}$$
  - the graph is symmetric about the y-axis
  - as x approaches large positive values, y approaches large positive values
  - as x approaches large negative values, y approaches large positive values
  - the absolute value function has domain $\{x \in \mathbf{R}\}$ and range $\{y \in \mathbf{R} \mid y \geq 0\}$
  - every input in an absolute value returns an output that is non-negative

FURTHER *Your Understanding*

1. Arrange these values in order, from least to greatest:
   $|-5|, |20|, |-15|, |12|, |-25|$

2. Evaluate.
   a) $|-22|$
   c) $|-5-13|$
   e) $\dfrac{|-8|}{-4}$

   b) $-|-35|$
   d) $|4-7| + |-10+2|$
   f) $\dfrac{|-22|}{|-11|} + \dfrac{-16}{|-4|}$

3. Express using absolute value notation.
   a) $x < -3$ or $x > 3$
   c) $x \le -1$ or $x \ge 1$
   b) $-8 \le x \le 8$
   d) $x \ne \pm 5$

Communication | *Tip*

To show that a number is not included in the solution set, use an open dot at this value. A solid dot shows that this value is included in the solution set.

4. Graph on a number line.
   a) $|x| < 8$
   b) $|x| \ge 16$
   c) $|x| \le -4$
   d) $|x| > -7$

5. Rewrite using absolute value notation.
   a)

   b)

   c)

   d)

6. Graph $f(x) = |x - 8|$ and $g(x) = |-x + 8|$.
   a) What do you notice?
   b) How could you have predicted this?

7. Graph the following functions.
   a) $f(x) = |x - 2|$
   b) $f(x) = |x| + 2$
   c) $f(x) = |x + 2|$
   d) $f(x) = |x| - 2$

8. Compare the graphs you drew in question 7. How could you use transformations to describe the graph of $f(x) = |x + 3| - 4$?

9. Predict what the graph of $f(x) = |2x + 1|$ will look like. Verify your prediction using graphing technology.

10. Predict what the graph of $f(x) = 3 - |2x - 5|$ will look like. Verify your prediction using graphing technology.

1.3 Properties of Graphs of Functions

YOU WILL NEED
- graphing calculator

INVESTIGATE the Math

Two students created a game that they called "Which function am I?" In this game, players turn over cards that are placed face down and match the characteristics and properties with the correct functions. The winner is the player who has the most pairs at the end of the game.

The students have studied the following parent functions:

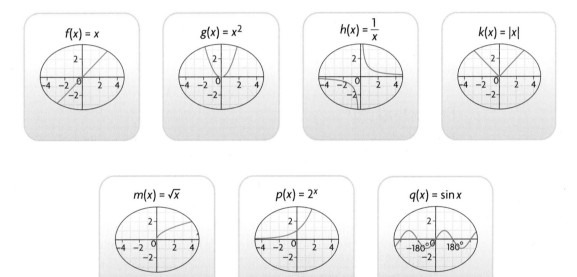

? Which criteria could the students use to differentiate between these different types of functions?

A. Graph each of these parent functions on a graphing calculator, and sketch its graph. State the domain and range of each function, and determine its zeros and y-intercepts.

B. Determine the intervals of increase and the intervals of decrease for each of the parent functions.

interval of increase

the interval(s) within a function's domain, where the y-values of the function get larger, moving from left to right

interval of decrease

the interval(s) within a function's domain, where the y-values of the function get smaller, moving from left to right

odd function

any function that has rotational symmetry about the origin; algebraically, all odd functions have the property
$f(-x) = -f(x)$

even function

any function that is symmetric about the y-axis; algebraically, all even functions have the property $f(-x) = f(x)$

continuous function

any function that does not contain any holes or breaks over its entire domain

discontinuity

a break in the graph of a function is called a point of discontinuity

C. State whether each parent function is an **odd function**, an **even function**, or neither.

D. Do any of the functions have vertical or horizontal asymptotes? If so, what are the equations of these asymptotes?

E. Which graphs are **continuous**? Which have **discontinuities**?

F. Complete the following statements to describe the end behaviour of each parent function.
 a) As x increases to large positive values, y ...
 b) As x decreases to large negative values, y ...

Communication | *Tip*

It is often convenient to use the symbol for infinity, ∞, and the following notation to write the end behaviour of a function:
 • For "As x increases to large positive values, y...," write "As $x \to \infty$, $y \to$ ..."
 • For "As x decreases to large negative values, y...," write "As $x \to -\infty$, $y \to$ ..."

G. Summarize your findings.

Reflecting

H. Which of the parent functions can be distinguished by their domain? Which can be distinguished by their range? Which can be distinguished by their zeros?

I. An increasing function is one in which the function's values increase from left to right over its entire domain. A decreasing function is one in which the function's values decrease from left to right over its entire domain. Which of the parent functions are increasing functions? Which are decreasing functions?

J. Which properties of each function would make the function easy to identify from a description of it?

APPLY *the Math*

| EXAMPLE **1** | Connecting the graph of a function with its characteristics |

Match each parent function card with a characteristic of its graph. Each card may only be used for one parent function.

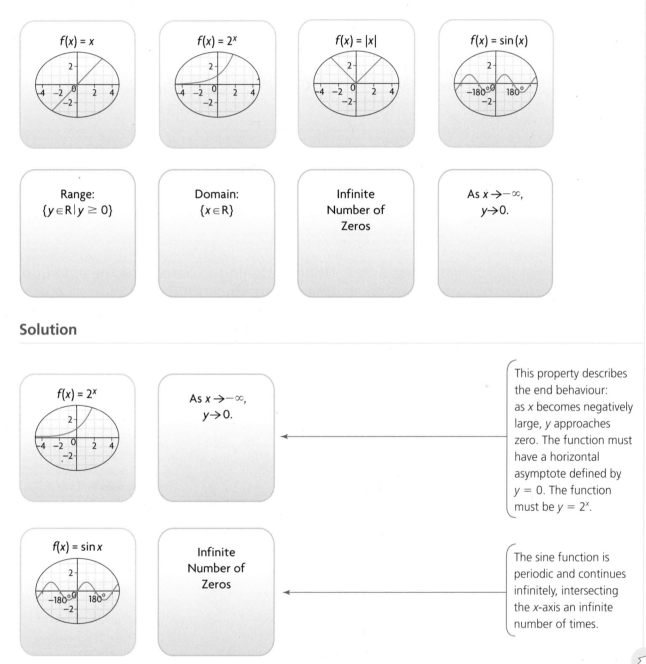

Solution

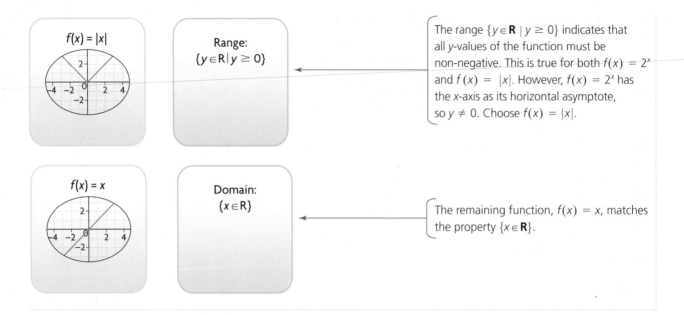

$f(x) = |x|$

Range:
$\{y \in \mathbf{R} \mid y \geq 0\}$

The range $\{y \in \mathbf{R} \mid y \geq 0\}$ indicates that all y-values of the function must be non-negative. This is true for both $f(x) = 2^x$ and $f(x) = |x|$. However, $f(x) = 2^x$ has the x-axis as its horizontal asymptote, so $y \neq 0$. Choose $f(x) = |x|$.

$f(x) = x$

Domain:
$\{x \in \mathbf{R}\}$

The remaining function, $f(x) = x$, matches the property $\{x \in \mathbf{R}\}$.

If you are given some characteristics of a function, you may be able to determine the equation of the function.

EXAMPLE 2   **Using reasoning to determine the equation of a parent function**

State which of the parent functions in this lesson have the following characteristics:

a) Domain $= \{x \in \mathbf{R}\}$
b) Range $= \{y \in \mathbf{R} \mid -1 \leq y \leq 1\}$

Solution

a) Domain $= \{x \in \mathbf{R}\}$

$f(x) = x$
$g(x) = x^2$
$h(x) = \dfrac{-1}{-x}$ (Domain $= \{x \in \mathbf{R} \mid x \neq 0\}$)
$k(x) = |x|$

$m(x) = \sqrt{x}$ (Domain $= \{x \in \mathbf{R} \mid x \geq 0\}$)
$p(x) = 2^x$
$q(x) = \sin x$

There are five parent functions that match this characteristic and two that do not.

b) Range $= \{y \in \mathbf{R} \mid -1 \leq y \leq 1\}$

$f(x) = x$ (Range $= \{y \in \mathbf{R}\}$)
$g(x) = x^2$ (Range $= \{y \in \mathbf{R} \mid y \geq 0\}$)
$k(x) = |x|$ (Range $= \{y \in \mathbf{R} \mid y \geq 0\}$)
$p(x) = 2^x$ (Range $= \{y \in \mathbf{R} \mid y \geq 0\}$)
$q(x) = \sin x$

Of these five functions, only the sine function has the range $\{y \in \mathbf{R} \mid -1 \leq y \leq 1\}$.

Visualizing what the graph of a function looks like can help you remember some of the characteristics of the function.

| EXAMPLE 3 | Connecting the characteristics of a function with its equation |

Which of the following are characteristics of the parent function $p(x) = 2^x$? Justify your reasoning.

a) The graph is decreasing for all values in the domain of $p(x)$.
b) The graph is continuous for all values in the domain of $p(x)$.
c) The function $p(x)$ is an even function.
d) The function $p(x)$ has no zeros.

Solution

$p(x) = 2^x$

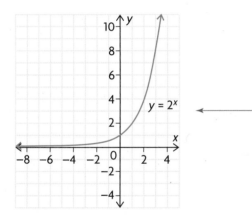

The function $p(x)$ is an exponential function with a base that is greater than 1.

This type of function is increasing for all values in its domain.

a) This function is increasing for all values in the domain of $p(x)$.

b) The graph is continuous for all values in the domain of $p(x)$. — This function has no breaks.

c) The function $p(x)$ is not an even function. — This type of function is not symmetric about the y-axis. $f(-x) = 2^{-x}$. This substitution does not result in $f(x)$.

d) The function $p(x)$ has no zeros. — As x approaches negative infinity, the graph gets arbitrarily close to the x-axis but does not intersect it.

Only b) and d) are characteristics of $p(x)$.

EXAMPLE **4**

Connecting the characteristics of a function with its equation and its graph

Determine a possible transformed parent function that has the following characteristics, and sketch the function:

- $D = \{x \in \mathbf{R}\}$
- $R = \{y \in \mathbf{R} \mid y \geq -2\}$
- decreasing on the interval $(-\infty, 0)$
- increasing on the interval $(0, \infty)$

Solution

Communication | **Tip**

The interval $(-\infty, 0)$ is described using interval notation and is equivalent to $x < 0$ in set notation. The use of round brackets in interval notation indicates that the endpoint is not included in the interval. The use of square brackets in interval notation indicates that the endpoint is included in the interval. For example, $[-3, 5)$ is equivalent to $-3 \leq x < 5$.

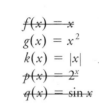

$f(x) = x$
$g(x) = x^2$
$k(x) = |x|$
$p(x) = 2^x$
$q(x) = \sin x$

List the functions that have domain $\{x \in \mathbf{R}\}$. Eliminate the functions that cannot have the range $\{y \in \mathbf{R} \mid y \geq -2\}$. Each of the remaining functions can be translated down two units to have this range.

Function	Intervals of Increase	Intervals of Decrease
$g(x) = x^2$	$(0, \infty)$	$(-\infty, 0)$
$k(x) = |x|$	$(0, \infty)$	$(-\infty, 0)$

State the intervals of increase and decrease for the two remaining functions. Check to see if these intervals match the given conditions. There are two possible parent functions that have the given characteristics.

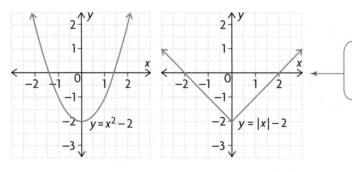

Sketch the graph of each parent function shifted 2 units down.

In Summary

Key Idea

Functions can be categorized based on their graphical characteristics:
- domain and range
- intervals of increase and decrease
- x-intercepts and y-intercepts
- symmetry (even/odd)
- continuity and discontinuity
- end behaviour

Need to Know

- Given a set of graphical characteristics, the type of function that has these characteristics can be determined by eliminating those that do not have these characteristics.
- Some characteristics are more helpful than others when determining the type of function.

CHECK Your Understanding

1. Which graphical characteristic is the least helpful for differentiating among the parent functions? Why?

2. Which graphical characteristic is the most helpful for differentiating among the parent functions? Why?

3. One of the seven parent functions examined in this lesson is transformed to yield a graph with these characteristics:
   - $D = \{x \in \mathbf{R}\}$
   - $R = \{y \in \mathbf{R} \mid y > 2\}$
   - As $x \to -\infty$, $y \to 2$.

   What is the equation of the transformed function?

PRACTISING

4. For each pair of functions, give a characteristic that the two functions
K have in common and a characteristic that distinguishes between them.

   a) $f(x) = \dfrac{1}{x}$ and $g(x) = x$ c) $f(x) = x$ and $g(x) = x^2$

   b) $f(x) = \sin x$ and $g(x) = x$ d) $f(x) = 2^x$ and $g(x) = |x|$

5. For each function, determine $f(-x)$ and $-f(-x)$ and compare it with $f(x)$. Use this to decide whether each function is even, odd, or neither.

   a) $f(x) = x^2 - 4$ d) $f(x) = 2x^3 + x$

   b) $f(x) = \sin x + x$ e) $f(x) = 2x^2 - x$

   c) $f(x) = \dfrac{1}{x} - x$ f) $f(x) = |2x + 3|$

6. Determine a possible parent function that could serve as a model for each of the following situations, and explain your choice.

    a) The number of marks away from the class average that a student's test score is

    b) The height of a person above the ground during several rotations of a Ferris wheel

    c) The population of Earth throughout time

    d) The amount of total money saved if you put aside exactly one dollar every day

7. Identify a parent function whose graph has the given characteristics.

    a) The domain is not all real numbers, and $f(0) = 0$.

    b) The graph has an infinite number of zeros.

    c) The graph is even and has no sharp corners.

    d) As x gets negatively large, so does y. As x gets positively large, so does y.

8. Each of the following situations involves a parent function whose graph has been translated. Draw a possible graph that fits the situation.

    a) The domain is $\{x \in \mathbf{R}\}$, the interval of increase is $(-\infty, \infty)$, and the range is $\{f(x) \in \mathbf{R} \mid f(x) > -3\}$.

    b) The range is $\{g(x) \in \mathbf{R} \mid 2 \le g(x) \le 4\}$.

    c) The domain is $\{x \in \mathbf{R} \mid x \ne 5\}$, and the range is $\{h(x) \in \mathbf{R} \mid h(x) \ne -3\}$.

9. Sketch a possible graph of a function that has the following characteristics:

- $f(0) = -1.5$
- $f(1) = 2$
- There is a vertical asymptote at $x = -1$.
- As x gets positively large, y gets positively large.
- As x gets negatively large, y approaches zero.

10. **a)** $f(x)$ is a quadratic function. The graph of $f(x)$ decreases on the interval $(-\infty, -2)$ and increases on the interval $(2, \infty)$. It has a y-intercept at $(0, 4)$. What is a possible equation for $f(x)$?

    b) Is there only one quadratic function, $f(x)$, that has the characteristics given in part a)?

    c) If $f(x)$ is an absolute value function that has the characteristics given in part a), is there only one such function? Explain.

11. $f(x) = x^2$ and $g(x) = |x|$ are similar functions. How might you describe the difference between the two graphs to a classmate, so that your classmate can tell them apart?

12. Copy and complete the following table. In your table, highlight the graphical characteristics that are unique to each function and could be used to distinguish it easily from other parent functions.

Parent Function	$f(x) = x$	$g(x) = x^2$	$h(x) = \dfrac{1}{x}$	$k(x) = |x|$	$m(x) = \sqrt{x}$	$p(x) = 2^x$	$r(x) = \sin x$
Sketch							
Domain							
Range							
Intervals of Increase							
Intervals of Decrease							
Location of Discontinuities and Asymptotes							
Zeros							
y-Intercepts							
Symmetry							
End Behaviours							

13. Linear, quadratic, reciprocal, absolute value, square root, exponential, and sine functions are examples of different types of functions, with different properties and characteristics. Why do you think it is useful to name these different types of functions?

Extending

14. Consider the parent function $f(x) = x^3$. Graph $f(x)$, and compare and contrast this function with the parent functions you have learned about in this lesson.

15. Explain why it is not necessary to have $h(x) = \cos(x)$ defined as a parent function.

16. Suppose that $g(x) = |x|$ is translated around the coordinate plane. How many zeros can its graph have? Discuss all possibilities, and give an example of each.

FREQUENTLY ASKED Questions

Q: **What is a function, and which of its representations is the best for solving problems and making predictions?**

A: A function is a relation between two variables, in which each input has a unique output. Functions can be represented using words, graphs, numbers, and algebra.

Word Example	Graphical Example	Numerical Example		Algebraic Example
One number is three more than twice another number.		Table of values: 	x	y	 -4 -5 -3 -3 -2 -1 -1 1 0 3 1 5	Mapping diagram:	$f(x) = 2x + 3$

The algebraic model is the most useful and most accurate. If you know the value of one variable, you can substitute this value into the function to create an equation, which can then be solved using an appropriate strategy. This leads to an accurate answer. Both numerical and graphical models are limited in their use because they represent the function for only small intervals of the domain and range. When using a graphical model, it may be necessary to interpolate or extrapolate. This can lead to approximate answers.

Q: **What is the absolute value function, and what are the characteristics of its graph?**

A: The absolute value function is $f(x) = |x|$. On a number line, $|x|$ is the distance of any value, x, from the origin. The absolute value function consists of two linear pieces, each defined by a different equation:

$$f(x) = \begin{cases} x, \text{ if } x \geq 0 \\ -x, \text{ if } x < 0 \end{cases}$$

This function has the following characteristics:

- x-intercept: $x = 0$
- y-intercept: $y = 0$
- domain: $D = \{x \in \mathbf{R}\}$; range: $\mathbf{R} = \{y \in \mathbf{R} \mid y \geq 0\}$
- interval of decrease: $(-\infty, 0)$; interval of increase: $(0, \infty)$
- end behaviour: As $x \to \infty$, $y \to \infty$; as $x \to -\infty$, $y \to \infty$.

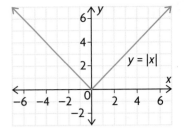

Q: **What is the difference between an odd function and an even function, and how are the parent functions differentiated by this characteristic?**

Study | Aid

- See Lesson 1.3, Examples 3 and 4.
- Try Mid-Chapter Review Questions 6, 7, and 8.

A: The graph of an odd function has rotational symmetry about the origin.
The graph of an even function is symmetric about the y-axis.

To test algebraically whether a function is odd or even, substitute $-x$ for x and simplify:

- If $f(-x) = -f(x)$, then the function is odd.
- If $f(-x) = f(x)$, then the function is even.

Odd Parent Functions: $f(x) = x$, $f(x) = \frac{1}{x}$, $f(x) = \sin x$

Even Parent Functions: $f(x) = x^2$, $f(x) = |x|$, $f(x) = \cos x$

Q: **What is a discontinuity, and what is a continuous function?**

Study | Aid

- See Lesson 1.3.
- Try Mid-Chapter Review Question 9.

A: A discontinuity is a break in the graph of a function. A function is continuous if it has no discontinuities; that is, no holes or breaks in its graph over its entire domain.

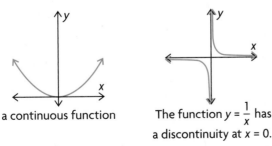

a continuous function

The function $y = \frac{1}{x}$ has a discontinuity at $x = 0$.

PRACTICE Questions

Lesson 1.1

1. Determine whether each relation is a function, and state its domain and range.

   a)

   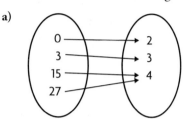

   b) $y = 2x + 3$

   c)

   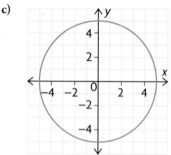

   d) $\{(2, 7), (1, 3), (2, 6), (10, -1)\}$

2. The height of a bungee jumper above the ground is modelled by the following data.

Time (s)	0	1	2	3	4	5	6	7	8	9	10
Height (m)	50	40	30	20	10	20	30	40	45	35	25

   a) Is the relationship between height and time a function? Explain.
   b) What is the domain?
   c) What is the range?

3. Determine the domain and range for each of the following and state whether it is a function:

   a) $f(x) = 3x + 1$ c) $y = \sqrt{5 - x}$
   b) $x^2 + y^2 = 9$ d) $x^2 - y = 2$

Lesson 1.2

4. Arrange the following values in order, from least to greatest:

   $|-3|, -|3|, |5|, |-4|, |0|$

5. Sketch the graph of each function.

   a) $f(x) = |x| + 3$ c) $f(x) = |-2x|$
   b) $f(x) = |x| - 2$ d) $f(x) = |0.5x|$

Lesson 1.3

6. Determine a parent function that matches each set of characteristics.

   a) The graph is neither even nor odd, and as $x \to \infty, y \to \infty$.
   b) $(-\infty, 0)$ and $(0, \infty)$ are both intervals of decrease.
   c) The domain is $[0, \infty)$.

7. Determine algebraically if each function is even, odd, or neither.

   a) $f(x) = |2x|$ c) $f(x) = x + 4$
   b) $f(x) = (-x)^2$ d) $f(x) = 4x^5 + 3x^3 - 1$

8. Each set of characteristics describes a parent function that has been shifted. Draw a possible graph, and state whether the graph is continuous.

   a) There is a vertical asymptote at $x = 1$ and a horizontal asymptote at $y = 3$.
   b) The range is $\{f(x) \in \mathbf{R} | -3 \le f(x) \le -1\}$.
   c) The interval of increase is $(-\infty, \infty)$, and there is a horizontal asymptote at $y = -10$.

9. Sketch a graph that has the following characteristics:

   - The function is odd.
   - The function is continuous.
   - The function has zeros at $x = -3, 0,$ and 3.
   - The function is increasing on the intervals $x \in (-\infty, -2)$ or $x \in (2, \infty)$.
   - The function is decreasing on the interval $x \in (-2, 2)$.

1.4   Sketching Graphs of Functions

GOAL

Apply transformations to parent functions, and use the most efficient methods to sketch the graphs of the functions.

YOU WILL NEED

- graph paper
- graphing calculator

INVESTIGATE the Math

The same transformations have been applied to six different parent functions, as shown below.

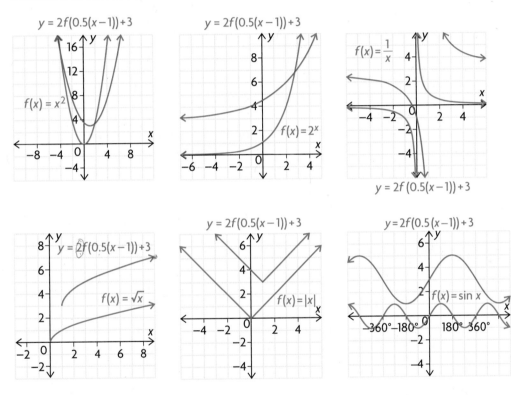

? How do the transformations defined by $y = 2f(0.5(x - 1)) + 3$ affect the characteristics of each parent function?

A. Identify the parent function for each graph.

$$(4, 2) \qquad (2 \, \sharp + 1) \qquad (2(\sharp) + 3)$$

$$(9, \; 7 \;)$$

B. Copy and complete the following table for each parent function.

Parent Fuction	$y = x^2$	$y = \dfrac{1}{x}$	$y = |x|$	$y = 2^x$	$y = \sqrt{x}$	$y = \sin x$
Domain						
Range						
Intervals of Increase						
Intervals of Decrease						
Turning Points						

turning point

a point on a curve where the function changes from increasing to decreasing, or vice versa; for example, A and B are turning points on the following curve

C. Identify the transformations (in the correct order) that were performed on each parent function to arrive at the transformed function.

D. State the transformation(s) that affected each of the following characteristics for each of the parent functions in the table above.
  i) domain
  ii) range
  iii) intervals of increase/decrease
  iv) turning points
  v) the equation(s) of any vertical asymptotes
  vi) the equation(s) of any horizontal asymptotes

E. What transformations to the graph of $y = f(x)$ result in the graph of $y = -\dfrac{1}{2}f(x + 2) - 1$?

Reflecting

F. For which parent functions are the domain, range, intervals of increase/decrease, and turning points affected when their graphs are transformed?

G. Describe the most efficient order that can be used to graph a transformed function when performing multiple transformations.

H. The most general equation of a transformed function is $y = af(k(x - d)) + c$, where a, k, c, and d are real numbers. Describe the transformations that would be performed on the parent function $y = f(x)$ in terms of the parameters a, k, c, and d.

APPLY the Math

| EXAMPLE **1** | Connecting transformations to the equation of a function |

State the function that would result from vertically compressing $y = f(x)$ by a factor of $\frac{1}{2}$ and then translating the graph 5 units to the right.

Solution

$y = \dfrac{1}{2}f(x)$ ⟵──────────── This is the function that has a vertical compression by a factor of $\frac{1}{2}$.

$y = \dfrac{1}{2}f(x - 5)$ ⟵──────────── This is the function has also has a translation 5 units to the right.

| EXAMPLE **2** | Connecting transformations to the characteristics of a function |

Use transformations to help you describe the characteristics of the transformed function $y = 3\sqrt{x} - 2$.

Solution

In the general function $y = af(k(x - d)) + c$, the parameters k and d affect the x-coordinates of each point on the parent function, and the parameters a and c affect the y-coordinates. Each point (x, y) on the parent function is mapped onto $\left(\dfrac{x}{k} + d, ay + c\right)$ on the transformed function.

⟵ The parameters k and a are related to stretches/compressions and reflections, while the parameters d and c are related to translations. Since division and multiplication must be performed before addition, all stretches/compression and reflections must be applied before any translations, due to the order of operations.

The equation $y = 3\sqrt{x} - 2$ ⟵── In this equation, $a = 3$ and $c = -2$.

indicates that two transformations have been applied to the parent function $y = \sqrt{x}$:

1. a vertical stretch by a factor of 3
2. a vertical translation 2 units down

$(x, y) \rightarrow (x, 3y)$

Parent Function $y = \sqrt{x}$	Stretched Function $y = 3\sqrt{x}$
(0, 0)	(0, 3(0)) = (0, 0)
(1, 1)	(1, 3(1)) = (1, 3)
(4, 2)	(4, 3(2)) = (4, 6)
(9, 3)	(9, 3(3)) = (9, 9)

Vertically stretching the graph by a factor of 3 occurs when all the y-coordinates on the graph of the parent function are multiplied by 3.

$(x, 3y) \rightarrow (x, 3y - 2)$

Stretched Function $y = 3\sqrt{x}$	Final Transformed Function $y = 3\sqrt{x} - 2$
(0, 0)	(0, 0 − 2) = (0, −2)
(1, 3)	(1, 3 − 2) = (1, 1)
(4, 6)	(4, 6 − 2) = (4, 4)
(9, 9)	(9, 9 − 2) = (9, 7)

Translating the graph 2 units down occurs when 2 is subtracted from all the y-coordinates on the graph of the stretched function.

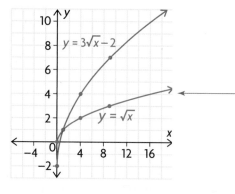

Plot the key points of $y = \sqrt{x}$ and the new points of the transformed function.

Since the domain of both the parent function and transformed function is the same, the interval of increase is also the same: $[0, \infty)$. The difference occurs in the range. The y-values of the transformed function increase faster than the y-values of the parent function.

These two transformations act on the y values only; there is no change to the x values. The domain is unchanged; it is $\{x \in \mathbf{R} \mid x \geq 0\}$. The range changes from $\{y \in \mathbf{R} \mid y \geq 0\}$ to $\{y \in \mathbf{R} \mid y \geq -2\}$.

EXAMPLE 3 — Reasoning about the characteristics of a transformed function

Graph the function $f(x) = \cos(x)$ and the transformed function $y = 2f(3x)$, where $0° \leq x \leq 360°$. State the impact of the transformations on the domain, range, intervals of increase/decrease, and turning points of the transformed function.

Solution

$$(x, y) \rightarrow \left(\tfrac{1}{3}x, 2y\right)$$

Parent Function $y = \cos(x)$	Final Transformed Function $y = 2\cos(3x)$
$(0°, 1)$	$\left(\tfrac{1}{3}(0°), 2(1)\right) = (0°, 2)$
$(90°, 0)$	$\left(\tfrac{1}{3}(90°), 2(0)\right) = (30°, 0)$
$(180°, -1)$	$\left(\tfrac{1}{3}(180°), 2(-1)\right) = (60°, -2)$
$(270°, 0)$	$\left(\tfrac{1}{3}(270°), 2(0)\right) = (90°, 0)$
$(360°, 1)$	$\left(\tfrac{1}{3}(360°), 2(1)\right) = (120°, 2)$

Apply a horizontal compression by a factor of $\tfrac{1}{3}$ and a vertical stretch by a factor of 2.

On the graph of $f(x) = \cos(x)$, multiply the x-coordinates by $\tfrac{1}{3}$ and the y-coordinates by 2.

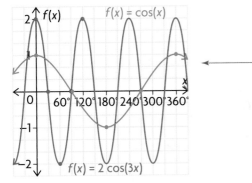

Plot the key points of the parent function and the transformed points.

Within the specified domain,

- the transformed function decreases on the intervals $(0°, 60°)$, $(120°, 180°)$, and $(240°, 300°)$ and increases on the intervals $(60°, 120°)$, $(180°, 240°)$, and $(300°, 360°)$
- the transformed function has the following turning points: $(60°, -2)$, $(120°, 2)$, $(180°, -2)$, $(240°, 2)$, and $(300°, -2)$

The domain consists of all real numbers; this is not changed by the horizontal compression and translation.
Domain = $\{x \in \mathbf{R}\}$.
The vertical stretch has changed the range from $\{y \in \mathbf{R} \mid -1 \leq y \leq 1\}$ to $\{y \in \mathbf{R} \mid -2 \leq y \leq 2\}$.

EXAMPLE **4**   Reasoning about the order of transformations

Describe the order in which you would apply the transformations defined by $y = -2f(3(x + 1)) - 4$ to $f(x) = \sqrt{x}$. Then state the impact of the transformations on the domain, range, intervals of increase/decrease, and end behaviours of the transformed function.

Solution

$$(x, y) \rightarrow \left(\frac{1}{3}x, -2y\right)$$

Parent Function $y = \sqrt{x}$	Stretched/Compressed Function $y = -2\sqrt{3x}$
$(0, 0)$	$\left(\frac{1}{3}(0), -2(0)\right) = (0, 0)$
$(1, 1)$	$\left(\frac{1}{3}(1), -2(1)\right) = \left(\frac{1}{3}, -2\right)$
$(4, 2)$	$\left(\frac{1}{3}(4), -2(2)\right) = \left(\frac{4}{3}, -4\right)$
$(9, 3)$	$\left(\frac{1}{3}(9), -2(3)\right) = (3, -6)$

Since multiplication must be done before addition, apply a horizontal compression by a factor of $\frac{1}{3}$, a vertical stretch by a factor of 2, and a reflection in the *x*-axis. To do this, multiply the *x*-coordinates of points on the parent function by $\frac{1}{3}$ and the *y*-coordinates by -2.

$$\left(\frac{1}{3}x, -2y\right) \rightarrow \left(\frac{1}{3}x - 1, -2y - 4\right)$$

Stretched/Compressed Function $y = -2\sqrt{3x}$	Final Transformed Function $y = -2\sqrt{3(x + 1)} - 4$
$(0, 0)$	$(0 - 1, 0 - 4) = (-1, -4)$
$\left(\frac{1}{3}, -2\right)$	$\left(\frac{1}{3} - 1, -2 - 4\right) = \left(-\frac{2}{3}, -6\right)$
$\left(\frac{4}{3}, -4\right)$	$\left(\frac{4}{3} - 1, -4 - 4\right) = \left(\frac{1}{3}, -8\right)$
$(3, -6)$	$(3 - 1, -6 - 4) = (2, -10)$

Apply all translations next. Translate the graph of $f(x) = -2f(3x)$ 1 unit to the left and 4 units down. To do this, subtract 1 from the *x*-coordinates and 4 from the *y*-coordinates of points on the previous function.

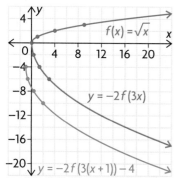

The transformed function is now a decreasing function on the interval $[-1, \infty)$.
The transformed function has the following end behaviours:

As $x \rightarrow -1, y \rightarrow -4$ and as $x \rightarrow \infty, y \rightarrow -\infty$.

Plot the points of the final transformed function. The horizontal translation changed the domain from $\{x \in \mathbf{R} \mid x \geq 0\}$ to $\{x \in \mathbf{R} \mid x \geq -1\}$.

The reflection in the *x*-axis and the vertical translation changed the range from $\{y \in \mathbf{R} \mid y \geq 0\}$ to $\{y \in \mathbf{R} \mid y \leq -4\}$.

In Summary

Key Ideas

- Transformations on a function $y = af(k(x - d)) + c$ must be performed in a particular order: horizontal and vertical stretches/compressions (including any reflections) must be performed before translations. All points on the graph of the parent function $y = f(x)$ are changed as follows: $(x, y) \rightarrow \left(\dfrac{x}{k} + d, ay + c\right)$

- When using transformations to graph, you can apply a and k together, and then c and d together, to get the desired graph in the fewest number of steps.

Need to Know

- The value of a determines whether there is a vertical stretch or compression, or a reflection in the x-axis:
  - When $|a| > 1$, the graph of $y = f(x)$ is stretched vertically by the factor $|a|$.
  - When $0 < |a| < 1$, the graph is compressed vertically by the factor $|a|$.
  - When $a < 0$, the graph is also reflected in the x-axis.
- The value of k determines whether there is a horizontal stretch or compression, or a reflection in the y-axis:
  - When $|k| > 1$, the graph is compressed horizontally by the factor $\dfrac{1}{|k|}$.
  - When $0 < |k| < 1$, the graph is stretched horizontally by the factor $\dfrac{1}{|k|}$.
  - When $k < 0$, the graph is also reflected in the y-axis.
- The value of d determines whether there is a horizontal translation:
  - For $d > 0$, the graph is translated to the right.
  - For $d < 0$, the graph is translated to the left.
- The value of c determines whether there is a vertical translation:
  - For $c > 0$, the graph is translated up.
  - For $c < 0$, the graph is translated down.

CHECK Your Understanding

1. State the transformations defined by each equation in the order they would be applied to $y = f(x)$.

   a) $y = f(x) - 1$

   b) $y = f(2(x - 1))$

   c) $y = -f(x - 3) + 2$

   d) $y = -2f(4x)$

   e) $y = -f(-(x + 2)) - 3$

   f) $y = \dfrac{1}{2}f\left(\dfrac{1}{4}(x - 5)\right) + 6$

2. Identify the appropriate values for a, k, c, and d in
$y = af(k(x - d)) + c$ to describe each set of transformations below.
   a) horizontal stretch by a factor of 2, vertical translation 3 units up,
       reflection in the x-axis
   b)

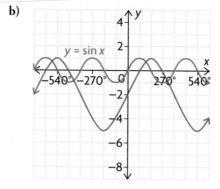

3. The point $(2, 3)$ is on the graph of $y = f(x)$. Determine the
   corresponding coordinates of this point on the graph of
   $y = -2(f(2(x + 5))) - 4$.

PRACTISING

4. The ordered pairs $(2, 3)$, $(4, 7)$, $(-2, 5)$, and $(-4, 6)$ belong to a
   function f. List the ordered pairs that belong to each of the following:
   a) $y = 2f(x)$ d) $y = f(x + 1) - 3$
   b) $y = f(x - 3)$ e) $y = f(-x)$
   c) $y = f(x) + 2$ f) $y = f(2x) - 1$

5. For each of the following equations, state the parent function and the
   K transformation that was applied. Graph the transformed function.

   a) $y = (x + 1)^2$ d) $y = \dfrac{1}{x} + 3$

   b) $y = 2|x|$ e) $y = 2^{0.5x}$

   c) $y = \sin(3x) + 1$ f) $y = \sqrt{2(x - 6)}$

6. State the domain and range of each function in question 5.

7. a) Graph the parent function $y = 2^x$ and the transformed function
       defined by $y = -2f(3(x - 1)) + 4$.
   b) State the impact of the transformations on the domain and range,
       intervals of increase/decrease, and end behaviours.
   c) State the equation of the transformed function.

8. The graph of $y = \sqrt{x}$ is stretched vertically by a factor of 3, reflected in the x-axis, and shifted 5 units to the right. Determine the equation that results from these transformations, and graph it.

9. The point $(1, 8)$ is on the graph of $y = f(x)$. Find the corresponding coordinates of this point on each of the following graphs.
   a) $y = 3f(x - 2)$
   b) $y = f(2(x + 1)) - 4$
   c) $y = -2f(-x) - 7$
   d) $y = -f(4(x + 1))$
   e) $y = -f(-x)$
   f) $y = 0.5f(0.5(x + 3)) + 3$

10. Given $f(x) = \sqrt{x}$, find the domain and range for each of the following:
   A
   a) $g(x) = f(x - 2)$
   b) $h(x) = 2f(x - 1) + 4$
   c) $k(x) = f(-x) + 1$
   d) $j(x) = 3f(2(x - 5)) - 3$

11. Greg thinks that the graphs of $y = 5x^2 - 3$ and $y = 5(x^2 - 3)$ are the same. Explain why he is incorrect.

12. Given $f(x) = x^3 - 3x^2$, $g(x) = f(x - 1)$, and $h(x) = -f(x)$, graph each function and compare $g(x)$ and $h(x)$ with $f(x)$.

13. Consider the parent function $y = x^2$.
   T
   a) Describe the transformation that produced the equation $y = 4x^2$.
   b) Describe the transformation that produced the equation $y = (2x)^2$.
   c) Show algebraically that the two transformations produce the same equation and graph.

14. Use a flow chart to show the sequence and types of transformations
   C required to transform the graph of $y = f(x)$ into the graph of $y = af(k(x - d)) + c$.

Extending

15. The point $(3, 6)$ is on the graph of $y = 2f(x + 1) - 4$. Find the original point on the graph of $y = f(x)$.

16. a) Describe the transformations that produce $y = f(3(x + 2))$.
   b) The graph of $y = f(3x + 6)$ is produced by shifting 6 units to the left and then compressing the graph by a factor of $\frac{1}{3}$. Why does this produce the same result as the transformations you described in part a)?
   c) Using $f(x) = x^2$ as the parent function, graph the transformations described in parts a) and b) to show that they result in the same transformed function.

Inverse Relations

GOAL

Determine the equation of an inverse relation and the conditions for an inverse relation to be a function.

LEARN ABOUT the Math

The owners of a candy company are creating a spherical container to hold their small chocolates. They are trying to decide what size to make the sphere and how much volume the sphere will hold, based on its radius.

The volume of a sphere is given by the relationship $V = \frac{4}{3}\pi r^3$.

? How can you use this relationship to find the radius of any sphere for a given volume?

EXAMPLE 1   Representing the inverse using a table of values and a graph

Use a table of values and a graphical model to represent the relationship between the radius of a sphere and any given volume.

Solution

$$V = \frac{4}{3}\pi r^3$$

Radius (cm)	Volume (cm³)
0.0	0.0
1.0	4.2
2.0	33.5
3.0	113.1
4.0	268.1
5.0	523.6
6.0	904.8
7.0	1436.8
8.0	2144.7
9.0	3053.6
10.0	4188.8

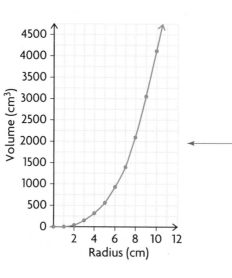

Radius is the independent variable, and volume is the dependent variable.

Create a table of values, and calculate the volume for a specific radius.

Draw a scatter plot of volume in terms of radius. Draw a smooth curve through the points since the function is continuous.

Volume (cm³)	Radius (cm)
0.0	0
4.2	1
33.5	2
113.1	3
268.1	4
523.6	5
904.8	6
1436.8	7
2144.7	8
3053.6	9
4188.8	10

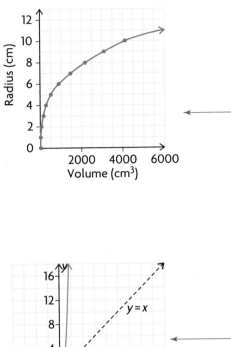

To graph radius in terms of volume, switch the variables in the table, making radius the dependent variable and volume the independent variable.

The red curve shows volume as the independent variable and radius as the dependent variable.

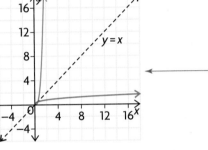

If we ignore units and plot both relations on the same graph, the red curve is a reflection of the blue curve in the line $y = x$. This is reasonable, given that the x-values and y-values were switched on the graph. The red curve is the inverse relation, and it is also a function.

The inverse was found by switching the independent and dependent variables in the table of values. The independent and dependent variables can also be switched in the equation of the relation to determine the equation of the inverse relation.

EXAMPLE **2**   Representing the inverse using an equation

Recall that the volume of a sphere is given by the relationship $V = \frac{4}{3}\pi r^3$.

Determine the equation of the inverse.

Solution

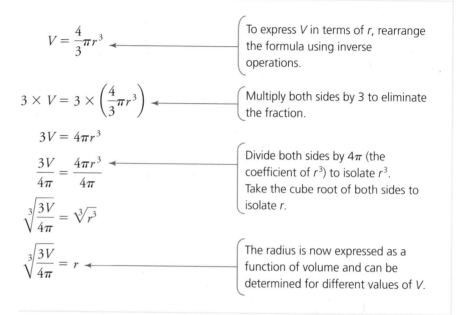

$$V = \frac{4}{3}\pi r^3$$

To express V in terms of r, rearrange the formula using inverse operations.

$$3 \times V = 3 \times \left(\frac{4}{3}\pi r^3\right)$$

Multiply both sides by 3 to eliminate the fraction.

$$3V = 4\pi r^3$$

$$\frac{3V}{4\pi} = \frac{4\pi r^3}{4\pi}$$

Divide both sides by 4π (the coefficient of r^3) to isolate r^3. Take the cube root of both sides to isolate r.

$$\sqrt[3]{\frac{3V}{4\pi}} = \sqrt[3]{r^3}$$

$$\sqrt[3]{\frac{3V}{4\pi}} = r$$

The radius is now expressed as a function of volume and can be determined for different values of V.

Reflecting

A.   Compare the domain and range of this function and its inverse.

B.   Will an **inverse of a function** always be a function? Explain.

C.   Why is it reasonable to switch the V and the r in Example 2 to determine the inverse relation?

APPLY the Math

| EXAMPLE 3 | Using an algebraic strategy to determine the inverse relation |

Given $f(x) = x^2$.

a) Find the inverse relation.

b) Compare the domain and range of the function and its inverse.

c) Determine if the inverse relation is also a function.

Solution

a) $y = x^2$ Rewrite the function using x and y.

         $x = y^2$ Interchange x and y in the relation.

    $\pm\sqrt{x} = \sqrt{y^2}$ Solve for y by taking the square root of both sides.

    $\pm\sqrt{x} = y$

b)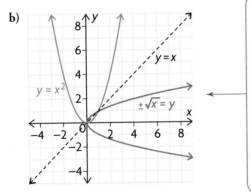

The graph of the inverse relation is a reflection of the original relation in the line $y = x$.

Only non-negative values of x work in the square root function. The square root of a negative number is undefined. Since $\pm$ in the inverse indicates that the output, y, will include both positive and negative values, the range will include all the real numbers.

> **Communication | Tip**
>
> The domain of the square root function is $\{x \in \mathbf{R} \mid x \geq 0\}$; we say the values of x are non-negative. The range of the exponential function $y = 2^x$ is $\{y \in \mathbf{R} \mid y > 0\}$; we say the values of y are positive. The distinction is because zero is neither negative nor positive.

The domain of $y = x^2$ is $\{x \in \mathbf{R}\}$. The range is $\{x \in \mathbf{R} \mid y \geq 0\}$.

The domain of the inverse relation is $\{x \in \mathbf{R} \mid x \geq 0\}$. The range is $\{y \in \mathbf{R}\}$.

c) The inverse relation is not a function, but it can be split in the middle into the two functions, $y = \sqrt{x}$ and $y = -\sqrt{x}$.

Based on the equation of the inverse relation, each input of x will have two outputs for y, one positive and one negative. The only exception is $x = 0$.

The inverse relation is useful to solve problems, particularly when you are given a value of the dependent variable and need to determine the value of the corresponding independent variable.

| EXAMPLE 4 | Selecting a strategy that involves the inverse relation to solve a problem |

Archaeologists use models for the relationship between height and footprint length to determine the height of a person based on the lengths of the bones they discover. The relationship between height, $h(x)$, in centimetres and footprint length, x, in centimetres is given by $h(x) = 1.1x + 143.6$. Use this relationship to predict the footprint length for a person who is 170 cm tall.

Solution

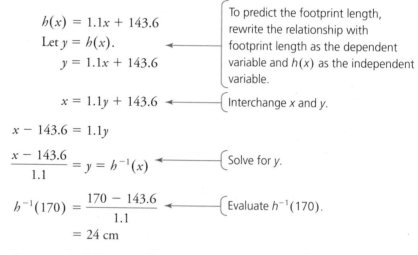

$$h(x) = 1.1x + 143.6$$
Let $y = h(x)$.
$$y = 1.1x + 143.6$$

To predict the footprint length, rewrite the relationship with footprint length as the dependent variable and $h(x)$ as the independent variable.

$$x = 1.1y + 143.6$$

Interchange x and y.

$$x - 143.6 = 1.1y$$

$$\frac{x - 143.6}{1.1} = y = h^{-1}(x)$$

Solve for y.

$$h^{-1}(170) = \frac{170 - 143.6}{1.1}$$

Evaluate $h^{-1}(170)$.

$$= 24 \text{ cm}$$

A person who is 170 cm tall may have a footprint length of 24 cm.

Communication | **Tip**

When an inverse relation is also a function, the notation $f^{-1}(x)$ can be used to define the inverse function.

In Summary

Key Ideas

- The inverse function of $f(x)$ is denoted by $f^{-1}(x)$. Function notation can only be used when the inverse is a function.
- The graph of the inverse function is a reflection in the line $y = x$.

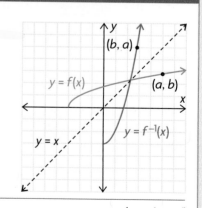

(*continued*)

Need to Know

- Not all inverse relations are functions. The domain and/or range of the original function may need to be restricted to ensure that the inverse of a function is also a function.
- To find the inverse algebraically, write the function equation using y instead of $f(x)$. Interchange x and y. Solve for y.
- If (a, b) represents a point on the graph of $f(x)$, then (b, a) represents a point on the graph of the corresponding f^{-1}.
- Given a table of values or a graph of a function, the independent and dependent variables can be interchanged to get a table of values or a graph of the inverse relation.
- The domain of a function is the range of its inverse. The range of a function is the domain of its inverse.

CHECK *Your Understanding*

1. Each of the following ordered pairs is a point on a function. State the corresponding point on the inverse relation.
   a) $(2, 5)$
   b) $(-5, -6)$
   c) $(4, -8)$
   d) $f(1) = 2$
   e) $g(-3) = 0$
   f) $h(0) = 7$

2. Given the domain and range of a function, state the domain and range of the inverse relation.
   a) $D = \{x \in \mathbf{R}\},\ R = \{y \in \mathbf{R}\}$
   b) $D = \{x \in \mathbf{R} \mid x \geq 2\},\ R = \{y \in \mathbf{R}\}$
   c) $D = \{x \in \mathbf{R} \mid x \geq -5\},\ R = \{y \in \mathbf{R} \mid y < 2\}$
   d) $D = \{x \in \mathbf{R} \mid x < -2\},\ R = \{y \in \mathbf{R} \mid -5 < y < 10\}$

3. Match the inverse relations to their corresponding functions.

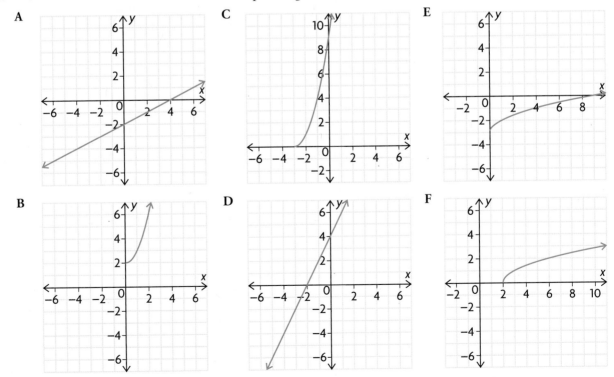

PRACTISING

4. Consider the function $f(x) = 2x^3 + 1$.

K

a) Find the ordered pair $(4, f(4))$ on the function.

b) Find the ordered pair on the inverse relation that corresponds to the ordered pair from part a).

c) Find the domain and range of f.

d) Find the domain and the range of the inverse relation of f.

e) Is the inverse relation a function? Explain.

5. Repeat question 4 for the function $g(x) = x^4 - 8$.

6. Graph each function and its inverse relation on the same set of axes. Determine whether the inverse relation is a function.

a) $f(x) = x^2 + 1$

b) $g(x) = \sin x$, where $-360° \leq x \leq 360°$

c) $h(x) = -x$

d) $m(x) = |x| + 1$

7. a) The equation $F = \frac{9}{5}C + 32$ can be used to convert a known

A Celsius temperature, C, to the equivalent Fahrenheit temperature, F. Find the inverse of this relation, and describe what it can be used for.

b) Use the equation given in part a) to convert 20 °C to its equivalent Fahrenheit temperature. Use the inverse relation to convert this Fahrenheit temperature back to its equivalent Celsius temperature.

8. a) The formula $A = \pi r^2$ is convenient for calculating the area of a circle when the radius is known. Find the inverse of the relation, and describe what it can be used for.

b) Use the equation given in part a) to calculate the area of a circle with a radius of 5 cm. (Express the area as an exact value in terms of π.) Use the inverse relation to calculate the radius of the circle with the area you calculated.

9. If $f(x) = kx^3 - 1$ and $f^{-1}(15) = 2$, find k.

T

10. Given the function $h(x) = 2x + 7$, find

a) $h(3)$

b) $h(9)$

c) $\dfrac{h(9) - h(3)}{9 - 3}$

d) $h^{-1}(3)$

e) $h^{-1}(9)$

f) $\dfrac{h^{-1}(9) - h^{-1}(3)}{9 - 3}$

11. Suppose that the variable a represents a particular student and $f(a)$ represents the student's overall average in all their subjects. Is the inverse relation of f a function? Explain.

12. Determine the inverse of each function.
   a) $f(x) = 3x + 4$ **c)** $g(x) = x^3 - 1$
   b) $h(x) = -x$ **d)** $m(x) = -2(x + 5)$

13. A function g is defined by $g(x) = 4(x - 3)^2 + 1$.
   a) Determine an equation for the inverse of $g(x)$.
   b) Solve for y in the equation for the inverse of $g(x)$.
   c) Graph $g(x)$ and its inverse using graphing technology.
   d) At what points do the graphs of $g(x)$ and its inverse intersect?
   e) State **restrictions** on the domain or range of g so that its inverse is a function.
   f) Suppose that the domain of $g(x)$ is $\{x \in \mathbf{R} \mid 2 \leq x \leq 5\}$. Is the inverse a function? Justify your answer.

14. A student writes, "The inverse of $y = -\sqrt{x + 2}$ is $y = x^2 - 2$." Explain why this statement is not true.

15. Do you have to restrict either the domain or the range of the function $y = \sqrt{x + 2}$ to make its inverse a function? Explain.

16. John and Katie are discussing inverse relationships. John says,
C "A function is a rule, and the inverse is the rule performed in reverse order with opposite operations. For example, suppose that you cube a number, divide by 4, and add 2. The inverse is found by subtracting 2, multiplying by 4, and taking the cube root." Is John correct? Justify your answer algebraically, numerically, and graphically.

Extending

17. $f(x) = x$ is an interesting function because it is its own inverse. Can you find three more functions that have the same property? Can you convince yourself that there are an infinite number of functions that satisfy this property?

18. The inverse relation of a function is also a function if the original function passes the horizontal line test (in other words, if any horizontal line hits the function in at most one location). Explain why this is true.

1.6 Piecewise Functions

YOU WILL NEED

- graph paper
- graphing calculator

GOAL

Understand, interpret, and graph situations that are described by piecewise functions.

LEARN ABOUT the Math

A city parking lot uses the following rules to calculate parking fees:

- A flat rate of \$5.00 for any amount of time up to and including the first hour
- A flat rate of \$12.50 for any amount of time over 1 h and up to and including 2 h
- A flat rate of \$13 plus \$3 per hour for each hour after 2 h

? How can you describe the function for parking fees in terms of the number of hours parked?

EXAMPLE 1 Representing the problem using a graphical model

Use a graphical model to represent the function for parking fees.

Solution

Time (h)	Parking Fee (\$)
0	0
0.25	5.00
0.50	5.00
1.00	5.00
1.25	12.50
1.50	12.50
2.00	12.50
2.50	14.50
3.00	16.00
4.00	19.00

Create a table of values.

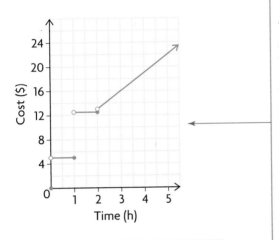

Plot the points in the table of values. Use a solid dot to include a value in an interval. Use an open dot to exclude a value from an interval.

There is a solid dot at (0, 0) and an open dot at (0, 5) because the parking fee at 0 h is $0.00.

There is a closed dot at (1, 5) and an open dot at (1, 12.50) because the parking fee at 1 h is $5.00.

There is a closed dot at (2, 12.50) and an open dot at (2, 13) because the parking fee at 2 h is $12.50.

The domain of this **piecewise function** is $x \geq 0$.

The function is linear over the domain, but it is discontinuous at $x = 0$, 1, and 2.

The last part of the graph continues in a straight line since the rate of change is constant after 2 h.

piecewise function
a function defined by using two or more rules on two or more intervals; as a result, the graph is made up of two or more pieces of similar or different functions

Each part of a piecewise function can be described using a specific equation for the interval of the domain.

EXAMPLE 2 Representing the problem using an algebraic model

Use an algebraic model to represent the function for parking fees.

Solution

$y_1 = 0$ if $x = 0$

$y_2 = 5$ if $0 < x \leq 1$

$y_3 = 12.50$ if $1 < x \leq 2$ — Write the relation for each rule.

$y_4 = 3x + 13$ if $x > 2$

$$f(x) = \begin{cases} 0, \text{ if } x = 0 \\ 5, \text{ if } 0 < x \le 1 \\ 12.50, \text{ if } 1 < x \le 2 \\ 3x + 13, \text{ if } x > 2 \end{cases}$$

Combine the relations into a piecewise function.

The domain of the function is $x \ge 0$.

The function is discontinuous at $x = 0$, 1, and 2 because there is a break in the function at each of these points.

Reflecting

A. How do you sketch the graph of a piecewise function?

B. How do you create the algebraic representation of a piecewise function?

C. How do you determine from a graph or from the algebraic representation of a piecewise function if there are any discontinuities?

APPLY the Math

EXAMPLE 3   Representing a piecewise function using a graph

Graph the following piecewise function.

$$f(x) = \begin{cases} x^2, \text{ if } x < 2 \\ 2x + 3, \text{ if } x \ge 2 \end{cases}$$

Solution

Create a table of values.

$f(x) = x^2$

x	f(x)
−2	4
−1	1
0	0
1	1
2	4

$f(x) = 2x + 3$

x	f(x)
2	7
3	9
4	11
5	13
6	15

From the equations given, the graph consists of part of a parabola that opens up and a line that rises from left to right.

Both tables include $x = 2$ since this is where the description of the function changes.

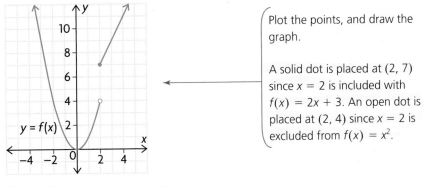

Plot the points, and draw the graph.

A solid dot is placed at (2, 7) since $x = 2$ is included with $f(x) = 2x + 3$. An open dot is placed at (2, 4) since $x = 2$ is excluded from $f(x) = x^2$.

$f(x)$ is discontinuous at $x = 2$.

EXAMPLE 4 | Representing a piecewise function using an algebraic model

Determine the algebraic representation of the following piecewise function.

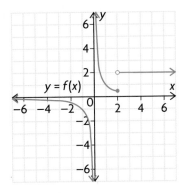

Solution

$$f(x) = \begin{cases} \dfrac{1}{x}, & \text{if } x \leq 2 \\ 2, & \text{if } x > 2 \end{cases}$$

The graph is made up of two pieces. One piece is part of the reciprocal function defined by $y = \frac{1}{x}$ when $x \leq 2$. The other piece is a horizontal line defined by $y = 2$ when $x > 2$. The solid dot indicates that point $\left(2, \frac{1}{2}\right)$ belongs with the reciprocal function.

EXAMPLE **5**

Reasoning about the continuity of a piecewise function

Is this function continuous at the points where it is pieced together? Explain.

$$g(x) = \begin{cases} x + 1, \text{ if } x \le 0 \\ 2x + 1, \text{ if } 0 < x < 3 \\ 4 - x^2, \text{ if } x \ge 3 \end{cases}$$

Solution

The function is continuous at the points where it is pieced together if the functions being joined have the same y-values at these points.

| The graph is made up of three pieces. One piece is part of an increasing line defined by $y = x + 1$ when $x \le 0$. The second piece is an increasing line defined by $y = 2x + 1$ when $0 < x < 3$. The third piece is part of a parabola that opens down, defined by $y = 4 - x^2$ when $x \ge 3$.

Calculate the values of the function at $x = 0$ using the relevant equations:

$y = x + 1 \qquad y = 2x + 1$

$y = 0 + 1 \qquad y = 2(0) + 1$

$y = 1 \qquad\quad y = 1$

The two y-values are the same, so the two linear pieces join each other at $x = 0$.

Calculate the values of the function at $x = 3$ using the relevant equations:

$y = 2x + 1 \qquad y = 4 - x^2$

$y = 2(3) + 1 \quad y = 4 - 3^2$

$y = 7 \qquad\qquad y = -5$

The two y-values are different, so the second linear piece does not join with the parabola at $x = 3$.

The function is discontinuous, since there is a break in the graph at $x = 3$.

Verify by graphing.

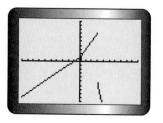

Tech | **Support**

For help using a graphing calculator to graph a piecewise function, see Technical Appendix, T-16.

In Summary

Key Ideas

- Some functions are represented by two or more "pieces." These functions are called piecewise functions.
- Each piece of a piecewise function is defined for a specific interval in the domain of the function.

Need to Know

- To graph a piecewise function, graph each piece of the function over the given interval.
- A piecewise function can be either continuous or not. If all the pieces of the function join together at the endpoints of the given intervals, then the function is continuous. Otherwise, it is discontinuous at these values of the domain.

CHECK *Your Understanding*

1. Graph each piecewise function.

   a) $f(x) = \begin{cases} 2, \text{if } x < 1 \\ 3x, \text{if } x \geq 1 \end{cases}$

   d) $f(x) = \begin{cases} |x + 2|, \text{if } x \leq -1 \\ -x^2 + 2, \text{if } x > -1 \end{cases}$

   b) $f(x) = \begin{cases} -2x, \text{if } x < 0 \\ x + 4, \text{if } x \geq 0 \end{cases}$

   e) $f(x) = \begin{cases} \sqrt{x}, \text{if } x < 4 \\ 2^x, \text{if } x \geq 4 \end{cases}$

   c) $f(x) = \begin{cases} |x|, \text{if } x \leq -2 \\ -x^2, \text{if } x > -2 \end{cases}$

   f) $f(x) = \begin{cases} \dfrac{1}{x}, \text{if } x < 1 \\ -x, \text{if } x \geq 1 \end{cases}$

2. State whether each function in question 1 is continuous or not. If not, state where it is discontinuous.

3. Write the algebraic representation of each piecewise function, using function notation.

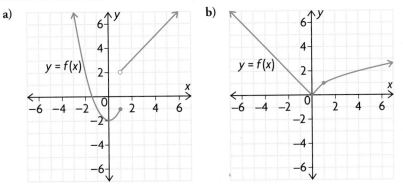

4. State the domain of each piecewise function in question 3, and comment on the continuity of the function.

PRACTISING

5. Graph the following piecewise functions. Determine whether each
K function is continuous or not, and state the domain and range of the
function.

a) $f(x) = \begin{cases} 2, \text{ if } x < -1 \\ 3, \text{ if } x \geq -1 \end{cases}$

c) $f(x) = \begin{cases} x^2 + 1, \text{ if } x < 2 \\ 2x + 1, \text{ if } x \geq 2 \end{cases}$

b) $f(x) = \begin{cases} -x, \text{ if } x \leq 0 \\ x, \text{ if } x > 0 \end{cases}$

d) $f(x) = \begin{cases} 1, \text{ if } x < -1 \\ x + 2, \text{ if } -1 \leq x \leq 3 \\ 5, \text{ if } x > 3 \end{cases}$

6. Graham's long-distance telephone plan includes the first 500 min per
A month in the $15.00 monthly charge. For each minute after
500 min, Graham is charged $0.02. Write a function that describes
Graham's total long-distance charge in terms of the number of long
distance minutes he uses in a month.

7. Many income tax systems are calculated using a tiered method. Under
a certain tax law, the first $100 000 of earnings are subject to a 35%
tax; earnings greater than $100 000 and up to $500 000 are subject to
a 45% tax. Any earnings greater than $500 000 are taxed at 55%.
Write a piecewise function that models this situation.

8. Find the value of k that makes the following function continuous.
T Graph the function.
$$f(x) = \begin{cases} x^2 - k, \text{ if } x < -1 \\ 2x - 1, \text{ if } x \geq -1 \end{cases}$$

9. The fish population, in thousands, in a lake at any time, x, in years is
modelled by the following function:
$$f(x) = \begin{cases} 2^x, \text{ if } 0 \leq x \leq 6 \\ 4x + 8, \text{ if } x > 6 \end{cases}$$
This function describes a sudden change in the population at time
$x = 6$, due to a chemical spill.
a) Sketch the graph of the piecewise function.
b) Describe the continuity of the function.
c) How many fish were killed by the chemical spill?
d) At what time did the population recover to the level it was before
the chemical spill?
e) Describe other events relating to fish populations in a lake that
might result in piecewise functions.

10. Create a flow chart that describes how to plot a piecewise function with two pieces. In your flow chart, include how to determine where the function is continuous.

11. **C** An absolute value function can be written as a piecewise function that involves two linear functions. Write the function $f(x) = |x + 3|$ as a piecewise function, and graph your piecewise function to check it.

12. The demand for a new CD is described by

$$D(p) = \begin{cases} \dfrac{1}{p^2}, \text{ if } 0 < p \le 15 \\ 0, \text{ if } p > 15 \end{cases}$$

where D is the demand for the CD at price p, in dollars. Determine where the demand function is discontinuous and continuous.

Extending

13. Consider a function, $f(x)$, that takes an element of its domain and rounds it down to the nearest 10. Thus, $f(15.6) = 10$, while $f(21.7) = 20$ and $f(30) = 30$. Draw the graph, and write the piecewise function. You may limit the domain to $x \in [0, 50]$. Why do you think graphs like this one are often referred to as *step functions*?

14. Explain why there is no value of k that will make the following function continuous.

$$f(x) = \begin{cases} 5x, \text{ if } x < -1 \\ x + k, \text{ if } -1 \le x \le 3 \\ 2x^2, \text{ if } x > 3 \end{cases}$$

15. The *greatest integer function* is a step function that is written as $f(x) = [x]$, where $f(x)$ is the greatest integer less than or equal to x. In other words, the greatest integer function rounds any number down to the nearest integer. For example, the greatest integer less than or equal to the number $[5.3]$ is 5, while the greatest integer less than or equal to the number $[-5.3]$ is -6. Sketch the graph of $f(x) = [x]$.

16. a) Create your own piecewise function using three different transformed parent functions.
    b) Graph the function you created in part a).
    c) Is the function you created continuous or not? Explain.
    d) If the function you created is not continuous, change the interval or adjust the transformations used as required to change it to a continuous function.

1.7 Exploring Operations with Functions

GOAL

Explore the properties of the sum, difference, and product of two functions.

A popular coffee house sells iced cappuccino for $4 and hot cappuccino for $3. The manager would like to predict the relationship between the outside temperature and the total daily revenue from each type of cappuccino sold. The manager discovers that every 1 °C increase in temperature leads to an increase in the sales of cold drinks by three cups per day and to a decrease in the sales of hot drinks by five cups per day.

The function $f(x) = 3x + 10$ can be used to model the number of iced cappuccinos sold.

The function $g(x) = -5x + 200$ can be used to model the number of hot cappuccinos sold.

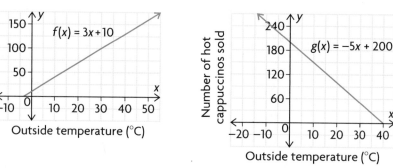

In both functions, x represents the daily average outside temperature. In the first function, $f(x)$ represents the daily average number of iced cappuccinos sold. In the second function, $g(x)$ represents the daily average number of hot cappuccinos sold.

? How does the outside temperature affect the daily revenue from cappuccinos sold?

A. Make a table of values for each function, with the temperature in intervals of 5°, from 0° to 40°.

B. What does $h(x) = f(x) + g(x)$ represent?

C. Simplify $h(x) = (3x + 10) + (-5x + 200)$.

D. Make a table of values for the function in part C, with the temperature in intervals of $5°$, from $0°$ to $40°$. How do the values compare with the values in each table you made in part A? How do the domains of $f(x)$, $g(x)$, and $h(x)$ compare?

E. What does $h(x) = f(x) - g(x)$ represent?

F. Simplify $h(x) = (3x + 10) - (-5x + 200)$.

G. Make a table of values for the function in part F, with the temperature in intervals of $5°$, from $0°$ to $40°$. How do the values compare with the values in each table you made in part A? How do the domains of $f(x)$, $g(x)$, and $h(x)$ compare?

H. What does $R(x) = 4f(x) + 3g(x)$ represent?

I. Simplify $R(x) = 4(3x + 10) + 3(-5x + 200)$.

J. Make a table of values for the function in part I, with the temperature in intervals of $5°$, from $0°$ to $40°$. How do the values compare with the values in each table you made in part A? How do the domains of $f(x)$, $g(x)$, and $R(x)$ compare?

K. How does temperature affect the daily revenue from cappuccinos sold?

Reflecting

L. Explain how the sum function, $h(x)$, would be different if
a) both $f(x)$ and $g(x)$ were increasing functions
b) both $f(x)$ and $g(x)$ were decreasing functions

M. What does the function $k(x) = g(x) - f(x)$ represent? Is its graph identical to the graph of $h(x) = f(x) - g(x)$? Explain.

N. Determine the function $h(x) = f(x) \times g(x)$. Does this function have any meaning in the context of the daily revenue from cappuccinos sold? Explain how the table of values for this function is related to the tables of values you made in part A.

O. If you are given the graphs of two functions, explain how you could create a graph that represents
a) the sum of the two functions
b) the difference between the two functions
c) the product of the two functions

FURTHER *Your Understanding*

1. Let $f = \{(-4, 4), (-2, 4), (1, 3), (3, 5), (4, 6)\}$ and
   $g = \{(-4, 2), (-2, 1), (0, 2), (1, 2), (2, 2), (4, 4)\}$.
   Determine:

   a) $f + g$ b) $f - g$ c) $g - f$ d) fg

2. Use the graphs of f and g to sketch the graphs of $f + g$.

   a)   b)

   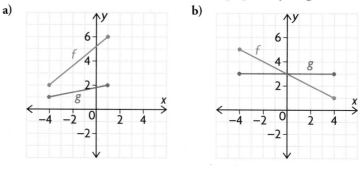

3. Use the graphs of f and g to sketch the graphs of $f - g$.

   a)   b)

   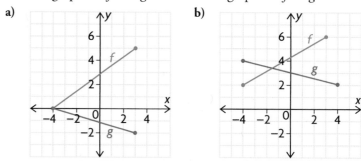

4. Use the graphs of f and g to sketch the graphs of fg.

a)   b)

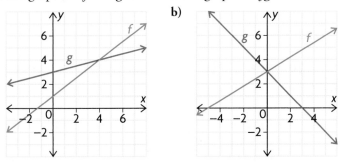

5. Determine the equation of each new function, and then sketch its graph.
  a) $h(x) = f(x) + g(x)$, where $f(x) = x^2$ and $g(x) = -x^2$
  b) $p(x) = m(x) - n(x)$, where $m(x) = x^2$ and $n(x) = -7x + 12$
  c) $r(x) = s(x) + t(x)$, where $s(x) = |x|$ and $t(x) = 2^x$
  d) $a(x) = b(x) \times c(x)$, where $b(x) = x$ and $c(x) = x^2$

6. a) Using the graphs you sketched in question 5, compare and contrast the relationship between the properties of the original functions and the properties of the new function.
  b) Which properties of the original functions determined the properties of the new function?

7. Let $f(x) = x + 3$ and $g(x) = -x^2 + 5$, $x \in \mathbf{R}$.
  a) Sketch each graph on the same set of axes.
  b) Make a table of values for $-3 \leq x \leq 3$, and determine the corresponding values of $h(x) = f(x) \times g(x)$.
  c) Use the table to sketch $h(x)$ on the same axes. Describe the shape of the graph.
  d) Determine the algebraic model for $h(x)$. What is its degree?
  e) What is the domain of $h(x)$? How does this domain compare with the domains of $f(x)$ and $g(x)$?

8. Let $f(x) = x^2 + 2$ and $g(x) = x^2 - 2$, $x \in \mathbf{R}$.
  a) Sketch each graph on the same set of axes.
  b) Make a table of values for $-3 \leq x \leq 3$, and determine the corresponding values of $h(x) = f(x) \times g(x)$.
  c) Use the table to sketch $h(x)$ on the same axes. Describe the shape of the graph.
  d) Determine the algebraic model for $h(x)$. What is its degree?
  e) What is the domain of $h(x)$?

FREQUENTLY ASKED Questions

Study | Aid

- See Lesson 1.4, Examples 2, 3, and 4.
- Try Chapter Review Questions 7, 8, and 9.

Q: **In what order are transformations performed on a function?**

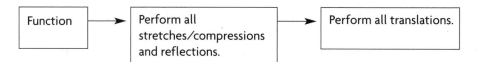

A: All stretches/compressions (vertical and horizontal) and reflections can be applied at the same time by multiplying the x- and y-coordinates on the parent function by the appropriate factors. Both vertical and horizontal translations can then be applied by adding or subtracting the relevant numbers to the x- and y-coordinates of the points.

Study | Aid

- See Lesson 1.5, Examples 1, 2, and 3.
- Try Chapter Review Questions 10 to 13.

Q: **How do you find the inverse relation of a function?**

A: You can find the inverse relation of a function numerically, graphically, or algebraically.

To find the inverse relation of a function numerically, using a table of values, switch the values for the independent and dependent variables.

$f(x)$	f^{-1}
(x, y)	(y, x)

To find the inverse relation graphically, reflect the graph of the function in the line $y = x$. This is accomplished by switching the x- and y-coordinates in each ordered pair.

To find the algebraic representation of the inverse relation, interchange the positions of the x- and y-variables in the function and solve for y.

Q: Is an inverse of a function always a function?

A: No; if an element in the domain of the original function corresponds to more than one number in the range, then the inverse relation is not a function.

Study | Aid

• See Lesson 1.5, Examples 1, 2, and 3.
• Try Chapter Review Questions 10 to 13.

Q: What is a piecewise function?

A: A piecewise function is a function that has two or more function rules for different parts of its domain.

For example, the function defined by $f(x) = \begin{cases} -x^2, & \text{if } x < 0 \\ -x + 1, & \text{if } x \geq 0 \end{cases}$

consists of two pieces. The first equation defines half of a parabola that opens down when $x < 0$. The second equation defines a decreasing line with a y-intercept of 1 when $x \geq 0$. The graph confirms this.

Study | Aid

• See Lesson 1.6, Examples 1, 2, 3, and 4.
• Try Chapter Review Questions 14 to 17.

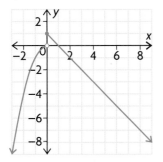

Q: If you are given the graphs or equations of two functions, how can you create a new function?

A: You can create a new function by adding, subtracting, or multiplying the two given functions.

This can be done graphically by adding, subtracting, or multiplying the y-coordinates in each pair of ordered pairs that have identical x-coordinates.

This can be done algebraically by adding, subtracting, or multiplying the expressions for the dependent variable and then simplifying.

Study | Aid

• See Lesson 1.7.
• Try Chapter Review Questions 18 to 21.

PRACTICE Questions

Lesson 1.1

1. Determine whether each relation is a function, and state its domain and range.

a)

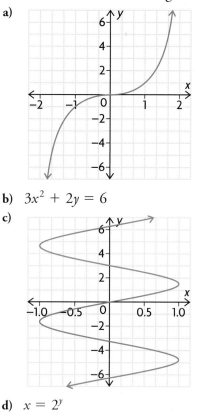

b) $3x^2 + 2y = 6$

c)

d) $x = 2^y$

2. A cell phone company charges a monthly fee of $30, plus $0.02 per minute of call time.
   a) Write the monthly cost function, $C(t)$, where t is the amount of time in minutes of call time during a month.
   b) Find the domain and range of C.

Lesson 1.2

3. Graph $f(x) = 2|x + 3| - 1$, and state the domain and range.

4. Describe this interval using absolute value notation.

$$\xleftarrow{\hspace{1cm}} -4\ -3\ -2\ -1\ \ 0\ \ 1\ \ 2\ \ 3\ \ 4 \xrightarrow{\hspace{1cm}}$$

Lesson 1.3

5. For each pair of functions, give a characteristic that the two functions have in common and a characteristic that distinguishes them.
   a) $f(x) = x^2$ and $g(x) = \sin x$
   b) $f(x) = \dfrac{1}{x}$ and $g(x) = x$
   c) $f(x) = |x|$ and $g(x) = x^2$
   d) $f(x) = 2^x$ and $g(x) = x$

6. Identify the intervals of increase/decrease, the symmetry, and the domain and range of each function.
   a) $f(x) = 3x$
   b) $f(x) = x^2 + 2$
   c) $f(x) = 2^x - 1$

Lesson 1.4

7. For each of the following equations, state the parent function and the transformations that were applied. Graph the transformed function.
   a) $y = |x + 1|$
   b) $y = -0.25\sqrt{3(x + 7)}$
   c) $y = -2\sin(3x) + 1,\ 0 \le x \le 360°$
   d) $y = 2^{-2x} - 3$

8. The graph of $y = x^2$ is horizontally stretched by a factor of 2, reflected in the x-axis, and shifted 3 units down. Find the equation that results from the transformation, and graph it.

9. $(2, 1)$ is a point on the graph of $y = f(x)$. Find the corresponding point on the graph of each of the following functions.
   a) $y = -f(-x) + 2$
   b) $y = f(-2(x + 9)) - 7$
   c) $y = f(x - 2) + 2$
   d) $y = 0.3f(5(x - 3))$
   e) $y = 1 - f(1 - x)$
   f) $y = -f(2(x - 8))$

Lesson 1.5

10. For each point on a function, state the corresponding point on the inverse relation.

a) $(1, 2)$ d) $f(5) = 7$

b) $(-1, -9)$ e) $g(0) = -3$

c) $(0, 7)$ f) $h(1) = 10$

11. Given the domain and range of a function, state the domain and range of the inverse relation.

a) $D = \{x \in \mathbf{R}\}$, $R = \{y \in \mathbf{R} | -2 < y < 2\}$

b) $D = \{x \in \mathbf{R} | x \geq 7\}$, $R = \{y \in \mathbf{R} | y < 12\}$

12. Graph each function and its inverse relation on the same set of axes. Determine whether the inverse relation is a function.

a) $f(x) = x^2 - 4$ b) $g(x) = 2^x$

13. Find the inverse of each function.

a) $f(x) = 2x + 1$ b) $g(x) = x^3$

Lesson 1.6

14. Graph the following function. Determine whether it is discontinuous and, if so, where. State the domain and the range of the function.

$$f(x) = \begin{cases} 2x, & \text{if } x < 1 \\ x + 1, & \text{if } x \geq 1 \end{cases}$$

15. Write the algebraic representation for the following piecewise function, using function notation.

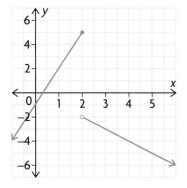

16. If $f(x) = \begin{cases} x^2 + 1, & \text{if } x < 1 \\ 3x, & \text{if } x \geq 1 \end{cases}$

is $f(x)$ continuous at $x = 1$? Explain.

17. A telephone company charges $30 a month and gives the customer 200 free call minutes. After the 200 min, the company charges $0.03 a minute.

a) Write the function using function notation.

b) Find the cost for talking 350 min in a month.

c) Find the cost for talking 180 min in a month.

Lesson 1.7

18. Given $f = \{(0, 6), (1, 3), (4, 7), (5, 8)\}$ and $g = \{(-1, 2), (1, 4), (2, 3), (4, 8), (8, 9)\}$, determine the following.

a) $f(x) + g(x)$

b) $f(x) - g(x)$

c) $[f(x)][g(x)]$

19. Given $f(x) = 2x^2 - 2x$, $-2 \leq x \leq 3$ and $g(x) = -4x$, $-3 \leq x \leq 5$, graph the following.

a) f d) $f - g$

b) g e) fg

c) $f + g$

20. $f(x) = x^2 + 2x$ and $g(x) = x + 1$. Match the answer with the operation.

Answer: Operation:

a) $x^3 + 3x^2 + 2x$ A $f(x) + g(x)$

b) $-x^2 - x + 1$ B $f(x) - g(x)$

c) $x^2 + 3x + 1$ C $g(x) - f(x)$

d) $x^2 + x - 1$ D $f(x) \times g(x)$

21. $f(x) = x^3 + 2x^2$ and $g(x) = -x + 6$,

a) Complete the table.

x	-3	-2	-1	0	1	2
f(x)						
g(x)						
(f + g)(x)						

b) Use the table to graph $f(x)$ and $g(x)$ on the same axes.

c) Graph $(f + g)(x)$ on the same axes as part b).

d) State the equation of $(f + g)(x)$.

e) Verify the equation of $(f + g)(x)$ using two of the ordered pairs in the table.

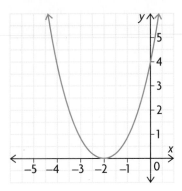

1. Consider the graph of the relation shown.
   a) Is the relation a function? Explain.
   b) State the domain and range.

2. Given the following information about a function:
   - $D = \{x \in \mathbf{R}\}$
   - $R = \{y \in \mathbf{R} \mid y \geq -2\}$
   - decreasing on the interval $(-\infty, 0)$
   - increasing on the interval $(0, \infty)$
   a) What is a possible parent function?
   b) Draw a possible graph of the function.
   c) Describe the transformation that was performed.

3. Show algebraically that the function $f(x) = |3x| + x^2$ is an even function.

4. Both $f(x) = x^2$ and $g(x) = 2^x$ have a domain of all real numbers. List as many characteristics as you can to distinguish the two functions.

5. Describe the transformations that must be applied to $y = x^2$ to obtain the function $f(x) = -(x + 3)^2 - 5$, then graph the function.

6. Given the graph shown, describe the transformations that were performed to get this function. Write the algebraic representation, using function notation.

7. $(3, 5)$ is a point on the graph of $y = f(x)$. Find the corresponding point on the graph of each of the following relations.
   a) $y = 3f(-x + 1) + 2$ b) $y = f^{-1}(x)$

8. Find the inverse of $f(x) = -2(x + 1)$.

9. A certain tax policy states that the first \$50 000 of income is taxed at 5% and any income above \$50 000 is taxed at 12%.
   a) Calculate the tax on \$125 000.
   b) Write a function that models the tax policy.

10. a) Sketch the graph of $f(x)$ where $f(x) = \begin{cases} 2^x + 1, & \text{if } x < 0 \\ \sqrt{x} + 3, & \text{if } x \geq 0 \end{cases}$
    b) Is $f(x)$ continuous over its entire domain? Explain.
    c) State the intervals of increase and decrease.
    d) State the domain and range of this function.

Modelling with Functions

In 1950, a team of chemists led by Dr. W. F. Libby developed a method for determining the age of any natural specimen, up to approximately 60 000 years of age. Dr. Libby's method is based on the fact that all living materials contain traces of carbon-14. His method involves measuring the percent of carbon-14 that remains when a specimen is found.

The percent of carbon-14 that remains in a specimen after various numbers of years is shown in the table below.

Years	Carbon-14 Remaining (%)
5 730	50.0
11 460	25.0
17 190	12.5
22 920	6.25
28 650	3.125
34 380	1.5625

? How can you use the function $P(t) = 100(0.5)^{\frac{t}{5730}}$ to model this situation and determine the age of a natural specimen?

A. What percent of carbon is remaining for $t = 0$? What does this mean in the context of Dr. Libby's method?

B. Draw a graph of the function $P(t) = 100(0.5)^{\frac{t}{5730}}$, using the given table of values.

C. What is a reasonable domain for $P(t)$? What is a reasonable range?

D. Determine the approximate age of a specimen, given that $P(t) = 70$.

E. Draw the graph of the inverse function.

F. What information does the inverse function provide?

G. What are the domain and range of the inverse function?

Task | *Checklist*

✔ Did you show all your steps?

✔ Did you draw and label your graphs accurately?

✔ Did you determine the age of the specimen that had 70% carbon-14 remaining?

✔ Did you explain your thinking clearly?

Functions: Understanding Rates of Change

▶ **GOALS**

You will be able to

- Calculate an average rate of change of a function given a table of values, a graph, or an equation

- Estimate the instantaneous rate of change of a function given a table of values, a graph, or an equation

- Interpret the average rate of change of a function over a given interval

- Interpret the instantaneous rate of change of a function at a given point

- Solve problems that involve rate of change

❓ At what point on this hill is the speed of the roller coaster the fastest?

SKILLS AND CONCEPTS *You Need*

Study Aid

• For help, see the Review of Essential Skills found at the Nelson Advanced Functions website.

Question	Appendix
1	R–5
3	R–6
4	R–8
6	R–12

1. Determine the slope of the line through each pair of points.
   a) A $(2, 3)$ and B $(5, 7)$
   b) C $(3, -1)$ and D $(-4, 5)$

2. Calculate the finite differences for each table, identify the type of function that each table represents, and provide a reason for your choice.

a)

x	1	2	3	4	5	6
y	1	-1	-5	-13	-29	-61

b)

x	1	2	3	4	5	6
y	0	11	28	51	80	115

3. Determine the zeros for each of the following functions.
   a) $g(x) = 2x^2 - x - 6$
   b) $h(x) = 2^x - 1$
   c) $j(x) = \sin(x - 45°), 0° \le x \le 360°$
   d) $k(x) = 2\cos x, -360° \le x \le 0°$

4. Given $y = f(x)$, describe how the graph of $f(x)$ is transformed in each of the following functions.
   a) $y = \frac{1}{2}f(x)$
   b) $y = 2f(x - 4)$
   c) $y = -3f(x) + 7$
   d) $y = 5f(x - 3) - 2$

5. Suppose you invest \$1000 in a savings account that pays $8\%/a$ compounded annually.
   a) Write an equation for the amount of money you will have after t years.
   b) How much money will you have after three years?
   c) Does the amount of money in your account increase at a constant rate each year? Explain.

6. The height above the ground of one of the seats of a Ferris wheel, in metres, can be modelled by the function $h(t) = 8 + 7\sin(15°t)$, where t is measured in seconds.
   a) What is the maximum and minimum height reached by any seat?
   b) How long does one seat on this ride take to rotate back to its starting point?
   c) After 30 s, what will the height of the seat be?

7. Create a chart to show what you know about rates of change in **linear** and **nonlinear relations**.

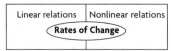

APPLYING *What You Know*

Safe Driving

It is important for drivers to know how much time they need to come to a safe stop. The time needed to stop depends on the speed of the vehicle.

The following table gives safe stopping distances on dry pavement.

Speed (km/h)	Reaction-Time Distance (m)	Braking Distance (m)	Overall Stopping Distance (m)
0	0.00	0.00	0.00
20	8.33	1.77	10.10
40	16.67	7.09	23.77
60	25.00	15.96	40.96
80	33.33	28.38	61.71
100	41.67	44.35	86.02

? What might be realistic reaction-time distances, braking distances, and overall stopping distances for speeds of 70 km/h and 120 km/h?

A. What type of function best models the reaction-time distances for the given speeds? Explain how you know.

B. Sketch a graph and determine an equation for the type of function you chose in part A, using the data in the table.

C. What type of function best models the braking distances for the given speeds? Explain how you know.

D. Sketch a graph and determine an equation for the type of function you chose in part C, using the data in the table.

E. Do any of the three distances in the table increase at a constant rate? Explain.

F. What other factors, in addition to the speed of the vehicle, may affect the overall stopping distance?

G. Use the graphs and equations you found to predict the reaction times, braking distances, and overall stopping distances, in metres, for speeds of 70 km/h and 120 km/h.

Determining Average Rate of Change

average rate of change

in a relation, the change in the quantity given by the dependent variable (Δy) divided by the corresponding change in the quantity represented by the independent variable (Δx); for a function $y = f(x)$, the average rate of change in the internal $x_1 \le x \le x_2$ is $\dfrac{\Delta y}{\Delta x} = \dfrac{f(x_2) - f(x_1)}{x_2 - x_1}$

GOAL

Calculate and interpret the average rate of change on an interval of the independent variable.

LEARN ABOUT the Math

The following table represents the growth of a bacteria population over a 10 h period.

Time (h)	0	2	4	6	8	10
Number of Bacteria	850	1122	1481	1954	2577	3400

? During which 2 h interval did the bacteria population grow the fastest?

EXAMPLE 1   Reasoning about rate of change

Use the data in the table of values to determine the 2 h interval in which the bacteria population grew the fastest.

Solution A: Using a table

Time Interval (h)	Δb = Change in Number of Bacteria	Δt = Change in Time (h)	$\dfrac{\Delta b}{\Delta t}$ = Average Rate of Change (bacteria/h)
$0 \le t \le 2$	$1122 - 850 = 272$	$2 - 0 = 2$	$\dfrac{272}{2} = 136$
$2 \le t \le 4$	$1481 - 1122 = 359$	$4 - 2 = 2$	$\dfrac{359}{2} = 179.5$
$4 \le t \le 6$	$1954 - 1481 = 473$	$6 - 4 = 2$	$\dfrac{473}{2} = 236.5$
$6 \le t \le 8$	$2577 - 1954 = 623$	$8 - 6 = 2$	$\dfrac{623}{2} = 311.5$
$8 \le t \le 10$	$3400 - 2577 = 823$	$10 - 8 = 2$	$\dfrac{823}{2} = 411.5$

Calculate the **average rate of change** in the dependent variable (bacteria population) for each 2 h interval. Divide the change in the number of bacteria by the corresponding change in time (2 h for each interval). Identify the interval with the greatest change in population.

The greatest change in the bacteria population occurred during the last 2 h, when the population increased by an average of 412 bacteria per hour.

The average rate of change is expressed using the units of the two related quantities.

Solution B: Using points on a graph

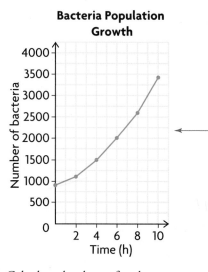

Bacteria Population Growth

Create a scatter plot using the data in the table of values. Draw a **secant line** that passes through each pair of the endpoints for each 2 h interval. The slope of each secant line is equivalent to the average rate of change in the number of bacteria over each interval.

From the graph, it appears that the secant line with the greatest slope occurs during the last interval, from 8 to 10 h.

secant line

a line that passes through two points on the graph of a relation

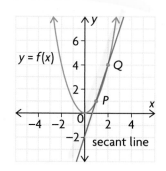

secant line

Calculate the slope of each secant line to verify.

$$m_1 = \frac{1122 - 850}{2 - 0} = \frac{272}{2}$$

$$= 136$$

Recall that $m = \frac{y_2 - y_1}{x_2 - x_1}$, where (x_1, y_1) and (x_2, y_2) are points on the line.

In the first interval, the secant line passes through $(0, 850)$ and $(2, 1122)$.

$$m_2 = \frac{1481 - 1122}{4 - 2}$$

$$= 179.5$$

Perform the same calculations for the other intervals.

$$m_3 = \frac{1954 - 1481}{6 - 4}$$

$$= 236.5$$

$$m_4 = \frac{2577 - 1954}{8 - 6}$$

$$= 311.5$$

$$m_5 = \frac{3400 - 2577}{10 - 8}$$

$$= 411.5$$

The greatest change in the bacteria population occurred when the secant line is the steepest, during the last 2 h. The bacteria population increased by an average of 412 bacteria per hour in this interval.

Slope has no units, but average rate of change does.

Reflecting

A. Why is the average rate of change of the bacteria population positive on each interval, and what does this mean? How is this represented by the secant lines on the graph of the data?

B. How is calculating an average rate of change like calculating the slope of a secant line?

C. Why does rate of change have units, even though slope does not?

D. Why is the rate of change in the bacteria population not a constant?

APPLY the Math

EXAMPLE **2**	Reasoning about average rates of change in linear relationships

Sarah rents a car from a rental company. She is charged $35 a day, plus a fee of $0.15/km for the distances she drives each day. The equation $C(d) = 0.15d + 35$ can be used to calculate her daily cost to rent the car, where $C(d)$ is her daily cost in dollars and d is the daily distance she drives in kilometres.

Discuss the average rate of change of her daily costs in relation to the distance she drives.

Solution

Graph the equation $C(d) = 0.15d + 35$.

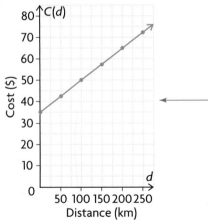

Daily Car Rental Cost

The relationship is linear, so the rate of change in the daily cost is constant. This means that the average rate of change between any two points on the graph is always constant. The secant lines that are drawn between any two pairs of points on the graph have the same slope.

Using the distance interval $0 \leq d \leq 100$,

$$\frac{\Delta C}{\Delta d} = \frac{C(100) - C(0)}{100 - 0}$$

$$= \frac{50 - 35}{100} = \$0.15/\text{km}$$

> Calculate some average rates of change in the daily cost, using different distance intervals to verify.

Using the distance interval $100 \leq d \leq 250$,

$$\frac{\Delta C}{\Delta d} = \frac{C(250) - C(100)}{250 - 100}$$

$$= \frac{72.50 - 50}{150} = \$0.15/\text{km}$$

The farther she drives each day, the more she will pay to rent the car. However, the rate at which the daily cost increases does not change. For every additional kilometre she drives, her daily cost increases by $0.15.

EXAMPLE 3 Using a graph to determine the average rate of change

Andrew drains the water from a hot tub. The tub holds 1600 L of water. It takes 2 h for the water to drain completely. The volume V, in litres, of water remaining in the tub at various times t, in minutes, is shown in the table and graph.

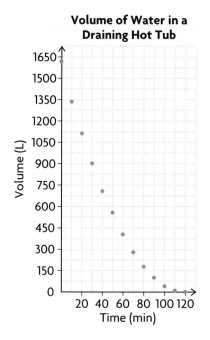

Volume of Water in a Draining Hot Tub

Time (min)	Volume (L)
0	1600
10	1344
20	1111
30	900
40	711
50	544
60	400
70	278
80	178
90	100
100	44
110	10
120	0

a) Calculate the average rate of change in volume during each of the following time intervals.

    i) $30 \leq t \leq 90$ **iii)** $90 \leq t \leq 110$

    ii) $60 \leq t \leq 90$ **iv)** $110 \leq t \leq 120$

b) Why is the rate of change in volume negative during each of these time intervals?

c) Does the hot tub drain at a constant rate? Explain.

Solution

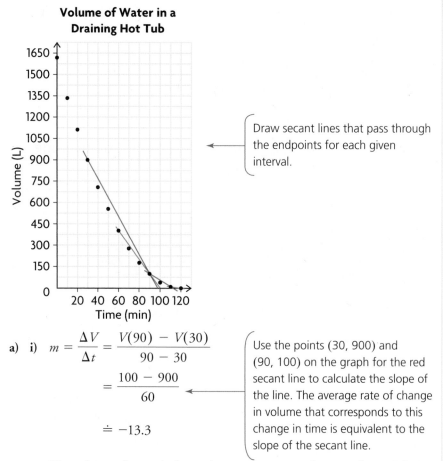

Volume of Water in a Draining Hot Tub

Draw secant lines that pass through the endpoints for each given interval.

a) **i)**
$$m = \frac{\Delta V}{\Delta t} = \frac{V(90) - V(30)}{90 - 30}$$
$$= \frac{100 - 900}{60}$$
$$\doteq -13.3$$

Use the points (30, 900) and (90, 100) on the graph for the red secant line to calculate the slope of the line. The average rate of change in volume that corresponds to this change in time is equivalent to the slope of the secant line.

The volume of water is decreasing, on average, at the rate of 13.3 L/min between 30 min and 90 min.

ii)
$$m = \frac{\Delta V}{\Delta t} = \frac{V(90) - V(60)}{90 - 60}$$
$$= \frac{100 - 400}{30}$$
$$= -10$$

Use the points (60, 400) and (90, 100) on the graph for the blue secant line to calculate its slope.

The volume of water is decreasing, on average, at the rate of 10 L/min between 60 min and 90 min.

iii) $m = \dfrac{\Delta V}{\Delta t} = \dfrac{V(110) - V(90)}{110 - 90}$ Use the points (90, 100) and (110, 10) on the graph for the green secant line to calculate its slope.

$= \dfrac{10 - 100}{20}$

$= -4.5$

The volume of water is decreasing, on average, at the rate of 4.5 L/min between 90 min and 110 min.

iv) $m = \dfrac{\Delta V}{\Delta t} = \dfrac{V(120) - V(110)}{120 - 110}$ Use the points (110, 10) and (120, 0) on the graph for the purple secant line to calculate its slope.

$= \dfrac{0 - 10}{10}$

$= -1$

The volume of water is decreasing, on average, at the rate of 1 L/min between 110 min and 120 min.

b) The volume decreases as the time increases. So the numerator in each slope calculation is negative, while the denominator is positive. This makes the **rational number** that represents the rate of change negative.

The water is flowing out of the tub, so the volume that remains in the tub decreases with time.

c) The water is not draining at a constant rate over the 2 h period. This can be seen from the graph, because it is a non-linear relationship. The water is draining from the tub faster over time intervals at the beginning of the 2 h period. As the volume of water decreases, the pressure also decreases, causing the water to flow out of the tub more slowly.

Looking at the slope calculations, the slopes of the red and blue secant lines have a greater **magnitude** than the slopes of the green and purple secant lines. Also, the slopes of the secant lines between points over each 10 min interval are smaller in magnitude as time increases.

magnitude
the absolute value of a quantity

If you are given the equation of a relation or function, the average rate of change on a given interval can be calculated.

EXAMPLE 4 | Using an equation to determine the average rate of change

A rock is tossed upward from a cliff that is 120 m above the water. The height of the rock above the water is modelled by $h(t) = -5t^2 + 10t + 120$, where $h(t)$ is the height in metres and t is time in seconds.

a) Calculate the average rate of change in height during each of the following time intervals.

   i) $0 \le t \le 1$ **ii)** $1 \le t \le 2$ **iii)** $2 \le t \le 3$ **iv)** $3 \le t \le 4$

b) As the time increases, what do you notice about the average rate of change in height during each 1 s interval? What does this mean?

c) Describe what the average rate of change means in this situation.

Solution

a) i) $\dfrac{\Delta h}{\Delta t} = \dfrac{h(1) - h(0)}{1 - 0}$

$= \dfrac{125 - 120}{1} = 5 \text{ m/s}$

ii) $\dfrac{\Delta h}{\Delta t} = \dfrac{h(2) - h(1)}{2 - 1}$

$= \dfrac{120 - 125}{1} = -5 \text{ m/s}$

iii) $\dfrac{\Delta h}{\Delta t} = \dfrac{h(3) - h(2)}{3 - 2}$

$= \dfrac{105 - 120}{1} = -15 \text{ m/s}$

iv) $\dfrac{\Delta h}{\Delta t} = \dfrac{h(4) - h(3)}{4 - 3}$

$= \dfrac{80 - 105}{1} = -25 \text{ m/s}$

> Substitute $t = 1$ and $t = 0$ into the equation to determine $h(1)$ and $h(0)$.
>
> Calculate the change in height. Divide by the corresponding change in time to determine the average rate of change.
>
> Repeat this process for the other three intervals.

b) The average rates of change are positive and then negative because the rock's height increases and then decreases. The average rates of change in height are also changing for each 1 s interval. After 1 s, as time increases, the rock is dropping a greater distance. The magnitude of the average rates of change are increasing. The rock is not falling at a constant rate.

> Between 0 s and 1 s, the rock rises 5 m.
> Between 1 s and 2 s, the rock drops 5 m.
> Between 2 s and 3 s, the rock drops 15 m.
> Between 3 s and 4 s, the rock drops 25 m.

c) Since the rate of change compares a change in distance over an interval of time, the rate of change represents the speed of the rock over the interval.

> In this situation, as time increases, the rock picks up speed once it has passed its maximum height, because the distance it drops increases with each second.

In Summary

Key Ideas

- The average rate of change is the change in the quantity represented by the dependent variable (Δy) divided by the corresponding change in the quantity represented by the independent variable (Δx) over an interval. Algebraically, the average rate of change for any function $y = f(x)$ over the interval $x_1 \le x \le x_2$ can be determined by

$$\text{Average rate of change} = \frac{\text{change in } y}{\text{change in } x}$$

$$= \frac{\Delta y}{\Delta x}$$

$$= \frac{f(x_2) - f(x_1)}{x_2 - x_1}$$

- Graphically, the average rate of change for any function $y = f(x)$ over the interval $x_1 \le x \le x_2$ is equivalent to the slope of the secant line passing through two points (x_1, y_1) and (x_2, y_2).

$$\text{Average rate of change} = m_{secant} = \frac{\text{change in } y}{\text{change in } x}$$

$$= \frac{\Delta y}{\Delta x}$$

$$= \frac{y_2 - y_1}{x_2 - x_1}$$

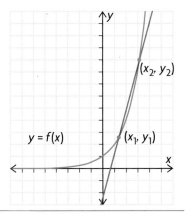

Need to Know

- Average rate of change is expressed using the units of the two quantities that are related to each other.
- A positive average rate of change indicates that the quantity represented by the dependent variable is increasing on the specified interval, compared with the quantity represented by the independent variable. Graphically, this is indicated by a secant line that has a positive slope (the secant line rises from left to right).
- A negative average rate of change indicates that the quantity represented by the dependent variable is decreasing on the specified interval, compared with the quantity represented by the independent variable. Graphically, this is indicated by a secant line that has a negative slope (the secant line falls from left to right).
- All linear relationships have a constant rate of change. Average rate of change calculations over different intervals of the independent variable give the same result.
- Nonlinear relationships do not have a constant rate of change. Average rate of change calculations over different intervals of the independent variable give different results.

CHECK Your Understanding

1. Calculate the average rate of change for the function $g(x) = 4x^2 - 5x + 1$ over each interval.
   a) $2 \leq x \leq 4$
   b) $2 \leq x \leq 3$
   c) $2 \leq x \leq 2.5$
   d) $2 \leq x \leq 2.25$
   e) $2 \leq x \leq 2.1$
   f) $2 \leq x \leq 2.01$

2. An emergency flare is shot into the air. Its height, in metres, above the ground at various times in its flight is given in the following table.

Time (s)	0.0	0.5	1.0	1.5	2.0	2.5	3.0	3.5	4.0
Height (m)	2.00	15.75	27.00	35.75	42.00	45.75	47.00	45.75	42.00

   a) Determine the average rate of change in the height of the flare during each interval.
   i) $1.0 \leq t \leq 2.0$
   ii) $3.0 \leq t \leq 4.0$
   b) Use your results from part a) to explain what is happening to the height of the flare during each interval.

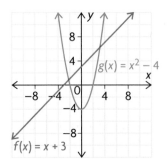

3. Given the functions $f(x)$ and $g(x)$ shown on the graph, discuss how the average rates of change, $\frac{\Delta y}{\Delta x}$, differ in each relationship.

PRACTISING

4. This table shows the growth of a crowd at a rally over a 3 h period.

K

Time (h)	0.0	0.5	1.0	1.5	2.0	2.5	3.0
Number of People	0	176	245	388	402	432	415

   a) Determine the average rate of change in the size of the crowd for each half hour of the rally.
   b) What do these numbers represent?
   c) What do positive and negative rates of change mean in this situation?

Day	Cumulative Distance (km)
0	0
1	203
2	396
3	561
4	739.5
5	958
6	1104

5. a) The cumulative distance travelled over several days of the 2007 Tour de France bicycle race is shown in the table to the left. Calculate the average rate of change in cumulative distance travelled between consecutive days.
   b) Does the Tour de France race travel over the same distance each day? Explain.

6. What is the average rate of change in the values of the function $f(x) = 4x$ from $x = 2$ to $x = 6$? What about from $x = 2$ to $x = 26$? What do your results indicate about $f(x)$?

7. Shelly has a cell phone plan that costs \$39 per month and allows her 250 free anytime minutes. Any minutes she uses over the 250 free minutes cost \$0.10 per minute. The function

$$C(m) = \begin{cases} 39, \text{ if } 0 \le m \le 250 \\ 0.10(m - 250) + 39, \text{ if } m > 250 \end{cases}$$

can be used to determine her monthly cell phone bill, where $C(m)$ is her monthly cost in dollars and m is the number of minutes she talks. Discuss how the average rate of change in her monthly cost changes as the minutes she talks increases.

8. The population of a city has continued to grow since 1950. The
A population P, in thousands, and the time t, in years, since 1950 are given in the table below and in the graph.

Time, t (years)	0	10	20	30	40	50	60
Population, P (thousands)	5	10	20	40	80	160	320

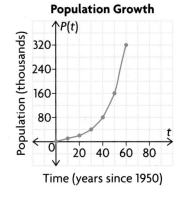

Population Growth

a) Calculate the average rate of change in population for the following intervals of time.
   i) $0 \le t \le 20$ iii) $40 \le t \le 60$
   ii) $20 \le t \le 40$ iv) $0 \le t \le 60$
b) Is the population growth constant?
c) To predict what the population will be in 2050, what assumptions must you make?

9. During the Apollo 14 mission, Alan Shepard hit a golf ball on the Moon. The function $h(t) = 18t - 0.8t^2$ models the height of the golf ball's trajectory on the Moon, where $h(t)$ is the height, in metres, of the ball above the surface of the Moon and t is the time in seconds. Determine the average rate of change in the height of the ball over the time interval $10 \le t \le 15$.

10. A company that sells sweatshirts finds that the profit can be modelled by $P(s) = -0.30s^2 + 3.5s + 11.15$, where $P(s)$ is the profit, in thousands of dollars, and s is the number of sweatshirts sold (expressed in thousands).
a) Calculate the average rate of change in profit for the following intervals.
   i) $1 \le s \le 2$ ii) $2 \le s \le 3$ iii) $3 \le s \le 4$ iv) $4 \le s \le 5$
b) As the number of sweatshirts sold increases, what do you notice about the average rate of change in profit on each sweatshirt? What does this mean?
c) Predict if the rate of change in profit will stay positive. Explain what this means.

11. The population of a town is modelled by
$P(t) = 50t^2 + 1000t + 20\ 000$, where $P(t)$ is the size of the
population and t is the number of years since 2000.
   a) Use graphing technology to graph $P(t)$.
   b) Predict if the average rate of change in the population size will be
   greater closer to the year 2000 or farther in the future. Explain how
   you made your prediction.
   c) Calculate the average rate of change in the population size for each
   time period.
      i) 2000–2010   **iii)** 2005–2015
      ii) 2002–2012   **iv)** 2010–2020
   d) Evaluate your earlier prediction using the data you developed when
   answering part c).

12. Your classmate was absent today and phones you for help with today's
C lesson. Share with your classmate
   a) two real-life examples of when someone might calculate an average
   rate of change (one positive and one negative)
   b) an explanation of when an average rate of change might be useful
   c) an explanation of how an average rate of change is calculated

13. Vehicles lose value over time. A car is purchased for $23 500, but is
T worth only $8750 after eight years. What is the average annual rate of
   change in the value of the car, as a percent?

14. Complete the following table by providing a definition in your own
   words, a personal example, and a visual representation of an average
   rate of change.

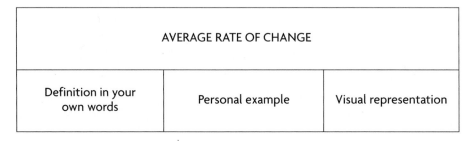

AVERAGE RATE OF CHANGE		
Definition in your own words	Personal example	Visual representation

Extending

15. The function $F(x) = -0.005x^2 + 0.8x + 12$ models the
   relationship between a certain vehicle's speed and fuel economy, where
   $F(x)$ is the fuel economy in kilometres per litre and x is the speed of
   the vehicle in kilometres per hour. Determine the rate of change in fuel
   economy for 10 km/h intervals in speed, and use your results to
   determine the speed that gives the best fuel economy.

2.2 Estimating Instantaneous Rates of Change from Tables of Values and Equations

GOAL

Estimate and interpret the rate of change at a particular value of the independent variable.

YOU WILL NEED

• graphing calculator or graphing software

INVESTIGATE the Math

A small pebble was dropped into a 3.0 m tall cylindrical tube filled with thick glycerine. A motion detector recorded the time and the total distance that the pebble fell after its release. The table below shows some of the measurements between 6.0 s and 7.0 s after the initial drop.

Time, t (s)	6.0	6.2	6.4	6.6	6.8	7.0
Distance, $d(t)$ (cm)	208.39	221.76	235.41	249.31	263.46	277.84

? How can you estimate the rate of change in the distance that the pebble fell at exactly $t = 6.4$ s?

A. Calculate the average rate of change in the distance that the pebble fell during each of the following time intervals.

   i) $6.0 \leq t \leq 6.4$ **iii)** $6.4 \leq t \leq 7.0$ **v)** $6.4 \leq t \leq 6.6$

   ii) $6.2 \leq t \leq 6.4$ **iv)** $6.4 \leq t \leq 6.8$

B. Use your results for part A to estimate the **instantaneous rate of change** in the distance that the pebble fell at exactly $t = 6.4$ s. Explain how you determined your estimate.

C. Calculate the average rate of change in the distance that the pebble fell during the time interval $6.2 \leq t \leq 6.6$. How does your calculation compare with your estimate?

instantaneous rate of change

the exact rate of change of a function $y = f(x)$ at a specific value of the independent variable $x = a$; estimated using average rates of change for small intervals of the independent variable very close to the value $x = a$

Reflecting

D. Why do you think each of the intervals you used to calculate the average rate of change in part A included 6.4 as one of its endpoints?

E. Why did it make sense to examine the average rates of change using time intervals on both sides of $t = 6.4$ s? Which of these intervals provided the best estimate for the instantaneous rate of change at $t = 6.4$ s?

F. Even though 6.4 is not an endpoint of the interval used in the average rate of change calculation in part C, explain why this calculation gave a reasonable estimate for the instantaneous rate of change at $t = 6.4$ s.

G. Using the table of values given, is it possible to get as accurate an estimate of the instantaneous rate of change for $t = 7.0$ s as you did for $t = 6.4$ s? Explain.

APPLY the Math

> **EXAMPLE 1** Selecting a strategy to estimate instantaneous rate of change using an equation

The population of a small town appears to be growing exponentially. Town planners think that the equation $P(t) = 35\,000\,(1.05)^t$, where $P(t)$ is the number of people in the town and t is the number of years after 2000, models the size of the population. Estimate the instantaneous rate of change in the population in 2015.

Solution A: Selecting a strategy using intervals

preceding interval

an interval of the independent variable of the form $a - h \leq x \leq a$, where h is a small positive value; used to determine an average rate of change

Using a **preceding interval** in which $14 \leq t \leq 15$,

$$\frac{\Delta P}{\Delta t} = \frac{P(15) - P(14)}{15 - 14}$$

$$\doteq \frac{72\,762 - 69\,298}{15 - 14}$$

$$= \frac{3464}{1}$$

$$= 3464 \text{ people/year}$$

> Calculate average rates of change using some dates that precede the year 2015. Since 2015 is 15 years after 2000, use $t = 15$ to represent the year 2015.
>
> Use $14 \leq t \leq 15$ and $14.5 \leq t \leq 15$ as preceding intervals (intervals on the left side of 15) to calculate the average rates of change in the population.

Using a preceding interval in which $14.5 \leq t \leq 15$,

$$\frac{\Delta P}{\Delta t} = \frac{P(15) - P(14.5)}{15 - 14.5}$$

$$\doteq \frac{72\,762 - 71\,009}{15 - 14.5}$$

$$= 3506 \text{ people/year}$$

following interval

an interval of the independent variable of the form $a \leq x \leq a + h$, where h is a small positive value; used to determine an average rate of change

Using a **following interval** in which $15 \leq t \leq 16$,

$$\frac{\Delta P}{\Delta t} = \frac{P(16) - P(15)}{16 - 15}$$

$$\doteq \frac{76\,401 - 72\,762}{16 - 15}$$

$$= 3639 \text{ people/year}$$

> Calculate average rates of change using some dates that follow the year 2015. Use $15 \leq t \leq 16$ and $15 \leq t \leq 15.5$ as following intervals (intervals on the right side of 15) to calculate the average rates of change in the population.

Using a following interval in which $15 \leq t \leq 15.5$,

$$\frac{\Delta P}{\Delta t} = \frac{P(15.5) - P(15)}{15.5 - 15}$$

$$\doteq \frac{74\,559 - 72\,762}{15.5 - 15}$$

$$= 3594 \text{ people/year}$$

As the size of the preceding interval decreases, the average rate of change increases.

As the size of the following interval decreases, the average rate of change decreases. ← Examine the average rates of change in population on both sides of $t = 15$ to find a trend.

The instantaneous rate of change in the population is somewhere between the values above.

$$\text{Estimate} = \frac{3506 + 3594}{2}$$

$$= 3550 \text{ people/year}$$

Make an estimate using the average of the two calculations for smaller intervals on either side of $t = 15$.

Solution B: Selecting a different interval strategy

Calculate some average rates of change using intervals that have the year 2015 as their midpoint.

Using a **centred interval** in which $14 \leq t \leq 16$,

$$\frac{\Delta P}{\Delta t} = \frac{P(16) - P(14)}{16 - 14}$$

$$\doteq \frac{76\,401 - 69\,298}{16 - 14}$$

$$\doteq 3552 \text{ people/year}$$

Using a centred interval in which $14.5 \leq t \leq 15.5$,

$$\frac{\Delta P}{\Delta t} = \frac{P(15.5) - P(14.5)}{15.5 - 14.5}$$

$$\doteq \frac{74\,559 - 71\,009}{15.5 - 14.5}$$

$$= 3550 \text{ people/year}$$

Use $14 \leq t \leq 16$ and $14.5 \leq t \leq 15.5$ as centred intervals (intervals with 15 as their midpoint) to calculate the average rates of change in the population. Examine the corresponding rates of change to find a trend. Using centred intervals allows you to move in gradually to the value that you are interested in. Sometimes this is called the *squeeze technique*.

centred interval

an interval of the independent variable of the form $a - h \leq x \leq a + h$, where h is a small positive value; used to determine an average rate of change

The instantaneous rate of change in the population is about 3550 people/year. ← The average rates of change are very similar. Make an estimate using the smallest centred interval.

| EXAMPLE **2** | **Selecting a strategy to estimate the instantaneous rate of change** |

The volume of a cubic crystal, grown in a laboratory, can be modelled by $V(x) = x^3$, where $V(x)$ is the volume measured in cubic centimetres and x is the side length in centimetres. Estimate the instantaneous rate of change in the crystal's volume with respect to its side length when the side length is 5 cm.

Solution A: Squeezing the centred intervals

Look at the average rates of change near $x = 5$ using a series of centred intervals that get progressively smaller. By using intervals that get systematically smaller and smaller, you can make a more accurate estimate for the instantaneous rate of change than if you were to use intervals that are all the same size.

Using $4.5 \leq x \leq 5.5$,

$$\frac{\Delta V}{\Delta x} = \frac{166.375 - 91.125}{5.5 - 4.5}$$

$$= 75.25 \text{ cm}^3/\text{cm}$$

Using $4.9 \leq x \leq 5.1$,

$$\frac{\Delta V}{\Delta x} = \frac{132.651 - 117.649}{5.1 - 4.9}$$

$$= 75.01 \text{ cm}^3/\text{cm}$$

> In this case, use $4.5 \leq x \leq 5.5$, then $4.9 \leq x \leq 5.1$, and finally $4.99 \leq x \leq 5.01$.

Using $4.99 \leq x \leq 5.01$,

difference quotient

if $P(a, f(a))$ and $Q(a + h, f(a + h))$ are two points on the graph of $y = f(x)$, then the instantaneous rate of change of y with respect to x at P can be estimated using $\frac{\Delta y}{\Delta x} = \frac{f(a + h) - f(a)}{h}$, where h is a very small number. This expression is called the difference quotient.

$$\frac{\Delta V}{\Delta x} = \frac{125.751\,501 - 124.251\,499}{5.01 - 4.99}$$

$$= 75.0001 \text{ cm}^3/\text{cm}$$

When the side length of the cube is exactly 5 cm, the volume of the cube is increasing at the rate of 75 cm³/cm.

> As the interval gets smaller, the average rate of change in the volume of the cube appears to be getting closer to 75 cm³/cm. So it seems that the instantaneous rate of change in volume should be 75 cm³/cm.

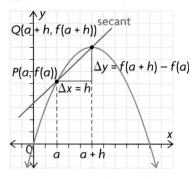

Solution B: Using an algebraic approach and a general point

Write the **difference quotient** for the average rate of change in volume as the side length changes between 5 and any value: $(5 + h)$.

$$\frac{\Delta V}{\Delta x} = \frac{(5 + h)^3 - 125}{5 + h - 5}$$

$$= \frac{(5 + h)^3 - 125}{h}$$

> Use two points. Let one point be $(5, 5^3)$ or $(5, 125)$ because you are investigating the rate of change for $V(x) = x^3$ when $x = 5$. Let the other point be $(5 + h, (5 + h)^3)$, where h is a very small number, such as 0.01 or -0.01.

Let $h = -0.01$.

$$\frac{\Delta V}{\Delta x} = \frac{(5 + (-0.01))^3 - 125}{h}$$

$$= \frac{124.251\,499 - 125}{-0.01}$$

$$= 74.8501 \text{ cm}^3/\text{cm}$$

> The value $h = -0.01$ corresponds to a very small preceding interval, where $4.99 \leq x \leq 5$. This gives an estimate of the instantaneous rate of change when the side length changes from 4.99 cm to 5 cm.

Let $h = 0.01$.

$$\frac{\Delta V}{\Delta x} = \frac{(5 + 0.01)^3 - 125}{0.01}$$

$$= \frac{125.751\,501 - 125}{0.01}$$

$$= 75.1501 \text{ cm}^3/\text{cm}$$

> The value $h = 0.01$ corresponds to a very small following interval, where $5 \leq x \leq 5.01$. This gives an estimate of the instantaneous rate of change when the side length changes from 5 cm to 5.01 cm.

The instantaneous rate of change in the volume of the cube is somewhere between the two values calculated.

$$\text{Estimate} = \frac{74.8501 + 75.1501}{2}$$

$$\doteq 75.0001 \text{ cm}^3/\text{cm}$$

> Determine an estimate using the average of the two calculations on either side of $x = 5$.

EXAMPLE 3   Selecting a strategy to estimate an instantaneous rate of change

The following table shows the temperature of an oven as it heats from room temperature to $400°F$.

Time (min)	0	1	2	3	4	5	6	7	8	9	10
Temperature (°F)	70	125	170	210	250	280	310	335	360	380	400

a) Estimate the instantaneous rate of change in temperature at exactly 5 min using the given data.

b) Estimate the instantaneous rate of change in temperature at exactly 5 min using a quadratic model.

Solution

a) Using the interval $2 \leq t \leq 8$,

$$\frac{\Delta T}{\Delta t} = \frac{360 - 170}{8 - 2}$$

$$\doteq 31.67°F/\text{min}$$

> Choose some centred intervals around 5 min. Examine the average rates of change as the intervals of time get smaller, and find a trend.

Tech | Support

For help using a graphing calculator to create scatter plots and determine an algebraic model using quadratic regression, see Technical Appendix, T-11.

Using the interval $3 \leq t \leq 7$,

$$\frac{\Delta T}{\Delta t} = \frac{335 - 210}{7 - 3}$$

$$= 31.25°\text{F/min}$$

Using the interval $4 \leq t \leq 6$,

$$\frac{\Delta T}{\Delta t} = \frac{310 - 250}{6 - 4}$$

$$= 30°\text{F/min}$$

As the centred intervals around 5 min get smaller, it appears that the average rates of change in the temperature of the oven get closer to about 30°F/min.

b)

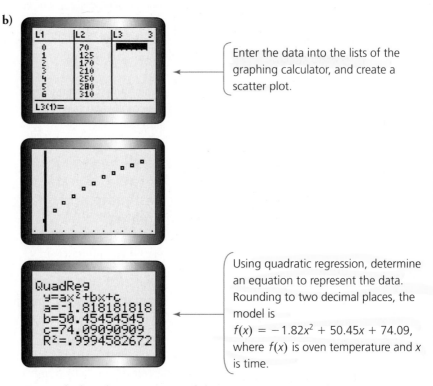

Enter the data into the lists of the graphing calculator, and create a scatter plot.

Using quadratic regression, determine an equation to represent the data. Rounding to two decimal places, the model is

$f(x) = -1.82x^2 + 50.45x + 74.09$,

where $f(x)$ is oven temperature and x is time.

Next, calculate the average rate of change in oven temperature using a very small centred interval near $x = 5$. For example, use $4.99 \leq x \leq 5.01$.

Interval	$\Delta f(x)$	Δx	$\dfrac{\Delta f(x)}{\Delta x}$
$4.99 \leq x \leq 5.01$	$f(5.01) - f(4.99)$ $\doteq 281.16 - 280.52$ $= 0.64$	$5.01 - 4.99$ $= 0.02$	$0.64/0.02$ $= 32°\text{F/min}$

The instantaneous rate of change in temperature at 5 min is about $32°\text{F/min}$.

In Summary

Key Idea

- The instantaneous rate of change of the dependent variable is the rate at which the dependent variable changes at a specific value of the independent variable, $x = a$.

Need to Know

- The instantaneous rate of change of the dependent variable, in a table of values or an equation of the relationship, can be estimated using the following methods:
  - Using a series of preceding ($a - h \leq x \leq a$) and following ($a \leq x \leq a + h$) intervals: Calculate the average rate of change by keeping one endpoint of each interval fixed. (This is $x = a$, the location where the instantaneous rate of change occurs.) Move the other endpoint of the interval closer and closer to the fixed point from either side by making h smaller and smaller. Based on the trend for the average rates of change, make an estimate for the instantaneous rate of change at the specific value.
  - Using a series of centred intervals ($a - h \leq x \leq a + h$): Calculate the average rate of change by picking endpoints for each interval on either side of $x = a$, where the instantaneous rate of change occurs. Choose these endpoints so that the value where the instantaneous rate of change occurs is the midpoint of the interval. Continue to calculate the average rate of change by moving both endpoints closer and closer to where the instantaneous rate of change occurs. Based on the trend, make an estimate for the instantaneous rate of change.
  - Using the difference quotient and a general point: Calculate the average rate of change using the location where the instantaneous rate of change occurs $(a, f(a))$ and a general point $(a + h, f(a + h))$, i.e., $\frac{f(a + h) - f(a)}{h}$. Choose values for h that are very small, such as ± 0.01 or ± 0.001. The smaller the value used for h, the better the estimate will be.
- The best estimate for the instantaneous rate of change occurs when the interval used to calculate the average rate of change is made as small as possible.

CHECK *Your Understanding*

1. **a)** Copy and complete the tables, if $f(x) = 5x^2 - 7$.

Preceding Interval	$\Delta f(x)$	Δx	Average Rate of Change, $\dfrac{\Delta f(x)}{\Delta x}$
$1 \leq x \leq 2$	$13 - (-2) = 15$	$2 - 1 = 1$	
$1.5 \leq x \leq 2$	8.75	0.5	
$1.9 \leq x \leq 2$			
$1.99 \leq x \leq 2$			

Following Interval	$\Delta f(x)$	Δx	Average Rate of Change, $\dfrac{\Delta f(x)}{\Delta x}$
$2 \le x \le 3$	$38 - 13 = 25$	$3 - 2 = 1$	
$2 \le x \le 2.5$	11.25	0.5	
$2 \le x \le 2.1$			
$2 \le x \le 2.01$			

b) Based on the trend in the average rates of change, estimate the instantaneous rate of change when $x = 2$.

2. A soccer ball is kicked into the air. The following table of values shows the height of the ball above the ground at various times during its flight.

Time (s)	0.0	0.5	1.0	1.5	2.0	2.5	3.0	3.5	4.0	4.5	5.0
Height (m)	0.5	11.78	20.6	26.98	30.9	32.38	31.4	27.98	22.1	13.78	3.0

a) Estimate the instantaneous rate of change in the height of the ball at exactly $t = 2.0$ s using the preceding and following interval method.

b) Estimate the instantaneous rate of change in the height of the ball at exactly $t = 2.0$ s using the centred interval method.

c) Which estimation method do you prefer? Explain.

3. A population of raccoons moves into a wooded area. At t months, the number of raccoons, $P(t)$, can be modelled using the equation $P(t) = 100 + 30t + 4t^2$.

a) Determine the population of raccoons at 2.5 months.

b) Determine the average rate of change in the raccoon population over the interval from 0 months to 2.5 months.

c) Estimate the rate of change in the raccoon population at exactly 2.5 months.

d) Explain why your answers for parts a), b), and c) are different.

PRACTISING

4. For the function $f(x) = 6x^2 - 4$, estimate the instantaneous rate of change for the given values of x.

a) $x = -2$ b) $x = 0$ c) $x = 4$ d) $x = 8$

5. An object is sent through the air. Its height is modelled by the function $h(x) = -5x^2 + 3x + 65$, where $h(x)$ is the height of the object in metres and x is the time in seconds. Estimate the instantaneous rate of change in the object's height at 3 s.

6. A family purchased a home for $125 000. Appreciation of the home's value, in dollars, can be modelled by the equation $H(t) = 125\,000(1.06)^t$, where $H(t)$ is the value of the home and t is the number of years that the family owns the home. Estimate the instantaneous rate of change in the home's value at the start of the eighth year of owning the home.

7. The population of a town, in thousands, is described by the
Ⓚ function $P(t) = -1.5t^2 + 36t + 6$, where t is the number of years after 2000.
   a) What is the average rate of change in the population between the years 2000 and 2024?
   b) Does your answer to part a) make sense? Does it mean that there was no change in the population from 2000 to 2024?
   c) Explain your answer to part b) by finding the average rate of change in the population from 2000 to 2012 and from 2012 to 2024.
   d) For what value of t is the instantaneous rate of change in the population 0?

8. Jacelyn purchased a new car for $18 999. The yearly depreciation of the value of the car can be modelled by the equation $V(t) = 18\,999(0.93)^t$, where $V(t)$ is the value of the car and t is the number of years that Jacelyn owns the car. Estimate the instantaneous rate of change in the value of the car when the car is 5 years old. What does this mean?

9. A diver is on the 10 m platform, preparing to perform a dive. The
Ⓐ diver's height above the water, in metres, at time t can be modelled using the equation $h(t) = 10 + 2t - 4.9t^2$.
   a) Determine when the diver will enter the water.
   b) Estimate the rate at which the diver's height above the water is changing as the diver enters the water.

10. To make a snow person, snow is being rolled into the shape of a
Ⓣ sphere. The volume of a sphere is given by the function $V(r) = \frac{4}{3}\pi r^3$, where r is the radius in centimetres. Use two different methods to estimate the instantaneous rate of change in the volume of the snowball with respect to the radius when $r = 5$ cm.

11. David plans to drive to see his grandparents during his winter break. How can he determine his average speed for a part of his journey along the way? Be as specific as possible. Describe the steps he must take and the information he must know.

12. The following table shows the temperature of an oven as it cools.

Time (min)	0	1	2	3	4	5	6
Temperature (°F)	400	390	375	350	330	305	270

a) Use the data in the table to estimate the instantaneous rate of change in the temperature of the oven at exactly 4 min.
b) Use a graphing calculator to determine a quadratic model. Use your quadratic model to estimate the instantaneous rate of change in the temperature of the oven at exactly 4 min.
c) Discuss why your answers for parts a) and b) are different.
d) Which is the better estimate? Explain.

13. In a table like the one below, list all the methods that can be used to
C estimate the instantaneous rate of change. What are the advantages and disadvantages of each method?

Method of Estimating Instantaneous Rate of Change	Advantage	Disadvantage

Extending

14. Concentric circles form when a stone is dropped into a pool of water.
a) What is the average rate of change in the area of one circle with respect to the radius as the radius grows from 0 cm to 100 cm?
b) How fast is the area changing with respect to the radius when the radius is 120 cm?

15. A crystal in the shape of a cube is growing in a laboratory. Estimate the rate at which the surface area is changing with respect to the side length when the side length of the crystal is 3 cm.

16. A spherical balloon is being inflated. Estimate the rate at which its surface area is changing with respect to the radius when the radius measures 20 cm.

2.3 Exploring Instantaneous Rates of Change Using Graphs

GOAL

Estimate instantaneous rates of change using slopes of lines.

EXPLORE the Math

In the previous lesson, you used numerical and algebraic techniques to estimate instantaneous rates of change. Graphically, you have seen that the average rate of change is equivalent to the slope of a secant line that passes through two points on the graph of a function.

? How can you use the slopes of secant lines to estimate the instantaneous rate of change?

A. Enter the function $f(x) = x^2$ into the equation editor of your graphing calculator, graph it, and draw a sketch of the graph.

B. On your sketch, draw a secant line that passes through the points $(1, f(1))$ and $(3, f(3))$.

C. Calculate the slope of the secant line. Copy the table and record the slope. Calculate and record the slopes of other secant lines using the points listed.

Points	Slope of Secant
$(1, f(1))$ and $(3, f(3))$	
$(1, f(1))$ and $(2, f(2))$	
$(1, f(1))$ and $(1.5, f(1.5))$	
$(1, f(1))$ and $(1.1, f(1.1))$	
$(1, f(1))$ and $(1.01, f(1.01))$	

D. Create a formula for calculating the slope of any secant line that passes through $(1, f(1))$ and the general point $(x, f(x))$.

E. Enter this formula into Y1 of the equation editor.

F. Set the TBLSET feature of your graphing calculator by scrolling down and across so that the cursor is over Ask in the Indpnt: row of the screen as shown.

G. Confirm that the first slope you calculated in part C, for the secant line that passes through the points $(1, f(1))$ and $(3, f(3))$, is correct by entering $X = 3$ in the TABLE on your graphing calculator. (If there are already x-values in the table, delete them by moving the cursor over each value and pressing ⬭ DEL ⬭.)

Tech | Support

For help using the TBLSET and TABLE features of a graphing calculator, see Technical Appendix, T-6.

H. On your sketch, draw another secant line that passes through the points $(1, f(1))$ and $(2, f(2))$. Calculate its slope by entering X = 2 in the TABLE on your graphing calculator, and compare this to the slope in the table you created in part F.

I. Draw and calculate three other secant lines, always using $(1, f(1))$ as a fixed point and moving the other points closer to $(1, f(1))$ each time. You can do this by using the points given in the table in part C.

J. Examine your sketch and your table of secant slopes. Describe what happens to each secant line in your sketch, and compare this with the values of the slopes in your table as the points get closer and closer to the fixed point $(1, f(1))$.

tangent line

a line that touches the graph at only one point, P, within a small interval of a relation; it could, but does not have to, cross the graph at another point outside this interval. The tangent line goes in the same direction as the relation at point P (called the point of tangency).

K. Estimate the slope of the **tangent line** to the curve $f(x) = x^2$ at the point $(1, f(1))$ by examining the trend in the secant slopes you calculated.

L. Repeat parts B to K using the points in the table below.

Points	Slope of Secant
$(1, f(1))$ and $(-1, f(-1))$	
$(1, f(1))$ and $(0, f(0))$	
$(1, f(1))$ and $(0.5, f(0.5))$	
$(1, f(1))$ and $(0.9, f(0.9))$	
$(1, f(1))$ and $(0.99, f(0.99))$	

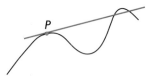

Tech | **Support**

For help using the graphing calculator to draw tangent lines, see Technical Appendix, T-17.

M. Verify your estimates by drawing the tangent line to the graph of $f(x) = x^2$ at $x = 1$ using your graphing calculator.

N. Repeat parts B to L with two other functions of your choice. Use two different types of functions, such as an exponential function, a **sinusoidal function**, or a different quadratic function.

Reflecting

O. What happens to the slopes of the secant lines as the points move closer to the fixed point?

P. How do the slopes of the secant lines relate to the slope of the tangent line when $x = 1$? Explain.

Q. How is estimating the slope of a tangent like estimating the instantaneous rate of change?

In Summary

Key Ideas

- The slope of a secant line is equivalent to the average rate of change over the interval defined by the *x*-coordinates of the two points that are used to define the secant line.
- The slope of a tangent at a point on a graph is equivalent to the instantaneous rate of change of a function at this point.

Need to Know

- The slope of a tangent cannot be calculated directly using the slope formula, because the coordinates of only one point are known. The slope can be estimated, however, by calculating the slopes of a series of secant lines that go through the fixed point of tangency P and points that get closer and closer to this fixed point, Q_1, Q_2, and Q_3.

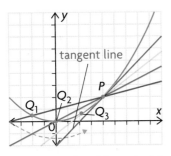

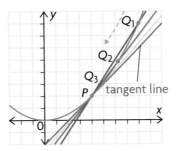

As Q approaches P from the left, the slope of QP increases and approaches the slope of the tangent line.

As Q approaches P from the right, the slope of QP decreases and approaches the slope of the tangent line.

FURTHER *Your Understanding*

1. Graph each of the following functions using a graphing calculator, and then sketch the graph. On your sketch, draw a series of secant lines that you could use to estimate the slope of the tangent when $x = 2$. Calculate and record the slopes of these secant lines. Use the slopes to estimate the slope of the tangent line when $x = 2$.

   a) $f(x) = 3x^2 - 5x + 1$
   b) $f(x) = 3^x + 1$
   c) $f(x) = \sqrt{x + 2}$
   d) $f(x) = 2x - 7$

2. Verify your estimates for each function in question 1 by drawing the tangent line when $x = 2$ on your graphing calculator.

3. a) For each of the following sets of functions, estimate the slopes of the tangents at the given values of x.
   b) What do all the slopes in each set of functions have in common?

Set A
$f(x) = -x^2 + 6x - 4$ when $x = 3$
$g(x) = \sin x$ when $x = 90°$
$h(x) = x^2 + 4x + 11$ when $x = -2$
$j(x) = 5$ when $x = 1$

Set B
$f(x) = 3x^2 + 2x - 1$ when $x = 2$
$g(x) = 2^x + 3$ when $x = 1$
$h(x) = 5x + 4$ when $x = 3$
$j(x) = \sin x$ when $x = 60°$

Set C
$f(x) = 3x^2 + 2x - 1$ when $x = -1$
$g(x) = -2^x + 3$ when $x = 0$
$h(x) = -3x + 5$ when $x = 2$
$j(x) = \sin x$ when $x = 120°$

4. The following table gives the temperature of an oven as it heats up.

Time (min)	0	1	2	3	4	5	6	7	8	9	10	11	12	13	14
Temperature (°F)	70	125	170	210	250	280	310	335	360	380	400	415	430	440	445

   a) Graph the data.
   b) Draw a **curve of best fit** and the tangent line at $x = 5$.
   c) Determine the slope of the tangent line using the y-intercept of the tangent line and the point of tangency $(5, 280)$.
   d) Estimate the instantaneous rate of change in temperature at exactly 5 min using a centred interval from the table of values.
   e) Compare your answers to parts c) and d).

5. In the first two sections of this chapter, you calculated the slopes of successive secant lines to estimate the slope of a tangent line, and you calculated the average rate of change to estimate the instantaneous rate of change. How are these two calculations similar and different?

6. a) On graph paper, sketch the graph of $f(x) = x^2$.
   b) Draw the secant line that passes through $(1, 2)$ and $(2, 4)$.
   c) Estimate the location of the point of tangency on the graph of $f(x)$ whose tangent line has the same slope as the secant line you drew in part b).

FREQUENTLY ASKED Questions

Q: **What is the difference between the average rate of change and the instantaneous rate of change?**

A: The average rate of change of a quantity represented by a dependent variable occurs over an interval of the independent variable. The instantaneous rate of change of a quantity represented by a dependent variable occurs at a single value of the independent variable. As a result, average rate of change can be represented graphically using secant lines, while instantaneous rate of change can be represented graphically using tangent lines.

Q: **How do you determine the average rate of change?**

A1: To determine the average rate of change from a table of values or from the equation of any function $y = f(x)$, over the interval between the x-coordinates of points (x_1, y_1) and (x_2, y_2), divide the change in y by the change in x.

$$
\begin{aligned}
\text{Average rate of change} &= \frac{\text{change in } y}{\text{change in } x} \\
&= \frac{\Delta y}{\Delta x} \\
&= \frac{y_2 - y_1}{x_2 - x_1} \\
&= \frac{f(x_2) - f(x_1)}{x_2 - x_1}
\end{aligned}
$$

A2: To determine the average rate of change from the graph of a function, calculate the slope of the secant line that passes through the two points that define the interval on the graph. The slope is equivalent to the average rate of change on the defined interval.

> **Study Aid**
> - See Lesson 2.1, Example 1.
> - Try Mid-Chapter Review Question 1.

> **Study Aid**
> - See Lesson 2.1, Examples 2 to 4.
> - Try Mid-Chapter Review Questions 1 and 2.

Study | *Aid*

• See Lesson 2.2, Examples 1, 2, and 3, and Lesson 2.3.
• Try Mid-Chapter Review Questions 2 to 5.

Q: How can you estimate the instantaneous rate of change?

A1: Calculate the average rate of change for values that are very close to the location where the instantaneous rate of change occurs. You can use preceding and following intervals, or you can use centred intervals. Use your results to find the trend and then estimate the instantaneous rate of change.

A2: Calculate the average rate of change using the difference quotient with the location where the instantaneous rate of change occurs $(a, f(a))$ and a general point $(a + h, f(a + h))$:

$$\frac{f(a + h) - f(a)}{h}$$

Choose values for h that are very small.

A3: Draw a tangent line at the point where the instantaneous rate of change occurs. Calculate the slope of this line.

For example, to estimate the instantaneous rate of change of $f(x) = -2x^2 + 14x - 20$ at the point $(3, 4)$, graph $f(x)$ and draw a tangent line at $(3, 4)$.
Use the points $(3, 4)$ and $(1, 0)$ on the tangent line to calculate the slope of the tangent line.

$$\text{Slope} = \frac{0 - 4}{1 - 3}$$
$$= 2$$

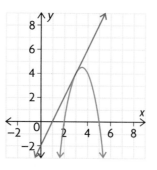

So the instantaneous rate of change in y with respect to x is about 2.

PRACTICE Questions

Lesson 2.1

1. The following table gives the amount of water that is used on a farm during the first six months of the year.

Month	Volume (1000 of m³)
January	3.00
February	3.75
March	3.75
April	4.00
May	5.10
June	5.50

   a) Plot the data in the table on a graph.
   b) Find the rate of change in the volume of water used between consecutive months.
   c) Between which two months is the change in the volume of water used the greatest?
   d) Determine the average rate of change in the volume of water used between March and June.

Lesson 2.2

2. A city's population (in tens of thousands) is modelled by the function $P(t) = 1.2(1.05)^t$, where t is the number of years since 2000. Examine the equation for this function and its graph.
   a) What can you conclude about the average rate of change in population between consecutive years as time increases?
   b) Estimate the instantaneous rate of change in population in 2010.

3. The height of a football that has been kicked can be modelled by the function $h(t) = -5t^2 + 20t + 1$, where $h(t)$ is the height in metres and t is the time in seconds.
   a) What is the average rate of change in height on the interval $0 \le t \le 2$ and on the interval $2 \le t \le 4$?

   b) Use the information given in part a) to find the time for which the instantaneous rate of change in height is 0 m/s. Verify your response.

4. The movement of a certain glacier can be modelled by $d(t) = 0.01t^2 + 0.5t$, where d is the distance, in metres, that a stake on the glacier has moved, relative to a fixed position, t days after the first measurement was made. Estimate the rate at which the glacier is moving after 20 days.

5. Create a graphic organizer, such as a web diagram, mind map, or concept map, for rate of change. Include both average rate of change and instantaneous rate of change in your graphic organizer.

Lesson 2.3

6. Create a table to estimate the slope of the tangent to $y = x^3 + 1$ at $P(2, 9)$. Be sure to approach P from both directions.

7. Estimate the slope of the tangent line in the graph of this function.

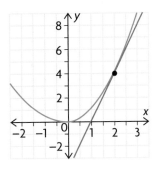

8. Explain what the answer for question 7 represents.

9. Graph the function $f(x) = 0.5x^2 + 5x - 15$ using your graphing calculator. Estimate the instantaneous rate of change for each value of x.
   a) $x = -5$ c) $x = 0$
   b) $x = -1$ d) $x = 3$

2.4 Using Rates of Change to Create a Graphical Model

YOU WILL NEED

• graphing calculator or graphing software

GOAL

Represent verbal descriptions of rates of change using graphs.

LEARN ABOUT the Math

Today Steve walked to his part-time job. As he started walking, he sped up for 3 min. Then he walked at a constant pace for another 2 min. When he realized that he would be early for work, he slowed down. His walk ended and he came to a complete stop once he reached his destination 10 min after he started.

? What would the speed versus time graph of Steve's walk to work look like?

EXAMPLE 1   Representing the situation with a graph

Create a speed versus time graph for Steve's walk to work.

Solution A: Assuming that he changed speed at a constant rate

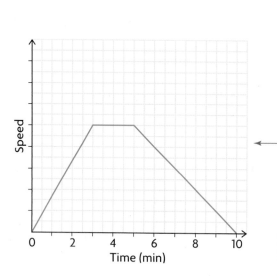

Because Steve was speeding up, his speed increased as time increased. His speed increased at a constant rate, so the graph should be a straight line with a positive slope that begins at (0, 0) and ends at $x = 3$.

Between 3 min and 5 min, Steve walked at the same rate, so his speed did not change. The graph should be a horizontal line that connects to the first line.

After 5 min, Steve slowed down at a constant rate, decreasing his speed as time increased, so you might draw a straight line with a negative slope that begins at $x = 5$ and ends at $x = 10$.

Solution B: Assuming that he walked at a variable speed

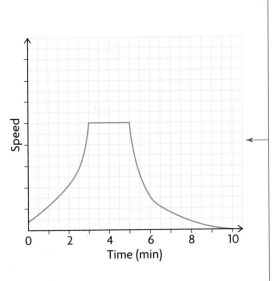

Because Steve was speeding up, his speed increased as time increased. His speed increased at a variable rate, so you might draw an increasing curve that starts at (0, 0) and ends at $x = 3$.

Between 3 min and 5 min, Steve walked at the same rate, so his speed did not change. The graph should be a horizontal line that connects to the first line.

After 5 min, Steve slowed down at a variable rate, decreasing his speed as time increased, so you might draw a decreasing curve that begins at $x = 5$ and ends at $x = 10$.

Reflecting

A. Which details in the given description were most important for determining the shape of the graph?

B. Are these the only two graphs that could represent Steve's walk to work? Explain.

APPLY the Math

EXAMPLE 2   **Representing the situation with a graph**

A flask, a beaker, and a graduated cylinder are being filled with water. The rate at which the water flows from the tap is the same when filling all three containers. Draw possible water level versus time graphs for the three containers.

Solution

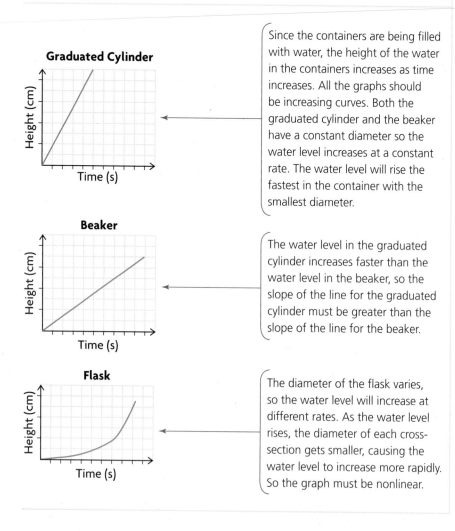

Graduated Cylinder

Since the containers are being filled with water, the height of the water in the containers increases as time increases. All the graphs should be increasing curves. Both the graduated cylinder and the beaker have a constant diameter so the water level increases at a constant rate. The water level will rise the fastest in the container with the smallest diameter.

Beaker

The water level in the graduated cylinder increases faster than the water level in the beaker, so the slope of the line for the graduated cylinder must be greater than the slope of the line for the beaker.

Flask

The diameter of the flask varies, so the water level will increase at different rates. As the water level rises, the diameter of each cross-section gets smaller, causing the water level to increase more rapidly. So the graph must be nonlinear.

EXAMPLE 3   Using a graph to determine the rate of change

A cyclist is observed moving at a speed of 10 m/s. She begins to slow down at a constant rate and, 4 s later, is at a speed of 5 m/s. She continues to slow down at a different constant rate and finally comes to a stop 6 s later.
a) Sketch a graph of speed versus time.
b) What is the average rate of change of the cyclist's speed in the first 4 s?
c) Estimate the instantaneous rate of change in speed at 3 s.

Solution

a)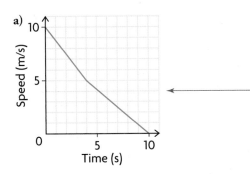

The cyclist begins at 10 m/s and slows down at a constant rate. Place a point at (0, 10) and another at (4, 5), and connect the points with a straight line.

Because the cyclist stops at 10 s, her speed is 0 m/s. Place another point at (10, 0), and connect it to the previous point with a straight line.

b) Average rate of change $= \dfrac{5 - 10}{4 - 0}$

$= -1.25$

To determine the average rate of change of the cyclist's speed in the first 4 s, calculate the slope of the secant line between (0, 10) and (4, 5).

The cyclist's speed is decreasing at the rate of 1.25 m/s².

c) The equation of the line for the first part of the graph is $y = -\dfrac{5}{4}x + 10$, since the slope is $-\dfrac{5}{4}$ and the y-intercept is 10.

When $x = 3.1$, $y = 6.125$.
When $x = 2.9$, $y = 6.375$.

Substitute $x = 3.1$ and $x = 2.9$ into the equation of the line. These values are close to $x = 3$, but on opposite sides of it. Determine the corresponding y-values.

Average rate of change $= \dfrac{\Delta y}{\Delta x}$

$= \dfrac{6.125 - 6.375}{3.1 - 2.9}$

$= -1.25$ m/s²

Calculate the average rate of change between these points, and estimate the instantaneous rate of change based on your answer.

The instantaneous rate of change is the same as the average rate of change calculated in part b). This should not be surprising, since the tangent line at $x = 3$ has the same slope as the secant line on the interval $0 \le x \le 4$.

Recall that the rate of change of a linear function is constant, so the rate of change at 3 s will be same as the rate of change at any time between 0 s and 4 s.

EXAMPLE **4**   Using reasoning to represent and
analyze a situation

Adam and his friend are testing a motion sensor. Adam stands 0.5 m in front of
the sensor and then walks 4 m away from it at a constant rate for 10 s. Next,
Adam walks 1 m toward the sensor for 5 s and then waits there for another 5 s.
a) Draw a distance versus time graph for Adam's motion sensor walk.
b) What is the average rate of change in his distance in the first 10 s?
c) What are the instantaneous rates of change at $t = 1$ s and $t = 7$ s?
d) What is the average rate of change in the next 5 s?
e) What are the instantaneous rates of change at $t = 12$ s and $t = 14$ s?
f) What is the instantaneous rate of change at $t = 18$ s?
g) Draw a speed versus time graph for Adam's motion sensor walk.

Solution

a)

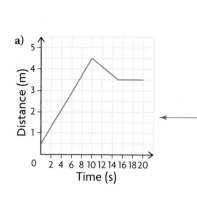

The graph begins with a straight line since the
rate at which Adam walks is constant. The
graph has a positive slope since he walks away
from the sensor, and his distance from the
sensor increases as time increases.

Adam starts 0.5 m from the sensor. Use (0, 0.5)
as the distance intercept.

Adam walks 4 m away from the sensor at a
constant rate for 10 s, so use the point
(10, 4.5).

Adam then walks toward the sensor. The line
has a negative slope, because his distance from
the sensor decreases as time increases. The line
is not very steep because he is walking slowly.

The graph ends with a horizontal line that
has a slope of 0 because Adam is not moving.
The slope indicates that his distance from the
sensor does not change.

b) Average rate of change
= slope of secant

$$= \frac{4.5 - 0.5}{10 - 0}$$

Calculate the slope of the secant line
between the points (0, 0.5) and (10, 4.5).

$$= 0.4$$

Adam's distance from the
sensor is increasing, on
average, by 0.4 m/s.

c) Instantaneous rate of change
  = slope of tangent
  = 0.4 ←

Adam's distance from the sensor is increasing. He is moving away from the sensor at a rate of 0.4 m/s.

> Estimate the slopes of the tangent lines at 1 s and 7 s. Both of the tangent lines have the same slope as the secant line since the graph is linear on the interval $0 \leq t \leq 10$.

d) Average rate of change
  = slope of secant
  $= \dfrac{3.5 - 4.5}{15 - 10}$ ←
  $= -0.2$

Adam's distance from the sensor is decreasing. He is moving toward the sensor at a rate of 0.2 m/s.

> Calculate the slope of the secant line between the points (10, 4.5) and (15, 3.5).

e) Instantaneous rate of change
  = slope of tangent
  $= -0.2$ ←

Adam's distance from the sensor is decreasing by 0.2 m/s at 12 s and 14 s.

> Estimate the slope of the tangent lines at 12 s and 14 s. As in part c), both of these tangent lines have the same slope as the secant line since the graph is linear on the interval $10 < t \leq 15$.

f) Instantaneous rate of change
  = slope of tangent
  = 0 ←

Adam's distance from the sensor is not changing at 18 s.

> Estimate the slope of the tangent line at 18 s. Again, the tangent line has the same slope as the secant line since the graph is linear on the interval $15 < t \leq 20$. Since the line is horizontal, its slope is 0.

g)

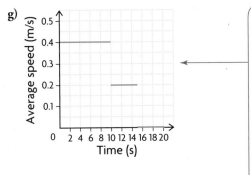

> There are three different speeds at which Adam walks, over three different intervals of time. Using the previous calculations,
> Speed = 0.4 m/s when $0 \leq t \leq 10$
> Speed = 0.2 m/s when $10 < t \leq 15$
> Speed = 0 m/s when $15 < t \leq 20$
> Note that speed is a non-negative quantity.
> $$\text{Speed} = \left| \frac{\Delta d}{\Delta t} \right|$$

In Summary

Key Ideas

- In a problem that involves movement, a possible graph shows **displacement** (distance, height, or depth) versus time. Distance, height, or depth is the dependent variable, and time is the independent variable. The rate of change in these relationships is speed:

$$\text{Speed} = \left| \frac{\text{change in displacement}}{\text{change in time}} \right|, \quad S = \left| \frac{\Delta d}{\Delta t} \right|$$

- On a displacement (distance, height, or depth) versus time graph, the magnitude of the slope of a secant line represents the average speed on the corresponding interval. The magnitude of the slope of a tangent line represents the instantaneous speed at a specific point. As a result, observing how the slopes of tangent lines change at different points on a graph gives you insight into how the speed changes over time.

Need to Know

- When the rate of change of displacement (or speed) is constant:

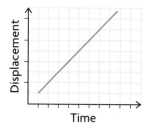

An increasing line indicates that displacement increases as time increases.

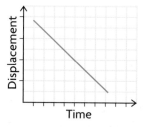

A decreasing line indicates that displacement decreases as time increases.

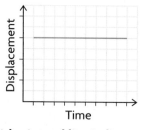

A horizontal line indicates that there is no change in displacement as time increases.

(continued)

- When the rate of change of displacement (or speed) is variable, an increasing curve indicates that displacement increases as time increases.

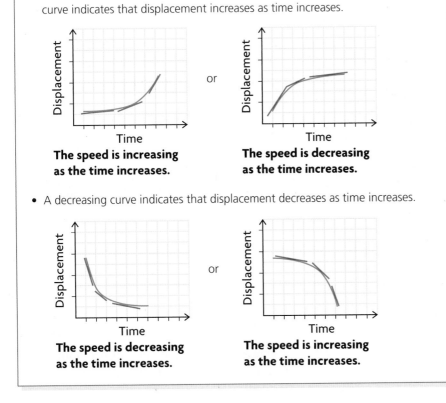

or

The speed is increasing as the time increases.

The speed is decreasing as the time increases.

- A decreasing curve indicates that displacement decreases as time increases.

or

The speed is decreasing as the time increases.

The speed is increasing as the time increases.

CHECK *Your Understanding*

1. The following graphs show distance versus time. Match each graph with the description given below.

a)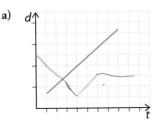

b)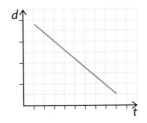

c)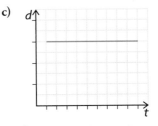

A Distance is decreasing over time.

B There is no change in distance over time.

C Distance is increasing over time.

2. Which of the graphs in question 1 show that the speed is constant? Explain.

3. Jan stands 5 m away from a motion sensor and then walks 4 m toward it at a constant rate for 5 s. Then she walks 2 m away from the location where she changed direction at a variable rate for the next 3 s. She stops and waits at this location for 2 s. Draw a distance versus time graph to show Jan's motion sensor walk.

PRACTISING

4. Rachel climbed Mt. Fuji while in Japan. There are 10 levels to the mountain. She was able to drive to Level 5, where she began her climb.
  - She walked at a constant rate for 40 min from Level 5 to Level 6.
  - She slowed slightly but then continued at a constant rate for a total of 90 min from Level 6 to Level 7.
  - She decided to eat and rest there, which took approximately 2 h.
  - From Level 7 to Level 8, a 40 min trip, she travelled at a constant rate.
  - Continuing on to Level 9, a 45 min trip, she decreased slightly to a new constant rate.
  - During most of the 1 h she took to reach Level 10, the top of Mt. Fuji, she maintained a constant rate. As she neared the top, however, she accelerated.

a) Using the information given and the following table, draw an elevation versus time graph to describe Rachel's climb.

Level	5	6	7	8	9	10
Elevation (m)	2100	2400	2700	3100	3400	3740

b) Calculate Rachel's average speed over each part of her climb.
c) Draw a speed versus time graph to describe Rachel's climb.

5. The containers shown are being filled with water at a constant rate.
K Draw a graph of the water level versus time for each container.
  a) a 2 L plastic pop bottle   **b)** a vase

6. John is riding a bicycle at a constant cruising speed along a flat road. He slows down as he climbs a hill. At the top of the hill, he speeds up, back to his constant cruising speed on a flat road. He then accelerates down the hill. He comes to another hill and coasts to a stop as he starts to climb.
  a) Sketch a possible graph to show John's speed versus time, and another graph to show his distance travelled versus time.
  b) Sketch a possible graph of John's elevation (in relation to his starting point) versus time.

7. A swimming pool is 50 m long. Kommy swims from one end of the
A pool to the other end in 45 s. He rests for 10 s and then takes 55 s to
swim back to his starting point.

  a) Use the information given to find the average speed for Kommy's
  first length of the pool.

  b) What is the average speed for Kommy's second length of the pool?

  c) If you were to graph Kommy's distance versus time for his first
  and second lengths of the pool, how would the two graphs
  compare? How is this related to Kommy's speed?

  d) Draw a distance versus time graph for Kommy's swim.

  e) What is Kommy's speed at time $t = 50$?

  f) Draw a speed versus time graph for Kommy's swim.

8. The following graphs show speed versus time. Match each graph with
the description given below.

a)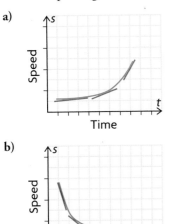

c)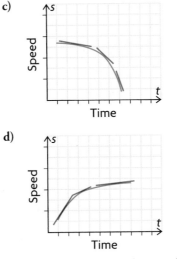

b)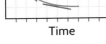

d)

  A The rate at which the
  speed increases is increasing
  as time increases.

  B The rate at which the
  speed increases is decreasing
  as time increases.

  C The rate at which the speed
  decreases is decreasing as
  time increases.

  D The rate at which the speed
  decreases is increasing as
  time increases.

9. A jockey is warming up a horse. Whenever the jockey has the horse
T accelerate or decelerate, she does so at a nonconstant rate—at first
slowly and then more quickly. The jockey begins by having the horse
trot around the track at a constant rate. She then increases the rate to a
canter and allows the horse to canter at a constant rate for several laps.
Next, she slowly begins to decrease the speed of the horse to a trot and
then to a walk. To finish, the jockey walks the horse around the track
once. Draw a speed versus time graph to represent this situation.

10. a) Describe how you would walk toward or away from a motion sensor detector to give each distance versus time graph shown below.

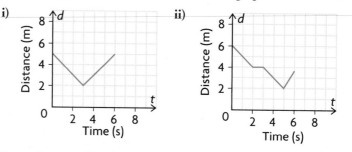

i)
ii)

b) For each part of each graph, determine the speed at which you must walk.

11. A cross-country runner is training for a marathon. His training program requires him to run at different speeds for different lengths of time. His program also requires him to accelerate and decelerate at a constant rate. Today he begins by jogging for 10 min at a rate of 5 miles per hour. He then spends 1 min accelerating to a rate of 10 miles per hour. He stays at this rate for 5 min. He then decelerates for 1 min to a rate of 7 miles per hour. He stays at this rate for 30 min. Finally, to cool down, he decelerates for 2 min to a rate of 3 miles per hour. He stays at this rate for a final 10 min and then stops.

a) Make a speed versus time graph to represent this situation.

b) What is the instantaneous rate of change in the runner's speed at 10.5 min?

c) Calculate the runner's average rate at which he changed speeds from minute 11 to minute 49.

d) Explain why your answer for part c) does not accurately represent the runner's training schedule from minute 11 to minute 49.

12. Create a scenario that could be used to create either a distance versus time graph or a speed versus time graph. Exchange your scenario with a partner and create the corresponding graph.

Extending

13. Two women are running on the same track. One has just finished her workout and is decelerating—at first slowly and then more quickly as she comes to a complete stop. The other woman is just starting her workout and is accelerating—at first quickly and then more slowly as she reaches her target speed. Use one graph to illustrate the rates of both women.

14. A graph displays changes in rate of speed versus time. The graph has straight lines from point to point. If the graph had been drawn to display changes in distance versus time, how would it be different?

2.5 Solving Problems Involving Rates of Change

GOAL

Use rates of change to solve problems that involve functions.

YOU WILL NEED

• dynamic geometry software, spreadsheet, or graphing calculator

INVESTIGATE the Math

A theatre company's profit $P(x)$, in dollars, is described by the equation $P(x) = -60x^2 + 1800x + 16\,500$, where x is the cost of a ticket in dollars.

? What ticket price will give the maximum profit?

A. Calculate the average rate of change in profit for each interval of ticket prices:

$12 \le x \le 15$	$15 \le x \le 17$
$14 \le x \le 15$	$15 \le x \le 16$
$14.5 \le x \le 15$	$15 \le x \le 15.5$
$14.8 \le x \le 15$	$15 \le x \le 15.2$

B. What do all the values for the first four rate of change calculations have in common? The last four?

C. Use your results to estimate the instantaneous rate of change when $x = 15$.

D. Graph the profit function. Where does the maximum occur on your graph and what ticket price gives this maximum profit?

Reflecting

E. What is the relationship between the instantaneous rate of change in profit and the cost of a ticket at the point where the maximum profit occurs? How do you know?

F. How else could you use your graph and your knowledge of rates of change to verify that a maximum occurs at this point?

G. What would the tangent line look like at the point where a maximum occurs on your graph?

H. Explain how you could use tangents and rates of change to identify the value where a minimum occurs on a graph.

APPLY the Math

EXAMPLE 1

Selecting a strategy to identify the location of a minimum value

Leonard is riding a Ferris wheel. Leonard's elevation $h(t)$, in metres above the ground at time t in seconds, can be modelled by the function $h(t) = 5 \cos \left(4(t - 10)^\circ\right) + 6$. Shu thinks that Leonard will be closest to the ground at 55 s. Do you agree? Support your answer.

Solution

Using $t = 54$ and $t = 55$,
Average rate of change in elevation

$$= \frac{h(55) - h(54)}{55 - 54}$$

$$\doteq \frac{1 - 1.0122}{1}$$

$$= -0.0122 \text{ m/s}$$

> Estimate the instantaneous rate of change in height near $t = 55$. If it is equal to zero, then a minimum could happen there.

Using $t = 56$ and $t = 55$,
Average rate of change in elevation

$$= \frac{h(56) - h(55)}{56 - 55}$$

$$\doteq \frac{1.0122 - 1}{1}$$

$$= 0.0122 \text{ m/s}$$

A minimum could occur at $t = 55$.
$h(54) = 1.0122$, $h(55) = 1$, and
$h(56) = 1.0122$

> Since the rate of change in height using a point to the left of $t = 55$ is negative, and using a point to the right of $t = 55$ is positive, and since both are close to 0, the instantaneous rate of change could be zero at $t = 55$.

Since the estimate of the instantaneous rate of change at $t = 55$ is zero, and since $h(55)$ is less than both $h(54)$ and $h(56)$, Leonard is closest to the ground at $t = 55$ s, just as Shu predicted.

> Check that $h(55)$ is really lower than $h(54)$ and $h(56)$ to be sure that a minimum occurs at $t = 55$.

| EXAMPLE **2** | Selecting an algebraic strategy to identify the location of a minimum value |

Show that the minimum value for the function $f(x) = x^2 + 4x - 21$ happens when $x = -2$.

Solution

Estimate the slope of the tangent to the curve when $a = -2$ by writing an equation for the slope of any secant line on the graph of $f(x)$.

$$m = \frac{f(-2 + h) - f(-2)}{h}$$

$$= \frac{(-2 + h)^2 + 4(-2 + h) - 21 - (-25)}{h}$$

$$= \frac{4 - 4h + h^2 - 8 + 4h + 4}{h}$$

$$= \frac{h^2}{h}$$

$$= h$$

> To estimate the slope of the tangent at $x = -2$, use two points and the difference quotient. For one point, use $(-2, -25)$, the point where you want the tangent line to be. For the other point, use the general point on the graph of $f(x)$, for example, $(-2 + h, f(-2 + h))$.

To estimate the slope of the tangent to the curve when $x = -2$, replace h with small values.

When $h = -0.01$, $m = -0.01$.
When $h = 0.01$, $m = 0.01$.

> Since the slope of the tangent is close to 0, there could be a minimum value at $x = -2$.

Take the average of these rates of change to improve your estimate of the instantaneous rate of change at $x = -2$.

$$\text{Instantaneous rate of change} = \frac{0.01 + (-0.01)}{2}$$

$$= 0$$

$f(-1.9) = -24.99$
$f(-2) = -25$
$f(-2.1) = -24.99$

> Use two values of x that are close to -2, but on opposite sides of it, to calculate values for the function. Compare these values for the function to the value at $x = -2$.

Since the slope of the tangent is equal to zero when $x = -2$, and since the values of the function when $x = -2.1$ and $x = -1.9$ are greater than the value when $x = -2$, a minimum value occurs at $x = -2$.

EXAMPLE **3**

Selecting a strategy that involves instantaneous rate of change to solve a problem

Tim has a culture of 25 bacteria that is growing at a rate of 15%/h. He observes the culture for 12 h. During this time period, when is the instantaneous rate of change the greatest?

Solution

Determine an algebraic model for the situation.

$$P(t) = 25(1.15)^t \longleftarrow$$

This situation involves exponential growth. The algebraic model will be in the form $y = ab^x$, where a represents the initial size of the population, 25, and b is 1 + the growth rate, which is 15%.

Graph the algebraic model over the given domain, $0 \leq t \leq 12$, using a suitable window setting. $\longleftarrow$

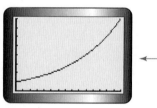

It looks like the instantaneous rate of change is the greatest near the end of the time period, because the graph is increasing faster then.

Estimate the instantaneous rate of change at $t = 10$ and $t = 12$ by drawing tangent lines at each of these points.

Tech | **Support**

For help using the graphing calculator to draw tangent lines, see Technical Appendix, T-17.

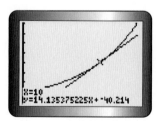

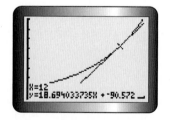

At $x = 10$, the slope of the tangent line is about 14.1. So here the bacteria population is increasing by about 14 bacteria per hour.

At $x = 12$, the slope of the tangent line is about 18.7. At this point, the bacteria population is increasing by about 19 bacteria per hour.

The instantaneous rate of change is the greatest at 12 h.

In Summary

Key Idea

- The instantaneous rate of change is zero at both a maximum point and a minimum point. As a result, the tangent lines drawn at these points will be horizontal lines.

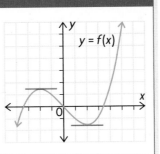

Need to Know

- If the instantaneous rate of change is negative before the value where the rate of change is zero and positive after this value, then a minimum occurs. Graphically, the tangent lines must have a negative slope before the minimum point and a positive slope after.
- If the instantaneous rate of change is positive before the value where the rate of change is zero and negative after this value, then a maximum occurs. Graphically, the tangent lines must have a positive slope before the maximum point and a negative slope after.

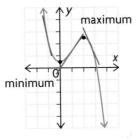

CHECK *Your Understanding*

1. The cost of running an assembly line can be modelled by the function $C(x) = 0.3x^2 - 0.9x + 1.675$, where $C(x)$ is the cost per hour in thousands of dollars and x is the number of items produced per hour in thousands. The most economical production level occurs when 1500 items are produced. Verify this using the appropriate calculations for rate of change in cost.

2. For a person at rest, the function $P(t) = -20 \cos(300°t) + 100$ models blood pressure, in millimetres of mercury (mm Hg), at time t seconds. What is the rate of change in blood pressure at 3 s?

3. If a function has a maximum value at $(a, f(a))$, what do you know about the slopes of the tangent lines at the following points?
   a) points to the left of, and very close to, $(a, f(a))$
   b) points to the right of, and very close to, $(a, f(a))$

4. If a function has a minimum value at $(a, f(a))$, what do you know about the slopes of the tangent lines at the following points?
   a) points to the left of, and very close to, $(a, f(a))$
   b) points to the right of, and very close to, $(a, f(a))$

PRACTISING

5. For each function, the point given is the maximum or minimum.
 K Use the difference quotient to verify that the slope of the tangent at this point is zero.
  a) $f(x) = 0.5x^2 + 6x + 7.5; (-6, -10.5)$
  b) $f(x) = -6x^2 + 6x + 9; (0.5, 10.5)$
  c) $f(x) = 5 \sin(x); (90°, 5)$
  d) $f(x) = -4.5 \cos(2x); (0°, -4.5)$

6. Use an algebraic strategy to verify that the point given for each function is either a maximum or a minimum.
  a) $f(x) = x^2 - 4x + 5; (2, 1)$
  b) $f(x) = -x^2 - 12x + 5.75; (-6, 41.75)$
  c) $f(x) = x^2 - 9x; (4.5, -20.25)$
  d) $f(x) = 3 \cos(x); (0°, 3)$
  e) $f(x) = x^3 - 3x; (-1, 2)$
  f) $f(x) = -x^3 + 12x - 1; (2, 15)$

7. A pilot who is flying at an altitude of 10 000 feet is forced to eject
 A from his airplane. The path that his ejection seat takes is modelled by the equation $h(t) = -16t^2 + 90t + 10\,000$, where $h(t)$ is his altitude in feet and t is the time since his ejection in seconds. Estimate at what time, t, the pilot is at a maximum altitude. Explain how the maximum altitude is related to the slope of the tangent line at certain points.

8. a) Graph each function using a graphing calculator. Then find the minimum or maximum point for the function.
  i) $f(x) = x^2 + 10x - 15$ iii) $f(x) = 4x^2 - 26x - 3$
  ii) $f(x) = -3x^2 + 45x + 16$ iv) $f(x) = -0.5x^2 + 6x + 0.45$
  b) Draw tangent lines on either side of the points you found in part a).
  c) Explain how the tangent lines you drew confirm the existence of the minimum or maximum points you found in part a).

9. a) Find the maximum *and* minimum values for each exponential
 T growth or decay equation on the given interval.
  i) $y = 100(0.85)^t$, for $0 \le t \le 5$
  ii) $y = 35(1.15)^x$, for $0 \le x \le 10$
  b) Examine your answers for part a). Use your answers to hypothesize about where the maximum value will occur in a given range of values, $a \le x \le b$. Explain and support your hypothesis thoroughly.

10. The height of a diver above the water is modelled by the function $h(t) = -5t^2 + 5t + 10$, where t represents the time in seconds and $h(t)$ represents the height in metres. Use the appropriate calculations for the rate of change in height to show that the diver reaches her maximum height at $t = 0.5$ s.

11. The top of a flagpole sways back and forth in high winds. The function $f(t) = 8 \sin(180°t)$ represents the displacement, in centimetres, that the flagpole sways from vertical, where t is the time in seconds. The flagpole is vertical when $f(t) = 0$. It is 8 cm to the right of its resting place when $f(t) = 8$, and 8 cm to the left of its resting place when $f(t) = -8$. If the flagpole is observed for 2 s, it appears to be farthest to the left when $t = 1.5$ s. Is this observation correct? Justify your answer using the appropriate calculations for the rate of change in displacement.

12. The weekly revenue for battery sales at Discount H hardware store
C can be modelled by the function $R(x) = -x^2 + 10x + 30\,000$, where revenue, R, and the cost of a package of batteries, x, are in dollars. The maximum revenue occurs when a package of batteries costs \$5. Write detailed instructions, using the appropriate calculations for the rate of change in revenue, to verify that the maximum revenue occurs when a package of batteries costs \$5. Exchange instructions with a partner. Follow your partner's instructions to verify when the maximum revenue occurs.

Extending

13. Explain how to determine the value of x that gives a maximum for a transformed sine function in the form $y = a \sin(k(x - d)) + c$, if the maximum for $y = \sin x$ occurs at $(90°, 1)$.

14. The speedometer in a car shows the vehicle's instantaneous velocity, or rate of change in position, at any moment. Every 5 s, Myra records the speedometer reading in a vehicle driven by a friend. She then plots these values. When Myra begins considering rates of change shown on her graph, what quantity is she looking at? Explain what different scenarios on Myra's graph mean, such as, her graph is increasing, but the rate of change between points on her graph is decreasing.

15. Estimate the instantaneous rate of change for $f(x) = x^2$ at $x = -2, -1, 2$, and 3. Does there appear to be a rule for determining the instantaneous rate of change for the function at given values of x? If so, state the rule. Repeat for $f(x) = x^3$.

FREQUENTLY ASKED Questions

Study | *Aid*

- See Lesson 2.4, Examples 1, 2, and 3.
- Try Chapter Review Questions 8, 9, and 10.

Q: **What descriptions could be given to produce the following speed versus time graphs? Explain.**

Graph A   **Graph B**

A: Graph A: A person walks at the same rate for 10 s and then slows down and comes to a stop at 18 s. This is shown in the graph because the horizontal line means that the person is walking at the same rate, and the straight line with a negative slope means that the person is slowing down at a constant rate.

Graph B: A person walks, increasing speed at a variable rate for 8 s and then decreasing speed at a variable rate. From 11 s to 20 s, the person walks at the same rate.

Study | *Aid*

- See Lesson 2.5, Examples 1, 2, and 3.
- Try Chapter Review Questions 11 and 13.

Q: **How can you verify, for a given value of the independent variable, where a maximum or minimum occurs using rate of change calculations?**

A: Check to see if the instantaneous rate of change is equal to zero at any point where a maximum or minimum might occur. If it does, then a maximum or minimum could occur there. Graphically, the tangent line must be horizontal at this point.

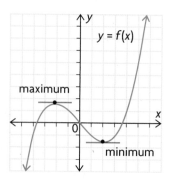

If the instantaneous rate of change is positive before the point where the rate of change is zero, and negative after, then a maximum occurs. Graphically, the tangent lines must have a positive slope before the maximum point and a negative slope after.

If the instantaneous rate of change is negative before the point where the rate of change is zero, and positive after, then a minimum occurs. Graphically, the tangent lines must have a negative slope before the minimum point and a positive slope after.

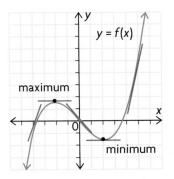

Q: When solving problems that require you to estimate the value for the instantaneous rate of change in a relationship at a specific point, what does the sign of this estimated value indicate?

A: The sign of the estimated value of the instantaneous rate of change gives you information about what is happening to the values of the dependent variable in the relationship at that exact point in time. If the instantaneous rate of change is positive (indicated graphically by a tangent line that rises from left to right), then the values for the dependent variable are increasing. If the instantaneous rate of change is negative (indicated graphically by a tangent line that falls from left to right), then the values for the dependent variable are decreasing.

Q: Can the difference quotient $\dfrac{f(a + h) - f(a)}{h}$ be used to determine both average and instantaneous rates of change?

A: Yes. For any function $y = f(x)$, the difference quotient provides a formula for calculating the average rate of change between two points $(a, f(a))$ and $(a + h, f(a + h))$. In both the case of average and instantaneous rate of change, h is the difference between the values for the independent variable that define the interval on which the rate of change is being calculated. In the case of instantaneous rate of change, h is made arbitrarily small so that this interval is close to 0. The calculation approximates the instantaneous rate of change when two points on $y = f(x)$ are chosen that are very, very close to each other.

Study | *Aid*
- See Lesson 2.5, Example 2.
- Try Chapter Review Question 12.

PRACTICE Questions

Lesson 2.1

1. The following table shows the daily number of watches sold at a shop and the amount of money made from the sales.

Number of Watches (w)	Revenue (r) ($)
25	437.50
17	297.50
20	350.00
12	210.00
24	420.00

a) Does the data in the table appear to follow a linear relation? Explain.
b) Graph the data. How does the graph compare with your hypothesis?
c) What is the average rate of change in revenue from $w = 20$ to $w = 25$?
d) What is the cost of one watch, and how does this cost relate to the graph?

2. The graph shows the height above the ground of a person riding a Ferris wheel.

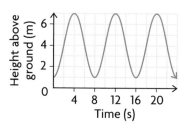

a) Calculate the average rate of change in height on the interval $[0, 4]$.
b) Calculate the average rate of change in height on the interval $[4, 8]$.
c) Discuss the similarities and differences in your answers to parts a) and b).

3. A company is opening a new office. The initial expense to set up the office is $10 000, and the company will spend another $2500 each month in utilities until the new office opens.
a) Write the equation that represents the company's total expenses in terms of months until the office opens.
b) What is the average rate of change in the company's expenses from $3 \leq m \leq 6$?
c) Do you expect this rate of change to vary? Why or why not?

Lesson 2.2

4. An investment's value, $V(t)$, is modelled by the function $V(t) = 2500(1.15)^t$, where t is the number of years after funds are invested.
a) To find the instantaneous rate of change in the value of the investment at $t = 4$, what intervals on either side of 4 would you choose? Why?
b) Use your intervals from part a) to find the instantaneous rate of change in the value of the investment at $t = 4$.

5. The height, in centimetres, of a piston attached to a turning wheel at time t, in seconds, is modelled by the equation $y = 2 \sin (120°t)$.
a) Examine the equation, and select a strategy for finding the instantaneous rate of change in the piston's height at $t = 12$ s.
b) Use your strategy from part a) to find the instantaneous rate of change at $t = 12$ s.

Lesson 2.3

6. For the graph shown, estimate the slope of the tangent line at each point.

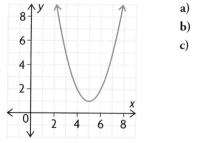

a) $(4, 2)$
b) $(5, 1)$
c) $(7, 5)$

7. Use a graphing calculator to graph the equation $y = 5x^2 + 3x + 7$. Then use your calculator to estimate the instantaneous rate of change for each value of x.

a) $x = -4$ c) $x = -0.3$
b) $x = -2$ d) $x = 2$

Lesson 2.4

8. A sculptor makes a vase for flowers. The radius and circumference of the vase increase as the height of the vase increases. The vase is filled with water. Draw a possible graph of the height of the water as time increases.

9. A newspaper carrier delivers papers on her bicycle. She bikes to the first neighbourhood at a rate of 10 km/h. She slows down at a constant rate over a period of 7 s, to a speed of 5 km/h, so that she can deliver her papers. After travelling at this rate for 3 s, she sees one of her customers and decides to stop. She slows at a constant rate until she stops. It takes her 6 s to stop.

a) Draw a graph of the newspaper carrier's rate over time for the time period after she arrives at the first neighbourhood.
b) What is the average rate of change in speed over the first 7 s?
c) What is the average rate of change in speed from second 7 to 12 seconds.
d) What is the instantaneous rate of change in speed at 12 s?

10. The graph shows the height of a roller coaster versus time. Describe how the vertical speed of the roller coaster will vary as it travels along the track from A to G. Sketch a graph to show the vertical speed of the roller coaster.

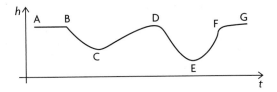

Lesson 2.5

11. A maximum or minimum is given for each of the following functions. Select a strategy, and verify whether the point given is a maximum or a minimum.

a) $f(x) = x^2 - 10x + 7$; $(5, -18)$
b) $g(x) = -x^2 - 6x - 4$; $(-3, 5)$
c) $h(x) = -2x^2 + 68x + 75$; $(17, 653)$
d) $j(x) = \sin(-2x)$; $(45°, -1)$
e) $k(x) = -4\cos(x + 25)$; $(-25°, -4)$
f) $m(x) = \frac{1}{20}(x^3 + 2x^2 - 15x)$; $\left(-3, \frac{9}{5}\right)$

12. a) For each function, find the equation for the slope of the secant line between any general point on the function $(a + h, f(a + h))$ and the given x-coordinate of another point.
  i) $f(x) = x^2 - 30x$; $a = 2$
  ii) $g(x) = -4x^2 - 56x + 16$; $a = -1$

b) Use each slope equation you found in part a) to estimate the slope of the tangent line at the point with the given x-coordinate.

13. a) Explain how the instantaneous rates of change differ on either side of a maximum point of a function.
b) Explain how the instantaneous rates of change differ on either side of a minimum point of a function.

14. a) Use graphing technology to graph $f(x) = x^4 - 2x^2$.
b) Use the graph to estimate the locations of the maximum and minimum values of this function.
c) Explain how tangent lines can be used to verify the locations you identified in part b).
d) Confirm your estimates by using the maximum and minimum operations on the graphing calculator.

1. A speedboat driver is testing a new boat. He begins the test by steadily increasing the boat's speed until he reaches 3 kn (knots) over a period of 1 min. Because he is in a no-wake zone, he stays at this speed for 5 min. After leaving the no-wake zone, he steadily increases the speed of the boat to 25 kn over a period of 2 min. He stays at this speed for 5 min and then increases the speed of the boat to 45 kn over a period of 1 min. After staying at this speed for 5 min, he decelerates the boat at a steady rate over a period of 4 min until he comes to a stop.
   a) Draw a graph of the boat's speed versus time. Remember to label your data points.
   b) What is the average rate of change in speed from $t = 6$ to $t = 8$ and from $t = 8$ to $t = 13$? How are the two rates different? What does this tell you about the speed of the boat during these two intervals of time?
   c) What is the instantaneous rate of change in speed at $t = 7$?

2. A cup of hot cocoa left on a desk in a classroom had its temperature measured once every minute. The graph shows the relationship between the temperature of the cocoa, in degrees Celsius, and time, in minutes.

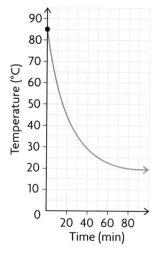

   a) Determine the slope of the secant line that passes through the points $(5, 70)$ and $(50, 25)$.
   b) What does the answer to part a) mean in this context?
   c) Estimate the slope of the tangent line at the point $(30, 35)$.
   d) What does the answer to part b) mean in this context?
   e) Discuss what happens to the rate at which the cup of cocoa cools over the 90 min period.

3. The profit $P(x)$ of a cosmetics company, in thousands of dollars, is given by $P(x) = -5x^2 + 400x - 2550$, where x is the amount spent on advertising in thousands of dollars.
   a) Calculate the average rate of change in profit on the interval $8 \leq x \leq 10$.
   b) Estimate the instantaneous rate of change in profit when $x = 50$.
   c) Discuss the significance of the signs in your answers to parts a) and b).

4. Estimate the instantaneous rate of change for each function at each point given. Identify any point that is a maximum/minimum value.
   a) $h(p) = 2p^2 + 3p$; $p = -1, -0.75$, and 1
   b) $k(x) = -0.75x^2 + 1.5x + 13$; $x = -2, 4$, and 1

Investigating Rates of Change in Body Temperature

Use either a Calculator Based Laboratory (CBL) and temperature probe or a thermometer with a Fahrenheit scale to measure your body temperature for 2 min. Then allow the temperature probe or thermometer to return to room temperature for an additional minute.

❓ **What happens to the average and instantaneous rate of change in temperature as the probe or thermometer heats up and cools?**

A. Collect data every 5 s for the 3 min interval. For the first 2 min, hold the thermometer or probe tightly in your hands. After 2 min, release the thermometer or probe and allow it to rest on the desk for one more minute. Use the data you collected to draw a graph of temperature versus time.

B. Determine where the temperature was the highest and the lowest.

C. Was there any time when the temperature remained fairly constant?

D. When was the temperature increasing? When was it decreasing?

E. Determine the average rate of change over the interval when the temperature
  i) increased
  ii) decreased
  iii) remained fairly constant

F. At what point did the greatest rate of change in temperature occur? At what point was the temperature rising most rapidly? At what point was the temperature falling most rapidly?

Task | *Checklist*

✔ Did you label your graph accurately?

✔ Did you use appropriate points to determine the average rate of change?

✔ Did you use an appropriate technique to determine the instantaneous rate of change?

✔ Did you interpret your graph correctly to draw reasonable conclusions?

Chapter

3

Polynomial Functions

▶ GOALS

You will be able to

- Identify and describe key characteristics of polynomial functions
- Divide one polynomial by another polynomial
- Factor polynomial expressions
- Solve problems that involve polynomial equations and inequalities graphically and algebraically

? A fractal object displays properties of self-similarity. The fractal shown was created using a computer, the polynomial function $f(z) = 35z^9 - 180z^7 + 378z^5 - 420z^3 + 315z$, and a process called iteration. How can you estimate the number of zeros that this polynomial function has?

SKILLS AND CONCEPTS *You Need*

Study | *Aid*

- For help, see the Review of Essential Skills found at the Nelson Advanced Functions website.

Question	Appendix
1	R-2
2	R-3
3	R-6
4	R-8
5	R-9

1. Expand and simplify each of the following expressions.
   a) $2x^2(3x - 11)$
   c) $4x(2x - 5)(3x + 2)$
   b) $(x - 4)(x + 6)$
   d) $(5x - 4)(x^2 + 7x - 8)$

2. Factor each of the following expressions completely.
   a) $x^2 + 3x - 28$
   b) $2x^2 - 18x + 28$

3. Solve each of the following equations. Round your answer to two decimal places, if necessary.
   a) $3x + 7 = x - 5$
   c) $x^2 + 11x + 24 = 0$
   b) $(x + 3)(2x - 9) = 0$
   d) $6x^2 + 22x = 8$

4. Describe the transformations that must be applied to $y = x^2$ to create the graph of each of the following functions.
   a) $y = \dfrac{1}{4}(x - 3)^2 + 9$
   b) $y = \left(\dfrac{1}{2}x\right)^2 - 7$

5. Write the equation of each function shown below.

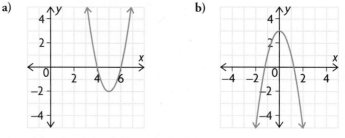

   a)
   b)

6. Graph each of the following functions.
   a) $y = 3(x + 5)^2 - 4$
   b) $y = 2x^2 - 12x + 5$

7. Use finite differences to classify each set of data as linear, quadratic, or other.

a)
x	y
-2	56.4
-1	50.6
0	45
1	39.6
2	34.4

b)
x	y
-2	11
-1	5
0	2
1	7
2	13

c)
x	y
-2	2
-1	6
0	18
1	54
2	162

d)
x	y
-2	7
-1	6.5
0	6
1	5.5
2	5

8. Create a concept web that shows the connections between each of the following for the function $f(x) = 3x^2 + 24x + 36$: the y-intercept, factored form, vertex form, axis of symmetry, direction of opening, zeroes, minimum value, value of the discriminant, and translations of the parent function.

   On each arrow, write a brief description of the process you would use to obtain the information.

APPLYING *What You Know*

Examining Patterns

In the late 18th century, seven-year-old Carl Friedrich Gauss noticed a pattern that allowed him to determine the sum of the numbers from 1 to 100 very quickly. He realized that you could add 1 and 100, and then multiply by half of the largest number (50) to get 5050.

YOU WILL NEED
- graph paper

 Are there formulas for calculating the sum of the first n natural numbers and the sums of consecutive squares of natural numbers?

A. Copy and complete each table, then calculate the **finite differences** until they are constant.

B. Graph each relationship in part A on graph paper.

C. Use your graphs and finite differences to make a **conjecture** about the type of model that would fit the data in each table (linear, quadratic, or other).

D. Use a graphing calculator and the regression operation to verify your conjectures in part C.

E. Use the equations you found in part D to calculate the sum of the first five natural numbers and the sum of the squares of the first five natural numbers.

F. Verify that your calculations in part E are correct by comparing your sums with the values in both tables when $n = 5$.

G. Use the equation you found to verify that the sum of the natural numbers from 1 to 100 is 5050.

H. Use the equation you found to determine the sum of the squares of the natural numbers from 1 to 100.

Table 1

n	Sum up to n ($f(n)$)
1	1
2	$1 + 2 = 3$
3	$1 + 2 + 3 = 6$
4	
5	
6	
7	
8	
9	
10	

Table 2

n	Sum of the squares up to n^2 ($g(n)$)
1	1
2	$1^2 + 2^2 = 5$
3	$1^2 + 2^2 + 3^2 = 14$
4	
5	
6	
7	
8	
9	
10	

Exploring Polynomial Functions

YOU WILL NEED

- graphing calculator or graphing software

GOAL

Identify polynomial functions.

EXPLORE the Math

Beth knows that linear functions result in graphs of straight lines, while quadratic functions result in parabolas. She wonders what happens when the **degree** of a function is larger than 2. Beth searched for polynomials on the Internet and found the following table.

These are polynomial expressions.	These are not polynomial expressions.
$3x^2 - 5x + 3$	$\sqrt{x} + 5x^3$
$-4x + 5x^7 - 3x^4 + 2$	$\dfrac{1}{2x + 5}$
$\frac{2}{5}x^3 - 3x^5 + 4$	$6x^3 + 5x^2 - 3x + 2 + 4x^{-1}$
$\sqrt{4}x^3 - \frac{\sqrt{5}}{3}x^2 + 2x - \frac{1}{4}$	$\dfrac{3x^2 + 5x - 1}{2x^2 + x - 3}$
$3x - 5$	$4^x + 5$
-7	$\sin(x - 30)$
$-4x$	$x^2y + 3x - 4y^{-2}$
$(2x - 3)(x + 1)^2$	$3x^3 + 4x^{2.5}$

Communication | Tip

A polynomial expression in one variable is usually written with the powers arranged from highest to lowest degrees, as in $5x^3 - 7x^2 + 4x + 3$. The phrase "polynomial expression" is often shortened to just "polynomial."

? What makes an expression a *polynomial* expression, and what do functions that involve polynomial expressions look like graphically and algebraically?

A. Look carefully at the expressions in the two columns of the table. What do all of the polynomial expressions have in common?

B. The expressions in the right column are not polynomials. How are they different from the polynomial expressions in the left column?

C. In your own words, define a polynomial expression.

D. The simplest polynomial functions are functions that contain a single term. Use a graphing calculator to graph each of the following polynomial functions. Then copy and complete the table.

Polynomial Function	Type	Sketch of Graph	Description of Graph	Domain and Range	Existence of Asymptotes?
$f(x) = x$	linear				
$f(x) = x^2$	quadratic				
$f(x) = x^3$	cubic				
$f(x) = x^4$	quartic				
$f(x) = x^5$	quintic				

E. Which polynomial functions in part D have similar graphical characteristics? How are the equations of these functions related?

F. For each function in part D, create a table of values for $-3 \leq x \leq 3$. Calculate the finite differences until they are constant. What do you notice?

G. Create equations for four different polynomial functions that are neither linear nor quadratic. Make sure that each function has a different degree and contains at least three terms. Graph each function on a graphing calculator, make a detailed sketch, and create a table of finite differences.

H. Create equations for four non-polynomial functions. Make detailed sketches of their graphs, and create a table of finite differences.

I. Compare and contrast the graphs, the equations, and the finite difference tables for the polynomial and non-polynomial functions you created. Explain how you can tell whether or not a function is a polynomial by looking at
  i) its graph
  ii) its equation
  iii) its finite difference table

Reflecting

J. Explain how you can tell whether a polynomial equation is a function and not just a relation.

K. Why are the equations of the form $y = mx + b$ and $y = ax^2 + bx + c$ examples of polynomial functions?

polynomial functions

a function of the form $f(x) = a_n x^n + a_{n-1} x^{n-1} + \ldots + a_2 x^2 + a_1 x + a_0$, where $a_0, a_1, \ldots, a_n$ are real numbers and n is a whole number; the equation of a polynomial function is defined by a polynomial expression, as in $f(x) = 5x^3 + 6x^2 - 3x + 7$

Communication | *Tip*

Polynomial functions are named according to their degree. Polynomial functions of degree 1, 2, 3, 4, and 5 are commonly called linear, **quadratic**, **cubic**, **quartic**, and **quintic** functions, respectively.

L. As the degree of a polynomial function increases, describe what happens to
  i) the graph of the function
  ii) the finite differences

M. Would you change your definition in part C now, after having completed part G? Explain.

In Summary

Key Idea

- A polynomial in one variable is an expression of the form $a_nx^n + a_{n-1}x^{n-1} + \ldots + a_2x^2 + a_1x + a_0$, where $a_0, a_1, \ldots, a_n$ are real numbers and n is a whole number. The expression contains only one variable, with the powers arranged in descending order. For example, $2x + 5$, $3x^2 + 2x - 1$, and $5x^4 + 3x^3 - 6x^2 + 5x - 8$.

Need to Know

- In any polynomial expression, the exponents on the variable must be whole numbers.
- A polynomial function is any function that contains a polynomial expression in one variable. The degree of the function is the highest exponent in the expression. For example, $f(x) = 6x^3 - 3x^2 + 4x - 9$ has a degree of 3.
- The nth finite differences of a polynomial function of degree n are constant.
- The domain of a polynomial function is the set of real numbers, $\{x \in \mathbf{R}\}$.
- The range of a polynomial function may be all real numbers, or it may have a lower bound or an upper bound (but not both).
- The graphs of polynomial functions do not have horizontal or vertical asymptotes.
- The graphs of polynomial functions of degree zero are horizontal lines. The shape of other graphs depends on the degree of the function. Five typical shapes are shown for various degrees:

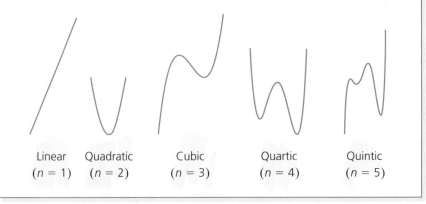

| Linear | Quadratic | Cubic | Quartic | Quintic |
| ($n = 1$) | ($n = 2$) | ($n = 3$) | ($n = 4$) | ($n = 5$) |

FURTHER *Your Understanding*

1. Determine which graphs represent polynomial functions. Explain how you know.

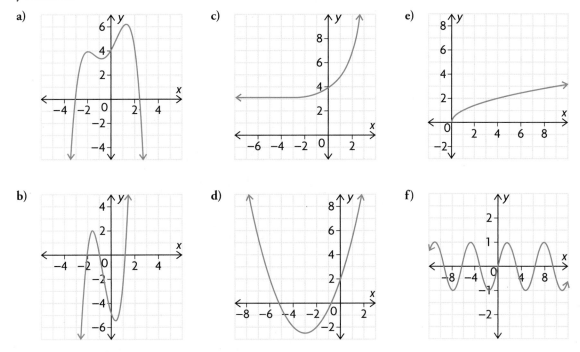

a)

c)

e)

b)

d)

f)

2. Determine whether each function is a polynomial function or another type of function. Justify your decision.

a) $f(x) = 2x^3 + x^2 - 5$

b) $f(x) = x^2 + 3x - 2$

c) $y = 2x - 7$

d) $y = \sqrt{x + 1}$

e) $y = \dfrac{x^2 - 4x + 1}{x + 2}$

f) $f(x) = x(x - 1)^2$

3. Use finite differences to determine the type of polynomial function that could model each relationship.

a) Michelle earns \$200 per week, plus 5% of sales.

Sales	0	500	1000	1500	2000
Earnings ($)	200	225	250	275	300

b) A model rocket is launched from the roof of a school.

Time (s)	0	1	2	3	4
Height above Ground (m)	10	25	30	25	10

c) The volume of a box varies at different widths.

Width (cm)	1	2	3	4	5
Volume (cm³)	200	225	250	275	300

d) The input for a function gives a certain output.

Input	0	1	2	3	4	5	6
Output	200	204	232	308	456	700	1064

4. Graph the function $y = 2^x$ on the domain $0 \leq x \leq 3$.
   a) Explain why a person who sees only the graph you created (not the equation) might think that the graph represents a polynomial function.
   b) Explain why this function is not a polynomial function.

5. Draw a graph of a polynomial function that satisfies all of the following characteristics:
   - $f(-3) = 16, f(3) = 0$, and $f(-1) = 0$
   - The y-intercept is 2.
   - $f(x) \geq 0$ when $x < 3$.
   - $f(x) \leq 0$ when $x > 3$.
   - The domain is the set of real numbers.

6. Explain why there are many different graphs that fit different combinations of the characteristics in question 5. Draw two graphs that are different from each other, and explain how they satisfy some, but not all, of the characteristics in question 5.

7. Create equations for a linear, a quadratic, a cubic, and a quartic polynomial function that all share the same y-intercept of 5.

8. Complete the following chart to summarize your understanding of polynomials.

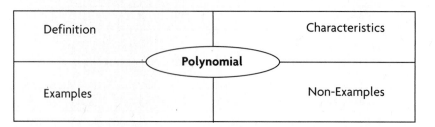

3.2 Characteristics of Polynomial Functions

GOAL

Investigate the turning points and end behaviours of polynomial functions.

YOU WILL NEED

- graphing calculator or graphing software

INVESTIGATE the Math

Karel knows that he can describe the graph of a linear function from its equation, using the slope and the y-intercept. He can also describe the graph of a quadratic function from its equation, using the vertex, y-intercept, and the direction of opening. Now he is wondering whether he can describe the graphs of polynomial functions of higher degree, using characteristics that can be predicted from their equations.

? How can you predict some of the characteristics of a polynomial function from its equation?

A. The graphs of some polynomial functions are shown below and on the following page.

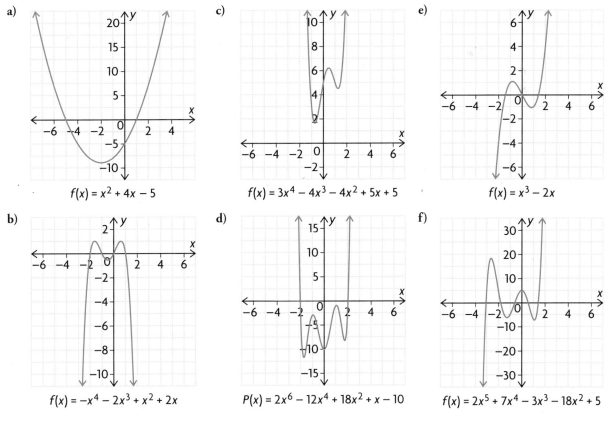

a) $f(x) = x^2 + 4x - 5$

b) $f(x) = -x^4 - 2x^3 + x^2 + 2x$

c) $f(x) = 3x^4 - 4x^3 - 4x^2 + 5x + 5$

d) $P(x) = 2x^6 - 12x^4 + 18x^2 + x - 10$

e) $f(x) = x^3 - 2x$

f) $f(x) = 2x^5 + 7x^4 - 3x^3 - 18x^2 + 5$

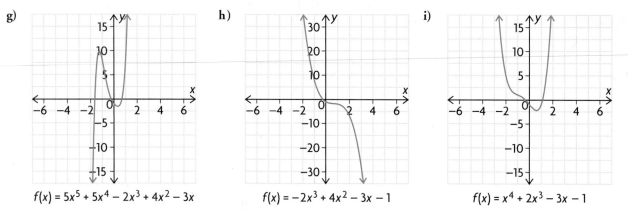

g)

$f(x) = 5x^5 + 5x^4 - 2x^3 + 4x^2 - 3x$

h)

$f(x) = -2x^3 + 4x^2 - 3x - 1$

i)

$f(x) = x^4 + 2x^3 - 3x - 1$

Copy the following table, and complete it using the remaining equations and graphs given.

Equation and Graph	Degree	Even or Odd Degree?	Leading Coefficient	End Behaviours		Number of Turning Points
				$x \to -\infty$	$x \to +\infty$	
a) $f(x) = x^2 + 4x - 5$	2	even	+1	$y \to +\infty$	$y \to +\infty$	1

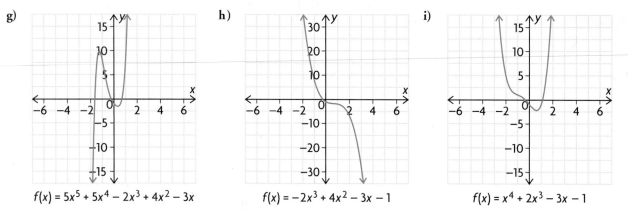

leading coefficient

the coefficient of the term with the highest degree in a polynomial

B. Describe any patterns that you see in your table.

C. Create two new polynomial functions of degree greater than 2, one of even degree and one of odd degree. Do these new polynomial functions support your observations in part B?

D. What do you think is the maximum number of turning points that a polynomial function of degree n can have?

E. Graph the following functions using a graphing calculator. Copy each graph and its equation into the appropriate column of a table like the one shown on the next page.

   i) $f(x) = x^4 - 2x^2 + 1$ vi) $f(x) = x^5 - 3x$

   ii) $f(x) = x^3 + 3x^2 - 2x - 5$ vii) $f(x) = x^2 - 3x + 4$

   iii) $f(x) = \dfrac{1}{2}x^{10} - \dfrac{1}{3}x^4 + x^2$ viii) $f(x) = 2x^7 - 3x^3 + 2x$

   iv) $f(x) = x^3 + x$ ix) $f(x) = -3x^4 + 2x^3 - 3x + 1$

   v) $f(x) = -2x^6 + 3x^4$ x) $f(x) = x^2 - x$

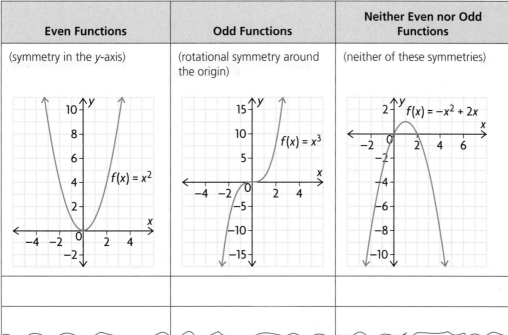

Even Functions	Odd Functions	Neither Even nor Odd Functions
(symmetry in the y-axis)	(rotational symmetry around the origin)	(neither of these symmetries)

F. Determine $f(-x)$ for each function in your table. Discuss any patterns that you see.

G. Is every function of even degree an even function? Why or why not?

H. Is every function of odd degree an odd function? Why or why not?

I. How can you use the equation of a polynomial function to describe its end behaviours, number of turning points, and symmetry?

Reflecting

J. Why must all polynomial functions of even degree have an absolute maximum or absolute minimum ?

K. Why must all polynomial functions of odd degree have at least one zero?

L. Can the graph of a polynomial function have no zeros? Explain.

M. Examine all the graphs you have investigated and their equations. Is it possible to predict the maximum number of zeros that a graph will have if you are given its equation? Explain.

absolute maximum/ absolute minimum

the greatest/least value attained by a function for all values in its domain

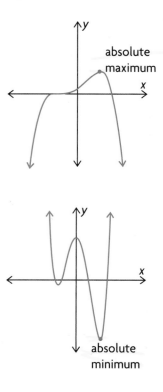

APPLY the Math

EXAMPLE 1   Reasoning about characteristics of a given polynomial function

Describe the end behaviours of each function, the possible number of turning points, and the possible number of zeros. Use these characteristics to sketch possible graphs of the function.

a) $f(x) = -3x^5 + 4x^3 - 8x^2 + 7x - 5$ b) $g(x) = 2x^4 + x^2 + 2$

Solution

a) $f(x) = -3x^5 + 4x^3 - 8x^2 + 7x - 5$

The degree is odd, so the function has opposite end behaviours. The leading coefficient is negative, so the graph must extend from the second quadrant to the fourth quadrant.

As $x \to -\infty, y \to +\infty$.

As $x \to +\infty, y \to -\infty$.

> If x is a very large negative number, such as -1000, $-3x^5$ will have a large positive value and will have a greater effect on the value of the function than the other terms. Therefore, the graph will pass through the second quadrant. For very large positive values of x, $-3x^5$ will have a large negative value. Therefore, the graph will extend into the fourth quadrant.

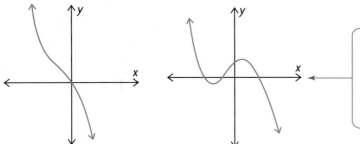

> Using the end behaviours of the function, sketch possible graphs of a fifth-degree polynomial.
>
> To pass through the second quadrant and extend into the fourth quadrant, the graph must have an even number of turning points.

$f(x)$ may have zero, two, or four turning points.

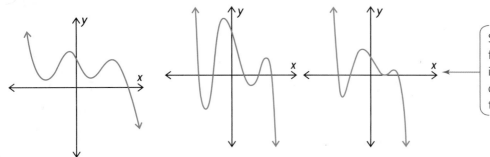

> Since the function is a fifth-degree polynomial, it must have at least one zero and no more than five zeros.

$f(x)$ may have one, two, three, four, or five zeros.

b) $g(x) = 2x^4 + x^2 + 2$

The degree is even, so the function has the same end behaviours. The leading coefficient is positive, so the graph must extend from the second quadrant to the first quadrant.

As $x \to -\infty$, $y \to +\infty$.

As $x \to +\infty$, $y \to +\infty$.

> If x is a very large negative number, $2x^4$ will have a large positive value and will have a greater effect on the value of the function than the other terms. Therefore, the graph will pass through the second quadrant. For very large positive values of x, $2x^4$ will have a large positive value. Therefore, the graph will extend into the first quadrant.

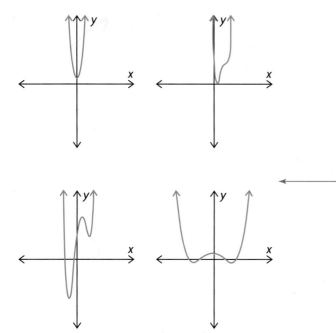

> Using the end behaviours of the function, sketch possible graphs of a fourth-degree polynomial.
>
> To start in the second quadrant and end in the first quadrant, the graph must have an odd number of turning points.
>
> Since the function is a fourth-degree polynomial, it may have anywhere from zero to four x-intercepts.

$f(x)$ may have one or three turning points and zero, one, two, three, or four zeros.

What could the graph of a polynomial function that has range $\{y \in \mathbf{R} \mid y \leq 10\}$ and three turning points look like? What can you conclude about its equation?

Solution

End behaviours of the function:

As $x \to -\infty, y \to -\infty$.

As $x \to +\infty, y \to -\infty$.

> Since the range has an upper limit, both ends of the function extend downward toward $-\infty$ in the third and fourth quadrants. For this to occur, the leading coefficient in the equation must be negative.

The function has at least two zeros.

> Because the function has a maximum value that is positive and both ends extend downward, the function must cross the x-axis at least twice.

The function has an even degree.

> Since the function has an absolute maximum, it must have an even degree. This is confirmed by the end behaviours, because they are the same.

The degree of the function is at least 4.

> It is not possible to be sure about the degree of the function, but the degree must be at least one more than the number of turning points.

Here are some possible graphs of the function.

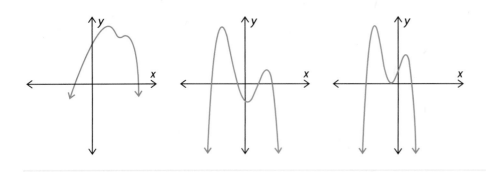

In Summary

Key Ideas

- Polynomial functions of the same degree have similar characteristics.
- The degree and the leading coefficient in the equation of a polynomial function indicate the end behaviours of the graph.
- The degree of a polynomial function provides information about the shape, turning points, and zeros of the graph.

Need to Know

End Behaviours

- An odd-degree polynomial function has opposite end behaviours.
  - If the leading coefficient is negative, then the function extends from the second quadrant to the fourth quadrant; that is, as $x \to -\infty$, $y \to \infty$ and as $x \to \infty$, $y \to -\infty$.

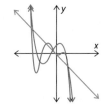

  - If the leading coefficient is positive, then the function extends from the third quadrant to the first quadrant; that is, as $x \to -\infty$, $y \to -\infty$ and as $x \to \infty$, $y \to \infty$.

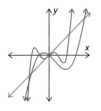

- An even-degree polynomial function has the same end behaviours.
  - If the leading coefficient is negative, then the function extends from the third quadrant to the fourth quadrant; that is, as $x \to \pm\infty$, $y \to -\infty$.

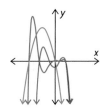

  - If the leading coefficient is positive, then the function extends from the second quadrant to the first quadrant; that is, as $x \to \pm\infty$, $y \to \infty$.

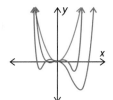

Turning Points

- A polynomial function of degree n has at most $n - 1$ turning points.

Number of Zeros

- A polynomial function of degree n may have up to n distinct zeros.
- A polynomial function of odd degree must have at least one zero.
- A polynomial function of even degree may have no zeros.

Symmetry

- Some polynomial functions are symmetrical in the y-axis. These are even functions, where $f(-x) = f(x)$.
- Some polynomial functions have rotational symmetry about the origin. These are odd functions, where $f(-x) = -f(x)$.
- Most polynomial functions have no symmetrical properties. These are functions that are neither even nor odd, with no relationship between $f(-x)$ and $f(x)$.

CHECK *Your Understanding*

1. State the degree, leading coefficient, and end behaviours of each polynomial function.
   a) $f(x) = -4x^4 + 3x^2 - 15x + 5$
   b) $g(x) = 2x^5 - 4x^3 + 10x^2 - 13x + 8$
   c) $p(x) = 4 - 5x + 4x^2 - 3x^3$
   d) $h(x) = 2x(x - 5)(3x + 2)(4x - 3)$

2. a) Determine the minimum and maximum number of turning points for each function in question 1.
   b) Determine the minimum and maximum number of zeros that each function in question 1 may have.

3. For each of the following graphs, decide if
   a) the function has an even or odd degree
   b) the leading coefficient is positive or negative

i)
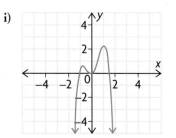

iii)
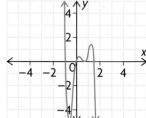

v)
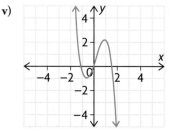

ii)
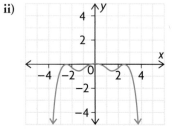

iv)
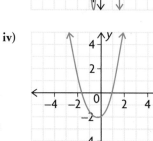

vi)
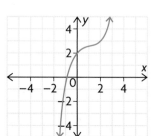

PRACTISING

4. Describe the end behaviour of each polynomial function using the degree and the leading coefficient.
   a) $f(x) = 2x^2 - 3x + 5$
   b) $f(x) = -3x^3 + 2x^2 + 5x + 1$
   c) $f(x) = 5x^3 - 2x^2 - 2x + 6$
   d) $f(x) = -2x^4 + 5x^3 - 2x^2 + 3x - 1$
   e) $f(x) = 0.5x^4 + 2x^2 - 6$
   f) $f(x) = -3x^5 + 2x^3 - 4x$

5. Use end behaviours, turning points, and zeros to match each polynomial equation with the most likely graph below. Explain.

a) $y = 2x^3 - 4x^2 + 3x + 2$ d) $y = x^4 - x^3 - 4x^2 + 5x$

b) $y = -4x^4 + 3x^2 + 4$ e) $y = -2x^5 + 3x^4 + 6x^3 - 10x^2 + 2x + 5$

c) $y = x^2 + 3x - 5$ f) $y = 3x^3 + 5x^2 - 3x + 1$

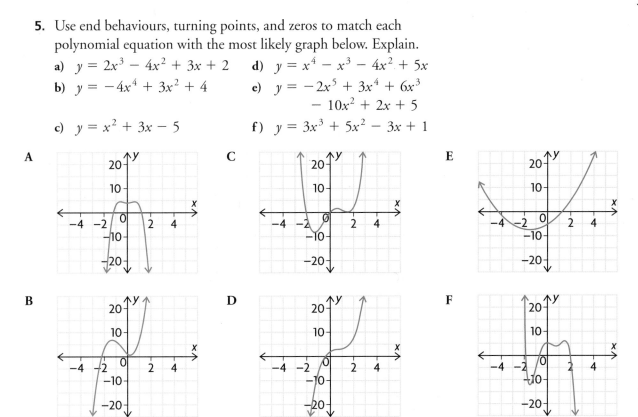

6. Give an example of a polynomial function that has each of the following end behaviours:

a) As $x \to -\infty$, $y \to -\infty$ and as $x \to \infty$, $y \to \infty$.

b) As $x \to \pm\infty$, $y \to \infty$.

c) As $x \to \pm\infty$, $y \to -\infty$.

d) As $x \to -\infty$, $y \to \infty$ and as $x \to \infty$, $y \to -\infty$.

7. Sketch the graph of a polynomial function that satisfies each set of conditions.

a) degree 4, positive leading coefficient, 3 zeros, 3 turning points

b) degree 4, negative leading coefficient, 2 zeros, 1 turning point

c) degree 4, positive leading coefficient, 1 zero, 3 turning points

d) degree 3, negative leading coefficient, 1 zero, no turning points

e) degree 3, positive leading coefficient, 2 zeros, 2 turning points

f) degree 4, two zeros, three turning points, Range $= \{y \in \mathbf{R} \mid y \leq 5\}$

8. Explain why odd-degree polynomial functions can have only local maximums and minimums, but even-degree polynomial functions can have absolute maximums and minimums.

9. Rei noticed that the graph of the function $f(x) = ax^b - cx$ is symmetrical with respect to the origin, and that it has some turning points. Does the graph have an odd or even number of turning points?

10. Sketch an example of a cubic function with a graph that intersects the *x*-axis at each number of points below.

    a) only one point   **b)** two different points **c)** three different points

11. Sketch an example of a quartic function with a graph that intersects the *x*-axis at each number of points below.

    a) no points   **d)** three different points

    b) only one point   **e)** four different points

    c) two different points

12. The graph of a polynomial function has the following characteristics:
- Its domain and range are the set of all real numbers.
- There are turning points at $x = -2, 0,$ and 3.

    a) Draw the graphs of two different polynomial functions that have these three characteristics.

    b) What additional characteristics would ensure that only one graph could be drawn?

13. The mining town of Brighton was founded in 1900. Its
A population, *y*, in hundreds, is modelled by the equation
$y = -0.1x^4 + 0.5x^3 + 0.4x^2 + 10x + 7$, where *x* is the number of years since 1900.

    a) What was the population of the town in 1900?

    b) Based on the equation, describe what happened to the population of Brighton over time. Justify your answer.

14. *f* is a polynomial function of degree *n*, where *n* is a positive even integer. Decide whether each of the following statements is true or false. If the statement is false, give an example that illustrates why it is false.

    a) *f* is an even function.

    b) *f* cannot be an odd function.

    c) *f* will have at least one zero.

    d) As $x \rightarrow \infty, y \rightarrow \infty$ and as $x \rightarrow -\infty, y \rightarrow \infty$.

15. If you needed to predict the graph or equation of a polynomial function and were only allowed to ask three questions about the function, what questions would you ask to help you the most? Why?

Extending

16. a) Suppose that $f(x) = ax^2 + bx + c$. What must be true about the coefficients if *f* is an even function?

    b) Suppose that $g(x) = ax^3 + bx^2 + cx + d$. What must be true about the coefficients if *g* is an odd function?

Characteristics of Polynomial Functions in Factored Form

GOAL

Determine the equation of a polynomial function that describes a particular graph or situation, and vice versa.

YOU WILL NEED

- graphing calculator or graphing software

INVESTIGATE the Math

The graphs of the functions $f(x) = x^2 - 4x - 12$ and $g(x) = 2x - 12$ are shown.

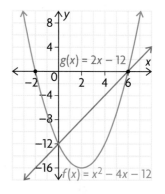

? What is the relationship between the real **roots** of a polynomial equation and the x-intercepts of the corresponding polynomial function?

A. Solve the equations $f(x) = 0$ and $g(x) = 0$ using the given functions. Compare your solutions with the graphs of the functions. What do you notice?

B. Create a cubic function from the **family of polynomial functions** of the form $h(x) = a(x - p)(x - q)(x - r)$.

C. Graph $y = h(x)$ on a graphing calculator. Describe the shape of the graph near each zero, and compare the shape to the **order** of each factor in the equation of the function.

D. Solve $h(x) = 0$, and compare your solutions with the zeros of the graph of the corresponding function. What do you notice?

E. Repeat parts B through D using a quartic function.

F. Repeat parts C and D using $m(x) = (x - 2)^2(x + 3)$. How would you describe the shape of the graph near the zero with the repeated factor?

G. Repeat parts C and D using $n(x) = (x - 2)^3(x + 3)$. How would you describe the shape of the graph near the zero with the repeated factor?

H. What relationship exists between the x-intercepts of the graph of a polynomial function and the roots of the corresponding equation?

family of polynomial functions

a set of polynomial functions whose equations have the same degree and whose graphs have common characteristics; for example, one type of quadratic family has the same zeros or x-intercepts

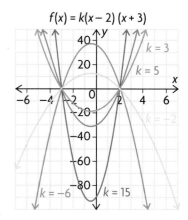

order

the exponent to which each factor in an algebraic expression is raised; for example, in $f(x) = (x - 3)^2(x - 1)$, the order of $(x - 3)$ is 2 and the order of $(x - 1)$ is 1

Reflecting

I. How does a squared factor in the equation of a polynomial function affect the shape of the graph near its corresponding zero?

J. How does a cubed factor in a polynomial function affect the shape of the graph near its corresponding zero?

K. Why does the relationship you described in part H make sense?

APPLY the Math

EXAMPLE **1**	Using reasoning to draw a graph from the equation of a polynomial function

Sketch a possible graph of the function $f(x) = -(x + 2)(x - 1)(x - 3)^2$.

Solution

Let $x = 0$.

$f(x) = -(0 + 2)(0 - 1)(0 - 3)^2$ ⟵ — Calculate the y-intercept.

$\quad = -(2)(-1)(-3)^2$

$\quad = 18$

$0 = -(x + 2)(x - 1)(x - 3)^2$ ⟵

$x = -2, x = 1,$ or $x = 3$

> Determine the x-intercepts by letting $f(x) = 0$. Use the factors to solve the resulting equation for x.

Use values of x that fall between the x-intercepts as test values to determine the location of the function above or below the x-axis.

$$\xleftarrow{\quad\underset{-2}{+}\qquad\qquad\underset{1}{+}\quad\underset{3}{+}\qquad} x$$

$f(-3) = -144 \quad f(-1) = 32 \qquad f(2) = -4 \quad f(4) = -18$

> Since the function lies below the x-axis on both sides of $x = 3$, the graph must just touch the x-axis and not cross over at this point. The order of 2 on the factor $(x - 3)^2$ confirms the parabolic shape near $x = 3$.

Determine the end behaviours of the function.

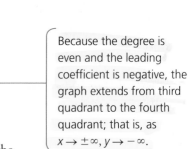

$(0, 18)$

$(-2, 0)$ $(1, 0)$ $(3, 0)$ x

$f(x) = -(x + 2)(x - 1)(x - 3)^2$

> Because the degree is even and the leading coefficient is negative, the graph extends from third quadrant to the fourth quadrant; that is, as $x \rightarrow \pm\infty, y \rightarrow -\infty$.

This is a possible graph of $f(x)$ estimating the locations of the turning points.

EXAMPLE 2   Using reasoning to determine the equation of a function from given information

Write the equation of a cubic function that has zeros at -2, 3, and $\frac{2}{5}$.
The function also has a y-intercept of 6.

Solution

$$f(x) = a(x + 2)(x - 3)(5x - 2)$$

Use the zeros of the function to create factors for the correct family of polynomials. Since this function has three zeros and it is cubic, the order of each factor must be 1.

$$6 = a(0 + 2)(0 - 3)(5(0) - 2)$$
$$6 = a(2)(-3)(-2)$$
$$6 = 12a$$
$$a = \frac{1}{2}$$

Use the y-intercept to calculate the value of a.

Substitute $x = 0$ and $y = 6$ into the equation, and solve for a.

$$f(x) = \frac{1}{2}(x + 2)(x - 3)(5x - 2)$$

Write the equation in factored form.

EXAMPLE 3   Representing the graph of a polynomial function with its equation

a) Write the equation of the function shown below.
b) State the domain and range of the function.

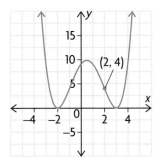

Solution

Write the equation of the correct family of polynomials using factors created from the zeros.

a) $y = a(x + 2)^2(x - 3)^2$

Because the function must have positive values on both sides of the x-intercepts, the factors are squared. The parabolic shape of the graph near the zeros $x = -2$ and $x = 3$ confirms the order of 2 on the factors $(x + 2)^2$ and $(x - 3)^2$.

Let $x = 2$ and $y = 4$.

Substitute the coordinates of the point marked on the graph into the equation.

$4 = a(2 + 2)^2(2 - 3)^2$
$4 = a(4)^2(-1)^2$
$4 = 16a$

Solve to determine the value of a.

$a = \dfrac{1}{4}$

$y = \dfrac{1}{4}(x + 2)^2(x - 3)^2$

Write the equation in factored form.

b) Domain $= \{x \in \mathbf{R}\}$
Range $= \{y \in \mathbf{R} \mid y \geq 0\}$

All polynomial functions have their domain over the entire set of real numbers.

The graph has an absolute minimum value of 0 when $x = -2$ and $x = 3$. All other values of the function are greater than this.

EXAMPLE 4   Representing the equation of a polynomial function with its graph

Sketch the graph of $f(x) = x^4 + 2x^3$.

Solution

$$f(x) = x^4 + 2x^3$$
$$= x^3(x + 2)$$

> Write the equation in factored form by dividing out the common factor of x^3.

The zeros are $x = 0$ and $x = -2$.

> Determine the zeros, the order of the factors, and the shape of the graph near the zeros. The graph has a cubic shape at $x = 0$, since the factor x^3 has an order of 3. The graph has a linear shape near $x = -2$ since the factor $(x + 2)$ has an order of 1.

The y-intercept is $f(0) = 0^4 + 2(0)^3 = 0$.

> Determine the y-intercept by letting $x = 0$.

End behaviours:
As $x \to \pm\infty$, $y \to \infty$.

> Determine the end behaviours. The function has an even degree, so the end behaviours are the same. The leading coefficient is positive, so the graph extends from the second quadrant to the first quadrant.

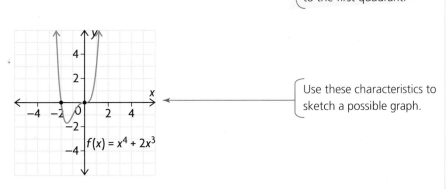

> Use these characteristics to sketch a possible graph.

While playing in the surf, a dolphin jumped twice into the air before diving deep below the surface of the water. The path of the dolphin is shown on the following graph.

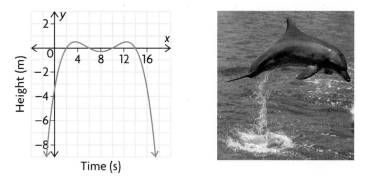

Write the equation of the polynomial function that represents the height of the dolphin relative to the surface of the water.

Solution

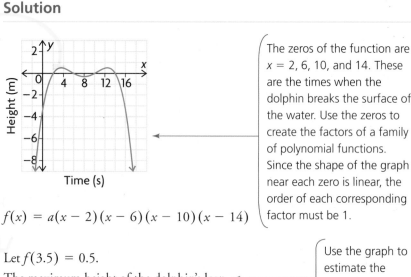

The zeros of the function are $x = 2, 6, 10,$ and 14. These are the times when the dolphin breaks the surface of the water. Use the zeros to create the factors of a family of polynomial functions. Since the shape of the graph near each zero is linear, the order of each corresponding factor must be 1.

$$f(x) = a(x - 2)(x - 6)(x - 10)(x - 14)$$

Let $f(3.5) = 0.5$.

The maximum height of the dolphin's leap was about 0.5 m when x was about 3.5 s.

Use the graph to estimate the maximum height of the dolphin's leap.

$$0.5 = a(3.5 - 2)(3.5 - 6)(3.5 - 10)(3.5 - 14)$$
$$0.5 = a(1.5)(-2.5)(-6.5)(-10.5)$$
$$0.5 = -255.9375a$$
$$a \doteq -0.002$$

Solve the equation to determine the value of a.

$$f(x) = -0.002(x - 2)(x - 6)(x - 10)(x - 14)$$

Write the equation in factored form.

In Summary

Key Idea

- The zeros of the polynomial function $y = f(x)$ are the same as the roots of the related polynomial equation, $f(x) = 0$.

Need to Know

- To determine the equation of a polynomial function in factored form, follow these steps:
  - Substitute the zeros $(x_1, x_2, \ldots, x_n)$ into the general equation of the appropriate family of polynomial functions of the form $y = a(x - x_1)(x - x_2)\ldots(x - x_n)$.
  - Substitute the coordinates of an additional point for x and y, and solve for a to determine the equation.
- If any of the factors of a polynomial function are linear, then the corresponding x-intercept is a point where the curve passes through the x-axis. The graph has a linear shape near this x-intercept.

$y = \frac{1}{10}(x + 2)(x + 1)(x - 4)(x - 5)$

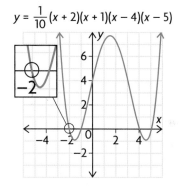

- If any of the factors of a polynomial function are squared, then the corresponding x-intercepts are turning points of the curve and the x-axis is tangent to the curve at these points. The graph has a parabolic shape near these x-intercepts.

$y = \frac{1}{10}(x + 3)^2(x - 2)$

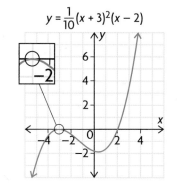

- If any of the factors of a polynomial function are cubed, then the corresponding x-intercepts are points where the x-axis is tangent to the curve and also passes through the x-axis. The graph has a cubic shape near these x-intercepts.

$y = \frac{1}{5}(x + 3)^3(x - 1)$

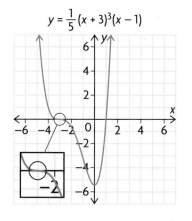

CHECK Your Understanding

1. Match each equation with the most suitable graph. Explain your reasoning.

   a) $f(x) = 2(x + 1)^2(x - 3)$ c) $f(x) = -2(x + 1)(x - 3)^2$

   b) $f(x) = 2(x + 1)^2(x - 3)^2$ d) $f(x) = x(x + 1)(x - 3)(x - 5)$

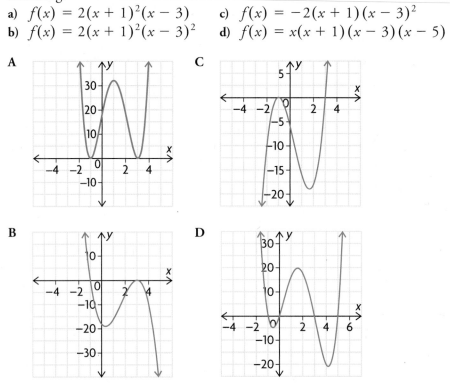

2. Sketch a possible graph of each function.

   a) $f(x) = -(x - 4)(x - 1)(x + 5)$ b) $g(x) = x^2(x - 6)^3$

3. Each member of a family of quadratic functions has zeros at $x = -1$ and $x = 4$.

   a) Write the equation of the family, and then state two functions that belong to the family.

   b) Determine the equation of the member of the family that passes through the point $(5, 9)$. Graph the function.

4. Write the equation of each function.

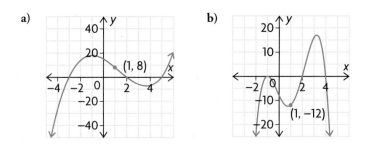

PRACTISING

5. Organize the following functions into families.

A $y = 2(x - 3)(x + 5)$

G $y = \frac{1}{2}(x - 3)(x + 5)$

B $y = -1.8(x - 3)^2(x + 5)$

H $y = -5(x + 8)(x)(x + 6)$

C $y = -x(x + 6)(x + 8)$

I $y = (x - 3)(x + 5)$

D $y = 2(x + 5)(x + 3)^2$

J $y = \frac{3}{5}(x + 5)(x + 3)^2$

E $y = (x - 3)^2(x + 5)$

K $y = \frac{x(x + 6)(x + 8)}{4}$

F $y = x(x + 6)(x + 8)$

L $y = 2(x + 5)(x^2 + 6x + 9)$

6. Sketch the graph of each function.
   a) $y = x(x - 4)(x - 1)$
   b) $y = -(x - 1)(x + 2)(x - 3)$
   c) $y = x(x - 3)^2$
   d) $y = (x + 1)^3$
   e) $y = x(2x + 1)(x - 3)(x - 5)$
   f) $y = x^2(3x - 2)^2$

7. a) Sketch an example of a cubic function with the given zeros. Then write the equation of the function.

   i) $-3, 0, 2$ iii) $-1, 4$ (order 2)

   ii) -2 (order 3)   iv) $3, -\frac{1}{2}$ (order 2)

   b) Are all the characteristics of the graphs unique? Explain.

8. Sketch an example of a quartic function with the given zeros, and write the equation of the function. Then write the equations of two other functions that belong to the same family.

   a) $-5, -3, 2, 4$ c) $-2, \frac{3}{4}, 5$ (order 2)

   b) -2 (order 2), 3 (order 2)   d) 6 (order 4)

9. Sketch the graph of each function.
   a) $y = 3x^3 - 48x$ c) $y = x^3 - 9x^2 + 27x - 27$
   b) $y = x^4 + 4x^3 + 4x^2$ d) $y = -x^4 - 15x^3 - 75x^2 - 125x$

10. Sketch the graph of a polynomial function that satisfies each set of conditions.
    a) degree 4, positive leading coefficient, 3 zeros, 3 turning points
    b) degree 4, negative leading coefficient, 2 zeros, 1 turning point
    c) degree 4, positive leading coefficient, 2 zeros, 3 turning points
    d) degree 3, negative leading coefficient, 1 zero, no turning points

Year	Profit or Loss (in thousands of dollars)
1990	−216
1991	−88
1992	0
1993	54
1994	80
1995	84
1996	72
1997	50
1998	24
1999	0
2000	−16
2001	−18
2002	0
2003	44
2004	120

11. **A** A company's profits and losses during a 15-year period are shown in the table.

   a) Sketch a graph of the data, using years since 1990 as the values of the independent variable.

   b) If x represents the number of years since 1990 (with 1990 being year 0), write the polynomial equation that models the data.

   c) Is this trend likely to continue? What restrictions should be placed on the domain of the function so that it is realistic?

12. **K** Determine the equation of the polynomial function from each graph.

   a)

   b)

13. **a)** Determine the quadratic function that has zeros at -3 and -5, if $f(7) = -720$.

   b) Determine the cubic function that has zeros at -2, 3, and 4, if $f(5) = 28$.

14. **T** The function $f(x) = kx^3 - 8x^2 - x + 3k + 1$ has a zero when $x = 2$. Determine the value of k. Graph $f(x)$, and determine all the zeros. Then rewrite $f(x)$ in factored form.

15. **C** Describe what you know about the graphs of each family of polynomials, in as much detail as possible.

   a) $y = a(x - 2)^2(x - 4)^2$ **b)** $y = a(x + 4)(x - 3)^2$

Extending

16. Square corners cut from a 30 cm by 20 cm piece of cardboard create a box when the 4 remaining tabs are folded upwards. The volume of the box is $V(x) = x(30 - 2x)(20 - 2x)$, where x represents the height.

   a) Calculate the volume of a box with a height of 2 cm.

   b) Calculate the dimensions of a box with a volume of 1000 cm^3.

   c) Solve $V(x) > 0$, and discuss the meaning of your solution in the context of the question.

   d) State the restrictions in the context of the question.

3.4

Transformations of Cubic and Quartic Functions

Describe and perform transformations on cubic and quartic functions.

YOU WILL NEED

- graphing calculator or graphing software

INVESTIGATE the Math

The graphs of the parent cubic function $y = x^3$ and a second function, which is a transformation of the parent function, are shown.

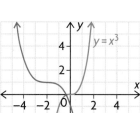

❓ How do the graphs of $y = a(k(x - d))^3 + c$ and $y = a(k(x - d))^4 + c$ relate to the graphs of $y = x^3$ and $y = x^4$?

A. Use dynamic geometry software to create a Cartesian grid with an x-axis and y-axis.

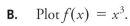

B. Plot $f(x) = x^3$.

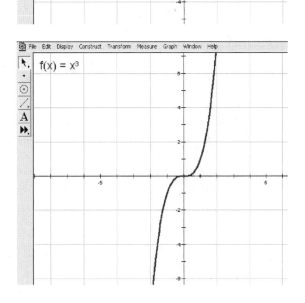

Tech | Support

For information about how to use *The Geometer's Sketchpad* to plot functions, see Technical Appendix, T-19.

C. Define four new parameters: $a = 1$, $k = 1$, $d = 1$, and $c = 0$.

D. Create and plot $g(x) = a(k(x - d))^3 + c$. Describe how the new graph, $g(x)$, is related to the graph of the parent function, $f(x)$.

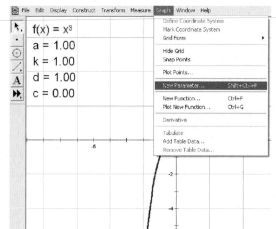

E. Make a conjecture about how changing the parameter a in the function $g(x)$ will affect the graph of the parent function, $f(x)$.

F. Change the value of a at least four times using integers and rational numbers. Record the effect of each change on the graph. Make sure that you use both positive and negative values.

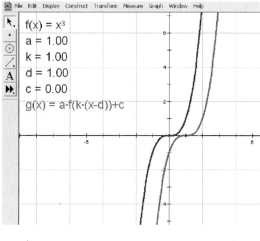

G. Repeat parts E and F for each of the other parameters $(k, d,$ and $c)$.

H. Repeat parts A to G for the quartic function $f(x) = x^4$.

Reflecting

I. Describe the transformations that must be applied to the graph of the function $f(x) = x^3$ to create the graph of $y = a(k(x - d))^3 + c$.

J. Describe the transformations that must be applied to the graph of the function $f(x) = x^4$ to create the graph of $y = a(k(x - d))^4 + c$.

K. Do you think your descriptions in parts I and J can be applied to transformations of the function $f(x) = x^n$ for all possible values of n? Explain.

APPLY the Math

EXAMPLE 1 | Using reasoning to determine transformations

Describe the transformations that must be applied to $y = x^3$ to graph $y = -8\left(\frac{1}{2}x + 1\right)^3 - 3$, and then graph this function.

Solution A: Using the equation as given

$$y = -8\left(\frac{1}{2}x + 1\right)^3 - 3$$

$$y = -8\left(\frac{1}{2}(x + 2)\right)^3 - 3 \longleftarrow$$

> Factor the coefficient of x so that the function is in the form $y = a(k(x - d))^3 + c$.

$y = x^3$ is

- vertically stretched by a factor of 8 and reflected in the x-axis
- horizontally stretched by a factor of 2
- translated 2 units left
- translated 3 units down

$$
\begin{cases}
a = -8 \\
k = \dfrac{1}{2} \\
d = -2 \\
c = -3
\end{cases}
$$

$y = x^3$

x	y
-2	-8
-1	-1
0	0
1	1
2	8

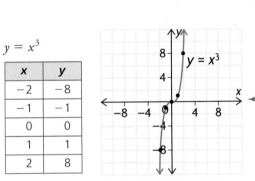

> Begin with the parent function to be transformed and its key points.

$(x, y) \rightarrow (2x, -8y)$

$y = x^3$	$y = -8\left(\frac{1}{2}x\right)^3$
$(-2, -8)$	$(2(-2), -8(-8)) = (-4, 64)$
$(-1, -1)$	$(2(-1), -8(-1)) = (-2, 8)$
$(0, 0)$	$(2(0), -8(0)) = (0, 0)$
$(1, 1)$	$(2(1), -8(1)) = (2, -8)$
$(2, 8)$	$(2(2), -8(8)) = (4, -64)$

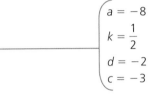

> Perform the stretches, reflections, and compressions first. Multiply the x-coordinates of the key points by 2. Multiply the y-coordinates of the key points by -8.

$$(2x, -8y) \rightarrow (2x - 2, -8y - 3)$$

$y = -8\left(\frac{1}{2}x\right)^3$	$y = -8\left(\frac{1}{2}(x + 2)\right)^3 - 3$
$(-4, 64)$	$(-4 - 2, 64 - 3) = (-6, 61)$
$(-2, 8)$	$(-2 - 2, 8 - 3) = (-4, 5)$
$(0, 0)$	$(0 - 2, 0 - 3) = (-2, -3)$
$(2, -8)$	$(2 - 2, -8 - 3) = (0, -11)$
$(4, -64)$	$(4 - 2, -64 - 3) = (2, -67)$

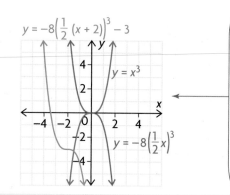

Perform the translations last. Subtract 2 from the x-coordinate and 3 from the y-coordinate of each point on the red graph to obtain the corresponding point on the blue graph.

Solution B: Simplifying the equation first

$$y = -8\left(\frac{1}{2}x + 1\right)^3 - 3$$

$$y = -8\left(\frac{1}{2}(x + 2)\right)^3 - 3$$

$$y = -8\left(\frac{1}{2}\right)^3 (x + 2)^3 - 3$$

$$y = -(x + 2)^3 - 3$$
$$y = -(x + 2)^3 - 3$$

Factor out the coefficient of x, and apply the exponent to both parts of the product.

Simplify.

$y = x^3$ is
- vertically reflected in the x-axis
- translated 2 units to the left
- translated 3 units down

$a = -1$
$d = -2$
$c = -3$

$y = x^3$

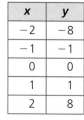

x	y
-2	-8
-1	-1
0	0
1	1
2	8

Begin with the graph of the parent function to be transformed.

$(x, y) \rightarrow (x, -y)$

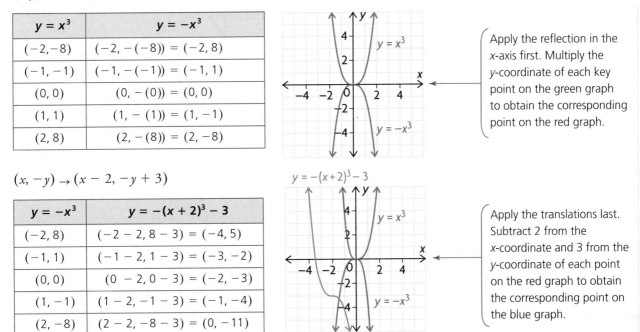

$y = x^3$	$y = -x^3$
$(-2, -8)$	$(-2, -(-8)) = (-2, 8)$
$(-1, -1)$	$(-1, -(-1)) = (-1, 1)$
$(0, 0)$	$(0, -(0)) = (0, 0)$
$(1, 1)$	$(1, -(1)) = (1, -1)$
$(2, 8)$	$(2, -(8)) = (2, -8)$

Apply the reflection in the x-axis first. Multiply the y-coordinate of each key point on the green graph to obtain the corresponding point on the red graph.

$(x, -y) \rightarrow (x - 2, -y + 3)$

$y = -x^3$	$y = -(x + 2)^3 - 3$
$(-2, 8)$	$(-2 - 2, 8 - 3) = (-4, 5)$
$(-1, 1)$	$(-1 - 2, 1 - 3) = (-3, -2)$
$(0, 0)$	$(0 - 2, 0 - 3) = (-2, -3)$
$(1, -1)$	$(1 - 2, -1 - 3) = (-1, -4)$
$(2, -8)$	$(2 - 2, -8 - 3) = (0, -11)$

Apply the translations last. Subtract 2 from the x-coordinate and 3 from the y-coordinate of each point on the red graph to obtain the corresponding point on the blue graph.

Note that the final graph, shown in blue, is the same from the two different solutions shown above. Two different sets of transformations have resulted in the same final graph.

EXAMPLE 2 — Selecting a strategy to determine the roots of a quartic function

Determine the x-intercept(s) of the function $y = 3(x + 6)^4 - 48$.

Solution A: Using algebra

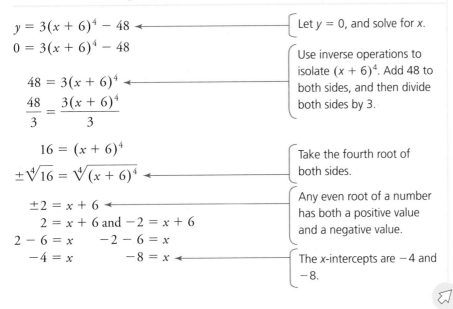

$y = 3(x + 6)^4 - 48$ — Let $y = 0$, and solve for x.

$0 = 3(x + 6)^4 - 48$

$48 = 3(x + 6)^4$

$\dfrac{48}{3} = \dfrac{3(x + 6)^4}{3}$

Use inverse operations to isolate $(x + 6)^4$. Add 48 to both sides, and then divide both sides by 3.

$16 = (x + 6)^4$

$\pm\sqrt[4]{16} = \sqrt[4]{(x + 6)^4}$ — Take the fourth root of both sides.

$\pm 2 = x + 6$

Any even root of a number has both a positive value and a negative value.

$2 = x + 6 \text{ and } -2 = x + 6$

$2 - 6 = x \qquad -2 - 6 = x$

$-4 = x \qquad -8 = x$ — The x-intercepts are -4 and -8.

Solution B: Using transformations and a graphing calculator

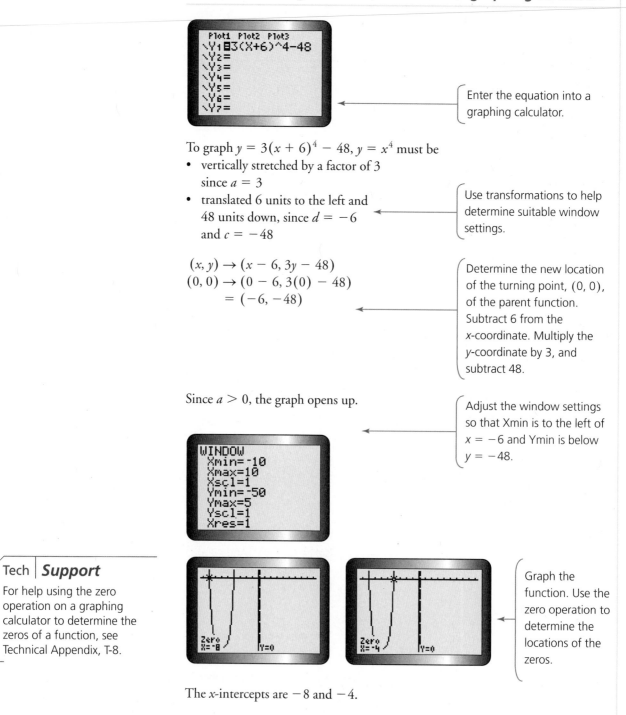

Enter the equation into a graphing calculator.

To graph $y = 3(x + 6)^4 - 48$, $y = x^4$ must be
- vertically stretched by a factor of 3 since $a = 3$
- translated 6 units to the left and 48 units down, since $d = -6$ and $c = -48$

Use transformations to help determine suitable window settings.

$$(x, y) \rightarrow (x - 6, 3y - 48)$$
$$(0, 0) \rightarrow (0 - 6, 3(0) - 48)$$
$$= (-6, -48)$$

Determine the new location of the turning point, $(0, 0)$, of the parent function. Subtract 6 from the x-coordinate. Multiply the y-coordinate by 3, and subtract 48.

Since $a > 0$, the graph opens up.

Adjust the window settings so that Xmin is to the left of $x = -6$ and Ymin is below $y = -48$.

Tech | **Support**

For help using the zero operation on a graphing calculator to determine the zeros of a function, see Technical Appendix, T-8.

Graph the function. Use the zero operation to determine the locations of the zeros.

The x-intercepts are -8 and -4.

In Summary

Key Ideas

- The polynomial function $y = a(k(x - d))^n + c$ can be graphed by applying transformations to the graph of the parent function $y = x^n$, where $n \in \mathbf{N}$. Each point (x, y) on the graph of the parent function changes to $\left(\dfrac{x}{k} + d, ay + c \right)$.

- When using transformations to graph a function in the fewest steps, you can apply a and k together, and then c and d together.

Need to Know

- In $y = a(k(x - d))^n + c$,
  - the value of a represents a vertical stretch/compression and possibly a vertical reflection
  - the value of k represents a horizontal stretch/compression and possibly a horizontal reflection
  - the value of d represents a horizontal translation
  - the value of c represents a vertical translation

CHECK *Your Understanding*

1. Match each function with the most likely graph. Explain your reasoning.

   a) $y = 2(x - 3)^3 + 1$

   b) $y = -\dfrac{1}{3}(x + 1)^3 - 1$

   c) $y = 0.2(x - 4)^4 - 3$

   d) $y = -1.5(x + 3)^4 + 4$

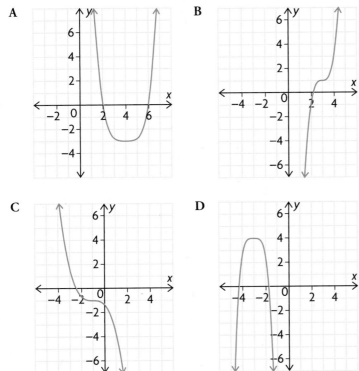

2. State the parent function that must be transformed to create the graph of each of the following functions. Then describe the transformations that must be applied to the parent function.

a) $y = \dfrac{5}{4}x^4 + 3$

b) $y = 3x - 4$

c) $y = (3x + 4)^3 - 7$

d) $y = -(x + 8)^4$

e) $y = -4.8(x - 3)(x - 3)$

f) $y = 2\left(\dfrac{1}{5}x + 7\right)^3 - 4$

3. Describe the transformations that were applied to the parent function to create each of the following graphs. Then write the equation of the transformed function.

a) parent function: $y = x^3$

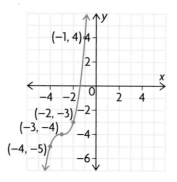

c) parent function: $y = x^4$

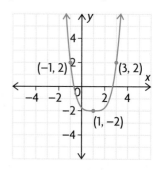

b) parent function: $y = x^4$

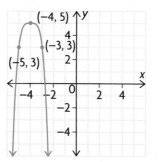

d) parent function: $y = x^3$

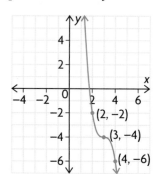

PRACTISING

4. Describe the transformations that were applied to $y = x^3$ to create each of the following functions.

K

a) $y = 12(x - 9)^3 - 7$

b) $y = \left(\dfrac{7}{8}(x + 1)\right)^3 + 3$

c) $y = -2(x - 6)^3 - 8$

d) $y = (x + 9)(x + 9)(x + 9)$

e) $y = -2(-3(x - 4))^3 - 5$

f) $y = \left(\dfrac{3}{4}(x - 10)\right)^3$

5. For each graph, determine the equation of the function in the form $y = a(x - h)^2 + k$. Then describe the transformations that were applied to $y = x^2$ to obtain each graph.

a)

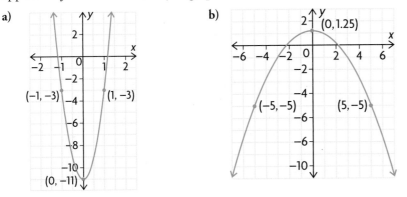

b)

6. The function $y = x^3$ has undergone the following sets of transformations. If $y = x^3$ passes through the points $(-1, -1)$, $(0, 0)$, and $(2, 8)$, list the coordinates of these transformed points on each new curve.

a) vertically compressed by a factor of $\frac{1}{2}$, horizontally compressed by a factor of $\frac{1}{5}$, and horizontally translated 6 units to the left

b) reflected in the y-axis, horizontally stretched by a factor of 2, and vertically translated 3 units up

c) reflected in the x-axis, vertically stretched by a factor of 3, horizontally translated 4 units to the right, and vertically translated $\frac{1}{2}$ of a unit down

d) vertically compressed by a factor of $\frac{1}{10}$, horizontally stretched by a factor of 7, and vertically translated 2 units down

e) reflected in the y-axis, reflected in the x-axis, and vertically translated $\frac{9}{10}$ of a unit up

f) horizontally stretched by a factor of 7, horizontally translated 4 units to the left, and vertically translated 2 units down

7. The graph shown is a result of transformations applied to $y = x^4$.
T Determine the equation of this transformed function.

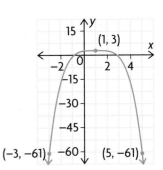

8. Dikembe has reflected the function $g(x) = x^3$ in the x-axis, vertically
A compressed it by a factor of $\frac{2}{3}$, horizontally translated it 13 units to the right, and vertically translated it 13 units down. Three points on the resulting curve are $\left(11, -\frac{23}{3}\right)$, $(13, -13)$, and $\left(15, -\frac{55}{3}\right)$. Determine the original coordinates of these three points on $g(x)$.

9. Determine the x-intercepts of each of the following polynomial functions. Round to two decimal places, if necessary.

a) $y = 2(x + 3)^4 - 2$
b) $y = (x - 2)^3 - 8$
c) $y = -3(x + 1)^4 + 48$
d) $y = -5(x + 6)^4 - 10$
e) $y = 4(x - 8)^4 - 12$
f) $y = -(2x + 5)^3 - 20$

10. Consider the function $y = 2(x - 4)^n + 1$, $n \in \mathbf{N}$.
   a) How many zeros will the function have if $n = 3$? Explain how you know.
   b) How many zeros will the function have if $n = 4$? Explain how you know.
   c) Make a general statement about the number of zeros that the function will have, for any value of n. Explain your reasoning.

11. a) For what values of n will the reflection of the function $y = x^n$ in the x-axis be the same as its reflection in the y-axis. Explain your reasoning.
   b) For what values of n will the reflections be different? Explain your reasoning.

12. Consider the function $y = x^3$.
   C a) Use algebraic and graphical examples to describe all the transformations that could be applied to this function.
   b) Explain why just creating a single table of values is not always the best way to sketch the graph of a function.

Extending

13. Can you create the graph of the function $y = 2(x - 1)(x + 4)(x - 5)$ by transforming the function $y = (x - 4)(x + 1)(x - 8)$? Explain.

14. Transform the graph of the function $y = (x - 1)^2(x + 1)^2$ to determine the roots of the function $y = 2(x - 1)^2(x + 1)^2 + 1$.

15. The function $f(x) = x^2$ was transformed by vertically stretching it, horizontally compressing it, horizontally translating it, and vertically translating it. The resulting function was then transformed again by reflecting it in the x-axis, vertically compressing it by a factor of $\frac{4}{5}$, horizontally compressing it by a factor of $\frac{1}{2}$, and vertically translating it 6 units down. The equation of the final function is $f(x) = -4(4(x + 3))^2 - 5$. What was the equation of the function after it was transformed the first time?

FREQUENTLY ASKED Questions

Q: **How can you tell whether an expression is a polynomial?**

A: A polynomial is an expression in which the coefficients are real numbers and the exponents on the variables are whole numbers.

For example, consider the following expressions:

$$3x^2 - 5x^3 + \frac{1}{2}x, \quad \sqrt{x} + 4x^2 - 3, \quad \frac{x+3}{2x-5}, \quad \sqrt{5}x^2 + 8x - 10$$

Only two of these expressions, $3x^2 - 5x^3 + \frac{1}{2}x$ and $\sqrt{5}x^2 + 8x - 10$, are polynomials.

Study | **Aid**
- See Lesson 3.1.
- Try Mid-Chapter Review Questions 1 and 2.

Q: **How can you describe the characteristics of the graph of a polynomial function by looking at its equation?**

A: The degree of the function and the sign of the leading coefficient can be used to determine the end behaviours of the graph.

Study | **Aid**
- See Lesson 3.2, Example 1.
- Try Mid-Chapter Review Questions 3 and 4.

- If the degree of the function is odd and the leading coefficient is
  - negative, then the function extends from above the x-axis to below the x-axis
  - positive, then the function extends from below the x-axis to above the x-axis

- If the degree of the function is even and the leading coefficient is
  - negative, then both ends of the function are below the x-axis
  - positive, then both ends of the function are above the x-axis

- For any polynomial function, the maximum number of turning points is one less than the degree of the function.

- If the degree of the function is
  - odd, then there must be an even number of turning points
  - even, then there must be an odd number of turning points

Q: **How can you sketch the graph of a polynomial function that is in factored form?**

A: The factors of the function can be used to determine the real roots of the corresponding polynomial equation. These roots are the x-intercepts of the graph. Use other characteristics of the function, such as end behaviours, turning points, and the order of each factor, to approximate the shape of the graph.

Study | **Aid**
- See Lesson 3.3, Example 2.
- Try Mid-Chapter Review Questions 5, 6, and 7.

For example, to sketch the graph of $y = -2(x + 3)(x + 1)(x - 4)$, first determine the x-intercepts. They are -3, -1, and 4. Because the order of each factor is 1, the graph has a linear shape near each zero. Because the leading coefficient is -2 and the degree is 3, the graph extends from the second quadrant to the fourth quadrant. There are, at most, two turning points.

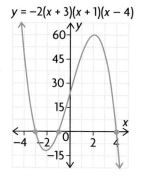

$y = -2(x + 3)(x + 1)(x - 4)$

Study | *Aid*

• See Lesson 3.4, Examples 1 and 2.
• Try Mid-Chapter Review Questions 8 and 9.

Q: **How can you sketch the graph of a polynomial function using transformations?**

A: If the equation is in the form $y = a(k(x - d))^n + c$, then transform the graph of $y = x^n$ as follows:

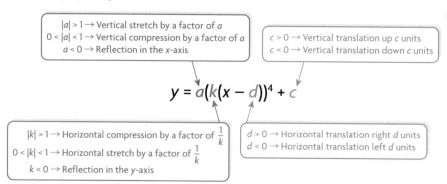

$|a| > 1 \rightarrow$ Vertical stretch by a factor of a
$0 < |a| < 1 \rightarrow$ Vertical compression by a factor of a
$a < 0 \rightarrow$ Reflection in the x-axis

$c > 0 \rightarrow$ Vertical translation up c units
$c < 0 \rightarrow$ Vertical translation down c units

$$y = a(k(x - d))^4 + c$$

$|k| > 1 \rightarrow$ Horizontal compression by a factor of $\frac{1}{k}$
$0 < |k| < 1 \rightarrow$ Horizontal stretch by a factor of $\frac{1}{k}$
$k < 0 \rightarrow$ Reflection in the y-axis

$d > 0 \rightarrow$ Horizontal translation right d units
$d < 0 \rightarrow$ Horizontal translation left d units

For example, to sketch the graph of $y = -2(x - 3)^4 + 5$, vertically stretch the graph of $y = x^4$ by a factor of 2, reflect it through the x-axis, and then translate it 3 units to the right and 5 units up. As a result of these transformations, every point (x, y) on the graph of $y = x^4$ changes to $(x + 3, -2y + 5)$.

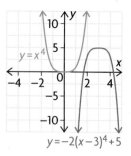

$y = -2(x-3)^4 + 5$

PRACTICE Questions

Lesson 3.1

1. Determine whether or not each function is a polynomial function. If it is not a polynomial function, explain why.

   a) $f(x) = \dfrac{2}{3}x^4 + x^2 - 1$

   b) $f(x) = x^{\frac{5}{2}} - 7x^2 + 3$

   c) $f(x) = \sqrt{10x^3} - 16x^2 + 15$

   d) $f(x) = \dfrac{x^2 + 4x + 2}{x - 2}$

2. For each of the following, give an example of a polynomial function that has the characteristics described.

   a) a function of degree 3 that has four terms
   b) a function of degree 4 that has three terms
   c) a function of degree 6 that has two terms
   d) a function of degree 5 that has five terms

Lesson 3.2

3. State the end behaviours of each of the following functions.

   a) $f(x) = -11x^3 + x^2 - 2$
   b) $f(x) = 70x^2 - 67$
   c) $f(x) = x^3 - 1000$
   d) $f(x) = -13x^4 - 4x^3 - 2x^2 + x + 5$

4. State whether each function has an even number of turning points or an odd number of turning points.

   a) $f(x) = 6x^3 + 2x$
   b) $f(x) = -20x^6 - 5x^3 + x^2 - 17$
   c) $f(x) = 22x^4 - 4x^3 + 3x^2 - 2x + 2$
   d) $f(x) = -x^5 + x^4 - x^3 + x^2 - x + 1$

Lesson 3.3

5. Sketch a possible graph of each of the following functions.

   a) $f(x) = -(x - 8)(x + 1)$
   b) $f(x) = 3(x + 3)(x + 3)(x - 1)$
   c) $f(x) = (x + 2)(x - 4)(x + 2)(x - 4)$
   d) $f(x) = -4(2x + 5)(x - 2)(x + 4)$

6. If the value of k is unknown, which of the following characteristics of the graph of $f(x) = k(x + 14)(x - 13)(x + 15)(x - 16)$ cannot be determined: the x-intercepts, the shape of the graph near each zero, the end behaviours, or the maximum number of turning points?

7. Determine the equation of the polynomial function that has the following zeros and passes through the point $(7, 5000)$: $x = 2$ (order 1), $x = -3$ (order 2), and $x = 5$ (order 1).

Lesson 3.4

8. Describe the transformations that were applied to $y = x^4$ to get each of the following functions.

   a) $y = -25(3(x + 4))^4 - 60$

   b) $y = 8\left(\dfrac{3}{4}x\right)^4 + 43$

   c) $y = (-13x + 26)^4 + 13$

   d) $y = \dfrac{8}{11}(-x)^4 - 1$

9. Describe the transformations that were applied to $y = x^3$ to produce the following graph.

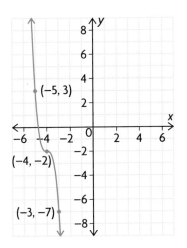

3.5 Dividing Polynomials

GOAL

Use a variety of strategies to determine the quotient when one polynomial is divided by another polynomial.

LEARN ABOUT the Math

Recall that long division can be used to determine the quotient of two numbers. For example, $107 \div 4$ can be evaluated as follows:

$$
\begin{array}{r}
26 \leftarrow \text{quotient} \\
\text{divisor} \rightarrow 4\overline{)107} \leftarrow \text{dividend} \\
8\downarrow \\
\overline{27} \\
24 \\
\overline{3} \leftarrow \text{remainder}
\end{array}
$$

Every division statement that involves numbers can be rewritten using multiplication and addition. The multiplication is the quotient, and the addition is the remainder. For example, since $107 = (4)(26) + 3$, then $\frac{107}{4} = 26 + \frac{3}{4}$. The quotient is 26, and the remainder is 3.

? How can you use a similar strategy to determine the quotient of $(3x^3 - 5x^2 - 7x - 1) \div (x - 3)$?

EXAMPLE 1   Selecting a strategy to divide a polynomial by a binomial

Determine the quotient of $(3x^3 - 5x^2 - 7x - 1) \div (x - 3)$.

Solution A: Using polynomial division

$$x - 3\overline{)3x^3 - 5x^2 - 7x - 1}$$

Focus on the *first terms* of the dividend and the divisor, and then determine the quotient when these terms are divided. Here, the first term of the dividend is $3x^3$ and the first term of the divisor is x.

$$
\begin{array}{r}
3x^2 \\
x - 3\overline{)3x^3 - 5x^2 - 7x - 1}
\end{array}
$$

Since $3x^3 \div x = 3x^2$, this becomes the first term of the quotient. Place $3x^2$ above the term of the dividend with the same degree.

$$
\begin{array}{r}
3x^2 \\
x - 3 \overline{)\ 3x^3 - 5x^2 - 7x - 1} \\
\underline{3x^3 - 9x^2 } \\
4x^2
\end{array}
$$

Multiply $3x^2$ by the divisor, and write the answer below the dividend. Make sure that you line up "like terms." $3x^2(x - 3) = 3x^3 - 9x^2$. Subtract this product from the dividend.

$$
\begin{array}{r}
3x^2 + \ 4x \\
x - 3 \overline{)\ 3x^3 - 5x^2 - \ 7x - 1} \\
\underline{-3x^3 + 9x^2 \downarrow} \\
4x^2 - \ 7x \\
\underline{4x^2 - 12x } \\
5x
\end{array}
$$

Now focus on x in the divisor $x - 3$ and $4x^2$ in the expression $4x^2 - 7x$. Determine the quotient when these terms are divided. Since $4x^2 \div x = 4x$, place $4x$ above the x in the dividend. Multiply $4x$ by the divisor. Write the answer below the last line (making sure that you line up like terms), and then subtract.

$$
\begin{array}{r}
3x^2 + \ 4x + \ 5 \\
x - 3 \overline{)\ 3x^3 - 5x^2 - \ 7x - \ 1}
\end{array}
$$

$3x^2(x - 3) \rightarrow$

$$
\begin{array}{r}
\underline{3x^3 - 9x^2 \downarrow \downarrow} \\
4x^2 - \ 7x
\end{array}
$$

$4x(x - 3) \rightarrow$

$$
\begin{array}{r}
\underline{4x^2 - 12x } \\
5x - \ 1
\end{array}
$$

$5(x - 3) \rightarrow$

$$
\begin{array}{r}
\underline{5x - 15} \\
14
\end{array}
$$

Repeat this process until the degree of the remainder is less than the degree of the divisor.

Since the divisor has degree 1, the remainder should be a constant.

$$
\begin{aligned}
&3x^3 - 5x^2 - 7x - 1 \\
&= (x - 3)(3x^2 + 4x + 5) + 14
\end{aligned}
$$

Write the multiplication statement that shows how the divisor, dividend, quotient, and remainder are all related.

$$
\begin{aligned}
&(x - 3)(3x^2 + 4x + 5) + 14 \\
&= 3x^3 + 4x^2 + 5x - 9x^2 \\
&\quad - 12x - 15 + 14 \\
&= 3x^3 - 5x^2 - 7x - 1
\end{aligned}
$$

To check, expand and simplify the right side of the division statement.

The result is the dividend, which confirms the division was done correctly.

Solution B: Using synthetic division

$(3x^3 - 5x^2 - 7x - 1) \div (x - 3) \to k = 3$

| 3 | 3 | −5 | −7 | −1 |

Synthetic division is an efficient way to divide a polynomial by a binomial of the form $(x - k)$.

Create a chart that contains the coefficients of the dividend, as shown. The dividend and binomial must be written with its terms in descending order, by degree.

| 3 | 3 | −5 | −7 | −1 |

$\downarrow$

$\times 3 \nearrow 9$

3

Bring the first term down. This is now the coefficient of the first term of the quotient.

Multiply it by k, and write the answer below the second term of the dividend.

| 3 | 3 | −5 | −7 | −1 |

add$\downarrow$

9

3   4

Now add the terms together.

| 3 | 3 | −5 | −7 | −1 |

add$\downarrow$

$9 \times 3 \nearrow 12$

3   4   5

Repeat this process for the answer you just obtained.

| 3 | 3 | −5 | −7 | −1 |

add$\downarrow$

9   $12 \times 3 \nearrow 15$

3   4   5   14

Repeat this process one last time.

| 3 | 3 | −5 | −7 | −1 |

9   12   15

3   4   5   14

$\underbrace{}$ $\uparrow$
coefficients of   remainder
quotient

The last number below the chart is the remainder. The first numbers are the coefficients of the quotient, starting with the degree that is one less than the original dividend.

$\underbrace{3x^2 + 4x + 5}$

$3x^3 - 5x^2 - 7x - 1$
$= (x - 3)(3x^2 + 4x + 5) + 14$

Write the corresponding multiplication statement.

Reflecting

A. When dividing an nth degree polynomial by a kth degree polynomial, what degree is the quotient? What degree is the remainder?

B. If you divide a number by another number and the remainder is zero, what can you conclude? Do you think you can make the same conclusion for polynomials? Explain.

C. If you had a divisor of $x + 5$, what value of k would you use in synthetic division?

APPLY the Math

EXAMPLE 2	Selecting a strategy to determine the remainder in polynomial division

Determine the remainder of $\dfrac{5x - 2x^3 + 3 + x^4}{1 + 2x + x^2}$.

Solution

$x^2 + 2x + 1 \overline{)x^4 - 2x^3 + 0x^2 + 5x + 3}$

Write the terms of the dividend and the quotient in descending order, by degree.

Since there is no x^2-term in the dividend, use 0 as the coefficient of x^2 to make the like terms line up properly.

$$
\begin{array}{r}
x^2 \\
x^2 + 2x + 1 \overline{)\ x^4 - 2x^3 + 0x^2 + 5x + 3} \\
\underline{x^4 + 2x^3 + 1x^2} \downarrow \\
-4x^3 - 1x^2 + 5x
\end{array}
$$

Follow the same steps that you use for long division with numbers.

$$
\begin{array}{r}
x^2 - 4x + 7 \\
x^2 + 2x + 1 \overline{)\ x^4 - 2x^3 + 0x^2 + 5x + 3} \\
x^2(x^2 + 2x + 1) \to \quad x^4 + 2x^3 + 1x^2 \\
-4x^3 - 1x^2 + 5x \\
-4x(x^2 + 2x + 1) \to \quad -4x^3 - 8x^2 - 4x \\
7x^2 + 9x + 3 \\
7(x^2 + 2x + 1) \to \quad 7x^2 + 14x + 7 \\
-5x - 4
\end{array}
$$

Repeat this process until the degree of the remainder is less than the degree of the divisor.

Since the divisor was degree 2, the remainder should be degree 1.

The remainder is $-5x - 4$.

$x^4 - 2x^3 + 5x + 3$
$= (x^2 + 2x + 1)(x^2 - 4x + 7) - 5x - 4$

Write the corresponding division statement.

EXAMPLE 3 Selecting a strategy to determine whether one polynomial is a factor of another polynomial

Determine whether $x + 2$ is a factor of $13x - 2x^3 + x^4 - 6$.

Solution

Use synthetic division to divide
$13x - 2x^3 + x^4 - 6$ by $x + 2$.

> Rearrange the terms of the dividend in descending order. An x^2-term, with a coefficient of 0, needs to be added to the dividend.

$(x^4 - 2x^3 + 0x^2 + 13x - 6) \div (x + 2)$

$$
\begin{array}{r|rrrrr}
-2 & 1 & -2 & 0 & 13 & -6 \\
   & \downarrow & -2 & 8 & -16 & 6 \\
\hline
   & 1 & -4 & 8 & -3 & 0
\end{array}
$$

> In this example, $k = -2$. Multiply and add to complete the chart.

$x + 2$ is a factor, and
so is $x^3 - 4x^2 + 8x - 3$.

$(x + 2)(x^3 - 4x^2 + 8x - 3)$

$= x^4 - 2x^3 + 0x^2 + 13x - 6$

> The quotient is $x^3 - 4x^2 + 8x - 3$, and the remainder is 0. Since the remainder is 0, $x + 2$ must be a factor of the dividend.

EXAMPLE 4 Selecting a strategy to determine the factors of a polynomial

$2x + 3$ is one factor of the function $f(x) = 6x^3 + 5x^2 - 16x - 15$. Determine the other factors. Then determine the zeros, and sketch a graph of the polynomial.

Solution

$(2x + 3) = 2\left(x + \dfrac{3}{2}\right)$

$\qquad = 2\left(x - \left(-\dfrac{3}{2}\right)\right) \to k = -\dfrac{3}{2}$

> To use synthetic division, the divisor must be of the form $(x - k)$. Rewrite the divisor by dividing out the common factor 2 (the coefficient of x).
>
> The division can now be done in two steps.

$$-\frac{3}{2} \begin{array}{|rrrr} 6 & 5 & -16 & -15 \\ \downarrow & -9 & 6 & 15 \\ \hline 6 & -4 & -10 & 0 \end{array} \longleftarrow$$

First, divide $6x^3 + 5x^2 - 16x - 15$ by $\left(x + \frac{3}{2}\right)$.
This means that
$$\frac{6x^3 + 5x^2 - 16x - 15}{\left(x + \frac{3}{2}\right)} = 6x^2 - 4x - 10 + \frac{0}{\left(x + \frac{3}{2}\right)}.$$

$$\frac{1}{2} \times \left[\frac{6x^3 + 5x^2 - 16x - 15}{\left(x + \frac{3}{2}\right)} \right]$$

$$= \frac{1}{2} \times \left[6x^2 - 4x - 10 + \frac{0}{\left(x + \frac{3}{2}\right)} \right] \longleftarrow$$

$$\frac{6x^3 + 5x^2 - 16x - 15}{2\left(x + \frac{3}{2}\right)} = \frac{6x^2}{2} - \frac{4x}{2} - \frac{10}{2} + \frac{0}{2\left(x + \frac{3}{2}\right)}$$

$$\frac{6x^3 + 5x^2 - 16x - 15}{(2x + 3)} = 3x^2 - 2x - 5 + 0$$

Second, since the original divisor was $(2x + 3)$ or $2\left(x + \frac{3}{2}\right)$, multiply both sides by $\frac{1}{2}$ to get the correct multiplication statement.

Notice what this means—we only needed to divide our solution by 2 in the synthetic division.

$$-\frac{3}{2} \begin{array}{|rrrr} 6 & 5 & -16 & -15 \\ \downarrow & -9 & 6 & 15 \\ \hline 6 & -4 & -10 & 0 \\ \div 2 & \div 2 & \div 2 & \div 2 \\ \hline 3 & -2 & -5 & 0 \end{array}$$

There is no remainder, which verifies that $2x + 3$ is a factor of the dividend.

$$f(x) = 6x^3 + 5x^2 - 16x - 15$$
$$= (2x + 3)(3x^2 - 2x - 5) \longleftarrow$$
$$= (2x + 3)(3x - 5)(x + 1)$$

Factor the quotient.

Since $f(x) = (2x + 3)(3x - 5)(x + 1)$, the zeros are $-\frac{3}{2}, \frac{5}{3}$, and -1.

Determine the zeros by setting each factor equal to zero and solving for x.

An approximate graph of $y = f(x)$ is shown below.

$f(x) = (2x + 3)(3x - 5)(x + 1)$

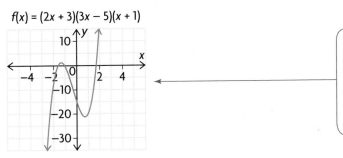

Use the zeros to locate and plot the x-intercepts. Determine the y-intercept, and plot this point. Examine the standard and factored forms of the equation to determine the end behaviours of the function and the shape of the graph near the zeros. Sketch the graph.

In Summary

Key Idea

- Polynomials can be divided in much the same way that numbers are divided.

Need to Know

- A polynomial can be divided by a polynomial of the same degree or less.
- Synthetic division is a shorter form of polynomial division. It can only be used when the divisor is linear (that is, $(x - k)$ or $(ax - k)$).
- When using polynomial or synthetic division,
  - terms should be arranged in descending order of degree, in both the divisor and the dividend, to make the division easier to perform
  - zero must be used as the coefficient of any missing powers of the variable in both the divisor and the dividend
- If the remainder of polynomial or synthetic division is zero, both the divisor and the quotient are factors of the dividend.

CHECK Your Understanding

1. **a)** Divide $x^4 - 16x^3 + 4x^2 + 10x - 11$ by each of the following binomials.

   i) $x - 2$ **ii)** $x + 4$ **iii)** $x - 1$

  b) Are any of the binomials in part a) factors of $x^4 - 16x^3 + 4x^2 + 10x - 11$? Explain.

2. State the degree of the quotient for each of the following division statements, if possible.

  a) $(x^4 - 15x^3 + 2x^2 + 12x - 10) \div (x^2 - 4)$
  b) $(5x^3 - 4x^2 + 3x - 4) \div (x + 3)$
  c) $(x^4 - 7x^3 + 2x^2 + 9x) \div (x^3 - x^2 + 2x + 1)$
  d) $(2x^2 + 5x - 4) \div (x^4 + 3x^3 - 5x^2 + 4x - 2)$

3. Complete the divisions in question 2, if possible.

4. Complete the following table.

Dividend	Divisor	Quotient	Remainder
$2x^3 - 5x^2 + 8x + 4$	$x + 3$	$2x^2 - 11x + 41$	
	$2x + 4$	$3x^3 - 5x + 8$	-3
$6x^4 + 2x^3 + 3x^2 - 11x - 9$		$2x^3 + x - 4$	-5
$3x^3 + x^2 - 6x + 16$	$x + 2$		8

PRACTISING

5. Calculate each of the following using long division.

K a) $(x^3 - 2x + 1) \div (x - 4)$

b) $(x^3 + 2x^2 - 6x + 1) \div (x + 2)$

c) $(2x^3 + 5x^2 - 4x - 5) \div (2x + 1)$

d) $(x^4 + 3x^3 - 2x^2 + 5x - 1) \div (x^2 + 7)$

e) $(x^4 + 6x^2 - 8x + 12) \div (x^3 - x^2 - x + 1)$

f) $(x^5 + 4x^4 + 9x + 8) \div (x^4 + x^3 + x^2 + x - 2)$

6. Calculate each of the following using synthetic division.

a) $(x^3 - 7x - 6) \div (x - 3)$

b) $(2x^3 - 7x^2 - 7x + 19) \div (x - 1)$

c) $(6x^4 + 13x^3 - 34x^2 - 47x + 28) \div (x + 3)$

d) $(2x^3 + x^2 - 22x + 20) \div (2x - 3)$

e) $(12x^4 - 56x^3 + 59x^2 + 9x - 18) \div (2x + 1)$

f) $(6x^3 - 2x - 15x^2 + 5) \div (2x - 5)$

7. Each divisor was divided into another polynomial, resulting in the given quotient and remainder. Find the other polynomial (the dividend).

a) divisor: $x + 10$, quotient: $x^2 - 6x + 9$, remainder: -1

b) divisor: $3x - 2$, quotient: $x^3 + x - 12$, remainder: 15

c) divisor: $5x + 2$, quotient: $x^3 + 4x^2 - 5x + 6$, remainder: $x - 2$

d) divisor: $x^2 + 7x - 2$, quotient: $x^4 + x^3 - 11x + 4$, remainder: $x^2 - x + 5$

8. Determine the remainder, r, to make each multiplication statement true.

a) $(2x - 3)(3x + 5) + r = 6x^2 + x + 5$

b) $(x + 3)(x + 5) + r = x^2 + 9x - 7$

c) $(x + 3)(x^2 - 1) + r = x^3 + 3x^2 - x - 3$

d) $(x^2 + 1)(2x^3 - 1) + r = 2x^5 + 2x^3 + x^2 + 1$

9. Each dividend was divided by another polynomial, resulting in the given quotient and remainder. Find the other polynomial (the divisor).

a) dividend: $5x^3 + x^2 + 3$, quotient: $5x^2 - 14x + 42$, remainder: -123

b) dividend: $10x^4 - x^2 + 20x - 2$, quotient: $10x^3 - 100x^2 + 999x - 9970$, remainder: $99\ 698$

c) dividend: $x^4 + x^3 - 10x^2 - 1$, quotient: $x^3 - 3x^2 + 2x - 8$, remainder: 31

d) dividend: $x^3 + x^2 + 7x - 7$, quotient: $x^2 + 3x + 13$, remainder: 19

10. Determine whether each binomial is a factor of the given polynomial.
    a) $x + 5, x^3 + 6x^2 - x - 30$
    b) $x + 2, x^4 - 5x^2 + 4$
    c) $x - 2, x^4 - 5x^2 + 6$
    d) $2x - 1, 2x^4 - x^3 - 4x^2 + 2x + 1$
    e) $3x + 5, 3x^6 + 5x^5 + 9x^2 + 17x - 1$
    f) $5x - 1, 5x^4 - x^3 + 10x - 10$

11. **A** The volume of a rectangular box is $(x^3 + 6x^2 + 11x + 6)$ cm^3. The box is $(x + 3)$ cm long and $(x + 2)$ cm wide. How high is the box?

12. a) $8x^3 + 10x^2 - px - 5$ is divisible by $2x + 1$. There is no remainder. Find the value of p.
    b) When $x^6 + x^4 - 2x^2 + k$ is divided by $1 + x^2$, the remainder is 5. Find the value of k.

13. The polynomial $x^3 + px^2 - x - 2, p \in \mathbf{R}$, has $x - 1$ as a factor. What is the value of p?

14. **T** Let $f(x) = x^n - 1$, where n is an integer and $n \geq 1$. Is $f(x)$ always divisible by $x - 1$? Justify your decision.

15. If the divisor of a polynomial, $f(x)$, is $x - 4$, then the quotient is $x^2 + x - 6$ and the remainder is 7.
    a) Write the division statement.
    b) Rewrite the division statement by factoring the quotient.
    c) Graph $f(x)$ using your results in part b).

16. **C** Use an example to show how synthetic division is essentially the same as regular polynomial division.

Extending

17. The volume of a cylindrical can is $(4\pi x^3 + 28\pi x^2 + 65\pi x + 50\pi)$ cm^3. The can is $(x + 2)$ cm high. What is the radius?

18. Divide.
    a) $(x^4 + x^3 y - xy^3 - y^4) \div (x^2 - y^2)$
    b) $(x^4 - 2x^3 y + 2x^2 y^2 - 2xy^3 + y^4) \div (x^2 + y^2)$

19. Is $x - y$ a factor of $x^3 - y^3$? Justify your answer.

20. If $f(x) = (x + 5)q(x) + (x + 3)$, what is the first multiple of $(x + 5)$ that is greater than $f(x)$?

Factoring Polynomials

GOAL

Make connections between a polynomial function and its remainder when divided by a binomial.

INVESTIGATE *the Math*

Consider the polynomial function $f(x) = x^3 + 4x^2 + x - 6$.

? How can you determine the factors of a polynomial function of degree 3 or greater?

A. For $f(x) = x^3 + 4x^2 + x - 6$, determine $f(2)$.

B. Determine the quotient of $\dfrac{f(x)}{x - 2}$, and state the remainder of the division. What do you notice?

C. Predict what the remainder of the division $\dfrac{f(x)}{x + 2}$ will be. What does this tell you about the relationship between $f(x)$ and $x + 2$?

D. Copy and complete the following table by choosing eight additional values of x. Use both positive and negative values. Leave space to add more columns in part E.

a	f(a)
2	20
−2	

E. Add the following two columns to your table, and complete your table for the other values of x.

a	f(a)	$\dfrac{f(x)}{x - a}$	Remainder
2	20	$\dfrac{f(x)}{x - 2} = x^2 + 6x + 13 + \dfrac{20}{x - 2}$	20

F. For which values of a in your table is $x - a$ a factor of $f(x)$? Can you see a pattern? Explain how you know there is a pattern.

G. How do the values of a that you identified in part F relate to the graph of $f(x)$?

H. Use your table and/or the graph to determine all the factors of $f(x)$.

I. Create a new factorable function, $g(x)$, and check whether the pattern you saw in part F exists for your new function.

Reflecting

J. What is the relationship between $f(a)$ and the quotient $\dfrac{f(x)}{x - a}$?

K. What is the value of $f(a)$ when $x - a$ is a factor?

L. How can you use your answer in part K to determine the factors of a polynomial?

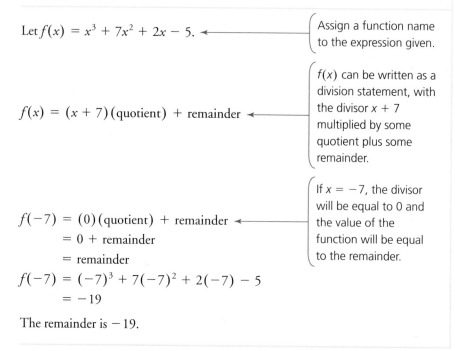

EXAMPLE 1   Using reasoning to determine a remainder

Determine the remainder when $x^3 + 7x^2 + 2x - 5$ is divided by $x + 7$.

Solution

Let $f(x) = x^3 + 7x^2 + 2x - 5$. ◄——————— Assign a function name to the expression given.

$f(x) = (x + 7)(\text{quotient}) + \text{remainder}$ ◄——————— $f(x)$ can be written as a division statement, with the divisor $x + 7$ multiplied by some quotient plus some remainder.

$f(-7) = (0)(\text{quotient}) + \text{remainder}$ ◄——————— If $x = -7$, the divisor will be equal to 0 and the value of the function will be equal to the remainder.
$\quad\quad = 0 + \text{remainder}$
$\quad\quad = \text{remainder}$

$f(-7) = (-7)^3 + 7(-7)^2 + 2(-7) - 5$
$\quad\quad = -19$

The remainder is -19.

remainder theorem

when a polynomial, $f(x)$, is divided by $x - a$, the remainder is equal to $f(a)$. If the remainder is zero, then $x - a$ is a factor of the polynomial. This can be used to help factor polynomials.

From Example 1, when $f(x)$ is divided by $x - 7$, the remainder is $f(7)$. This can be generalized into a theorem, known as the **remainder theorem**.

EXAMPLE 2 | Selecting tools and strategies to factor a polynomial

Factor $x^3 - 5x^2 - 2x + 24$ completely.

Solution

Let $f(x) = x^3 - 5x^2 - 2x + 24$. ←

Possible values of a: $\pm1, \pm2, \pm3, \pm4, \pm6, \pm8, \pm12, \pm24$

$x - a$ is a factor if $f(a) = 0$.

> Factors of $f(x)$ will be of the form $x - a$, since the leading coefficient of $f(x)$ is 1. Since a must divide into the constant term, the possible values of a are the factors of 24.

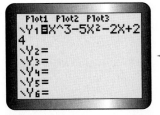

> Using a graphing calculator makes this process much faster. Enter the equation into Y1.

> In the home screen, enter Y1(1). This will give you the remainder when $f(x)$ is divided by $x - 1$.

$f(1) = 18$, so $x - 1$ is not a factor.

$f(-1) = 20$
$f(2) = 8$
$f(-2) = 0$

Therefore, $x + 2$ is a factor.

> Repeat this process until you find a value of a that results in a remainder of zero. The factor will be of the form $x - a$.

$$
\begin{array}{r|rrrr}
-2 & 1 & -5 & -2 & 24 \\
   &   & -2 & 14 & -24 \\
\hline
   & 1 & -7 & 12 & 0
\end{array}
$$

> Use synthetic or regular polynomial division to divide $f(x)$ by $x + 2$.

$$f(x) = (x + 2)(x^2 - 7x + 12)$$
$$= (x + 2)(x - 4)(x - 3)$$

> Factor the quotient.

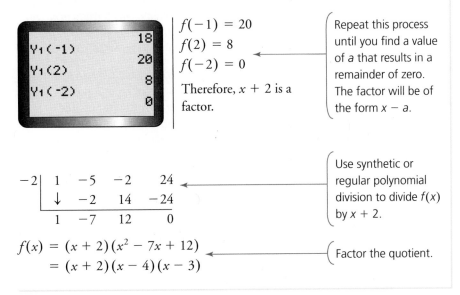

factor theorem

$x - a$ is a factor of $f(x)$, if and only if $f(a) = 0$

The **factor theorem** is a special case of the remainder theorem.

Communication | *Tip*

"A if and only if B" means that if A is true, then B is also true, and if B is true, then A is also true.

So "$x - a$ is a factor of $f(x)$, if and only if $f(a) = 0$" means that if $x - a$ is a factor of $f(x)$, then $f(a) = 0$, and if $f(a) = 0$, then $x - a$ is a factor of $f(x)$.

EXAMPLE **3**	Connecting the factor theorem to characteristics of the graph of a polynomial function

Sketch a graph of the function $y = 4x^4 + 6x^3 - 6x^2 - 4x$.

Solution

$$y = 4x^4 + 6x^3 - 6x^2 - 4x$$
$$= 2x(2x^3 + 3x^2 - 3x - 2)$$

First, divide out any common factors of the polynomial.

Let $f(x) = 2x^3 + 3x^2 - 3x - 2$.
$$f(1) = 2(1)^3 + 3(1)^2 - 3(1) - 2$$
$$= 0$$

Use the factor theorem to factor the remaining cubic.

$x - 1$ is a factor.

$$
\begin{array}{r|rrrr}
1 & 2 & 3 & -3 & -2 \\
  & \downarrow & 2 & 5 & 2 \\
\hline
  & 2 & 5 & 2 & 0
\end{array}
$$

Divide to determine the other factors.

$$y = 2x(x - 1)(2x^2 + 5x + 2)$$
$$= 2x(x - 1)(2x + 1)(x + 2)$$

Factor the quotient.

The function has zeros at $x = 0, 1, -\dfrac{1}{2}$, and -2.

State the zeros.

$y = 2x(x - 1)(2x + 1)(x + 2)$

Sketch a graph using the zeros and other characteristics from the standard and factored forms of the polynomial equations.

Since the degree is even and the leading coefficient is positive, the graph extends from the second quadrant to the first quadrant.

The function
$y = 4x^4 + 6x^3 - 6x^2 - 4x + 0$
has a y-intercept of 0.

Each factor of
$y = 2x(x - 1)(2x + 1)(x + 2)$
is order 1, so the graph has a linear shape near each zero.

EXAMPLE 4 Using a grouping strategy to factor polynomials

Factor $x^4 - 6x^3 + 2x^2 - 12x$.

Solution

$x^4 - 6x^3 + 2x^2 - 12x$
$= (x^4 - 6x^3) + (2x^2 - 12x)$ — Group the first two terms and last two terms together.

$= x^3(x - 6) + 2x(x - 6)$ — Divide out the common factors from each binominal.

$= (x - 6)(x^3 + 2x)$ — Divide out the common factor of $x - 6$.

$= x(x - 6)(x^2 + 2)$ — Divide out the common factor of x.

EXAMPLE 5 Connecting to prior knowledge to solve a problem

When $2x^3 - mx^2 + nx - 2$ is divided by $x + 1$, the remainder is -12 and $x - 2$ is a factor.
Determine the values of m and n.

Solution

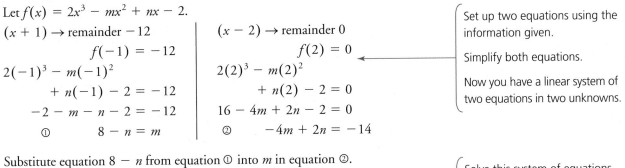

Let $f(x) = 2x^3 - mx^2 + nx - 2$.

$(x + 1) \rightarrow$ remainder -12 $(x - 2) \rightarrow$ remainder 0

$\qquad\qquad f(-1) = -12$ $f(2) = 0$

$2(-1)^3 - m(-1)^2$ $2(2)^3 - m(2)^2$

$\qquad + n(-1) - 2 = -12$ $+ n(2) - 2 = 0$

$-2 - m - n - 2 = -12$ $16 - 4m + 2n - 2 = 0$

① $8 - n = m$ ② $-4m + 2n = -14$

Set up two equations using the information given.

Simplify both equations.

Now you have a linear system of two equations in two unknowns.

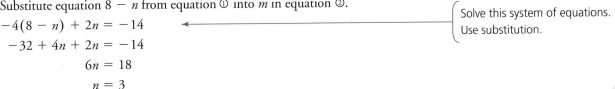

Substitute equation $8 - n$ from equation ① into m in equation ②.

$-4(8 - n) + 2n = -14$

$-32 + 4n + 2n = -14$

$\qquad\qquad 6n = 18$

$\qquad\qquad n = 3$

Solve this system of equations.
Use substitution.

$$8 - (3) = m$$
$$5 = m$$

Substitute $n = 3$ into ①.

$n = 3$ and $m = 5$

The original polynomial is
$f(x) = 2x^3 - 5x^2 + 3x - 2$.

To check, verify that $f(-1) = -12$ and $f(2) = 0$.

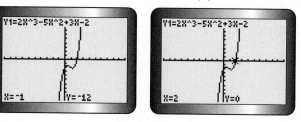

In Summary

Key Ideas

- The remainder theorem: When a polynomial, $f(x)$, is divided by $x - a$, the remainder is equal to $f(a)$.
- The factor theorem: $x - a$ is a factor of $f(x)$, if and only if $f(a) = 0$.

Need to Know

- To factor a polynomial, $f(x)$, of degree 3 or greater,
  - use the Factor Theorem to determine a factor of $f(x)$
  - divide $f(x)$ by $x - a$
  - factor the quotient, if possible
- If a polynomial, $f(x)$, has a degree greater than 3, it may be necessary to use the factor theorem more than once.
- Not all polynomial functions are factorable.

CHECK Your Understanding

1. a) Given $f(x) = x^4 + 5x^3 + 3x^2 - 7x + 10$, determine the remainder when $f(x)$ is divided by each of the following binomials, without dividing.
   i) $x - 2$
   ii) $x + 4$
   iii) $x - 1$

   b) Are any of the binomials in part a) factors of $f(x)$? Explain.

2. Which of the following functions are divisible by $x - 1$?
   a) $f(x) = x^4 - 15x^3 + 2x^2 + 12x - 10$
   b) $g(x) = 5x^3 - 4x^2 + 3x - 4$
   c) $h(x) = x^4 - 7x^3 + 2x^2 + 9x$
   d) $j(x) = x^3 - 1$

3. Determine all the factors of the function $f(x) = x^3 + 2x^2 - 5x - 6$.

PRACTISING

4. State the remainder when $x + 2$ is divided into each polynomial.

K
a) $x^2 + 7x + 9$
b) $6x^3 + 19x^2 + 11x - 11$
c) $x^4 - 5x^2 + 4$
d) $x^4 - 2x^3 - 11x^2 + 10x - 2$
e) $x^3 + 3x^2 - 10x + 6$
f) $4x^4 + 12x^3 - 13x^2 - 33x + 18$

5. Determine whether $2x - 5$ is a factor of each polynomial.

a) $2x^3 - 5x^2 - 2x + 5$
b) $3x^3 + 2x^2 - 3x - 2$
c) $2x^4 - 7x^3 - 13x^2 + 63x - 45$
d) $6x^4 + x^3 - 7x^2 - x + 1$

6. Factor each polynomial using the factor theorem.

a) $x^3 - 3x^2 - 10x + 24$
b) $4x^3 + 12x^2 - x - 15$
c) $x^4 + 8x^3 + 4x^2 - 48x$
d) $4x^4 + 7x^3 - 80x^2 - 21x + 270$
e) $x^5 - 5x^4 - 7x^3 + 29x^2 + 30x$
f) $x^4 + 2x^3 - 23x^2 - 24x + 144$

7. Factor fully.

a) $f(x) = x^3 + 9x^2 + 8x - 60$
b) $f(x) = x^3 - 7x - 6$
c) $f(x) = x^4 - 5x^2 + 4$
d) $f(x) = x^4 + 3x^3 - 38x^2 + 24x + 64$
e) $f(x) = x^3 - x^2 + x - 1$
f) $f(x) = x^5 - x^4 + 2x^3 - 2x^2 + x - 1$

8. Use the factored form of $f(x)$ to sketch the graph of each function in question 7.

9. The polynomial $12x^3 + kx^2 - x - 6$ has $2x - 1$ as one of its factors. Determine the value of k.

10. When $ax^3 - x^2 + 2x + b$ is divided by $x - 1$, the remainder is 10. When it is
A divided by $x - 2$, the remainder is 51. Find a and b.

11. Determine a general rule to help decide whether $x - a$ and $x + a$ are factors of
T $x^n - a^n$ and $x^n + a^n$.

12. The function $f(x) = ax^3 - x^2 + bx - 24$ has three factors. Two of these factors are $x - 2$ and $x + 4$. Determine the values of a and b, and then determine the other factor.

13. Consider the function $f(x) = x^3 + 4x^2 + kx - 4$. The remainder from $f(x) \div (x + 2)$ is twice the remainder from $f(x) \div (x - 2)$. Determine the value of k.

14. Show that $x - a$ is a factor of $x^4 - a^4$.

15. Explain why the factor theorem works.
C

Extending

16. Use the factor theorem to prove that $x^2 - x - 2$ is a factor of $x^3 - 6x^2 + 3x + 10$.

17. Prove that $x + a$ is a factor of $(x + a)^5 + (x + c)^5 + (a - c)^5$.

3.7 Factoring a Sum or Difference of Cubes

Factor the sum and difference of cubes.

LEARN ABOUT *the Math*

Megan has been completing her factoring homework, but she is stuck on the fourth question. She would prefer not to use the factor theorem, so she is hoping that there is a shortcut for factoring this type of polynomial.

$4x^2 - 9$	$16y^2 - 25$
$= (2x + 3)(2x - 3)$	$= (4y + 5)(4y - 5)$
$a^2 - 100$	$x^3 - 27$
$= (a + 10)(a - 10)$	$= ?$

? How can you factor a sum of cubes or a difference of cubes in one step?

EXAMPLE 1 | Selecting a strategy to factor a sum or difference of cubes

Factor the expressions $(ax)^3 - b^3$ and $(ax)^3 + b^3$ for your choice of values of a and b.

Solution A: Using a graph to factor a difference of cubes

Let $a = 1$ and $b = 2$.   ⟵ [Substitute values of a and b.

Then, $(ax)^3 - b^3 = x^3 - 8$.

$y = x^3 - 8$ is the same as $y = x^3$, translated 8 units down.

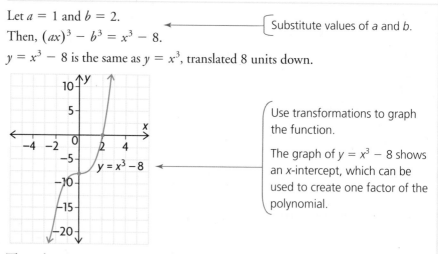

Use transformations to graph the function.

The graph of $y = x^3 - 8$ shows an x-intercept, which can be used to create one factor of the polynomial.

The only x-intercept is at 2, so $(x - 2)$ is one factor.

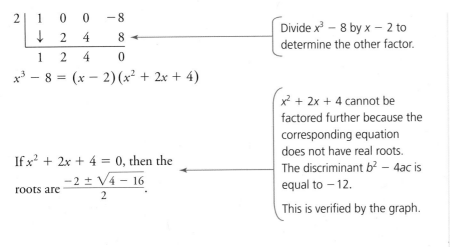

$$x^3 - 8 = (x - 2)(x^2 + 2x + 4)$$

Divide $x^3 - 8$ by $x - 2$ to determine the other factor.

If $x^2 + 2x + 4 = 0$, then the roots are $\dfrac{-2 \pm \sqrt{4 - 16}}{2}$.

$x^2 + 2x + 4$ cannot be factored further because the corresponding equation does not have real roots. The discriminant $b^2 - 4ac$ is equal to -12.

This is verified by the graph.

$$x^3 - 8 = (x - 2)(x^2 + 2x + 4)$$

Solution B: Using the factor theorem to factor a sum of cubes

Let $a = 2$ and $b = 3$.

Substitute values of a and b.

This gives the expression $f(x) = 8x^3 + 27$.

$f\left(-\dfrac{3}{2}\right) = 0$, so $2x + 3$ is a factor.

Use the factor theorem to determine one factor of $f(x)$.

$$-\dfrac{3}{2} \begin{array}{|ccccc} 8 & 0 & 0 & 27 \\ \downarrow & -12 & 18 & -27 \\ \hline 8 & -12 & 18 & 0 \end{array}$$

Divide to determine the other factors.

$$f(x) = \left(x + \dfrac{3}{2}\right)(8x^2 - 12x + 18)$$
$$= \left(x + \dfrac{3}{2}\right)(2)(4x^2 - 6x + 9)$$
$$f(x) = (2x + 3)(4x^2 - 6x + 9)$$

Multiplying $\left(x + \dfrac{3}{2}\right)$ by 2 results in the equivalent factor, $2x + 3$.

Solution C: Using a general solution

Let $a = 1$.

Substitute a value of 1 for a.

Then, $(ax)^3 - b^3 = x^3 - b^3$.

Let $f(x) = x^3 - b^3$.
$f(b) = 0$, so $(x - b)$ is a factor.

Use the factor theorem to determine one factor of $f(x)$.

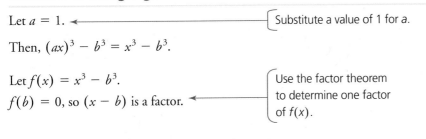

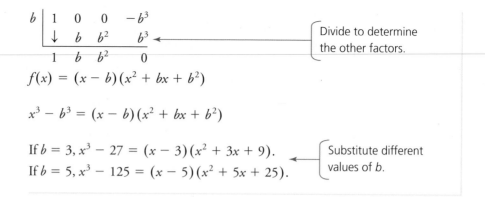

$$b \begin{array}{|cccc} 1 & 0 & 0 & -b^3 \\ \downarrow & b & b^2 & b^3 \\ \hline & 1 & b & b^2 & 0 \end{array}$$

Divide to determine the other factors.

$$f(x) = (x - b)(x^2 + bx + b^2)$$

$$x^3 - b^3 = (x - b)(x^2 + bx + b^2)$$

If $b = 3$, $x^3 - 27 = (x - 3)(x^2 + 3x + 9)$.

If $b = 5$, $x^3 - 125 = (x - 5)(x^2 + 5x + 25)$.

Substitute different values of b.

Reflecting

A. Why would an expression such as $x^3 - 8$ be called a *difference of cubes?*

B. Why would an expression such as $8x^3 + 27$ be called a *sum of cubes?*

C. Why was the quadratic formula useful for determining that the second factor could not be factored further?

D. State a general factorization for the difference of cubes, $A^3 - B^3$, and for the sum of cubes, $A^3 + B^3$.

APPLY the Math

EXAMPLE 2	Selecting a strategy to factor a polynomial

Factor the expression $27x^3 + 125$.

Solution

$27x^3 + 125$

$= (3x)^3 + (5)^3$

This is a sum of cubes.

Any sum of cubes can be factored as follows:
$A^3 + B^3 = (A + B)(A^2 - AB + B^2)$

$= (3x + 5)(9x^2 - 15x + 25)$

Use this factorization to write the two factors, if $A = 3x$ and $B = 5$.

EXAMPLE 3 | **Connecting prior knowledge to factor a polynomial**

Factor $7x^4 - 448x$.

Solution

$7x^4 - 448x$

$= 7x(x^3 - 64)$ ← | Divide out the common factor. This leaves a difference of cubes. Any difference of cubes can be factored as follows:
$A^3 - B^3 = (A - B)(A^2 + AB + B^2)$

$= 7x(x - 4)(x^2 + 4x + 16)$ ← | Use this factorization to write the factors, if $A = x$ and $B = 4$.

EXAMPLE 4 | **Selecting a strategy to factor a polynomial that is not obviously a cubic**

Factor the expression $x^9 - 512$ completely.

Solution

$x^9 - 512$

$= (x^3)^3 - (8)^3$ ← | Write the expression as the difference of two cubes.

$= (x^3 - 8)(x^6 + 8x^3 + 64)$ ← | Use the factorization $A^3 - B^3$ $= (A - B)(A^2 + AB + B^2)$ to factor the expression, if $A = x^3$ and $B = 8$.

$= (x - 2)(x^2 + 2x + 4)$
$(x^6 + 8x^3 + 64)$ ← | $(x^3 - 8)$ is also a difference of cubes, so factor it further using the pattern where $A = x$ and $B = 2$.

In Summary

Key Ideas

- An expression that contains two perfect cubes that are added together is called a sum of cubes and can be factored as follows:

$$A^3 + B^3 = (A + B)(A^2 - AB + B^2)$$

- An expression that contains perfect cubes where one is subtracted from the other is called a difference of cubes and can be factored as follows:

$$A^3 - B^3 = (A - B)(A^2 + AB + B^2)$$

CHECK Your Understanding

1. Using Solution C for Example 1 as a model, determine the factors of $x^3 + b^3$.

2. Factor each of the following expressions.
   a) $x^3 - 64$
   b) $x^3 - 125$
   c) $x^3 + 8$
   d) $8x^3 - 27$
   e) $64x^3 - 125$
   f) $x^3 + 1$
   g) $27x^3 + 8$
   h) $1000x^3 + 729$
   i) $216x^3 - 8$

3. Factor each expression.
   a) $64x^3 + 27y^3$
   b) $-3x^4 + 24x$
   c) $(x + 5)^3 - (2x + 1)^3$
   d) $x^6 + 64$

PRACTISING

4. Factor.
   K
   a) $x^3 - 343$
   b) $216x^3 - 1$
   c) $x^3 + 1000$
   d) $125x^3 - 512$
   e) $64x^3 - 1331$
   f) $343x^3 + 27$
   g) $512x^3 + 1$
   h) $1331x^3 + 1728$
   i) $512 - 1331x^3$

5. Factor each expression.
   a) $\dfrac{1}{27}x^3 - \dfrac{8}{125}$
   b) $-432x^5 - 128x^2$
   c) $(x - 3)^3 + (3x - 2)^3$
   d) $\dfrac{1}{512}x^9 - 512$

6. Jarred claims that the expression
   A $\dfrac{(a + b)(a^2 - ab + b^2) + (a - b)(a^2 + ab + b^2)}{2a^3}$ is equivalent to 1.
   Do you agree or disagree with Jarred? Justify your decision.

7. 1729 is a very interesting number. It is the smallest whole number that can be expressed as a sum of two cubes in two ways: $1^3 + 12^3$ and $9^3 + 10^3$. Use the factorization for the sum of cubes to verify that these sums are equal.

8. Prove that $(x^2 + y^2)(x^4 - x^2y^2 + y^4)(x^{12} - x^6y^6 + y^{12}) + 2x^9y^9$
   T equals $(x^9 + y^9)^2$ using the factorization for the sum of cubes.

9. Some students might argue that if you know how to factor a sum
   C of cubes, then you do not need to know how to factor a difference of cubes. Explain why you agree or disagree.

Extending

10. The number 1729, in question 7, is called a taxicab number.
    a) Use the Internet to find out why 1729 is called a taxicab number.
    b) Are there other taxicab numbers? If so, what are they?

FREQUENTLY ASKED *Questions*

Q: **How can you divide polynomials?**

A: You can divide polynomials using an algorithm similar to long division with numbers. If the divisor is a binomial, then you can use synthetic division.

For example, you can divide $3x^3 + 2x - 17$ by $x - 2$ as follows:

Study **Aid**

• See Lesson 3.5, Examples 1, 2, and 3.
• Try Chapter Review Questions 10, 11, and 12.

Using Synthetic Division

$(x - 2) \to k = 2$

$3x^3 + 2x - 17$
$= 3x^3 + 0x^2 + 2x - 17$

$$\begin{array}{r|rrrr} 2 & 3 & 0 & 2 & -17 \\ & \downarrow & 6 & 12 & 28 \\ \hline & 3 & 6 & 14 & 11 \end{array}$$

$3x^3 + 2x - 17$
$= (x - 2)(3x^2 + 6x + 14) + 11$

Using Regular Polynomial Division

$$\begin{array}{r} 3x^2 + 6x + 14 \\ x - 2 \overline{)3x^3 + 0x^2 + 2x - 17} \end{array}$$

$3x^2(x - 2) \to \underline{3x^3 - 6x^2}$
$\qquad\qquad\qquad 6x^2 + 2x$
$6x(x - 2) \to \qquad \underline{6x^2 - 12x}$
$\qquad\qquad\qquad\qquad 14x - 17$
$14(x - 2) \to \qquad\qquad \underline{14x - 28}$
$\qquad\qquad\qquad\qquad\qquad 11$

$3x^3 + 2x - 17 = (x - 2)(3x^2 + 6x + 14) + 11$

Q: **How do you factor a polynomial of degree 3 or greater?**

A1: Use the factor theorem to determine one factor of the polynomial, and then divide to determine the other factors.

For example, to factor $x^3 - 6x^2 - 13x + 42$, let $f(x) = x^3 - 6x^2 - 13x + 42$ and determine the first possible factor by finding a number the makes $f(x) = 0$.

Possibilities: $\pm 1, \pm 2, \pm 3, \pm 6, \pm 7, \pm 14, \pm 21, \pm 42$

$f(2) = (2)^3 - 6(2)^2 - 13(2) + 42 = 0$, so $x - 2$ is a factor.

Use synthetic division to find the other factor.

Study **Aid**

• See Lesson 3.6, Example 2.
• Try Chapter Review Questions 14 and 15.

$$\begin{array}{r|rrrr} 2 & 1 & -6 & -13 & 42 \\ & \downarrow & 2 & 8 & -42 \\ \hline & 1 & -4 & -21 & 0 \end{array}$$

$f(x) = (x - 2)(x^2 - 4x - 21)$ Factor the quotient.
$\quad = (x - 2)(x - 7)(x + 3)$

A2: Factor using the sum or difference of cubes pattern when appropriate:

$A^3 - B^3 = (A - B)(A^2 + AB + B^2)$
$A^3 + B^3 = (A + B)(A^2 - AB + B^2)$

For example, you can factor $27x^3 - 64$ as follows:
$27x^3 - 64$
$= (3x)^3 - (4)^3$
$= (3x - 4)(9x^2 + 12x + 16)$

Study **Aid**

• See Lesson 3.7, Examples 2 and 3.
• Try Chapter Review Questions 16, 17, and 18.

PRACTICE Questions

Lesson 3.1

1. Draw the graph of a polynomial function that has all of the following characteristics:
   - $f(2) = 10, f(-3) = 0$, and $f(4) = 0$
   - The y-intercept is 0.
   - $f(x) > 0$ when $x < -3$ and $0 < x < 4$.
   - $f(x) < 0$ when $-3 < x < 0$ and $x > 4$.
   - The range is the set of real numbers.

Lesson 3.2

2. Describe the end behaviours of this function.

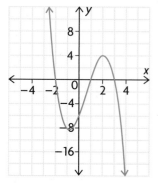

3. State the possible degree of each function, the sign of the leading coefficient, and the number of turning points.

   a)

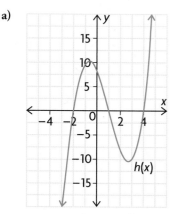

   b)

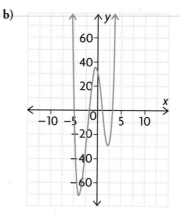

Lesson 3.3

4. For each of the following, write the equations of three cubic functions that have the given zeros and belong to the same family of functions.
   a) $-3, 6, 4$
   b) $5, -1, -2$
   c) $-7, 2, 3$
   d) $9, -5, -4$

5. For each of the following, write the equations of three quartic functions that have the given zeros and belong to the same family of functions.
   a) $-6, 2, 5, 8$
   b) $4, -8, 1, 2$
   c) $0, -1, 9, 10$
   d) $-3, 3, -6, 6$

6. Sketch the graph of $f(x) = (x - 3)(x + 2)(x + 5)$ using the zeros and end behaviours.

7. Determine the equation of the function with zeros at ± 1 and -2, and a y-intercept of -6. Then sketch the function.

Lesson 3.4

8. Describe the transformations that were applied to $y = x^2$ to obtain each of the following functions.
   a) $y = -2(x - 1)^2 + 23$
   b) $y = \left(\dfrac{12}{13}(x + 9)\right)^2 - 14$
   c) $y = x^2 - 8x + 16$
   d) $y = \left(x + \dfrac{3}{7}\right)\left(x + \dfrac{3}{7}\right)$
   e) $y = 40(-7(x - 10))^2 + 9$

9. The function $y = x^3$ has undergone each of the following sets of transformations. List three points on the resulting function.

a) vertically stretched by a factor of 25, horizontally compressed by a factor of $\frac{5}{6}$, horizontally translated 3 units to the right

b) reflected in the y-axis, horizontally stretched by a factor of 7, vertically translated 19 units down

c) reflected in the x-axis, vertically compressed by a factor of $\frac{6}{11}$, horizontally translated 5 units to the left, vertically translated 16 units up

d) vertically stretched by a factor of 100, horizontally stretched by a factor of 2, vertically translated 14 units up

e) reflected in the y-axis, vertically translated 45 units down

f) reflected in the x-axis, horizontally compressed by a factor of $\frac{7}{10}$, horizontally translated 12 units to the right, vertically translated 6 units up

Lesson 3.5

10. Calculate each of the following using long division.

a) $(2x^3 + 5x^2 + 3x - 4) \div (x + 5)$

b) $(x^4 + 4x^3 - 3x^2 - 6x - 7) \div (x^2 - 8)$

c) $(2x^4 - 2x^2 + 3x - 16)$ $\div (x^3 + 3x^2 + 3x - 3)$

d) $(x^5 - 8x^3 - 7x - 6)$ $\div (x^4 + 4x^3 + 4x^2 - x - 3)$

11. Divide each polynomial by $x + 2$ using synthetic division.

a) $2x^3 + 5x^2 - x - 5$

b) $3x^3 + 13x^2 + 17x + 3$

c) $2x^4 + 5x^3 - 16x^2 - 45x - 18$

d) $2x^3 + 4x^2 - 5x - 4$

12. Each divisor was divided into another polynomial, resulting in the given quotient and remainder. Determine the dividend.

a) divisor: $x - 9$, quotient: $2x^2 + 11x - 8$, remainder: 3

b) divisor: $4x + 3$, quotient: $x^3 - 2x + 7$, remainder: -4

c) divisor: $3x - 4$, quotient: $x^3 + 6x^2 - 6x - 7$, remainder: 5

d) divisor: $3x^2 + x - 5$, quotient: $x^4 - 4x^3 + 9x - 3$, remainder: $2x - 1$

Lesson 3.6

13. Without dividing, determine the remainder when $x^3 + 2x^2 - 6x + 1$ is divided by $x + 2$.

14. Factor each polynomial using the factor theorem.

a) $x^3 - 5x^2 - 22x - 16$

b) $2x^3 + x^2 - 27x - 36$

c) $3x^4 - 19x^3 + 38x^2 - 24x$

d) $x^4 + 11x^3 + 36x^2 + 16x - 64$

15. Factor fully.

a) $8x^3 - 10x^2 - 17x + 10$

b) $2x^3 + 7x^2 - 7x - 30$

c) $x^4 - 7x^3 + 9x^2 + 27x - 54$

d) $4x^4 + 4x^3 - 35x^2 - 36x - 9$

Lesson 3.7

16. Factor each difference of cubes.

a) $64x^3 - 27$ **c)** $343x^3 - 1728$

b) $512x^3 - 125$ **d)** $1331x^3 - 1$

17. Factor each sum of cubes.

a) $1000x^3 + 343$ **c)** $27x^3 + 1331$

b) $1728x^3 + 125$ **d)** $216x^3 + 2197$

18. a) Factor the expression $x^6 - y^6$ completely by treating it as a difference of squares.

b) Factor the same expression by treating it as a difference of cubes.

c) Explain any similarities or differences in your final results.

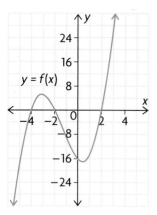

$y = f(x)$

1. **a)** Write the standard form of a general polynomial function. Then state the degree and leading coefficient of this function.
   b) What is the greatest number of turning points that this function can have?
   c) What is the greatest number of zeros that this function can have?
   d) If the least number of zeros is one, describe the degree of this function.
   e) A polynomial function is less than zero for all x. Describe the degree and the leading coefficient of this function.

2. Determine the equation of the polynomial function $y = f(x)$ shown. Express your answer in factored form.

3. Factor each expression.
   a) $2x^3 - x^2 - 145x - 72$ **b)** $(x - 7)^3 + (2x + 3)^3$

4. LaDainian graphed the cubic function $g(x) = x^3 - 4x^2$, and then vertically translated the graph 1 unit up. Does the resulting graph have fewer zeros, the same number of zeros, or more zeros than the original graph?

5. During which intervals of x is the graph of the function $f(x) = -(x + 3)(x + 5)(x - 1)$ below the x-axis?

6. Divide $6x^3 + x^2 - 12x + 5$ by $2x - 1$. Is the divisor a factor of the dividend?

7. The function $y = x^3$ has been vertically stretched by a factor of 5, horizontally compressed by a factor of $\frac{1}{2}$, horizontally translated 2 units to the right, and vertically translated 4 units up.
   a) Write the equation of the transformed function.
   b) The point $(1, 1)$ is on the parent function. Determine the new coordinates of this point on the transformed function.

8. Julie divided $x^4 + 3x^3 - 9x^2 + 6$ by a polynomial. Her answer was $x^3 - 2x^2 + x - 5$, with a remainder of 31. What polynomial did Julie divide by?

9. The function $f(x) = ax^4 + 8x^2$ has three turning points, an absolute maximum of 8, and one of its zeros at $x = 2$. Determine the value of a and the location of the other zeros. Then sketch the graph of $f(x)$.

Graph it!

The polynomial function $f(x) = ax^4 - 3x^3 - 63x^2 + 152x - b$ has one of its zeros at $x = 5$ and passes through the point $(-2, -560)$.

❓ **What might the graph of $f(x)$ look like?**

A. Use the given information to determine the values of a and b.

B. Use the given information to state one of the factors of $f(x)$.

C. Determine all the other factors of $f(x)$.

D. Use the factors to determine the zeros of $f(x)$.

E. Determine the end behaviours of $f(x)$.

F. Determine the y-intercept of $f(x)$.

G. Use all the characteristics you determined to sketch a possible graph of $f(x)$.

H. Verify your results using graphing technology. Discuss any differences between the graph and your sketch.

Task | *Checklist*

✔ Did you explain your thinking clearly?

✔ Did you justify your answers mathematically?

✔ Did you show all work and calculations?

✔ Did you check your calculations?

✔ Did you label your sketch properly?

Multiple Choice

1. What is the domain of the function
$f(x) = \dfrac{2}{5 - x}$?

   a) $\{x \in \mathbf{R} \mid x \neq -5\}$ c) $\{x \in \mathbf{R} \mid x \neq 0\}$
   b) $\{x \in \mathbf{R} \mid x \neq 5\}$ d) $\{x \in \mathbf{R}\}$

2. Which of these relations is *not* a function of x?

   a) $x = -y^2$ c) $y = \sqrt{x - 3}$
   b) $y = 2x^2$ d) $x + y = 3$

3. Which function can be represented by this graph?

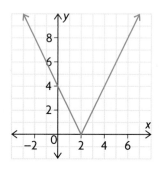

   a) $f(x) = |2x| - 4$ c) $f(x) = |2x - 4|$

   b) $f(x) = \left|\dfrac{1}{2}x - 2\right|$ d) $f(x) = |2x| + 4$

4. Which best describes
$f(x) = (x - 2)(x + 2)$?
   a) odd   c) neither a) nor b)
   b) even   d) both a) and b)

5. What transformations were applied to $y = |x|$
to obtain the equation $y = \left|\dfrac{1}{3}(x - 2)\right|$?

   a) horizontal compression by a factor of $\dfrac{1}{3}$,
   horizontal translation 2 units to the left
   b) horizontal stretch by a factor of 3,
   horizontal translation 2 units to the right
   c) horizontal translation 2 units to the right,
   horizontal stretch by a factor of 3
   d) horizontal translation 2 units to the right,
   horizontal compression by a factor of $\dfrac{1}{3}$

6. What is the equation of the parent function
of $f(x) = \dfrac{2}{x - 2} - 4$?

   a) $g(x) = 2^x$ c) $g(x) = x^2$

   b) $g(x) = \dfrac{2}{x}$ d) $g(x) = \dfrac{1}{x}$

7. The graph of $y = 2^x$ is stretched horizontally by
a factor of 5, and then translated 3 units down.
Which of the following is the resulting
equation?

   a) $f(x) = 2^{5(x-3)}$ c) $f(x) = 5^x - 3$
   b) $f(x) = 2^{\frac{1}{5}(x+3)}$ d) $f(x) = 2^{(\frac{1}{5}x)} - 3$

8. Which function has an inverse with the
domain $\{x \in \mathbf{R} \mid x \geq 5\}$?

   a) $y = 2x^2 + 5$ c) $y = 2|x| - 5$
   b) $y = 2(x - 5)^2$ d) $y = 2|x + 5|$

9. Which relation is the inverse of
$f(x) = 2x^2 - 4$?

   a) $y = \sqrt{2(x - 4)}$

   b) $y = \pm\sqrt{2(x - 4)}$

   c) $y = \pm\sqrt{\dfrac{x + 4}{2}}$

   d) $y = \sqrt{\dfrac{x + 4}{2}}$

10. Which function is *not* continuous?

   a) $f(x) = \begin{cases} 2x, & \text{if } x < 1 \\ x + 1, & \text{if } x \geq 1 \end{cases}$

   b) $f(x) = \begin{cases} (x - 2)^2, & \text{if } x \leq 2 \\ \sqrt{x - 2}, & \text{if } x > 2 \end{cases}$

   c) $f(x) = \begin{cases} \dfrac{1}{x}, & \text{if } x < -1 \\ -1, & \text{if } x \geq -1 \end{cases}$

   d) $f(x) = \begin{cases} 2x + 1, & \text{if } x < 2 \\ x + 2, & \text{if } x \geq 2 \end{cases}$

11. What is the average rate of change of the function $f(x) = x^3 - 2x^2 + 7$ over the interval $-1 \leq x \leq 3$?

a) 3 **b)** 4 **c)** 12 **d)** −3

12. Kristin and Husain are growing crystal gardens. Both of them started with a small seed crystal, which had a mass of about 0.1 g. In 3 days, Kristin's crystal grew to a mass of 5 g. In 10 days, Husain's crystal grew to a mass of 15 g. Whose crystal grew faster?

a) Kristin's
b) Husain's
c) The rates are equal.
d) There is not enough information to decide.

13. A submarine is descending from the surface. What is the best estimate of its instantaneous change in depth at $t = 3$ s?

Time, t (s)	Depth (m)
3	27
3.001	27.015002
3.01	27.1502
3.1	28.52
4	44

a) 15.2 m/s
b) 15.002 m/s
c) 15 m/s
d) 17 m/s

14. What is the best estimate of the instantaneous rate of change of $f(x) = 2^x - 2x + 1$ at $x = -1$?

a) −1.5 **b)** −3.5 **c)** −1.625 **d)** −1.65

15. For the following graph, what is the best estimate of the slope of the tangent at $x = 2$?

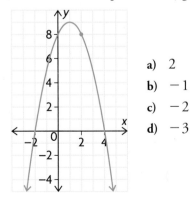

a) 2
b) −1
c) −2
d) −3

16. An athlete runs the first lap of a race slightly faster than the next two laps, and then runs the final lap the fastest. Which graph is the correct distance versus time graph for the athlete's run?

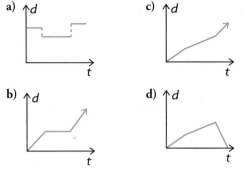

17. At $x = 5$, the function $f(x) = 13x - 1.3x^2 + 7.3$ has

a) a maximum
b) a minimum
c) both a maximum and a minimum
d) neither a maximum nor a minimum

18. For the function $f(x) = 2x^2 - 3x + 9$, what is the correct expression for the value of the difference quotient on the interval $3 \leq x \leq 3 + h$?

a) $2h^2 - 3h$ **c)** $4h - 3$
b) $4h + 9$ **d)** $2h + 9$

19. For the growth equation $y = 35(1.7)^x$, the maximum value over the domain $0 \leq x \leq 8$ is

a) $y = 1.7$ **c)** $y = 69.7$
b) $y = 2441.5$ **d)** $y = 35$

20. Which equation does *not* represent a polynomial function?

a) $f(x) = x^2 + 2$
b) $f(x) = (x + 1)(x - 2)(x - 3)(x - 4)$
c) $f(x) = 2^x - 3$
d) $f(x) = 3x - 2$

21. Which type of polynomial function *cannot* be represented by the following graph?

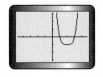

a) quadratic
b) cubic
c) quartic with three turning points
d) quartic with one turning point

22. Which statement is true for any cubic polynomial function?

a) As $x \to \pm\infty$, $y \to \infty$.

b) As $x \to \pm\infty$, the signs of y are opposite.

c) As $x \to \pm\infty$, $y \to -\infty$.

d) As $x \to \pm\infty$, the signs of y are same.

23. Which function could be represented by the following graph?

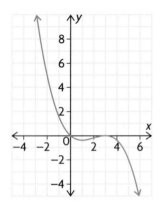

a) $y = 0.1x^2(x - 3)^2$

b) $y = -0.1x(x - 3)^2$

c) $y = -0.1x(x - 3)$

d) $y = -0.1x^2(x + 3)$

24. Which quartic function has zeros at $-2, 0, 1$, and 3, and satisfies $f(2) = 16$?

a) $f(x) = -2x^4 + 4x^3 + 10x^2 - 12x$

b) $f(x) = 2x^4 - 4x^3 - 10x^2 + 12x$

c) $f(x) = 2x^4 + 4x^3 - 10x^2 - 12x$

d) $f(x) = -2x^4 - 4x^3 + 10x^2 + 12x$

25. $y = x^3$ is stretched horizontally by a factor of 2, and then translated horizontally 3 units to the right. What is the equation of the resulting graph?

a) $y = (2(x + 3))^3$ c) $y = \left(\frac{1}{2}(x - 3)\right)^3$

b) $y = \left(\frac{1}{2}x\right)^3 - 3$ d) $y = (2x - 3)^3$

26. $x^3 - 2x^2 + 7x + 12$ is divided by $x^2 - 3x + 4$. What is the remainder?

a) $x^2 + 3x + 8$ c) $6x + 8$

b) $x + 4$ d) $-3x + 4$

27. What is the remainder when $x + 3$ is divided into $x^4 - 5x^2 + 12x + 16$?

a) 196   c) -2

b) 88   d) 16

28. The polynomial $2x^3 + kx^2 - 3x + 18$ has $x - 3$ as one of its factors. What is the value of k?

a) 4   c) -2

b) -7 d) 2

29. What is $27x^3 - 216$ in factored form?

a) $3(x - 2)(x^2 + 2x + 4)$

b) $27(x + 2)(x^2 - 2x + 4)$

c) $27(x - 2)(x^2 + 2x + 4)$

d) $(3x + 6)(9x^2 - 18x + 36)$

30. What are the factors of $(x + 3)^3 + 8$?

a) $(x^3 + 27)(8)$

b) $(x + 3)(x^2 - 3x + 17)$

c) $(x + 5)(x^2 + 4x + 7)$

d) $(x + 1)(x^2 - 4x + 7)$

31. The following container is being filled with water at a constant rate. Which graph shows the height of the water level versus time?

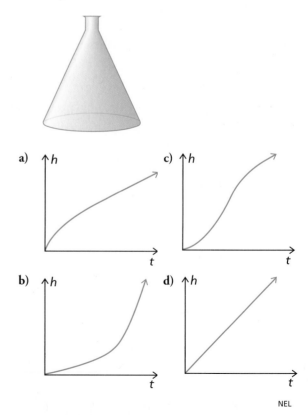

Investigations

Investigating Transformations of a Quadratic and its Inverse

32. a) Sketch the graphs of the parent function $f(x) = x^2$ and its inverse.

b) Apply various transformations to the graph of the parent function. Draw the graph of the inverse of each transformed function.

c) Describe how you could modify each transformed inverse you drew in part b) to make it into a function.

Investigating Rates of Change in a Cubic Function

33. Investigate various rates of change of the function $f(x) = x^3 - 6x^2 + 9x + 1$. Your investigation should include average rates of change and estimated rates of change at different points, including any maximum or minimum points.

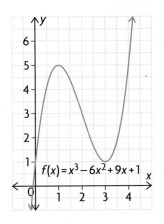

Graphing a Polynomial Function

34. a) Determine the equation of $f(x) = k(x + 1)^2(x - 2)(x - 4)$, if $(1, -24)$ is a point on the graph of $f(x)$.

b) Solve for p if $(3, p)$ is a point on the graph of $f(x)$.

c) State the end behaviours and the zeros of $f(x)$.

d) Determine the y-intercept of $f(x)$.

e) Use all the characteristics you determined to sketch a possible graph of $f(x)$.

Polynomial Equations and Inequalities

▶ **GOALS**

You will be able to

- Determine the roots of polynomial equations, with and without technology
- Solve polynomial inequalities, with and without technology
- Solve problems involving polynomial function models

> ❓ If a polynomial function models the height of the wake boarder above the surface of the water, how could you use the function to determine when he is above a given height or how quickly he is descending at any given time?

Study | Aid

- For help, see the Review of Essential Skills found at the Nelson Advanced Functions website.

Question	Appendix/Lesson
1, 4, 5	R-6
2	R-3, 3.6
3	3.3
6, 7	2.5

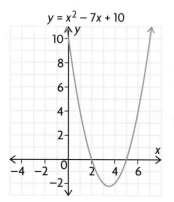

$y = x^2 - 7x + 10$

SKILLS AND CONCEPTS You Need

1. Solve the following linear equations.

   a) $5x - 7 = -3x + 17$

   b) $12x - 9 - 6x = 5 + 3x + 1$

   c) $2(3x - 5) = -4(3x - 2)$

   d) $\dfrac{2x + 5}{3} = 7 - \dfrac{x}{4}$

2. Factor the following expressions.

   a) $x^3 + x^2 - 30x$

   b) $x^3 - 64$

   c) $24x^4 + 81x$

   d) $2x^3 + 7x^2 - 18x - 63$

3. Sketch a graph of each of the following functions.

   a) $y = (x - 2)(x + 3)(x - 4)$

   b) $y = 2(x + 6)^3 - 10$

4. Given the graph of the function shown, determine the roots of the equation $x^2 - 7x + 10 = 0$.

5. Determine the roots of each of the following quadratic equations.

   a) $2x^2 = 18$

   b) $x^2 + 8x - 20 = 0$

   c) $6x^2 = 11x + 10$

   d) $x(x + 3) = 3 - 5x - x^2$

6. The graph below shows Erika's walk in front of a motion sensor.

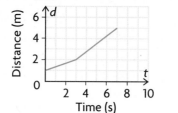

   a) In which time interval is she walking the fastest? Explain.

   b) Calculate the speeds at which she walks on the intervals $t \in (0, 3)$ and $t \in (3, 7)$.

   c) Is she moving away or toward the motion sensor? How do you know?

7. A T-ball player hits a baseball from a tee that is 0.5 m tall. The height of the ball is modelled by $h(t) = -5t^2 + 9.75t + 0.5$, where h is the height in metres at t seconds.

   a) How long is the ball in the air?

   b) Determine the average rate of change in the ball's height during the first second of flight.

   c) Estimate the instantaneous rate of change in the ball's height when it hits the ground.

8. Copy and complete the anticipation guide in your notes.

Statement	Agree	Disagree	Justification
The quadratic formula can only be used when solving a quadratic equation.			
Cubic equations always have three real roots.			
The graph of a cubic function always passes through all four quadrants.			
The graphs of all polynomial functions must pass through at least two quadrants.			
The expression $x^2 > 4$ is only true if $x > 2$.			
If you know the instantaneous rates of change for a function at $x = 2$ and $x = 3$, you can predict fairly well what the function looks like in between.			

APPLYING *What You Know*

Modelling a Situation with a Polynomial Function

Shown is a picture of the Gateway Arch located in St. Louis, Missouri, U.S.A. The arch is about 192 m wide and 192 m tall.

The city of St. Louis would like to hang a banner from the arch for their New Year celebrations. They have determined that the banner should be suspended from a horizontal cable that spans the arch 175 m off the ground to ensure optimal viewing around the city.

 Assuming that the arch is parabolic in shape, how long should the cable be?

A. Draw a sketch showing the arch on a coordinate grid using an appropriate scale.

B. Determine a quadratic function that could model the inside of the arch using vertex or factored form.

C. How did you predict what the sign of the leading coefficient in the function would be? Explain.

D. Use your model to determine the length of the cable needed to support the banner.

Solving Polynomial Equations

YOU WILL NEED

- graphing calculator or graphing software

GOAL

Solve polynomial equations using a variety of strategies.

LEARN ABOUT the Math

Amelia's family is planning to build another silo for grain storage, identical to those they have on their farm. The cylindrical portion of those they currently have is 15 m tall, and the silo's total volume is 684π m^3.

? What are the possible values for the radius of the new silo?

EXAMPLE 1	Representing a problem with a polynomial model

Determine possible values for the radius of the silo.

Solution

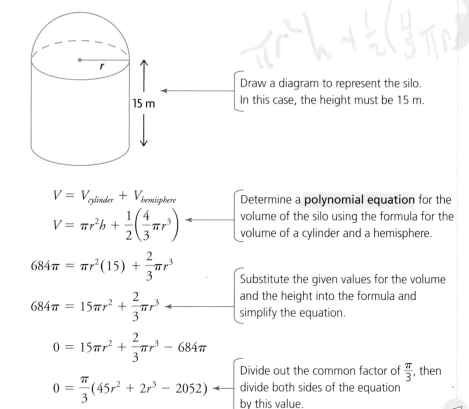

Draw a diagram to represent the silo. In this case, the height must be 15 m.

polynomial equation

an equation in which one polynomial expression is set equal to another (e.g., $x^3 - 5x^2 = 4x - 3$, or $5x^4 - 3x^3 + x^2 - 6x = 9$)

$$V = V_{cylinder} + V_{hemisphere}$$

$$V = \pi r^2 h + \frac{1}{2}\left(\frac{4}{3}\pi r^3\right)$$

Determine a **polynomial equation** for the volume of the silo using the formula for the volume of a cylinder and a hemisphere.

$$684\pi = \pi r^2(15) + \frac{2}{3}\pi r^3$$

$$684\pi = 15\pi r^2 + \frac{2}{3}\pi r^3$$

Substitute the given values for the volume and the height into the formula and simplify the equation.

$$0 = 15\pi r^2 + \frac{2}{3}\pi r^3 - 684\pi$$

$$0 = \frac{\pi}{3}(45r^2 + 2r^3 - 2052)$$

Divide out the common factor of $\frac{\pi}{3}$, then divide both sides of the equation by this value.

$$0 = 45r^2 + 2r^3 - 2052$$
$$0 = 2r^3 + 45r^2 - 2052 \leftarrow$$

Rewrite the polynomial in descending order of degree.

Let $f(r) = 2r^3 + 45r^2 - 2052 \leftarrow$

$$f(2) = 2(2)^3 + 45(2)^2 - 2052$$
$$= -1856$$
$$f(3) = 2(3)^3 + 45(3)^2 - 2052$$
$$= -1593$$
$$f(6) = 2(6)^3 + 45(6)^2 - 2052$$
$$= 0$$

Solve the equation by factoring the polynomial.

Since the roots of the equation are the x-intercepts of the related function, use the factor theorem to determine one factor.

By the factor theorem, $(r - 6)$ is a factor of $f(r)$.

$$(2r^3 + 45r^2 - 2052) \div (r - 6)$$

$$\begin{array}{r|rrrr} 6 & 2 & 45 & 0 & -2052 \\ & \downarrow & 12 & 342 & 2052 \\ \hline & 2 & 57 & 342 & 0 \end{array}$$

Use synthetic division to divide $f(r)$ by $(r - 6)$ to determine the other factor.

$$(r - 6)(2r^2 + 57r + 342) = 0$$

$$r - 6 = 0$$

$r = 6$ is one solution

Set each factor equal to zero and solve.

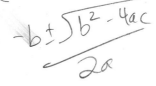

$$2r^2 + 57r + 342 = 0$$

$$a = 2, b = 57, c = 342$$

$$r = \frac{-b \pm \sqrt{b^2 - 4ac}}{2a}$$

$$r = \frac{-57 \pm \sqrt{(57)^2 - 4(2)(342)}}{2(2)}$$

$$r = \frac{-57 \pm \sqrt{513}}{4}$$

$$r = \frac{-57 + \sqrt{513}}{4} \quad \text{or} \quad r = \frac{-57 - \sqrt{513}}{4}$$

$$r \doteq -8.6 \qquad\qquad r \doteq -19.9$$

The second factor does not appear to be factorable, so use the quadratic formula to solve for the other roots.

The silo must have a radius of 6 m. $\leftarrow$

The radius cannot be negative, and so only the positive root can be the radius of the silo.

Reflecting

A. How could you verify the solutions you found, with and without using a graphing calculator?

B. What restriction was placed on the variable in the polynomial equation? Explain why this was necessary.

C. Do you think it is possible to solve all cubic and quartic equations using an algebraic strategy involving factoring? Explain.

APPLY the Math

EXAMPLE 2 Selecting a strategy to solve a cubic equation

Solve $4x^3 - 12x^2 - x + 3 = 0$.

Solution A: Using the factor theorem

Let $f(x) = 4x^3 - 12x^2 - x + 3$

Possible values for x where $f(x) = 0$:

$\pm 1, \pm 3, \pm\dfrac{1}{2}, \pm\dfrac{3}{2}, \pm\dfrac{1}{4}, \pm\dfrac{3}{4}$ ←

> Use the factor theorem and the related polynomial function to determine one factor of the equation. Numbers that could make $f(x) = 0$ are of the form $\frac{p}{q}$, where p is a factor of the constant term 3 and q is a factor of the leading coefficient 4.

$$f(1) = 4(1)^3 - 12(1)^2 - (1) + 3$$
$$= -6$$

$$f(-1) = 4(-1)^3 - 12(-1)^2 - (-1) + 3$$
$$= -12$$

$$f(3) = 4(3)^3 - 12(3)^2 - (3) + 3$$
$$= 0$$

By the factor theorem, $(x - 3)$ is a factor of $f(x)$.

$(4x^3 - 12x^2 - x + 3) \div (x - 3)$

$$
\begin{array}{r}
4x^2 + 0x - 1 \\
x - 3 \overline{)4x^3 - 12x^2 - x + 3} \\
\underline{4x^3 - 12x^2} \\
0x^2 - x \\
\underline{0x^2 - 0x} \\
-x + 3 \\
\underline{-x + 3} \\
0
\end{array}
$$

> Divide $f(x)$ by $(x - 3)$ to find the second factor using either long or synthetic division.

$(x - 3)(4x^2 - 1) = 0$ ←

> The quotient $4x^2 - 1$ is a difference of squares. Factor this.

$$(x - 3)(2x - 1)(2x + 1) = 0$$

$$x - 3 = 0 \text{ or } 2x - 1 = 0 \text{ or } 2x + 1 = 0$$

Set each of the factors equal to zero to solve.

$$x = 3 \qquad 2x = 1 \qquad 2x = -1$$

$$x = \frac{1}{2} \qquad x = -\frac{1}{2}$$

Check:

$$x = \frac{1}{2}$$

Verify the solutions by substitution.

$$x = -\frac{1}{2}$$

LS	RS	LS	RS
$4x^3 - 12x^2 - x + 3$	0	$4x^3 - 12x^2 - x + 3$	0

$$= 4\left(\frac{1}{2}\right)^3 - 12\left(\frac{1}{2}\right)^2$$

$$-\left(\frac{1}{2}\right) + 3$$

$$= \frac{1}{2} - 3 - \frac{1}{2} + 3$$

$$= 0$$

LS = RS ✓

$$= 4\left(-\frac{1}{2}\right)^3 - 12\left(-\frac{1}{2}\right)^2$$

$$-\left(-\frac{1}{2}\right) + 3$$

$$= -\frac{1}{2} - 3 + \frac{1}{2} + 3$$

$$= 0$$

LS = RS ✓

You only need to check $x = \frac{1}{2}$ and $-\frac{1}{2}$ since $x = 3$ was obtained using substitution.

The solutions to $4x^3 - 12x^2 - x + 3 = 0$ are $x = -\frac{1}{2}$, $x = \frac{1}{2}$, and $x = 3$.

Solution B: Factoring by grouping

$$4x^3 - 12x^2 - x + 3 = 0$$

$$4x^2(x - 3) - 1(x - 3) = 0$$

The first two terms and the last two terms have a common factor, so you can factor by grouping.

$$(x - 3)(4x^2 - 1) = 0$$

$$(x - 3)(2x - 1)(2x + 1) = 0$$

$$x - 3 = 0 \text{ or } 2x - 1 = 0 \text{ or } 2x + 1 = 0$$

Set each of the factors equal to zero to solve.

$$x = 3 \qquad 2x = 1 \text{ or } \qquad 2x = -1$$

$$x = \frac{1}{2} \qquad x = -\frac{1}{2}$$

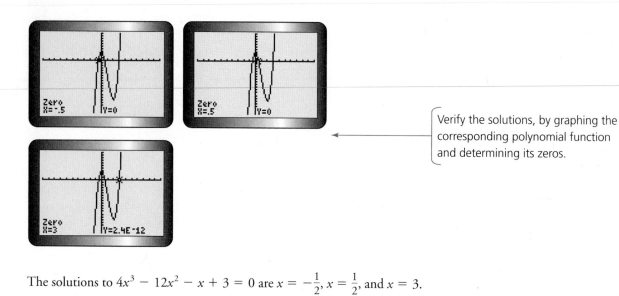

Verify the solutions, by graphing the corresponding polynomial function and determining its zeros.

The solutions to $4x^3 - 12x^2 - x + 3 = 0$ are $x = -\frac{1}{2}$, $x = \frac{1}{2}$, and $x = 3$.

EXAMPLE 3   Selecting tools to solve a question involving modelling

The paths of two orcas playing in the ocean were recorded by some oceanographers. The first orca's path could be modelled by the equation $h(t) = 2t^4 - 17t^3 + 27t^2 - 252t + 232$, and the second by $h(t) = 20t^3 - 200t^2 + 300t - 200$, where h is their height above/below the water's surface in centimetres and t is the time during the first 8 s of play. Over this 8-second period, at what times were the two orcas at the same height or depth?

Solution

$2t^4 - 17t^3 + 27t^2 - 252t + 232 = 20t^3 - 200t^2 + 300t - 200$

$2t^4 - 37t^3 + 227t^2 - 552t + 432 = 0$ ◄——

Since you are solving for the time when the heights or depths are the same, set the two equations equal to each other and use inverse operations to make the right side of the equation equal to zero.

Let $f(t) = 2t^4 - 37t^3 + 227t^2 - 552t + 432$ ◄——

Solve the equation by factoring.

Some possible values for t where $f(t) = 0$:

$\pm 1, \pm 2, \pm 3, \pm 4, \pm 6, \pm 8, \pm 9$

$f(1) = 72$

$f(2) = -28$

$f(3) = -18$

$f(4) = 0$

> Use the factor theorem to determine one factor of $f(t)$. Since the question specifies that the time is within the first 10 s, you only need to consider values of $\frac{p}{q}$ between 0 and 10. In this case, consider just the factors of 432.

By the factor theorem, $(t - 4)$ is a factor of $f(t)$.

$(2t^4 - 37t^3 + 227t^2 - 552t + 432) \div (t - 4)$

$$
\begin{array}{r|rrrrr}
4 & 2 & -37 & 227 & -552 & 432 \\
  & \downarrow & 8 & -116 & 444 & -432 \\
\hline
  & 2 & -29 & 111 & -108 & 0
\end{array}
$$

> Divide $f(t)$ by $(t - 4)$ to determine the second factor.

$f(t) = (t - 4)(2t^3 - 29t^2 + 111t - 108)$

$f(6) = -108$

$f(8) = -208$

$f(9) = 0$

> Since the second factor is cubic, you must continue looking for more zeros using the factor theorem. It is not necessary to recheck the values that were used in an earlier step, so carry on with the other possibilities.

By the factor theorem, $(t - 9)$ is a factor of $f(t)$.

$(2t^3 - 29t^2 + 111t - 108) \div (t - 9)$

$$
\begin{array}{r|rrrr}
9 & 2 & -29 & 111 & -108 \\
  & \downarrow & 18 & -99 & 108 \\
\hline
  & 2 & -11 & 12 & 0
\end{array}
$$

> Divide the cubic polynomial by $(t - 9)$ to determine the other factor.

$f(t) = (t - 4)(t - 9)(2t^2 - 11t + 12)$

> Factor the quadratic.

$ = (t - 4)(t - 9)(2t - 3)(t - 4)$

$ = (t - 4)^2(t - 9)(2t - 3)$

$(t - 4)^2 = 0, t - 9 = 0,$ or $2t - 3 = 0$

> Set each factor equal to zero and solve.

$t = 4 \qquad t = 9 \qquad t = 1.5$

The solutions that are valid on the given domain are $t = 1.5$ and $t = 4$.

> The polynomial functions given only model the orca's movement between 0 s and 8 s, so the solution $t = 9$ is inadmissable.

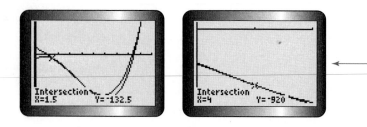

Graph both functions and adjust the window settings to determine the points of intersection to verify the solutions.

The orcas were at the same depth after 1.5 s and 4 s on the interval between 0 s and 8 s.

| EXAMPLE **4** | Selecting a strategy to solve a polynomial equation that is unfactorable |

Solve each of the following.

a) $x^4 + 5x^2 = -1$ **b)** $x^3 - 2x + 3 = 0$

Solution

a) $x^4 + 5x^2 = -1$ ←──────────── Add 1 to both sides of the equation to make the right side of the equation equal to zero.

$x^4 + 5x^2 + 1 = 0$

Let $f(x) = x^4 + 5x^2 + 1$ ←────── If the equation is factorable, then either $f(1)$ or $f(-1)$ should give a value of 0.

$f(1) = (1)^4 + 5(1)^2 + 1 = 7$

$f(-1) = (-1)^4 + 5(-1)^2 + 1 = 7$

The polynomial in this equation cannot be factored.

The function $f(x) = x^4 + 5x^2 + 1$ has an even degree and a positive leading coefficient, so its end behaviours are the same. In this case, as $x \to \pm\infty$, $y \to \infty$. This function has a degree of 4, so it could have 4, 3, 2, 1, or 0 x-intercepts.

Use the corresponding polynomial function to visualize the graph and determine the possible number of zeros.

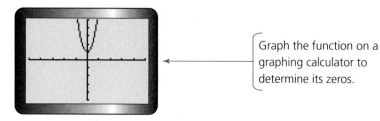

Graph the function on a graphing calculator to determine its zeros.

Based on the graph and the function's end behaviours, it never crosses the x-axis, so it has no zeros. As a result, the equation $x^4 + 5x = -1$ has no solutions.

b) $x^3 - 2x + 3 = 0$

Let $f(x) = x^3 - 2x + 3$ ←

$f(1) = (1)^3 - 2(1) + 3 = 2$

$f(-1) = (-1)^3 - 2(-1) + 3 = 4$

$f(3) = (3)^3 - 2(3) + 3 = 24$

$f(-3) = (-3)^3 - 2(-3) + 3 = -18$

> If the equation is factorable, then either $f(1)$, $f(-1)$, $f(3)$, or $f(-3)$ should equal 0.

> The polynomial in this equation cannot be factored.

The function $f(x) = x^3 - 2x^2 + 3$ has an odd degree and a positive leading coefficient, so its end behaviours are opposite. In this case, as $x \to \infty$, $y \to \infty$, and as $x \to -\infty$, $y \to -\infty$. This function has a degree of 3, so it could have 3, 2, or 1 x-intercepts.

> Use the corresponding polynomial function to visualize the graph and determine the possible number of zeros.

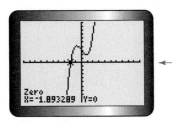

> Graph the function on a graphing calculator to determine its zeros.

Based on the graph and the function's end behaviours, it crosses the x-axis only once. The solution is $x \doteq -1.89$.

In Summary

Key Idea

- The solutions to a polynomial equation $f(x) = 0$ are the zeros of the corresponding polynomial function, $y = f(x)$.

Need to Know

- Polynomial equations can be solved using a variety of strategies:
  - algebraically using a factoring strategy
  - graphically using a table of values, transformations, or a graphing calculator
- Only some polynomial equations can be solved by factoring, since not all polynomials are factorable. In these cases, graphing technology must be used.
- When solving problems using polynomial models, it may be necessary to ignore the solutions that are outside the domain defined by the conditions of the problem.

CHECK Your Understanding

1. State the zeros of the following functions.
   a) $y = 2x(x - 1)(x + 2)(x - 2)$
   b) $y = 5(2x + 3)(4x - 5)(x + 7)$
   c) $y = 2(x - 3)^2(x + 5)(x - 4)$
   d) $y = (x + 6)^3(2x - 5)$
   e) $y = -5x(x^2 - 9)$
   f) $y = (x + 5)(x^2 - 4x - 12)$

2. Solve each of the following equations by factoring. Verify your solutions using graphing technology.
   a) $3x^3 = 27x$
   b) $4x^4 = 24x^2 + 108$
   c) $3x^4 + 5x^3 - 12x^2 - 20x = 0$
   d) $10x^3 + 26x^2 - 12x = 0$
   e) $2x^3 + 162 = 0$
   f) $2x^4 = 48x^2$

3. a) Determine the zeros of the function $y = 2x^3 - 17x^2 + 23x + 42$.
   b) Write the polynomial equation whose roots are the zeros of the function in part a).

4. Explain how you can solve
   $$x^3 + 12x^2 + 21x - 4 = x^4 - 2x^3 - 13x^2 - 4$$
   using two different strategies.

5. Determine the zeros of the function
   $$f(x) = 2x^4 - 11x^3 - 37x^2 + 156x \text{ algebraically.}$$
   Verify your solution using graphing technology.

PRACTISING

6. State the zeros of the following functions.
   a) $f(x) = x(x - 2)^2(x + 5)$
   b) $f(x) = (x^3 + 1)(x - 17)$
   c) $f(x) = (x^2 + 36)(8x - 16)$
   d) $f(x) = -3x^3(2x + 4)(x^2 - 25)$
   e) $f(x) = (x^2 - x - 12)(3x)$
   f) $f(x) = (x + 1)(x^2 + 2x + 1)$

7. Determine the roots algebraically by factoring.
   a) $x^3 - 8x^2 - 3x + 90 = 0$
   b) $x^4 + 9x^3 + 21x^2 - x - 30 = 0$
   c) $2x^3 - 5x^2 - 4x + 3 = 0$
   d) $2x^3 + 3x^2 = 5x + 6$
   e) $4x^4 - 4x^3 - 51x^2 + 106x = 40$
   f) $12x^3 - 44x^2 = -49x + 15$

8. Use graphing technology to find the real roots to two decimal places.

a) $x^3 - 7x + 6 = 0$

b) $x^4 - 5x^3 - 17x^2 + 3x + 18 = 0$

c) $3x^3 - 2x^2 + 16 = x^4 + 16x$

d) $x^5 + x^4 = 5x^3 - x^2 + 6x$

e) $105x^3 = 344x^2 - 69x - 378$

f) $21x^3 - 58x^2 + 10 = -18x^4 - 51x$

9. Solve each of the following equations.

K

a) $x^3 - 6x^2 - x + 30 = 0$

b) $9x^4 - 42x^3 + 64x^2 - 32x = 0$

c) $6x^4 - 13x^3 - 29x^2 + 52x = -20$

d) $x^4 - 6x^3 + 10x^2 - 2x = x^2 - 2x$

10. An open-topped box can be created by cutting congruent squares from each of the four corners of a piece of cardboard that has dimensions of 20 cm by 30 cm and folding up the sides. Determine the dimensions of the squares that must be cut to create a box with a volume of 1008 cm^3.

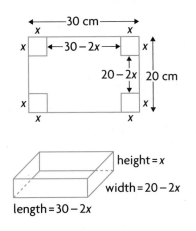

11. The Sickle-Lichti family members are very competitive card players.

A They keep score using a complicated system that incorporates positives and negatives. Maya's score for the last game night could be modelled by the function $S(x) = x(x - 4)(x - 6)$, $x < 10$, $x \in \mathbf{W}$, where x represents the game number.

a) After which game was Maya's score equal to zero?

b) After which game was Maya's score -5?

c) After which game was Maya's score 16?

d) Draw a sketch of the graph of $S(x)$ if $x \in \mathbf{R}$. Explain why this graph is *not* a good model to represent Maya's score during this game night.

12. The function $s(t) = -\frac{1}{2}gt^2 + v_0 t + s_0$ can be used to calculate s, the height above a planet's surface in metres, where g is the acceleration due to gravity, t is the time in seconds, v_0 is the initial velocity in metres per second, and s_0 is the initial height in metres. The acceleration due to gravity on Mars is $g = -3.92$ m/s^2. Find, to two decimal places, how long it takes an object to hit the surface of Mars if the object is dropped from 1000 m above the surface.

13. The distance of a ship from its harbour is modelled by the function $d(t) = -3t^3 + 3t^2 + 18t$, where t is the time elapsed in hours since departure from the harbour.
  a) Factor the time function.
  b) When does the ship return to the harbour?
  c) There is another zero of $d(t)$. What is it, and why is it not relevant to the problem?
  d) Draw a sketch of the function where $0 \le t \le 3$.
  e) Estimate the time that the ship begins its return trip back to the harbour.

14. During a normal 5 s respiratory cycle in which a person inhales and then exhales, the volume of air in a person's lungs can be modelled by $V(t) = 0.027t^3 - 0.27t^2 + 0.675t$, where the volume, V, is measured in litres at t seconds.
  a) What restriction(s) must be placed on t?
  b) If asked, "How many seconds have passed if the volume of air in a person's lungs is 0.25 L?" would you answer this question algebraically or by using graphing technology? Justify your decision.
  c) Solve the problem in part b).

15. Explain why the following polynomial equation has no real solutions:
$0 = 5x^8 + 10x^6 + 7x^4 + 18x^2 + 132$

16. Determine algebraically where the cubic polynomal function that has
  T zeros at 2, 3, and -5 and passes through the point $(4, 36)$ has a value of 120.

17. For each strategy below, create a cubic or quartic equation you might
  C solve by using that strategy (the same equation could be used more than once). Explain why you picked the equation you did.
  a) factor theorem   d) quadratic formula
  b) common factor   e) difference or sum of cubes
  c) factor by grouping   f) graphing technology

Extending

18. a) It is possible that a polynomial equation of degree 4 can have no real roots. Create such a polynomial equation and explain why it cannot have any real roots.
  b) Explain why a degree 5 polynomial equation must have at least one real root.

19. The factor theorem only deals with rational zeros. Create a polynomial of degree 5 that has no rational zeros. Explain why your polynomial has no rational zero but has at least one irrational zero.

Solving Linear Inequalities

GOAL

Solve linear inequalities.

YOU WILL NEED

- graphing calculator or graphing software

LEARN ABOUT the Math

In mathematics, you must be able to represent intervals and identify smaller sections of a relation or a set of numbers. You have used the following inequality symbols:

> greater than   < less than
≥ greater than or equal to   ≤ less than or equal to

When you write one of these symbols between two or more linear expressions, the result is called a **linear inequality**.

To solve an inequality, you have to find all the possible values of the variable that satisfy the inequality.

For example, $x = 2$ satisfies $3x - 1 < 8$, but so do $x = 2.9$, $x = -1$, and $x = -5$.

linear inequality

an inequality that contains an algebraic expression of degree 1 (e.g., $5x + 3 > 6x - 2$)

In fact, every real number less than 3 results in a number smaller than 8. So all real numbers less than 3 satisfy this inequality. The thicker part of the number line below represents this solution.

Communication | Tip

To show that a number is not included in the solution set, use an open dot at this value. A solid dot shows that this value is included in the solution set.

The solution to $3x - 1 < 8$ can be written in set notation as $\{x \in \mathbf{R} \mid x < 3\}$ or in interval notation $x \in (-\infty, 3)$.

? How can you determine algebraically the solution set to a linear inequality like $3x - 1 < 8$?

EXAMPLE **1** Selecting an inverse operation strategy to solve a linear inequality

Solve the linear inequality $3x - 1 < 8$.

Solution

$$3x - 1 < 8$$

$$3x - 1 + 1 < 8 + 1 \longleftarrow$$

$$3x < 9$$

Treat the inequality like a linear equation and use inverse operations to isolate x. Add 1 to both sides of the inequality and simplify.

$$\frac{3x}{3} < \frac{9}{3} \longleftarrow$$

Divide both sides of the inequality by 3.

$$x < 3$$

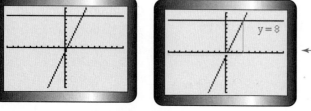

A number line helps visualize the solution.

Check $x = 0$.

LS	RS
$3x - 1$	8
$= 3(0) - 1$	
$= -1$	

$\text{LS} < \text{RS}$

Choose a value for x that is less than 3 to verify that any number in the solution set satisfies the original inequality.

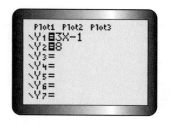

You can also verify the solution set using a graphing calculator. Graph each side of the inequality as a function.

```
Plot1 Plot2 Plot3
\Y1=3X-1
\Y2=8
\Y3=
\Y4=
\Y5=
\Y6=
\Y7=
```

The solution set is $\{x \in \mathbf{R} \mid x < 3\}$ or in interval notation $x \in (-\infty, 3)$.

The y-values on the line $y = 3x - 1$ that are less than 8 are found on all points that lie on the line below the horizontal line $y = 8$. This happens when x is smaller than 3.

Reflecting

A. How was solving a linear inequality like solving a linear equation? How was it different?

B. When checking the solution to an inequality, why is it not necessary for the left side to equal the right side?

C. Why do most linear equations have only one solution, but linear inequalities have many?

APPLY the Math

EXAMPLE **2**	Using reasoning to determine which operations preserve the truth of a linear inequality

Can you add, subtract, multiply, or divide both sides of an inequality by a non-zero value and still have a valid inequality?

Solution

$4 < 8$

$4 + 5 < 8 + 5$

$9 < 13$

⟵ Write a true inequality using two numbers. Add the same positive quantity to both sides.

The result is still true.

$4 + (-5) < 8 + (-5)$

$-1 < 3$

⟵ Add the same negative quantity to both sides of the initial inequality.

The result is still true.

$4 - 10 < 8 - 10$

$-6 < -2$

⟵ Subtract the same positive quantity from both sides of the initial inequality.

The result is still true.

$4 - (-3) < 8 - (-3)$

$7 < 11$

⟵ Subtract the same negative quantity from both sides of the initial inequality.

The result is still true.

$4(6) < 8(6)$

$24 < 48$

⟵ Multiply by the same positive quantity on both sides of the initial inequality.

The result is still true.

$$4(-2) < 8(-2)$$

$$-8 < -16$$

> Multiply by the same negative quantity on both sides of the initial inequality.

The result is false.
In this case, $-8 > -16$.

$$4 \div 2 < 8 \div 2$$

$$2 < 4$$

> Divide by the same positive quantity on both sides of the initial inequality.

The result is still true.

$$4 \div (-2) < 8 \div (-2)$$

$$-2 < -4$$

> Divide by the same negative quantity on both sides of the initial inequality.

The result is false.
In this case, $-2 > -4$.

Most of the operations preserve the validity of the inequality. The exception occurs when both sides are multiplied or divided by a negative number. In these two cases, reversing the inequality sign preserves the validity.

> Since algebraic expressions represent numbers, this conclusion applies to linear inequalities that contain variables.

EXAMPLE 3 | **Reflecting to verify a solution**

Solve the inequality $35 - 2x \geq 20$.

Solution

$$35 - 2x \geq 20$$

$$-2x \geq 20 - 35$$

$$-2x \geq -15$$

> Use inverse operations to isolate x. Subtract 35 from both sides and simplify.

$$\frac{-2x}{-2} \leq \frac{-15}{-2}$$

$$x \leq 7.5$$

> Divide both sides by -2. Since the division involves a negative number, reverse the inequality sign.

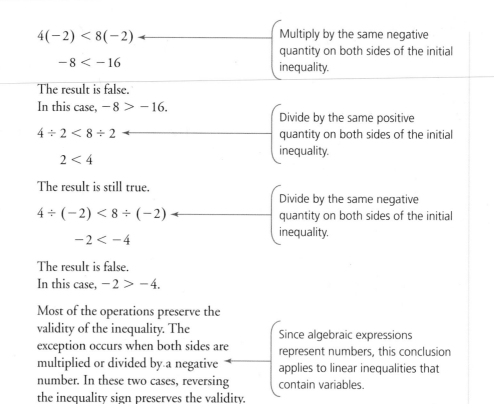

> Represent the solution on a number line.
> A solid dot is placed on 7.5 since this number is included in the solution set.

If $x = 5$, then

LS	RS
$35 - 2x$	20
$= 35 - 2(5)$	
$= 35 - 10$	
$= 25$	

LS $\geq$ RS: This is the desired outcome.

Test a value less than 7.5 and a value greater than 7.5 to verify the solution. Since $x = 5$ makes the inequality true and $x = 8$ makes the inequality false, the solution is correct.

If $x = 8$, then

LS	RS
$35 - 2x$	20
$= 35 - 2(8)$	
$= 35 - 16$	
$= 19$	

LS $\leq$ RS: This is <u>not</u> the desired outcome.

The solution set is $\{x \in \mathbf{R} | x \leq 7.5\}$ or in interval notation $x \in (-\infty, 7.5]$.

The value of 7.5 makes both sides equal. Since the inequality sign includes an equal sign, 7.5 must be part of the solution set.

EXAMPLE 4 Connecting the process of solving a double inequality to solving a linear inequality

Solve the inequality $30 \leq 3(2x + 4) - 2(x + 1) \leq 46$.

Solution

$30 \leq 3(2x + 4) - 2(x + 1) \leq 46$

This is a combination of two inequalities:
$30 \leq 3(2x + 4) - 2(x + 1)$ and $3(2x + 4) - 2(x + 1) \leq 46$.
A valid solution must satisfy both inequalities.
Expand using the distributive property and simplify.

$30 \leq 6x + 12 - 2x - 2 \leq 46$

$30 \leq 4x + 10 \leq 46$

$30 - 10 \leq 4x + 10 - 10 \leq 46 - 10$

Subtract 10 from all three parts of the inequality.

$20 \leq 4x \leq 36$

$$\frac{20}{4} \leq \frac{4x}{4} \leq \frac{36}{4}$$

$$5 \leq x \leq 9$$

> Divide all parts of the inequality by 4.

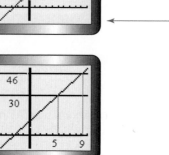

> A number line helps to visualize the solution. Solid dots are placed on 5 and 9 since these numbers are included in the solution set.

The solution using interval notation is

$$x \in [5, 9]$$

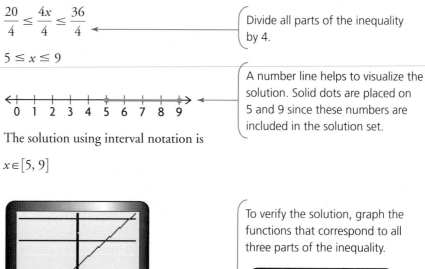

> To verify the solution, graph the functions that correspond to all three parts of the inequality.

The x-values that satisfy the inequality are the x-coordinates of points on the diagonal line defined by $y = 3(2x + 4) - 2(x + 1)$ whose y-values are bounded by 30 and 46.

In Summary

Key Idea

- You can solve a linear inequality using inverse operations in much the same way you solve linear equations.

Need to Know

- If you multiply or divide an inequality by a negative number, you must reverse the inequality sign.
- Most linear equations have only one solution, whereas linear inequalities have many solutions.
- A number line can help you visualize the solution set to an inequality. A solid dot is used to indicate that a number is included in the solution set, whereas an open dot indicates that a number is excluded.

CHECK *Your Understanding*

1. Solve the following inequalities graphically. Express your answer using set notation.
   a) $3x - 1 \le 11$
   b) $-x + 5 > -2$
   c) $x - 2 > 3x + 8$
   d) $3(2x + 4) \ge 2x$
   e) $-2(1 - 2x) < 5x + 8$
   f) $\dfrac{6x + 8}{5} \le 2x - 4$

2. Solve the following inequalities algebraically. Express your answer using interval notation.
   a) $2x - 5 \le 4x + 1$
   b) $2(x + 3) < -(x - 4)$
   c) $\dfrac{2x + 3}{3} \le x - 5$
   d) $2x + 1 \le 5x - 2$
   e) $-x + 1 > x + 1$
   f) $\dfrac{x + 4}{2} \ge \dfrac{x - 2}{4}$

3. Solve the double inequality $3 \le 2x + 5 < 17$ algebraically and illustrate your solution on a number line.

4. For each of the following inequalities, determine whether $x = 2$ is contained in the solution set.
   a) $x > -1$
   b) $5x - 4 > 3x + 2$
   c) $4(3x - 5) \ge 6x$
   d) $5x + 3 \le -3x + 1$
   e) $x - 2 \le 3x + 4 \le x + 14$
   f) $33 < -10x + 3 < 54$

PRACTISING

5. Solve the following algebraically. Verify your results graphically.
   K a) $2x - 1 \le 13$
   b) $-2x - 1 > -1$
   c) $2x - 8 > 4x + 12$
   d) $5(x - 3) \ge 2x$
   e) $-4(5 - 3x) < 2(3x + 8)$
   f) $\dfrac{x - 2}{3} \le 2x - 3$

6. For the following inequalities, determine if 0 is a number in the solution set.
   a) $3x \le 4x + 1$
   b) $-6x < x + 4 < 12$
   c) $-x + 1 > x + 12$
   d) $3x \le x + 1 \le x - 1$
   e) $x(2x - 1) \le x + 7$
   f) $x + 6 < (x + 2)(5x + 3)$

7. Solve the following inequalities algebraically.
   a) $-5 < 2x + 7 < 11$
   b) $11 < 3x - 1 < 23$
   c) $-1 \le -x + 9 \le 13$
   d) $0 \le -2(x + 4) \le 6$
   e) $59 < 7x + 10 < 73$
   f) $18 \le -12(x - 1) \le 48$

8. a) Create a linear inequality, with both constant and linear terms on each side, for which the solution is $x > 4$.

b) Create a linear inequality, with both constant and linear terms on each side, for which the solution is $x \leq \frac{3}{2}$.

9. The following number line shows the solution to a double inequality.

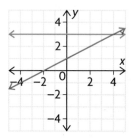

a) Write the solution using set notation.

b) Create a double inequality for which this is the solution set.

10. Which of the following inequalities has a solution. Explain.
$$x - 3 < 3 - x < x - 5 \text{ or } x - 3 > 3 - x > x - 5$$

11. Consider the following graph.

a) Write an inequality that is modelled by the graph.

b) Find the solution by examining the graph.

c) Confirm the solution by solving your inequality algebraically.

12. The relationship between Celsius and Fahrenheit is represented by
A $C = \frac{5}{9}(F - 32)$. In order to be comfortable, but also economical, the temperature in your house should be between $18\,°C$ and $22\,°C$.

a) Write this statement as a double linear inequality.

b) Solve the inequality to determine the temperature range in degrees Fahrenheit.

13. Some volunteers are making long distance phone calls to raise money for a charity. The calls are billed at the rate of $0.50 for the first 3 min and $0.10/min for each additional minute or part thereof. If each call cannot cost more that $2.00, how long can each volunteer talk to a prospective donor?

14. **a)** Find the equation that allows for the conversion of Celsius to Fahrenheit by solving the relation given in question 12 for F.
    b) For what values of C is the Fahrenheit temperature greater than the equivalent Celsius temperature?

15. The inequality $|2x - 1| < 7$ can be expressed as a double inequality.
    T
    a) Depict the inequality graphically.
    b) Use your graph to solve the inequality.

16. Will the solution to a double inequality always have an upper and
    C lower limit? Explain.

Extending

17. Some inequalities are very difficult to solve algebraically. Other methods, however, can be very helpful in solving such problems. Consider the inequality $2^x - 3 < x + 1$.
    a) Explain why solving the inequality might be very difficult to do algebraically.
    b) Describe an alternative method that could work, and use it to solve the inequality.

18. Some operations result in switching the direction of the inequality when done to both sides, but others result in maintaining the direction. For instance, if you add a constant to both sides, the direction is maintained, whereas multiplying both sides by a negative constant causes the sign to switch. For each of the following, determine if the inequality direction should be maintained, should switch, or if it sometimes switches and sometimes is maintained.
    a) cubing both sides
    b) squaring both sides
    c) making each side the exponent with 2 as the base, i.e., $3 < 5$, so $2^3 < 2^5$
    d) making each side the exponent with 0.5 as the base
    e) taking the reciprocal of both sides
    f) rounding both sides up to the nearest integer
    g) taking the square root of both sides

19. Solve each of the following, $x \in \mathbf{R}$. Express your answers using both set and interval notation and graph the solution set on a number line.
    a) $x^2 < 4$ **c)** $|2x + 2| < 8$
    b) $4x^2 + 5 \geq 41$ **d)** $-3x^3 \geq 81$

FREQUENTLY ASKED Questions

Study Aid

- See Lesson 4.1, Examples 1 to 4.
- Try Mid-Chapter Review Questions 1, 2, and 3.

Q: **How can you solve a polynomial equation?**

A1: You can use an algebraic strategy using the corresponding polynomial function, the factor theorem, and division to factor the polynomial. Set each factor equal to zero and solve for the independent variable. You will need to use the quadratic formula if one of the factors is a nonfactorable quadratic.

For example, to solve the equation

$2x^4 + x^3 - 19x^2 - 14x + 24 = 0$, let
$f(x) = 2x^4 + x^3 - 19x^2 - 14x + 24$. Possible values of x that make $f(x) = 0$ are numbers of the form $\frac{p}{q}$, where p is a factor of the constant term and q is a factor of the leading coefficient. Some possible values in this case are:

$$\frac{\pm 1, \pm 2, \pm 3, \pm 4, \pm 6, \pm 8, \pm 12, \pm 24}{\pm 1, \pm 2}$$

Since $f(-2) = 0$, by the factor theorem, $(x + 2)$ is a factor of $f(x)$. Determine $f(x) \div (x + 2)$ to find the other factor.

-2	2	1	-19	-14	24
$\downarrow$		-4	6	26	-24
	2	-3	-13	12	0

Now, $f(x) = (x + 2)(2x^3 - 3x^2 - 13x + 12)$.

Possible values of x that make the cubic polynomial 0 are numbers of the form:

$$\frac{\pm 1, \pm 2, \pm 3, \pm 4, \pm 6, \pm 12,}{\pm 2}$$

Since $f(3) = 0$, $(x - 3)$ is also a factor of $f(x)$. Divide the cubic polynomial by $(x - 3)$ to determine the other factor.

3	2	-3	-13	12
$\downarrow$		6	9	-12
	2	3	-4	0

So, $f(x) = (x + 2)(x - 3)(2x^2 + 3x - 4)$.

$x + 2 = 0$ or $x - 3 = 0$ or $2x^2 + 3x - 4 = 0$

$x = -2$ or $x = 3$

Since $2x^2 + 3x - 4$ is not factorable, use the quadratic formula to determine the other zeros.

$$x = \frac{-3 \pm \sqrt{3^2 - 4(2)(-4)}}{2(2)}$$

$$x = \frac{-3 \pm \sqrt{41}}{4}$$

$x \doteq -2.35$ or 0.85

The equation has four roots: $x = -2$, $x \doteq -2.35$, $x \doteq 0.85$, and $x = 3$.

A2: You can use a graphing strategy to find the zeros of a rearranged equation, or graph both sides of the equation separately and then determine the point(s) of intersection.

For example, to solve the equation $x^3 + 3x^2 - 7x + 4 = 3x^2 - 5x + 12$, enter both polynomials in the equation editor of the graphing calculator and then graph both corresponding functions. Use the intersect operation to determine the point of intersection of the two graphs.

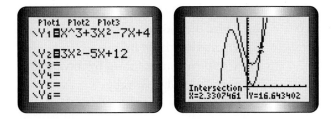

The solution is $x \doteq 2.33$.

Q: How can you solve a linear inequality?

A: You solve a linear inequality using inverse operations in much the same way you would solve a linear equation. If at any time you multiply or divide the inequality by a negative number, you must reverse the inequality sign.

> **Study | Aid**
> - See Lesson 4.2, Examples 1, 3, and 4.
> - Try Mid-Chapter Review Questions 4 to 8.

PRACTICE Questions

1. Determine the solutions for each of the following.
   a) $0 = -2x^3(2x - 5)(x - 4)^2$
   b) $0 = (x^2 + 1)(2x + 4)(x + 2)$
   c) $x^3 - 4x^2 = 7x - 10$
   d) $0 = (x^2 - 2x - 24)(x^2 - 25)$
   e) $0 = (x^3 + 2x^2)(x + 9)$
   f) $-x^4 = -13x^2 + 36$

2. Jude is diving from a cliff into the ocean. His height above sea level in metres is represented by the function $h(t) = -5(t - 0.3)^2 + 25$, where t is measured in seconds.
   a) Expand the height function.
   b) How high is the cliff?
   c) When does Jude hit the water?
   d) Determine where the function is negative. What is the significance of the negative values?

3. Chris makes an open-topped box from a 30 cm by 30 cm piece of cardboard by cutting out equal squares from the corners and folding up the flaps to make the sides. What are the dimensions of each square, to the nearest hundredth of a centimetre, so that the volume of the resulting box is 1000 cm^3?

Lesson 4.2

4. Solve the following inequalities algebraically and plot the solution on a number line.
   a) $2x - 4 < 3x + 7$
   b) $-x - 4 \le x + 4$
   c) $-2(x - 4) \ge 16$
   d) $2(3x - 7) > 3(7x - 3)$

5. Solve and state your solution using inverval notation.
   $$2x < \frac{3x + 6}{2} \le 4 + 2x$$

6. Create a linear inequality with both a constant and a linear term on each side and that has each of the following as a solution.
   a) $x > 7$
   b) $x \in (-\infty, -8)$
   c) $-1 \le x \le 7$
   d) $x \in [3, \infty)$

7. Consider the following functions.

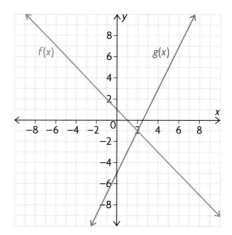

   a) Find the equations of the lines depicted.
   b) Solve the inequality $f(x) < g(x)$ by examining the graph.
   c) Confirm your solution by solving the inequality algebraically.

8. The New Network cell phone company charges $20 a month for service and $0.02 per minute of talking time. The My Mobile company charges $15 a month for service and $0.03 per minute of talking time.
   a) Write expressions for the total bill of each company.
   b) Set up an inequality that can be used to determine for what amount of time (in minutes) My Mobile is the better plan.
   c) Solve your inequality.
   d) Why did you have to put a restriction on the algebraic solution from part c)?

4.3 Solving Polynomial Inequalities

Solve polynomial inequalities.

YOU WILL NEED

- graphing calculator or graphing software

LEARN ABOUT the Math

The elevation of a hiking trail is modelled by the function $h(x) = 2x^3 + 3x^2 - 17x + 12$, where h is the height measured in metres above sea level and x is the horizontal position from a ranger station measured in kilometres. If x is negative, the position is to the west of the station, and if x is positive, the position is to the east. Since the trail extends 4.2 km to the west of the ranger station and 4 km to the east, the model is accurate where $x \in [-4.2, 4]$.

? How can you determine which sections of the trail are above sea level?

EXAMPLE 1 Selecting a strategy to solve the problem

At what distances from the ranger station is the trail above sea level?

Solution A: Using an algebraic strategy and a number line

$$2x^3 + 3x^2 - 17x + 12 > 0$$

The trail is above sea level when the height is positive, i.e., $h(x) > 0$. Write the mathematical model using a **polynomial inequality**.

polynomial inequality

an inequality that contains a polynomial expression (e.g., $5x^3 + 3x^2 - 6x \le 2$)

$$h(1) = 2(1)^3 + 3(1)^2 - 17(1) + 12$$
$$= 0 \text{ so } (x - 1) \text{ is a factor of } h(x)$$

Factor the corresponding function $y = h(x)$ to locate the x-intercepts. Use the factor theorem to determine the first factor.

1	2	3	−17	12
	↓	2	5	−12
	2	5	−12	0

$$h(x) = (x - 1)(2x^2 + 5x - 12)$$
$$0 = (x - 1)(2x - 3)(x + 4)$$

Set $h(x) = 0$. Set each factor equal to 0 and solve.

$$x = 1, \ x = \frac{3}{2}, \text{ or } x = -4$$

The x-intercepts are at -4, 1, and $\frac{3}{2}$. These numbers divide the domain of real numbers into four intervals:

$$x < -4, \ -4 < x < 1, \ 1 < x < \frac{3}{2}, \ x > \frac{3}{2}$$

Draw a number line and test points in each interval to see whether the function has a positive or negative value.

Interval	$x < -4$	$-4 < x < 1$	$1 < x < \frac{3}{2}$	$x > \frac{3}{2}$
Value of $h(x)$	$h(-5) = -78$	$h(0) = 12$	$h(1.2) \doteq -0.6$	$h(2) = 6$
Is $h(x) > 0$?	no	yes	no	yes

$$h(x) > 0 \text{ when } -4 < x < 1 \text{ and } x > \frac{3}{2}.$$

Identify the intervals where $h(x)$ is positive.

The hiking trail is above sea level from 4 km west of the ranger station to 1 km east, and for distances more than 1.5 km east.

Write a concluding statement.

Solution B: Using a graphing strategy

$$2x^3 + 3x^2 - 17x + 12 > 0$$

The trail is above sea level when the height is positive, i.e., $h(x) > 0$.

$$h(1) = 2(1)^3 + 3(1)^2 - 17(1) + 12$$
$$= 0 \text{ so } (x - 1) \text{ is a factor of } h(x)$$

1	2	3	−17	12
	↓	2	5	−12
	2	5	−12	0

Factor the corresponding function $y = h(x)$ to locate the x-intercepts. Use the factor theorem to determine the first factor.

$h(x) = (x - 1)(2x^2 + 5x - 12)$
$0 = (x - 1)(2x - 3)(x + 4)$

$x = 1, x = \dfrac{3}{2},$ or $x = -4$

> Set $h(x) = 0$.
> Set each factor equal to 0 and solve.

The x-intercepts are at -4, 1, and $\dfrac{3}{2}$.

$h(0) = 12$

> The y-intercept occurs when $x = 0$.

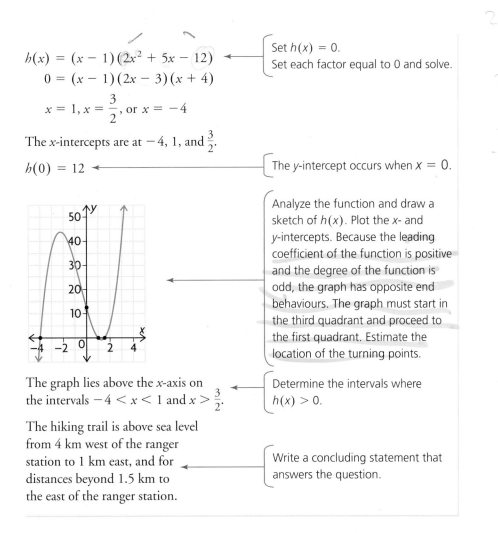

> Analyze the function and draw a sketch of $h(x)$. Plot the x- and y-intercepts. Because the leading coefficient of the function is positive and the degree of the function is odd, the graph has opposite end behaviours. The graph must start in the third quadrant and proceed to the first quadrant. Estimate the location of the turning points.

The graph lies above the x-axis on the intervals $-4 < x < 1$ and $x > \dfrac{3}{2}$.

> Determine the intervals where $h(x) > 0$.

The hiking trail is above sea level from 4 km west of the ranger station to 1 km east, and for distances beyond 1.5 km to the east of the ranger station.

> Write a concluding statement that answers the question.

Reflecting

A. When solving a polynomial inequality, which steps are the same as those used when solving a polynomial equation?

B. What additional steps must be taken when solving a polynomial inequality?

C. The zeros of $y = h(x)$ were used to identify the intervals where $h(x)$ was positive and negative but were not included in the solution set of $h(x) > 0$. Explain why.

D. How could you verify the solution set to the polynomial inequality using graphing technology?

APPLY *the Math*

EXAMPLE 2 | Selecting tools and strategies to solve a factorable polynomial inequality

Solve the inequality $x^3 - 2x^2 + 5x + 20 \geq 2x^2 + 14x - 16$.

Solution A: Using algebra and a factor table

$x^3 - 2x^2 + 5x + 20 \geq 2x^2 + 14x - 16$

$x^3 - 4x^2 - 9x + 36 \geq 0$ ⟵   Use inverse operations to make the right side of the inequality equal to zero.

$x^2(x - 4) - 9(x - 4) \geq 0$ ⟵   Factor the polynomial on the left by grouping.

$(x - 4)(x^2 - 9) \geq 0$

$(x - 4)(x - 3)(x + 3) \geq 0$

$(x - 4)(x - 3)(x + 3) = 0$ ⟵   Determine the roots of the corresponding polynomial equation.

The roots are -3, 3, and 4. These numbers divide the real numbers into four intervals:

$x < -3, \; -3 < x < 3, \; 3 < x < 4, \; x > 4$

	$x < -3$	$-3 < x < 3$	$3 < x < 4$	$x > 4$
$(x - 4)$	$-$	$-$	$-$	$+$
$(x - 3)$	$-$	$-$	$+$	$+$
$(x + 3)$	$-$	$+$	$+$	$+$
their product	$(-)(-)(-)$ $= -$	$(-)(-)(+)$ $= +$	$(-)(+)(+)$ $= -$	$(+)(+)(+)$ $= +$

Create a table to consider the sign of each factor in each of the intervals and examine the sign of their product. In this case, the intervals that correspond to a positive product are the solutions to the polynomial inequality.

$x^3 - 2x^2 + 5x + 20 \geq 2x^2 + 14x - 16$ when $-3 \leq x \leq 3$ or $x \geq 4$. ⟵   Write a concluding statement.

Solution B: Using graphing technology

Graph each side of the inequality as a separate function. Bold the graph of the second function (the quadratic) so you can distinguish one from the other. Experiment with different window settings to make the intersecting parts of the graph visible.

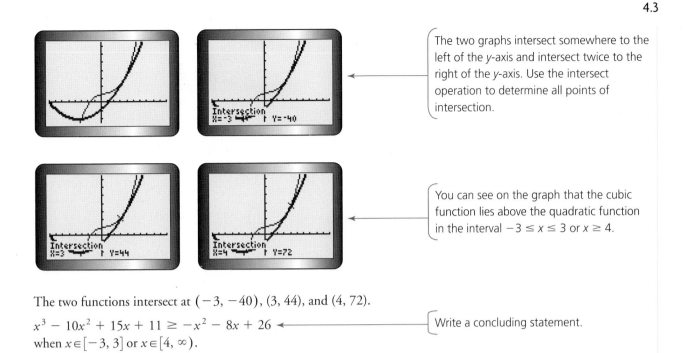

The two graphs intersect somewhere to the left of the y-axis and intersect twice to the right of the y-axis. Use the intersect operation to determine all points of intersection.

You can see on the graph that the cubic function lies above the quadratic function in the interval $-3 \leq x \leq 3$ or $x \geq 4$.

The two functions intersect at $(-3, -40)$, $(3, 44)$, and $(4, 72)$.

$x^3 - 10x^2 + 15x + 11 \geq -x^2 - 8x + 26$
when $x \in [-3, 3]$ or $x \in [4, \infty)$.

Write a concluding statement.

EXAMPLE 3   Selecting a strategy to solve a polynomial inequality that is unfactorable

The height of one section of the roller coaster can be described by the polynomial function $h(x) = \frac{1}{4\,000\,000}x^2(x - 30)^2(x - 55)^2$, where h is the height, measured in metres, and x is the position from the start, measured in metres along the ground.

When will the roller coaster car be more than 9 m above the ground?

Solution

Solve

$$\frac{1}{4\,000\,000}x^2(x-30)^2(x-55)^2 > 9$$

In this case, the solution set corresponds to all values of x where $h(x) > 9$. Using an algebraic approach involving factoring would be tedious, so use a graphing strategy.

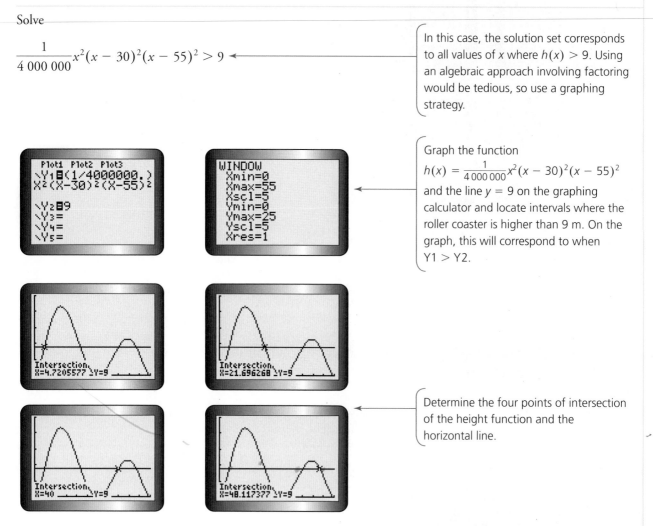

Graph the function
$$h(x) = \frac{1}{4\,000\,000}x^2(x-30)^2(x-55)^2$$
and the line $y = 9$ on the graphing calculator and locate intervals where the roller coaster is higher than 9 m. On the graph, this will correspond to when Y1 > Y2.

Determine the four points of intersection of the height function and the horizontal line.

The four points where the height function and the horizontal line intersect are approximately $(4.7, 9)$, $(21.7, 9)$, $(40, 9)$, and $(48.1, 9)$.

The roller coaster will be more than 9 m above the ground when it is between 4.7 m and 21.7 m from the starting point and between 40 m and 48.1 m from the starting point, as measured along the ground.

Y1 > Y2 when $4.7 < x < 21.7$ or $40 < x < 48.1$.

In Summary

Key Idea

- To solve a polynomial inequality algebraically, you must first determine the roots of the corresponding polynomial equation. Then you must consider the sign of the polynomial in each of the intervals created by these roots. The solution set is determined by the interval(s) that satisfy the given inequality.

Need to Know

- Some polynomial inequalities can be solved algebraically by
  - using inverse operations to move all terms to one side of the inequality
  - factoring the polynomial to determine the zeros of the corresponding polynomial equation
  - using a number line, a graph, or a factor table to determine the intervals on which the polynomial is positive or negative
- All polynomial inequalities can be solved using graphing technology by
  - graphing each side of the inequality as a separate function
  - determining the intersection point(s) of the functions
  - examining the graph to determine the intervals where one function is above or below the other, as required

  or

  - creating an equivalent inequality with zero on one side
  - identifying the intervals created by the zeros of the graph of the new function
  - finding where the graph lies above the x-axis (where $f(x) > 0$) or below (where $f(x) < 0$), as required

CHECK Your Understanding

1. Solve each of the following using a number line strategy. Express your answers using set notation.
   a) $(x + 2)(x - 3)(x + 1) \geq 0$
   b) $-2(x - 2)(x - 4)(x + 3) < 0$
   c) $(x - 3)(5x + 2)(4x - 3) < 0$
   d) $(x - 5)(4x + 1)(2x - 5) \geq 0$

2. For each graph shown, determine where $f(x) \leq 0$. Express your answers using interval notation.

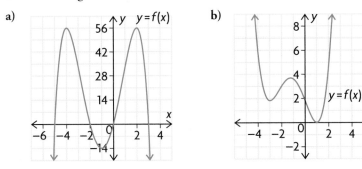

c)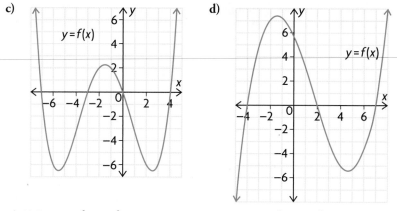

d)

3. If $f(x) = 2x^3 - x^2 + 3x + 10$ and $g(x) = x^3 + 3x^2 + 2x + 4$, determine when $f(x) > g(x)$ using a factor table strategy.

4. Solve the inequality $x^3 - 7x^2 + 4x + 12 > x^2 - 4x - 9$ using a graphing calculator.

PRACTISING

5. For each of the following polynomial functions, state the intervals
K where $f(x) > 0$.

a)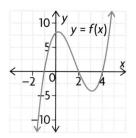

c)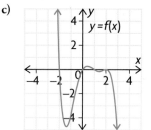

b)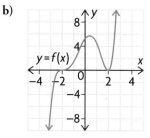

d)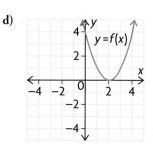

6. Solve the following inequalities.
  a) $(x - 1)(x + 1) > 0$
  b) $(x + 3)(x - 4) < 0$
  c) $(2x + 1)(x - 5) \geq 0$
  d) $-3x(x + 7)(x - 2) < 0$
  e) $(x - 3)(x + 1) + (x - 3)(x + 2) \geq 0$
  f) $2x(x + 4) - 3(x + 4) \leq 0$

7. Solve the following inequalities algebraically. Confirm your answer with a graph.
   a) $x^2 - 6x + 9 \geq 16$
   b) $x^4 - 8x < 0$
   c) $x^3 + 4x^2 + x \leq 6$
   d) $x^4 - 5x^2 + 4 > 0$
   e) $3x^3 - 3x^2 - 2x \leq 2x^3 - x^2 + x$
   f) $x^3 - x^2 - 3x + 3 > -x^3 + 2x + 5$

8. For the following pair of functions, determine when $f(x) < g(x)$.

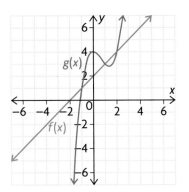

9. Consider $x^3 + 11x^2 + 18x + 10 > 10$.
   a) What is the equation of the corresponding function that could be graphed and used to solve this inequality?
   b) Explain how the graph of the corresponding function can be used in this case to solve the inequality.
   c) Solve this inequality algebraically.

10. Determine an expression for $f(x)$ in which $f(x)$ is a quartic function, $f(x) > 0$ when $-2 < x < 1$, $f(x) \leq 0$ when $x < -2$ or $x > 1$, $f(x)$ has a double root when $x = 3$, and $f(-1) = 96$.

11. The viscosity, v, of oil used in cars is related to its temperature, t, by the formula $v = -t^3 - 6t^2 + 12t + 50$, where each unit of t is equivalent to 50 °C.
   a) Graph the function on your graphing calculator.
   b) Determine the temperature range for which $v > 0$ to two decimal places.
   c) Determine the temperature ranges for which $15 < v < 20$ to two decimal places.

12. A rock is tossed from a platform and follows a parabolic path through the air. The height of the rock in metres is given by $h(t) = -5t^2 + 12t + 14$, where t is measured in seconds.
 a) How high is the rock off the ground when it is thrown?
 b) How long is the rock in the air?
 c) For what times is the height of the rock greater than 17 m?
 d) How long is the rock above a height of 17 m?

13. An open-topped box can be made from a sheet of aluminium
 Ⓐ measuring 50 cm by 30 cm by cutting congruent squares from the four corners and folding up the sides. Write a polynomial function to represent the volume of such a box. Determine the range of side lengths that are possible for each square that is cut out and removed that result in a volume greater than 4000 cm³.

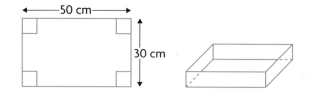

14. a) Without a calculator, explain why the inequality
 Ⓣ $2x^{24} + x^4 + 15x^2 + 80 < 0$ has no solution.
 b) Without a calculator, explain why
 $-4x^{12} - 7x^6 + 9x^2 + 20 < 30 + 11x^2$ has a solution of $-\infty < x < \infty$.

15. Explain why the following solution strategy fails, and then solve the inequality correctly.
 Solve: $(x + 1)(x - 2) > (x + 1)(-x + 6)$.
 Divide both sides by $x + 1$ and get $x - 2 > -x + 6$.
 Add x to both sides: $2x - 2 > 6$.
 Add 2 to both sides: $2x > 8$.
 Divide both sides by 2: $x > 4$.

16. Create a concept web that illustrates all of the different methods
 Ⓒ you could use to solve a polynomial inequality.

Extending

17. Use what you know about the factoring method to solve the following inequalities.
 a) $\dfrac{x^2 + x - 12}{x^2 + 5x + 6} < 0$
 b) $\dfrac{x^2 - 25}{x^3 + 6x^2 + 5x} > 0$

18. Solve the inequality $(x + 1)(x - 2)(2^x) \geq 0$ algebraically.

Rates of Change in Polynomial Functions

GOAL

Determine average and instantaneous rates of change in polynomial functions.

YOU WILL NEED

- graphing calculator or graphing software

LEARN ABOUT the Math

Emile is researching Canada's population growth. He obtained the data online and used graphing software to create the following graph and fit a curve to the data.

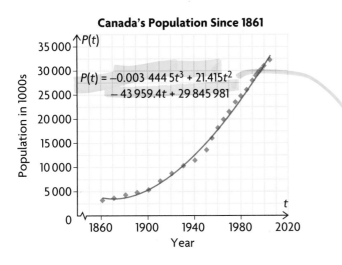

Canada's Population Since 1861

$P(t) = -0.003\ 444\ 5t^3 + 21.415t^2 - 43\ 959.4t + 29\ 845\ 981$

 Was Canada's population growing faster in 1997 or 2005?

Year	Population (1000s)
1861	3 230
1871	3 689
1881	4 325
1891	4 833
1901	5 371
1911	7 207
1921	8 788
1931	10 377
1941	11 507
1951	13 648
1956	16 081
1961	18 238
1966	20 015
1971	21 568
1976	23 550
1981	24 820
1986	26 101
1991	28 031
1994	29 036
1995	29 354
1996	29 672
1997	30 011
1998	30 301
2001	31 051
2006	32 249

EXAMPLE 1	Selecting tools and strategies to determine the instantaneous rate of change

Estimate the instantaneous rates of change in Canada's population in 1997 and 2005, and compare them.

Solution A: Using an algebraic strategy

Enter the equation into the graphing calculator.

Tech | *Support*

For help using the graphing calculator to evaluate a function at a given point, see Technical Appendix, T–3.

Average rate of change

$$= \frac{P(a + h) - P(a)}{h}$$

$h = 0.01$ ←

$$= \frac{P(1997 + 0.01) - P(1997)}{0.01}$$

$$= \frac{P(1997.01) - P(1997)}{0.01}$$

Use the difference quotient and a very small value for h where $a = 1997$ to estimate the instantaneous rate of change in 1997.

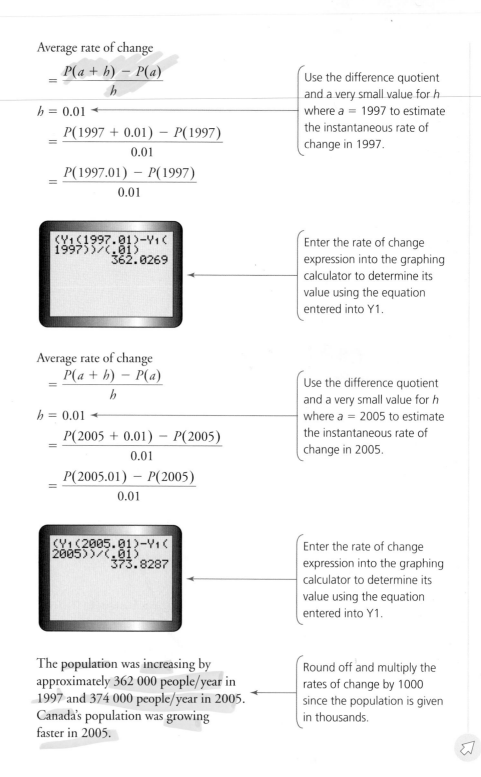

```
(Y₁(1997.01)-Y₁(
1997))/(.01)
        362.0269
```

Enter the rate of change expression into the graphing calculator to determine its value using the equation entered into Y1.

Average rate of change

$$= \frac{P(a + h) - P(a)}{h}$$

$h = 0.01$ ←

$$= \frac{P(2005 + 0.01) - P(2005)}{0.01}$$

$$= \frac{P(2005.01) - P(2005)}{0.01}$$

Use the difference quotient and a very small value for h where $a = 2005$ to estimate the instantaneous rate of change in 2005.

```
(Y₁(2005.01)-Y₁(
2005))/(.01)
        373.8287
```

Enter the rate of change expression into the graphing calculator to determine its value using the equation entered into Y1.

The population was increasing by approximately 362 000 people/year in 1997 and 374 000 people/year in 2005. Canada's population was growing faster in 2005.

Round off and multiply the rates of change by 1000 since the population is given in thousands.

Solution B: Using a graphing strategy

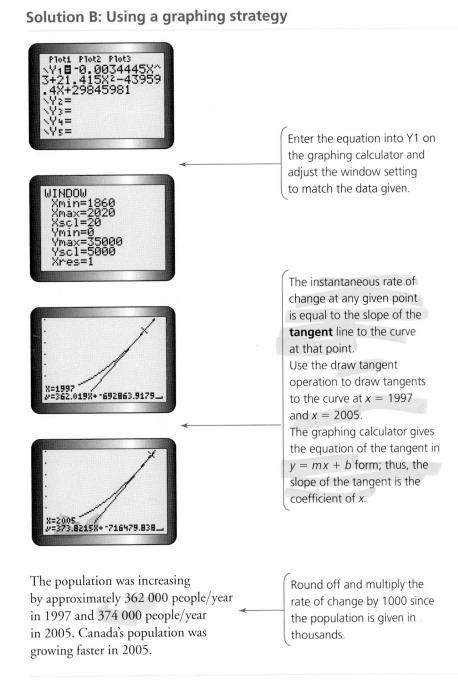

Enter the equation into Y1 on the graphing calculator and adjust the window setting to match the data given.

The instantaneous rate of change at any given point is equal to the slope of the **tangent** line to the curve at that point.
Use the draw tangent operation to draw tangents to the curve at $x = 1997$ and $x = 2005$.
The graphing calculator gives the equation of the tangent in $y = mx + b$ form; thus, the slope of the tangent is the coefficient of x.

Tech | **Support**

For help to draw tangent lines using the graphing calculator's draw operation, see Technical Appendix, T–17.

The population was increasing by approximately 362 000 people/year in 1997 and 374 000 people/year in 2005. Canada's population was growing faster in 2005.

Round off and multiply the rate of change by 1000 since the population is given in thousands.

Reflecting

A. The estimates for the instantaneous rates of change in population for 1997 and 2005 were both positive. Why does this make sense? Explain.

B. Explain how you could determine whether Canada's population was growing faster in 1880 or 1920 by just using the graph that was given.

C. Was Canada's population growing at a constant rate between 1860 and 2006? Explain.

APPLY *the Math*

EXAMPLE **2**	Selecting tools and strategies to determine the slope of a secant

Determine the average rate of change from $x = 2$ to $x = 5$ on the function $f(x) = (x - 3)^3 - 1$.

Solution A: Using an algebraic strategy

Average rate of change

$$= \frac{f(x_2) - f(x_1)}{x_2 - x_1}$$ ← Use the average rate of change formula for the interval $2 \leq x \leq 5$.

$$= \frac{f(5) - f(2)}{5 - 2}$$

$$= \frac{[(5 - 3)^3 - 1] - [(2 - 3)^3 - 1]}{3}$$

$$= \frac{7 - (-2)}{3}$$

$$= 3$$

Solution B: Using a graphing strategy

$f(x) = (x - 3)^3 - 1$ is a translation right 3 units and down 1 unit of the graph of $y = x^3$. ← Use transformations to sketch the graph of the function.

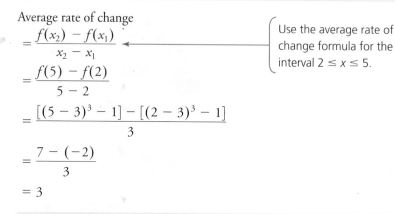

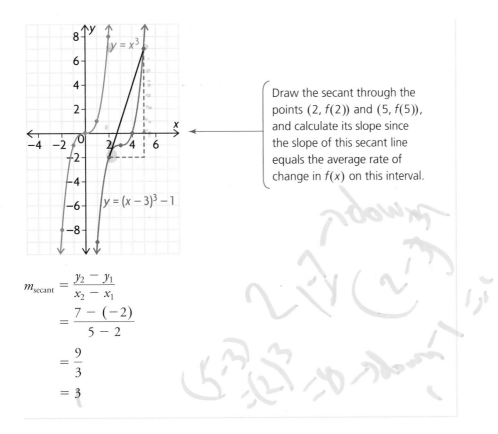

Draw the secant through the points $(2, f(2))$ and $(5, f(5))$, and calculate its slope since the slope of this secant line equals the average rate of change in $f(x)$ on this interval.

$$m_{\text{secant}} = \frac{y_2 - y_1}{x_2 - x_1}$$

$$= \frac{7 - (-2)}{5 - 2}$$

$$= \frac{9}{3}$$

$$= 3$$

EXAMPLE 3   Selecting tools and strategies to determine the slope of a tangent

The graph of a polynomial function is shown. Estimate the instantaneous rate of change in $f(x)$ at the point $(2, 0)$.

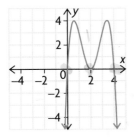

Solution A: Using an algebraic strategy

$$f(x) = ax(x - 2)^2(x - 4)$$

Determine the equation of the polynomial function. The graph has zeros at $x = 0$, 2, and 4. Since the graph is parabolic at $x = 2$, the factor $(x - 2)$ is squared.

$$3 = a(1)(1 - 2)^2(1 - 4)$$
$$3 = a(-3)$$
$$-1 = a$$

> Substitute the point $(1, 3)$ into the equation and solve for a.

$$f(x) = -x(x - 2)^2(x - 4)$$

> State the equation that represents the function.

$$\text{Slope} = \frac{f(a + h) - f(a)}{h}$$
$$= \frac{f(2 + h) - f(2)}{h}$$

> Use the difference quotient to estimate the slope of the tangent line at $(2, 0)$. In this case, $a = 2$ and $f(a) = f(2) = 0$.

Let $h = 0.001$

$$h = \frac{f(2.001) - f(2)}{0.001}$$
$$h = \frac{[-2.001(2.001 - 2)^2(2.001 - 4)] - 0}{0.001}$$
$$h \doteq \frac{0.000\ 004}{0.001}$$
$$h = 0.004$$

The instantaneous rate of change at $(2, 0)$ is approximately 0.

> The slope of the tangent line at a turning point on a polynomial function is 0.

Solution B: Using a graphing strategy

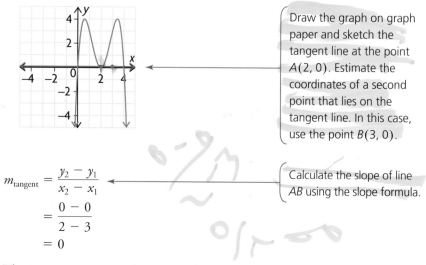

> Draw the graph on graph paper and sketch the tangent line at the point $A(2, 0)$. Estimate the coordinates of a second point that lies on the tangent line. In this case, use the point $B(3, 0)$.

$$m_{\text{tangent}} = \frac{y_2 - y_1}{x_2 - x_1}$$
$$= \frac{0 - 0}{2 - 3}$$
$$= 0$$

> Calculate the slope of line AB using the slope formula.

The instantaneous rate of change at $(2, 0)$ is 0.

In Summary

Key Idea

- The methods used previously to calculate average rate of change and estimate instantaneous rate of change can be used with polynomial functions.

Need to Know

- The average rate of change of a polynomial function $y = f(x)$ on the interval from $x_1 \leq x \leq x_2$ is $\dfrac{f(x_2) - f(x_1)}{x_2 - x_1}$. Graphically, this is equivalent to the slope of the secant line that passes through the points (x_1, y_1) and (x_2, y_2) on the graph of $y = f(x)$.

- The instantaneous rate of change of a polynomial function $y = f(x)$ at $x = a$ can be approximated by using the difference quotient $\dfrac{f(a + h) - f(a)}{h}$, where h is a very small value. Graphically, this is equivalent to estimating the slope of the tangent line by calculating the slope of the secant line that passes through the points $(a, f(a))$ and $(a + h, f(a + h))$.

- The instantaneous rate of change of a polynomial function $y = f(x)$ at any of its turning points is 0.

CHECK Your Understanding

1. Consider the graph showing a bicyclist's elevation relative to his elevation above sea level at the start of the race. The first 20 s of the race are shown.

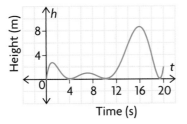

a) On which intervals will the tangent slope be positive? negative? zero?
b) What do these slopes tell you about the elevation of the bicyclist?

2. Consider the function $f(x) = 3(x - 2)^2 - 2$.
   a) Determine the average rate of change in $f(x)$ on each of the following intervals.
      i) $2 \leq x \leq 4$ ii) $2 \leq x \leq 6$ iii) $4 \leq x \leq 6$
   b) Estimate the instantaneous rate of change at $x = 4$.
   c) Explain why all the rates of change in $f(x)$ calculated in parts a) and b) are positive.
   d) State an interval on which the average rate of change in $f(x)$ will be negative.
   e) State the coordinates of a point where the instantaneous rate of change in $f(x)$ will be negative.

3. Consider the function $f(x) = x^3 - 4x^2 + 4x$.
   a) Estimate the instantaneous rate of change in $f(x)$ at $x = 2$.
   b) What does your answer to part a) tell you about the graph of the function at $x = 2$?
   c) Sketch a graph of $f(x)$ by first finding the zeros of $f(x)$ to verify your answer to part b).

4. You are given the following graph of $y = f(x)$.
   a) Calculate the average rate of change in $f(x)$ on the interval $4 \leq x \leq 5$.
   b) Estimate the coordinates of the point on the graph of $f(x)$ whose instantaneous rate of change in $f(x)$ is the same as that found in part a).

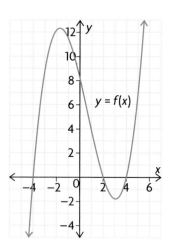

PRACTISING

5. For each of the following functions, calculate the average rate **K** of change on the interval $x \in [2, 5]$.
   a) $f(x) = 3x + 1$
   b) $t(x) = 3x^2 - 4x + 1$
   c) $g(x) = \dfrac{1}{x}$
   d) $d(x) = -x^2 + 7$
   e) $h(x) = 2^x$
   f) $v(x) = 9$

6. For each of the functions in question 5, estimate the instantaneous rate of change at $x = 3$.

7. Graph the function $f(x) = x^3 - 2x^2 + x$ by finding its zeros. Use the graph to estimate where the instantaneous rate of change is positive, negative, and zero.

8. A construction worker drops a bolt while working on a high-rise building 320 m above the ground. After t seconds, the bolt's height above the ground is s metres, where $s(t) = 320 - 5t^2$, $0 \leq t \leq 8$.
   a) Find the average velocity for the interval $3 \leq t \leq 8$.
   b) Find the bolt's velocity at $t = 2$.

9. Consider the function $f(x) = 3x^2 - 4x - 1$.
   a) Estimate the slope of the tangent line at $x = 1$.
   b) Find the y-coordinate of the point of tangency.
   c) Use the coordinates of the point of tangency and the slope to find the equation of the tangent line at $x = 1$.

10. The height, h, in metres of a toy rocket above the ground can be modelled **A** by the function $h(t) = -5t^2 + 50t$, where t represents time in seconds.
    a) Use an average speed to approximate the instantaneous speed at $t = 4$.
    b) Use an average speed to approximate the instantaneous speed at $t = 10$.
    c) What is the average speed over the interval from $t = 0$ s to $t = 10$?

11. The distance in kilometres of a boat from its dock can be modelled by the function $d(t) = \left(\frac{1}{200}\right)t^2(t-8)^2$, where t is in minutes and $t \in [0, 8]$. Sketch a graph that models this situation.

   a) Estimate when the instantaneous rate of change in distance to the dock is positive, negative, and zero.

   b) What happens to the boat when the instantaneous rate of change in distance is zero? What does it mean when the boat's rate of change in distance is negative?

12. Approximate the instantaneous rate of change at the zeros of the following function: $y = x^4 - 2x^3 - 8x^2 + 18x - 9$.

13. Consider the function $f(x) = x^2 + 3x - 5$.

   T a) Estimate the instantaneous rate of change at $x = 1$.

   b) Simplify the expression $\frac{f(x+h) - f(x)}{h}$.

   c) Examine the expression in part b) and discuss what happens as h becomes very close to 0.

   d) Use your result from part c) to come up with an expression for the instantaneous rate of change at the point x, and check your result from part a) using the expression.

14. Explain how instantaneous rates of change could be used to locate the
   C local maxima and local minima for a polynomial function.

Extending

15. Consider the function $f(x) = e^x$ (e is called Euler's Number where $e \doteq 2.7183$).

   a) Estimate the instantaneous rate of change at $x = 5$. Find $f(5)$.

   b) Repeat part a) with three more x-values.

   c) Generalize your findings.

16. Consider the function $f(x) = x^3 - 4x$.

   a) Estimate the slope of the tangent line at $x = 1$.

   b) Using the slope and the point of tangency, find the equation of the tangent line.

   c) The tangent line intersects the original graph one more time. Where? Graph both the original function and the tangent line to illustrate this.

17. Determine, to two decimal places, where the slope of a tangent line and the slope of the secant line that passes through $A(2, -4)$ and $B(3, 0)$ are equal on the graph of $f(x) = x^3 - 3x^2$.

FREQUENTLY ASKED Questions

Study Aid

- See Lesson 4.3, Examples 1, 2, and 3.
- Try Chapter Review Questions 10 to 13.

Q: **How do you solve a polynomial inequality?**

A1: Sometimes you can use an algebraic strategy if the polynomial is factorable. Use inverse operations to make one side of the inequality equal to zero, factor the polynomial to determine its zeros, then test values to the left, between, and to the right of the zeros to determine which intervals will satisfy the inequality. This can be done using a number line or a factor table.

For example, to solve $3x^3 - 4x^2 - 3x - 10 > 2x^3 - 6x^2 + 6x + 8$

$$x^3 + 2x^2 - 9x - 18 > 0$$
$$x^2(x + 2) - 9(x + 2) > 0$$
$$(x^2 - 9)(x + 2) > 0$$
$$(x + 3)(x - 3)(x + 2) > 0$$

The equation $(x + 3)(x - 3)(x + 2) = 0$ has solutions $x = -3$, $x = 3$, or $x = -2$. These numbers divide the domain of real numbers into the following intervals:

$x < -3$, $-3 < x < -2$, $-2 < x < 3$, and $x > 3$

Substitute values that lie in each interval into the original inequality, $3x^3 - 4x^2 - 3x - 10 > 2x^3 - 6x^2 + 6x + 8$.

Let $f(x) = 3x^3 - 4x^2 - 3x - 10$ and let $g(x) = 2x^3 - 6x^2 + 6x + 8$.

$x < -3$	$-3 < x < -2$	$-2 < x < 3$	$x > 3$
$f(-4) = -254$	$f(-2.5) = -74.375$	$f(1) = -14$	$f(4) = 106$
$g(-4) = -240$	$g(-2.5) = -75.75$	$g(1) = 10$	$g(4) = 64$
$f(x) < g(x)$	$f(x) > g(x)$	$f(x) < g(x)$	$f(x) > g(x)$

$3x^3 - 4x^2 - 3x - 10 > 2x^3 - 6x^2 + 6x + 8$ when $-3 < x < -2$ and $x > 3$.

A2: You can always use a graphing strategy using one of the following methods.

1. Treat each side of the inequality as two separate functions and graph them. Then determine their intersection points and identify the intervals for which one function is above or below the other, as required.

2. Create an equivalent inequality with zero on one side, and then identify the intervals created by the zeros of the graph of the corresponding function. Find where the graph lies above the x-axis (where $f(x) > 0$) or below (where $f(x) < 0$), as required.

For example, to solve $x^2 - 6x + 4 \geq x^3 - 8x^2 + 5x + 14$, use the graphing calculator to determine the intersection points for the functions.

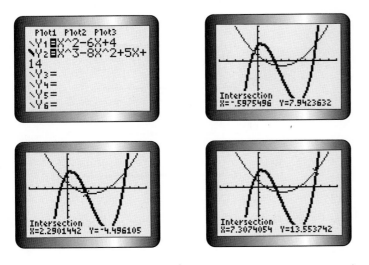

The two functions intersect when $x \doteq -0.598$, 2.290, and 7.307.

Refer to the graph to see where Y1 is above Y2 on the intervals defined by these three points. For example, for points to the left of $x = -0.598$, Y1 is above Y2.

So, $x^2 - 6x + 4 \geq x^3 - 8x^2 + 5x + 14$ when $x \leq -0.598$ and when $2.290 \leq x \leq 7.307$.

Q: **How do you calculate an average rate of change for a polynomial function?**

A: The average rate of change is the slope of a secant that connects two points on the function. To calculate the average rate of change on the interval $x_1 \leq x \leq x_2$ for a function, $f(x)$, calculate the average rate of change, $\dfrac{f(x_2) - f(x_1)}{x_2 - x_1}$.

> **Study | Aid**
> • See Lesson 4.4, Example 2.
> • Try Chapter Review Questions 14, 17, and 18.

Q: **How do you approximate the instantaneous rate of change for a polynomial function?**

A1: You can calculate the average rate of change for a very small interval on either side of the point at which you wish to calculate the instantaneous rate of change using the difference quotient $\dfrac{f(a + h) - f(a)}{h}$, where h is a very small value.

A2: You can graph the function, either by hand or by using a graphing calculator, and draw a tangent line at the required point and estimate its slope.

> **Study | Aid**
> • See Lesson 4.4, Examples 1 and 3.
> • Try Chapter Review Questions 15, 16, and 18.

PRACTICE Questions

Lesson 4.1

1. Solve each of the following equations by factoring.
   a) $x^4 - 16x^2 + 75 = 2x^2 - 6$
   b) $2x^2 + 4x - 1 = x + 1$
   c) $4x^3 - x^2 - 2x + 2 = 3x^3 - 2(x^2 - 1)$
   d) $-2x^2 + x - 6 = -x^3 + 2x - 8$

2. Solve the equation algebraically, and check your solution graphically:
   $18x^4 - 53x^3 + 52x^2 - 14x - 8 =$
   $3x^4 - x^3 + 2x - 8$

3. a) Write the equation of a polynomial $f(x)$ that has a degree of 4, zeros at $x = 1, 2, -2$, and -1, and has a y-intercept of 4.
   b) Determine the values of x where $f(x) = 48$.

4. An open-topped box is made from a rectangular piece of cardboard, with dimensions of 24 cm by 30 cm, by cutting congruent squares from each corner and folding up the sides. Determine the dimensions of the squares to be cut to create a box with a volume of 1040 cm³.

5. Between 1985 through 1995, the number of home computers, in thousands, sold in Canada is estimated by
   $C(t) = 0.92(t^3 + 8t^2 + 40t + 400)$,
   where t is in years and $t = 0$ for 1985.
   a) Explain why you can use this model to predict the number of home computers sold in 1993, but not to predict sales in 2005.
   b) Explain how to find when the number of home computer sales in Canada reached 1.5 million, using this model.
   c) In what year did home computer sales reach 1.5 million?

Lesson 4.2

6. For each number line given, write an inequality with both constant and linear terms on each side that has the corresponding solution.
   a)
   ```
   0  2  4  6  8  10 12 14
   ```
   b)
   ```
   -6 -4 -2  0  2  4  6
   ```
   c)
   ```
   -24    -18    -12    -6      0
   ```
   d)
   ```
   -9 -8 -7 -6 -5 -4 -3 -2 -1  0
   ```

7. Solve the following inequalities algebraically. State your answers using interval notation.
   a) $2(4x - 7) > 4(x + 9)$
   b) $\dfrac{x - 4}{5} \geq \dfrac{2x + 3}{2}$
   c) $-x + 2 > x - 2$
   d) $5x - 7 \leq 2x + 2$

8. Solve the following inequalities. State your answers using set notation.
   a) $-3 < 2x + 1 < 9$
   b) $8 \leq -x + 8 \leq 9$
   c) $6 + 2x \geq 0 \geq -10 + 2x$
   d) $x + 1 < 2x + 7 < x + 5$

9. A phone company offers two options. The first plan is an unlimited calling plan for $34.95 a month. The second plan is a $20.95 monthly fee plus $0.04 a minute for call time.
   a) When is the unlimited plan a better deal?
   b) Graph the situation to confirm your answer from part a).

Lesson 4.3

10. Select a strategy and determine the interval(s) for which each inequality is true.

   a) $(x + 1)(x - 2)(x + 3)^2 < 0$

   b) $\dfrac{(x - 4)(2x + 3)}{5} \geq \dfrac{2x + 3}{5}$

   c) $-2(x - 1)(2x + 5)(x - 7) > 0$

   d) $x^3 + x^2 - 21x + 21 \leq 3x^2 - 2x + 1$

11. Determine algebraically where the intervals of the function are positive and negative.
$$f(x) = 2x^4 - 2x^3 - 32x^2 - 40x$$

12. Solve the following inequality using graphing technology:
$$x^3 - 2x^2 + x - 3 \geq 2x^3 + x^2 - x + 1$$

13. In Canada, hundreds of thousands of cubic metres of wood are harvested each year. The function
$$f(x) = 1135x^4 - 8197x^3 + 15\,868x^2 - 2157x + 176\,608, \quad 0 \leq x \leq 4,$$ models the volume harvested, in cubic metres, from 1993 to 1997. Estimate the intervals (in years and months) when less than 185 000 m³ were harvested.

Lesson 4.4

14. For each of the following functions, determine the average rate of change in $f(x)$ from $x = 2$ to $x = 7$, and estimate the instantaneous rate of change at $x = 5$.

   a) $f(x) = x^2 - 2x + 3$

   b) $h(x) = (x - 3)(2x + 1)$

   c) $g(x) = 2x^3 - 5x$

   d) $v(x) = -x^4 + 2x^2 - 5x + 1$

15. Given the following graph, determine the intervals of x where the instantaneous rate of change is positive, negative, and zero.

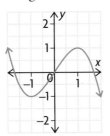

16. The height in metres of a projectile is modelled by the function $h(t) = -5t^2 + 25$, where t is the time in seconds.

   a) Find the point when the object hits the ground.

   b) Find the average rate of change from the point when the projectile is launched ($t = 0$) to the point in which it hits the ground.

   c) Estimate the object's speed at the point of impact.

17. Consider the function $f(x) = 2x^3 + 3x - 1$.

   a) Find the average rate of change from $x = 3$ to $x = 3.0001$.

   b) Find the average rate of change from $x = 2.9999$ to $x = 3$.

   c) Why are your answers so similar? Estimate the instantaneous rate of change at $x = 3$.

18. The incidence of lung cancer in Canadians per 100 000 people is shown below.

Year	Males	Females
1975	73.1	14.7
1980	83.2	21.7
1985	93.2	30.9
1990	92.7	36.5
1995	84.7	40.8
2000	78.6	46.4

Source: Cancer Bureau, Health Canada

   a) Use regression to determine a cubic function to represent the curve of best fit for both the male and female data.

   b) According to your models, when will more females have lung cancer than males?

   c) Was the incidence of lung cancer changing at a faster rate in the male or female population during the period fom 1975 to 2000? Justify your answer.

   d) Was the incidence of lung cancer changing at a faster rate in the male or female population in 1998? Justify your answer.

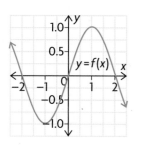

1. Solve for x in $3x^3 - 3x^2 - 7x + 5 = x^3 - 2x^2 - 1$.

2. Consider the graph shown of the function $y = f(x)$.
   a) Determine where $f(x)$ is positive, negative, and zero.
   b) Determine where the instantaneous rate of change in $f(x)$ is positive, negative, and zero. Find the average rate of change in $f(x)$ from $x = 1$ to $x = 2$.

3. A pizza company is advertising a special card. The card costs $50, but allows the owner to purchase pizzas for $5 each for one full year. Pizzas are normally $12 each.
   a) Write expressions that represent the cost of n pizzas with and without the card.
   b) How many pizzas would you have to purchase in a year to make the card worthwhile?

4. Solve the following inequalities.
   a) $4x - 5 < -2(x + 1)$
   b) $-4 \le -(3x + 1) \le 5$
   c) $(x + 1)(x - 5)(x + 2) > 0$
   d) $(2x - 4)^2(x + 3) \ge 0$

5. The height in metres of a projectile launched from the top of a building is given by $h(t) = -5t^2 + 20t + 15$, where t is the time in seconds since it was launched.
   a) How high was the projectile at the moment of launch?
   b) At what time does the projectile hit the ground?
   c) What is the average rate of change in height from the time the object was launched until the time it hit the ground?

6. Consider the following function: $f(x) = x^3 + x^2 + 1$.
   a) Estimate the slope of the tangent line at $x = 1$.
   b) What are the coordinates of the point of tangency?
   c) Determine the equation of the tangent line.

7. Explain why the polynomial $f(x) = 4x^{2008} + 2008x^4 + 4$ has no zeros.

8. The following number line shows the solution to a double inequality.

   $$\xleftarrow{} \overset{\circ}{\underset{-2}{}} \, \underset{-1}{|} \, \underset{0}{|} \, \underset{1}{|} \, \underset{2}{|} \, \underset{3}{|} \, \underset{4}{|} \, \underset{5}{|} \, \underset{6}{|} \, \overset{\circ}{\underset{7}{}} \xrightarrow{}$$

   a) Write the solution using set notation.
   b) Create a double inequality that has both a linear and a constant term for which this is the solution set.

9. A box that holds an expensive pen has square ends, and its length is 13 cm longer than its width. The volume of the box is 60 cm^3. Determine the dimensions of the box.

Flight of an Osprey

An observer in a fishing boat watched as an osprey dove under water and re-emerged with a fish in its talons. The following table shows the bird's estimated height above the water as given by that observer.

Time (s)	Height (m)
0	7
2	10
4	5
6	0
7	0
8	3

? Is the osprey travelling at its greatest speed when it hits the water?

A. Plot the given data on graph paper. What type of function best models these data?

B. Without using graphing technology, determine an equation to model the data and state a suitable domain.

C. Describe the osprey's flight, making reference to your graph and equation. Include information about the time, its height, direction of flight, and relative rate of ascent and descent (faster/slower).

D. According to your model, how long was the osprey under water? Does this seem reasonable? Explain.

E. According to your model, when was the osprey more than 6 m above the water?

F. Use your model to estimate the rate at which the osprey's height is changing at the time it hits the water.

G. Using tangent lines on your graph, do you think the rate you calculated in part F is the greatest at this point? Explain.

H. Check your result for part F using graphing technology by creating a scatter plot, determining the equation of the curve of best fit, and using it to find the slope of the appropriate tangent line.

I. Use the graphing calculator and the graph you created in part H to help you determine when the osprey's rate of change in height was greatest between 0 s and 8 s.

Task | **Checklist**

✔ Did you explain your thinking clearly?

✔ Did you justify your answers mathematically?

✔ Did you show all work and calculations?

✔ Did you check your calculations?

✔ Did you label your work properly?

Rational Functions, Equations, and Inequalities

▶ GOALS

You will be able to

- Graph the reciprocal functions of linear and quadratic functions

- Identify the key characteristics of rational functions from their equations and use these characteristics to sketch their graphs

- Solve rational equations and inequalities with and without graphing technology

- Determine average and instantaneous rates of change in situations that are modelled by rational functions

❓ When polluted water flows into a clean pond, how does the concentration of pollutant in the pond change over time? What type of function would model this change?

Study | Aid

- For help, see the Review of Essential Skills found at the Nelson Advanced Functions website.

Question	Appendix
1	R-3
2, 3, 4, 8	R-4
7	R-8

SKILLS AND CONCEPTS You Need

1. Factor each expression.

a) $x^2 - 3x - 10$ d) $9x^2 - 12x + 4$

b) $3x^2 + 12x - 15$ e) $3a^2 + a - 30$

c) $16x^2 - 49$ f) $6x^2 - 5xy - 21y^2$

2. Simplify each expression. State any restrictions on the variables, if necessary.

a) $\dfrac{12 - 8s}{4}$ d) $\dfrac{25x - 10}{5(5x - 2)^2}$

b) $\dfrac{6m^2 n^4}{18m^3 n}$ e) $\dfrac{x^2 + 3x - 18}{9 - x^2}$

c) $\dfrac{9x^3 - 12x^2 - 3x}{3x}$ f) $\dfrac{a^2 + 4ab - 5b^2}{2a^2 + 7ab - 15b^2}$

3. Simplify each expression, and state any restrictions on the variable.

a) $\dfrac{3}{5} \times \dfrac{7}{9}$ c) $\dfrac{x^2 - 4}{x - 3} \div \dfrac{x + 2}{12 - 4x}$

b) $\dfrac{2x}{5} \div \dfrac{x^2}{15}$ d) $\dfrac{x^3 + 4x^2}{x^2 - 1} \times \dfrac{x^2 - 5x + 6}{x^2 - 3x}$

4. Simplify each expression, and state any restrictions on the variable.

a) $\dfrac{2}{3} + \dfrac{6}{7}$ d) $\dfrac{5}{x - 3} - \dfrac{2}{x}$

b) $\dfrac{3x}{4} + \dfrac{5x}{6}$ e) $\dfrac{2}{x - 5} + \dfrac{y}{x^2 - 25}$

c) $\dfrac{1}{x} + \dfrac{4}{x^2}$ f) $\dfrac{6}{a^2 - 9a + 20} - \dfrac{8}{a^2 - 2a - 15}$

5. Solve and check.

a) $\dfrac{5x}{8} = \dfrac{15}{4}$ c) $\dfrac{4x}{5} - \dfrac{3x}{10} = \dfrac{3}{2}$

b) $\dfrac{x}{4} + \dfrac{1}{3} = \dfrac{5}{6}$ d) $\dfrac{x + 1}{2} - \dfrac{2x - 1}{3} = -1$

6. Sketch the graph of the reciprocal function $f(x) = \dfrac{1}{x}$ and describe its characteristics. Include the domain and range, as well as the equations of the asymptotes.

7. List the transformations that need to be applied to $y = \frac{1}{x}$ to graph each of the following reciprocal functions. Then sketch the graph.

a) $f(x) = \dfrac{1}{x + 3}$

c) $f(x) = -\dfrac{1}{2x} - 3$

b) $f(x) = \dfrac{2}{x - 1}$

d) $f(x) = \dfrac{2}{-3(x - 2)} + 1$

8. Describe the steps that are required to divide two rational expressions. Use your description to simplify $\dfrac{9y^2 - 4}{4y - 12} \div \dfrac{9y^2 + 12 + 4}{18 - 6y}$.

APPLYING *What You Know*

Painting Houses

Tony can paint the exterior of a house in six working days. Rebecca takes nine days to complete the same painting job.

? How long will Rebecca and Tony take to paint a similar house, if they work together?

A. What fraction of the job can Tony complete in one day? What fraction of the job can Rebecca complete?

B. Write a numerical expression to represent the fraction of the job that Rebecca and Tony can complete in one day, if they work together.

C. Let x represent the number of days that Rebecca and Tony, working together, will take to complete the job. Explain why $\frac{1}{x}$ represents the fraction of the job Rebecca and Tony will complete in one day when they work together.

D. Use your answers for parts B and C to write an equation. Determine the **lowest common denominator** for the **rational expressions** in your equation. Rewrite the equation using the lowest common denominator.

E. Solve the equation you wrote in part D by collecting like terms and comparing the numerators on the two sides of the equation.

F. What is the amount of time Rebecca and Tony will take to paint a similar house, when they work together?

Graphs of Reciprocal Functions

YOU WILL NEED

- graph paper
- coloured pencils or pens
- graphing calculator or graphing software

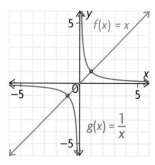

GOAL

Sketch the graphs of reciprocals of linear and quadratic functions.

INVESTIGATE the Math

Owen has noted some connections between the graphs of $f(x) = x$ and its reciprocal function $g(x) = \frac{1}{x}$.

- Both graphs are in the same quadrants for the same x-values.
- When $f(x) = 0$, there is a vertical asymptote for $g(x)$.
- $f(x)$ is always increasing, and $g(x)$ is always decreasing.

? How are the graphs of a function and its reciprocal function related?

A. Explain why the graphs of $f(x) = x$ and $g(x) = \frac{1}{x}$ are in the same quadrants over the same intervals. Does this relationship hold for $m(x) = -x$ and $n(x) = -\frac{1}{x}$? Does this relationship hold for any function and its reciprocal function? Explain.

B. What graphical characteristic in the reciprocal function do the zeros of the original function correspond to? Explain.

C. Explain why the reciprocal function $g(x) = \frac{1}{x}$ is decreasing when $f(x) = x$ is increasing. Does this relationship hold for $n(x) = -\frac{1}{x}$ and $m(x) = -x$? Explain how the increasing and decreasing intervals of a function and its reciprocal are related.

D. What are the y-coordinates of the points where $f(x)$ and $g(x)$ intersect? Will the points of intersection for any function and its reciprocal always have the same y-coordinates? Explain.

E. Explain why the graph of $g(x)$ has a horizontal asymptote. What is the equation of this asymptote? Will all reciprocal functions have the same horizontal asymptote? Explain.

F. On graph paper, draw the graph of $p(x) = x^2 - 4$. In a table like the one below, note the characteristics of the graph of $p(x)$ and use this information to help you determine the characteristics of the reciprocal function $q(x) = \dfrac{1}{x^2 - 4}$.

Characteristics	$p(x) = x^2 - 4$	$q(x) = \dfrac{1}{x^2 - 4}$
zeros and/or vertical asymptotes		
interval(s) on which the graph is above the x-axis (all values of the function are positive)		
interval(s) on which the graph is below the x-axis (all values of the function are negative)		
interval(s) on which the function is increasing		
interval(s) on which the function is decreasing		
point(s) where the y-value is 1		
point(s) where the y-value is -1		

G. On the same graph, draw the vertical asymptotes for the reciprocal function. Then use the rest of the information determined in part F to draw the graph for $q(x) = \dfrac{1}{x^2 - 4}$.

H. Verify your graphs by entering $p(x)$ and $q(x)$ in a graphing calculator using the "friendly" window setting shown.

I. Repeat parts F to H for the following pairs of functions.

    a) $p(x) = x + 2$ and $q(x) = \dfrac{1}{x + 2}$

    b) $p(x) = 2x - 3$ and $q(x) = \dfrac{1}{2x - 3}$

    c) $p(x) = (x - 2)(x + 3)$ and $q(x) = \dfrac{1}{(x - 2)(x + 3)}$

    d) $p(x) = (x - 1)^2$ and $q(x) = \dfrac{1}{(x - 1)^2}$

J. Write a summary of the relationships between the characteristics of the graphs of

    a) a linear function and its reciprocal function

    b) a quadratic function and its reciprocal function

Tech | *Support*

On a graphing calculator, the length of the display screen contains 94 pixels, and the width contains 62 pixels. When the domain, *Xmax-Xmin*, is cleanly divisible by 94, and the range, *Ymax-Ymin*, is cleanly divisible by 62, the window is friendly. This means that you can trace without using "ugly" decimals. A friendly window is useful when working with rational functions.

Use brackets when entering reciprocal functions in the Y = editor of a graphing calculator. For example, to graph the function $f(x) = \dfrac{1}{x^2 - 4}$, enter $Y1 = \dfrac{1}{(x^2 - 4)}$.

Reflecting

K. How did knowing the positive/negative intervals and the increasing/decreasing intervals for $p(x) = x^2 - 4$ help you draw the graph for $p(x) = \dfrac{1}{x^2 - 4}$?

L. Why are some numbers in the domain of a function excluded from the domain of its reciprocal function? What graphical characteristic of the reciprocal function occurs at these values?

M. What common characteristics are shared by all reciprocals of linear and quadratic functions?

APPLY the Math

EXAMPLE 1	Connecting the characteristics of a linear function to its corresponding reciprocal function

Given the function $f(x) = 2 - x$,
a) determine the domain and range, intercepts, positive/negative intervals, and increasing/decreasing intervals
b) use your answers for part a) to sketch the graph of the reciprocal function

Solution

a) $f(x) = 2 - x$ is a linear function.

$D = \{x \in \mathbf{R}\}$
$R = \{y \in \mathbf{R}\}$

⟵ The domain and range of most linear functions are the set of real numbers.

From the equation, the y-intercept is 2. ⟵
$f(x) = 0$ when $0 = 2 - x$
$\quad x = 2$

A linear function $f(x) = mx + b$ has y-intercept b.
The x-intercept occurs where $f(x) = 0$.

The x-intercept is 2.

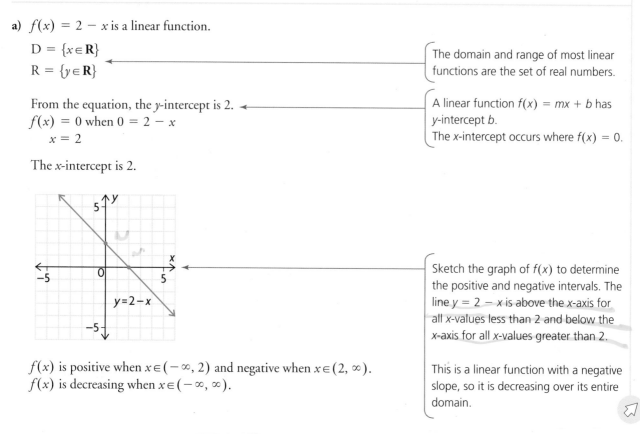

$y = 2 - x$

Sketch the graph of $f(x)$ to determine the positive and negative intervals. The line $y = 2 - x$ is above the x-axis for all x-values less than 2 and below the x-axis for all x-values greater than 2.

$f(x)$ is positive when $x \in (-\infty, 2)$ and negative when $x \in (2, \infty)$.
$f(x)$ is decreasing when $x \in (-\infty, \infty)$.

This is a linear function with a negative slope, so it is decreasing over its entire domain.

b) The reciprocal function is $g(x) = \dfrac{1}{2 - x}$.

$D = \{x \in \mathbf{R} \mid x \ne 2\}$

$R = \{y \in \mathbf{R} \mid y \ne 0\}$

The y-intercept is 0.5.

The vertical asymptote is $x = 2$
and the horizontal asymptote is $y = 0$.

The reciprocal function is positive
when $x \in (-\infty, 2)$ and negative
when $x \in (2, \infty)$.

It is increasing when $x \in (-\infty, 2)$
and when $x \in (2, \infty)$.

The graph of $g(x) = \dfrac{1}{2 - x}$ intersects

the graph of $g(x) = 2 - x$ at $(1, 1)$
and $(3, -1)$.

> All the y-values of points on the reciprocal function are reciprocals of the y-values on the original function.

> There is a vertical asymptote at the zero of the original function.
> The reciprocals of a linear function always have the x-axis as a horizontal asymptote.

> The positive/negative intervals are always the same for both functions.

> Because the original function is always decreasing, the reciprocal function is always increasing.

> The reciprocal of 1 is 1, and the reciprocal of -1 is -1. Thus, the two graphs intersect at any points with these y-values.

> Use all this information to sketch the graph of the reciprocal function.

EXAMPLE 2
Connecting the characteristics of a quadratic function to its corresponding reciprocal function

Given the function $f(x) = 9 - x^2$
a) determine the domain and range, intercepts, positive/negative intervals, and increasing/decreasing intervals
b) use your answers for part a) to sketch the graph of the reciprocal function

Solution

a) $f(x) = 9 - x^2$ is a quadratic function.

$D = \{x \in \mathbf{R}\}$

> The domain of a quadratic function is the set of real numbers.

$f(0) = 9$, so the y-intercept is 9.
$R = \{y \in \mathbf{R} \mid y \le 9\}$

> The graph of $f(x)$ is a parabola that opens down. The vertex is at $(0, 9)$, so $y \le 9$.

$$f(x) = 0 \Rightarrow 9 - x^2 = 0$$

$$(3 - x)(3 + x) = 0$$

$$x = \pm 3$$

> Factor and determine the x-intercepts.

The x-intercepts are -3 and 3.

> The parabola $y = 9 - x^2$ is above the x-axis for x-values between -3 and 3. The graph is below the x-axis for x-values less than -3 and for x-values greater than 3.

$f(x)$ is positive when $x \in (-3, 3)$ and negative when $x \in (-\infty, -3)$ and when $x \in (3, \infty)$.

$f(x)$ is increasing when $x \in (-\infty, 0)$ and decreasing when $x \in (0, \infty)$.

> The y-values increase as x increases from $-\infty$ to 0. The y-values decrease as x increases from 0 to ∞.

b) The reciprocal function is $g(x) = \dfrac{1}{9 - x^2}$.

The vertical asymptotes are $x = -3$ and $x = 3$.

$$D = \{x \in \mathbf{R} \,|\, x \neq \pm 3\}$$

> Vertical asymptotes occur at each zero of the original function, so these numbers must be excluded from the domain.

The horizontal asymptote is $y = 0$.

The y-intercept is $\dfrac{1}{9}$.

> The reciprocals of all quadratic functions have the x-axis as a horizontal asymptote. The y-intercept of the original function is 9, so the y-intercept of the reciprocal function is $\dfrac{1}{9}$.

There is a local minimum value at $\left(0, \dfrac{1}{9}\right)$.

$$R = \left\{y \in \mathbf{R} \,\middle|\, y < 0 \text{ or } y \geq \dfrac{1}{9}\right\}$$

> When the original function has a local maximum point, the reciprocal function has a corresponding local minimum point.

The reciprocal function is positive when $x \in (-3, 3)$ and negative when $x \in (-\infty, -3)$ and when $x \in (3, \infty)$. It is decreasing when $x \in (-\infty, -3)$ and when $x \in (-3, 0)$, and increasing when $x \in (0, 3)$ and when $x \in (3, \infty)$.

> The positive/negative intervals are always the same for both functions. Where the original function is decreasing, excluding the zeros, the reciprocal function is increasing (and vice versa).

$$f(x) = 1 \text{ when } 9 - x^2 = 1 \qquad \text{and} \quad f(x) = -1 \text{ when } 9 - x^2 = -1$$

$$-x^2 = 1 - 9 \qquad\qquad\qquad -x^2 = -1 - 9$$

$$-x^2 = -8 \qquad\qquad\qquad\qquad -x^2 = -10$$

$$x^2 = 8 \qquad\qquad\qquad\qquad\quad x^2 = 10$$

$$x = \pm 2\sqrt{2} \qquad\qquad\qquad\quad x = \pm \sqrt{10}$$

> A function and its reciprocal intersect at points where $y = \pm 1$. Solve the corresponding equations to determine the x-coordinates of the points of intersection.

The graph of $g(x) = \dfrac{1}{9 - x^2}$ intersects the graph of $f(x) = 9 - x^2$

at $(-2\sqrt{2}, 1), (2\sqrt{2}, 1)$ and at $(-\sqrt{10}, -1), (\sqrt{10}, -1)$.

> Use all this information to sketch the graph of the reciprocal function.

In Summary

Key Idea

- You can use key characteristics of the graph of a linear or quadratic function to graph the related reciprocal function.

Need to Know

- All the y-coordinates of a reciprocal function are the reciprocals of the y-coordinates of the original function.
- The graph of a reciprocal function has a vertical asymptote at each zero of the original function.
- A reciprocal function will always have $y = 0$ as a horizontal asymptote if the original function is linear or quadratic.
- A reciprocal function has the same positive/negative intervals as the original function.

(continued)

- Intervals of increase on the original function are intervals of decrease on the reciprocal function. Intervals of decrease on the original function are intervals of increase on the reciprocal function.
- If the range of the original function includes 1 and/or −1, the reciprocal function will intersect the original function at a point (or points) where the y-coordinate is 1 or −1.
- If the original function has a local minimum point, the reciprocal function will have a local maximum point at the same x-value (and vice versa).

A linear function and its reciprocal

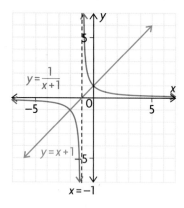

Both functions are negative when $x \in (-\infty, -1)$ and positive when $x \in (-1, \infty)$. The original function is increasing when $x \in (-\infty, \infty)$. The reciprocal function is decreasing when $x \in (-\infty, -1)$ or $(-1, \infty)$.

A quadratic function and its reciprocal

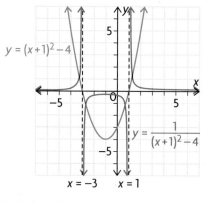

Both functions are negative when $x \in (-3, 1)$ and positive when $x \in (-\infty, -3)$ or $(1, \infty)$. The original function is decreasing when $x \in (-\infty, -1)$ and increasing when $x \in (-1, \infty)$. The reciprocal function is increasing when $x \in (-\infty, -3)$ or $(-3, -1)$ and decreasing when $x \in (-1, 1)$ or $(1, \infty)$.

CHECK *Your Understanding*

1. Match each function with its equation on the next page. Then identify which function pairs are reciprocals.

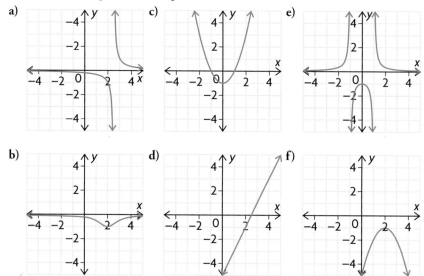

A $y = \dfrac{1}{-(x-2)^2 - 1}$

D $y = x^2 - 1$

B $y = \dfrac{1}{x^2 - 1}$

E $y = -(x-2)^2 - 1$

C $y = \dfrac{1}{2x - 5}$

F $y = 2x - 5$

2. For each pair of functions, determine where the zeros of the original function occur and state the equations of the vertical asymptotes of the reciprocal function, if possible.

   a) $f(x) = x - 6,\ g(x) = \dfrac{1}{x-6}$

   b) $f(x) = 3x + 4,\ g(x) = \dfrac{1}{3x+4}$

   c) $f(x) = x^2 - 2x - 15,\ g(x) = \dfrac{1}{x^2 - 2x - 15}$

   d) $f(x) = 4x^2 - 25,\ g(x) = \dfrac{1}{4x^2 - 25}$

   e) $f(x) = x^2 + 4,\ g(x) = \dfrac{1}{x^2 + 4}$

   f) $f(x) = 2x^2 + 5x + 3,\ g(x) = \dfrac{1}{2x^2 + 5x + 3}$

3. Sketch the graph of each function. Use your graph to help you sketch the graph of the reciprocal function.

   a) $f(x) = 5 - x$ b) $f(x) = x^2 - 6x$

PRACTISING

4. a) Copy and complete the following table.

x	-4	-3	-2	-1	0	1	2	3	4	5	6	7
$f(x)$	16	14	12	10	8	6	4	2	0	-2	-4	-6
$\dfrac{1}{f(x)}$												

   b) Sketch the graphs of $y = f(x)$ and $y = \dfrac{1}{f(x)}$.

   c) Find equations for $y = f(x)$ and $y = \dfrac{1}{f(x)}$.

5. State the equation of the reciprocal of each function, and determine the equations of the vertical asymptotes of the reciprocal. Verify your results using graphing technology.

   a) $f(x) = 2x$ e) $f(x) = -3x + 6$
   b) $f(x) = x + 5$ f) $f(x) = (x-3)^2$
   c) $f(x) = x - 4$ g) $f(x) = x^2 - 3x - 10$
   d) $f(x) = 2x + 5$ h) $f(x) = 3x^2 - 4x - 4$

6. Sketch the graph of the reciprocal of each function.

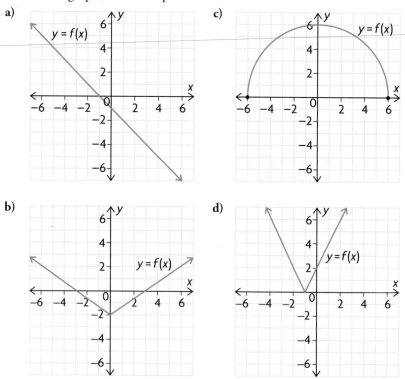

a)

b)

c)

d)

7. Sketch each pair of graphs on the same axes. State the domain and range of each reciprocal function.

a) $y = 2x - 5, y = \dfrac{1}{2x - 5}$

b) $y = 3x + 4, y = \dfrac{1}{3x + 4}$

8. Draw the graph of $y = f(x)$ and $y = \dfrac{1}{f(x)}$ on the same axes.

a) $f(x) = x^2 - 4$

b) $f(x) = (x - 2)^2 - 3$

c) $f(x) = x^2 - 3x + 2$

d) $f(x) = (x + 3)^2$

e) $f(x) = x^2 + 2$

f) $f(x) = -(x + 4)^2 + 1$

9. For each function, determine the domain and range, intercepts, positive/negative intervals, and increasing/decreasing intervals. State the equation of the reciprocal function. Then sketch the graphs of the original and reciprocal functions on the same axes.

a) $f(x) = 2x + 8$

b) $f(x) = -4x - 3$

c) $f(x) = x^2 - x - 12$

d) $f(x) = -2x^2 + 10x - 12$

10. Why do the graphs of reciprocals of linear functions always have vertical asymptotes, but the graphs of reciprocals of quadratic functions sometimes do not? Provide sketches of three different reciprocal functions to illustrate your answer.

11. An equation of the form $y = \dfrac{k}{x^2 + bx + c}$ has a graph that closely matches the graph shown. Find the equation. Check your answer using graphing technology.

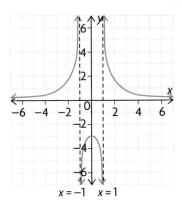

$x = -1 \quad x = 1$

12. A chemical company is testing the effectiveness of a new cleaning solution for killing bacteria. The test involves introducing the solution into a sample that contains approximately 10 000 bacteria. The number of bacteria remaining, $b(t)$, over time, t, in seconds is given by the equation $b(t) = 10\ 000\,\dfrac{1}{t}$.

a) How many bacteria will be left after 20 s?
b) After how many seconds will only 5000 bacteria be left?
c) After how many seconds will only one bacterium be left?
d) This model is not always accurate. Determine what sort of inaccuracies this model might have. Assume that the solution was introduced at $t = 0$.
e) Based on these inaccuracies, what should the domain and range of the equation be?

13. Use your graphing calculator to explore and then describe the key characteristics of the family of reciprocal functions of the form $g(x) = \dfrac{1}{x + n}$. Make sure that you include graphs to support your descriptions.

a) State the domain and range of $g(x)$.
b) For the family of functions $f(x) = x + n$, the y-intercept changes as the value of n changes. Describe how the y-intercept changes and how this affects $g(x)$.
c) If graphed, at what point would the two graphs $f(x)$ and $g(x)$ intersect?

14. Due to a basketball tournament, your friend has missed this class. Write a concise explanation of the steps needed to graph a reciprocal function using the graph of the original function (without using graphing technology). Use an example, and explain the reason for each step.

Extending

15. Sketch the graphs of the following reciprocal functions.

a) $y = \dfrac{1}{\sqrt{x}}$

b) $y = \dfrac{1}{x^3}$

c) $y = \dfrac{1}{2^x}$

d) $y = \dfrac{1}{\sin x}$

16. Determine the equation of the function in the graph shown.

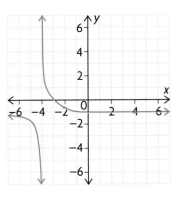

Exploring Quotients of Polynomial Functions

YOU WILL NEED

- graph paper
- coloured pencils or pens
- graphing calculator or graphing software

GOAL

Explore graphs that are created by dividing polynomial functions.

EXPLORE the Math

Each row shows the graphs of two polynomial functions.

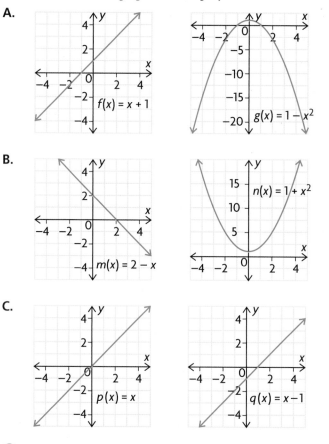

A.

$f(x) = x + 1$

$g(x) = 1 - x^2$

B.

$m(x) = 2 - x$

$n(x) = 1 + x^2$

rational function

a function that can be expressed as $f(x) = \frac{p(x)}{q(x)}$, where $p(x)$ and $q(x)$ are polynomial functions, $q(x) \neq 0$ (e.g., $f(x) = \frac{3x^2 - 1}{x + 1}$, $x \neq -1$, and $f(x) = \frac{1 - x}{x^2}$, $x \neq 0$, are rational functions, but $f(x) = \frac{1 + x}{\sqrt{2 - x}}$, $x \neq 2$, is not because its denominator is not a polynomial)

C.

$p(x) = x$

$q(x) = x - 1$

? What are the characteristics of the graphs that are created by dividing two polynomial functions?

A. Using the given functions, write the equation of the rational function $y = \frac{f(x)}{g(x)}$. Enter this equation into Y1 of the equation editor of a graphing calculator. Graph this equation using the window settings shown, and draw a sketch.

```
WINDOW
Xmin=-9.4
Xmax=9.4
Xscl=1
Ymin=-6.2
Ymax=6.2
Yscl=1
Xres=1
```

B. Describe the characteristics of the graph you created in part A by answering the following questions:

   i) Where are the zeros?

   ii) Are there any asymptotes? If so, where are they?

   iii) What are the domain and range of this function?

   iv) Is it a **continuous function**? Explain.

   v) Are there any values of $y = \dfrac{f(x)}{g(x)}$ that are undefined? What feature(s) of the graph is (are) related to these values?

   vi) Describe the end behaviours of this function.

   vii) Is the resulting graph a function? Explain.

C. Write the equation defined by $y = \dfrac{g(x)}{f(x)}$. Predict how the graph of this function will differ from the graph of $y = \dfrac{f(x)}{g(x)}$. Graph this function using your graphing calculator, and draw a sketch.

> **Tech | *Support***
>
> When entering a rational function into a graphing calculator, use brackets around the expression in the numerator and the expression in the denominator.

D. Describe the characteristics of the graph you created in part C by answering the questions in part B.

E. Repeat parts A through D for the functions in the other two rows.

F. Using graphing technology, and the same window settings you used in part A, explore the graphs of the following rational functions. Sketch each graph on separate axes, and note any holes or asymptotes.

   i) $f(x) = \dfrac{x^2 - 1}{x - 1}$ **v)** $f(x) = \dfrac{0.5x^2 + 1}{x - 1}$

   ii) $f(x) = \dfrac{3}{x + 1}$ **vi)** $f(x) = \dfrac{x^2 + 2x}{x + 1}$

   iii) $f(x) = \dfrac{x + 1}{x^2 - 2x - 3}$ **vii)** $f(x) = \dfrac{9x}{1 + x^2}$

   iv) $f(x) = \dfrac{x + 1}{x + 2}$ **viii)** $f(x) = \dfrac{2x^2 - 3}{x^2 + 1}$

G. Examine the graphs of the functions in parts i) and v) of part F at the point where $x = 1$. Explain why $f(x) = \dfrac{x^2 - 1}{x - 1}$ has a hole where $x = 1$, but $f(x) = \dfrac{0.5x^2 + 1}{x - 1}$ has a vertical asymptote. Identify the other functions in part F that have holes and the other functions that have vertical asymptotes.

H. Redraw the graph of the rational function $f(x) = \frac{0.5x^2 + 1}{x - 1}$. Then enter the equation $y = 0.5x + 0.5$ into Y2 of the equation editor. What do you notice? Examine all your other sketches in this exploration to see if any of the other functions have an **oblique asymptote**.

oblique asymptote

an asymptote that is neither vertical nor horizontal, but slanted

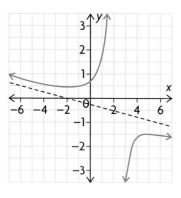

I. Examine the equations with graphs that have horizontal asymptotes in part F. Compare the degree of the expression in the numerator with the degree of the expression in the denominator. Is there a connection between the degrees in the numerator and denominator and the existence of horizontal asymptotes? Explain. Repeat for functions with oblique asymptotes.

J. Investigate several functions of the form $f(x) = \frac{ax + b}{cx + d}$. Note similarities and differences. Without graphing, how can you predict where a horizontal asymptote will occur?

K. Investigate graphs of quotients of quadratic functions. How are they different from graphs of quotients of linear functions?

L. Summarize the different characteristics of the graphs of rational functions.

Reflecting

M. How do the zeros of the function in the numerator help you graph the rational function? How do the zeros of the function in the denominator help you graph the rational function?

N. Explain how you can use the expressions in the numerator and the denominator of a rational function to decide if the graph has
  i) a hole
  ii) a vertical asymptote
  iii) a horizontal asymptote
  iv) an oblique asymptote

In Summary

Key Ideas

- The quotient of two polynomial functions results in a rational function which often has one or more discontinuities.
- The breaks or discontinuities in a rational function occur where the function is undefined. The function is undefined at values where the denominator is equal to zero. As a result, these values must be restricted from the domain of the function.
- The values that must be restricted from the domain of a rational function result in key characteristics that define the shape of the graph. These characteristics include a combination of vertical asymptotes (also called infinite discontinuities) and holes (also called point discontinuities).
- The end behaviours of many rational functions are determined by either horizontal asymptotes or oblique asymptotes.

Need to Know

- A rational function, $f(x) = \frac{p(x)}{q(x)}$, has a hole at $x = a$ if $\frac{p(a)}{q(a)} = \frac{0}{0}$. This occurs when $p(x)$ and $q(x)$ contain a common factor of $(x - a)$.

  For example, $f(x) = \frac{x^2 - 4}{x - 2}$ has the common factor of $(x - 2)$ in the numerator and the denominator. This results in a hole in the graph of $f(x)$ at $x = 2$.

- A rational function, $f(x) = \frac{p(x)}{q(x)}$, has a vertical asymptote at $x = a$ if $\frac{p(a)}{q(a)} = \frac{p(a)}{0}$.

  For example, $f(x) = \frac{x + 1}{x - 2}$ has a vertical asymptote at $x = 2$.

- A rational function, $f(x) = \frac{p(x)}{q(x)}$, has a horizontal asymptote only when the degree of $p(x)$ is less than or equal to the degree of $q(x)$. For example, $f(x) = \frac{2x}{x + 1}$ has a horizontal asymptote at $y = 2$.

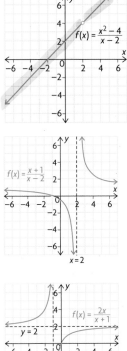

- A rational function, $f(x) = \frac{p(x)}{q(x)}$, has an oblique (slant) asymptote only when the degree of $p(x)$ is greater than the degree of $q(x)$ by exactly 1. For example, $f(x) = \frac{x^2 + 4}{x + 1}$ has an oblique asymptote.

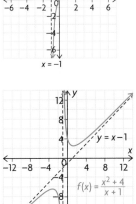

FURTHER *Your Understanding*

1. Without using graphing technology, match each equation with its corresponding graph. Explain your reasoning.

   a) $y = \dfrac{-1}{x - 3}$

   b) $y = \dfrac{x^2 - 9}{x - 3}$

   c) $y = \dfrac{1}{(x + 3)^2}$

   d) $y = \dfrac{x}{(x - 1)(x + 3)}$

   e) $y = \dfrac{1}{x^2 + 5}$

   f) $y = \dfrac{x^2}{x - 3}$

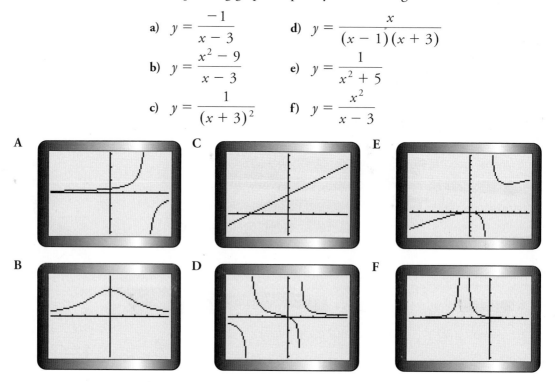

2. For each function, determine the equations of any vertical asymptotes, the locations of any holes, and the existence of any horizontal or oblique asymptotes.

   a) $y = \dfrac{x}{x + 4}$

   b) $y = \dfrac{1}{2x + 3}$

   c) $y = \dfrac{2x + 5}{x - 6}$

   d) $y = \dfrac{x^2 - 9}{x + 3}$

   e) $y = \dfrac{1}{(x + 3)(x - 5)}$

   f) $y = \dfrac{-x}{x + 1}$

   g) $y = \dfrac{3x - 6}{x - 2}$

   h) $y = \dfrac{-4x + 1}{2x - 5}$

   i) $y = \dfrac{8x}{4x + 1}$

   j) $y = \dfrac{x + 4}{x^2 - 16}$

   k) $y = \dfrac{x}{5x - 3}$

   l) $y = \dfrac{-3x + 1}{2x - 8}$

3. Write an equation for a rational function with the properties as given.

   a) a hole at $x = 1$

   b) a vertical asymptote anywhere and a horizontal asymptote along the x-axis

   c) a hole at $x = -2$ and a vertical asymptote at $x = 1$

   d) a vertical asymptote at $x = -1$ and a horizontal asymptote at $y = 2$

   e) an oblique asymptote, but no vertical asymptote

5.3 Graphs of Rational Functions of the Form $f(x) = \dfrac{ax + b}{cx + d}$

GOAL

Sketch the graphs of rational functions, given equations of the form $f(x) = \dfrac{ax + b}{cx + d}$.

INVESTIGATE the Math

The radius, in centimetres, of a circular juice blot on a piece of paper towel is modelled by $r(t) = \dfrac{1 + 2t}{1 + t}$, where t is measured in seconds. According to this model, the maximum size of the blot is determined by the location of the horizontal asymptote.

? How can you find the equation of the horizontal asymptote of a rational function of the form $f(x) = \dfrac{ax + b}{cx + d}$?

A. Without graphing, determine the domain, intercepts, vertical asymptote, and positive/negative intervals of the simple rational function $f(x) = \dfrac{x}{x + 1}$.

B. Copy the following tables, and complete them by evaluating $f(x)$ for each value of x. Examine the **end behaviour** of $f(x)$ by observing the trend in $f(x)$ as x grows positively large and negatively large. What value does $f(x)$ seem to approach?

$x \to \infty$	
x	$f(x) = \dfrac{x}{x + 1}$
10	
100	
1 000	
10 000	
100 000	
1 000 000	

$x \to -\infty$	
x	$f(x) = \dfrac{x}{x + 1}$
−10	
−100	
−1 000	
−10 000	
−100 000	
−1 000 000	

C. Write an equation for the horizontal asymptote of the function in part B.

D. Repeat parts A, B, and C for the functions $g(x) = \dfrac{4x}{x + 1}$, $h(x) = \dfrac{2x}{3x + 1}$, and $m(x) = \dfrac{3x - 2}{2x - 5}$.

E. Verify your results by graphing all the functions in part D on a graphing calculator. Note similarities and differences among the graphs.

F. Make a list of the equations of the functions and the equations of their horizontal asymptotes. Discuss how the degree of the numerator compares with the degree of the denominator. Explain how the leading coefficients of x in the numerator and the denominator determine the equation of the horizontal asymptote.

G. Determine the equation of the horizontal asymptote of the juice blot function $r(t) = \dfrac{1 + 2t}{1 + t}$. What does this equation tell you about the eventual size of the juice blot?

Reflecting

H. How do the graphs of rational functions with linear expressions in the numerator and denominator compare with the graphs of reciprocal functions?

I. Explain how you determined the equation of a horizontal asymptote from
  i) end behaviour tables
  ii) the equation of the function

APPLY the Math

EXAMPLE 1	Selecting a strategy to determine how a graph approaches a vertical asymptote

Determine how the graph of $f(x) = \dfrac{3x - 5}{x + 2}$ approaches its vertical asymptote.

Solution

$f(x) = \dfrac{3x - 5}{x + 2}$ has a vertical asymptote with the equation $x = -2$. Near this asymptote, the values of the function will grow very large in a positive direction or very large in a negative direction.

> $f(x)$ is undefined when $x = -2$.
> There is no common factor in the numerator and denominator.

Choose a value of x to the left and very close to -2. This value is less than -2.

$$f(-2.1) = \frac{3(-2.1) - 5}{(-2.1) + 2}$$
$$= 113$$

The graph of a rational function never crosses a vertical asymptote, so choose x-values that are very close to the vertical asymptote, on both sides, to determine the behaviour of the function.

On the left side of the vertical asymptote, the values of the function are positive. As $x \to -2, f(x) \to \infty$.

The function increases to large positive values as x approaches -2 from the left.

Choose a value of x to the right and very close to -2. This value is greater than -2.

$$f(-1.9) = \frac{3(-1.9) - 5}{(-1.9) + 2}$$
$$= -107$$

On the right side of the vertical asymptote, the values of the function are negative. As $x \to -2, f(x) \to -\infty$.

The function decreases to small negative values as x approaches -2 from the right.

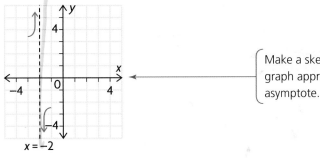

Make a sketch to show how the graph approaches the vertical asymptote.

EXAMPLE 2   Using key characteristics to sketch the graph of a rational function

For each function,

a) $f(x) = \dfrac{2}{x - 3}$ b) $f(x) = \dfrac{x - 2}{3x + 4}$ c) $f(x) = \dfrac{x - 3}{2x - 6}$

  i) determine the domain, intercepts, asymptotes, and positive/negative intervals
 ii) use these characteristics to sketch the graph of the function
iii) describe where the function is increasing or decreasing

Solution

a) $f(x) = \dfrac{2}{x-3}$

i) $D = \{x \in \mathbf{R} \mid x \neq 3\}$ ◄

> The function $f(x) = \dfrac{2}{x-3}$ is undefined when $x = 3$.

$f(0) = -\dfrac{2}{3}$, so the y-intercept is $-\dfrac{2}{3}$.

$f(x) \neq 0$, so there is no ◄ x-intercept.

> Any rational function equals zero when its numerator equals zero. The numerator is always 2, so $f(x)$ can never equal zero.

The line $x = 3$ is a vertical asymptote.
The line $y = 0$ is a horizontal asymptote.

> Since the numerator and denominator do not contain the common factor $(x - 3)$, $f(x)$ has a vertical asymptote at $x = 3$. Any rational function that is formed by a constant numerator and a linear function denominator has a horizontal asymptote at $y = 0$.

$f(x)$ is negative when $x \in (-\infty, 3)$ and positive when $x \in (3, \infty)$. ◄

> The numerator is always positive, so the denominator determines the sign of $f(x)$.
> $x - 3 < 0$ when $x < 3$
> $x - 3 > 0$ when $x > 3$

ii) Confirm the behaviour of $f(x)$ near the vertical asymptote.
$f(3.1) = 20$, so as $x \to 3, f(x) \to \infty$ on the right.
$f(2.9) = -20$, so as $x \to 3, f(x) \to -\infty$ on the left.

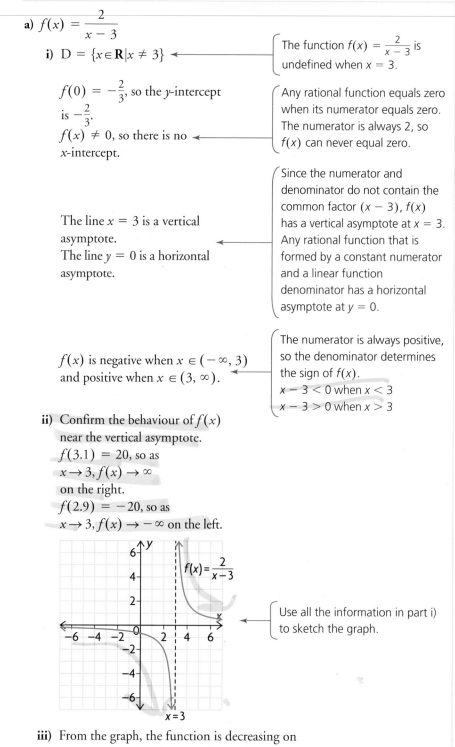

> Use all the information in part i) to sketch the graph.

iii) From the graph, the function is decreasing on its entire domain: when $x \in (-\infty, 3)$ and when $x \in (3, \infty)$.

b) $f(x) = \dfrac{x-2}{3x+4}$

i) $3x + 4 \neq 0$

$\qquad 3x \neq -4$

$\qquad x \neq -\dfrac{4}{3}$

$\qquad D = \left\{x \in \mathbf{R} \,\middle|\, x \neq -\dfrac{4}{3}\right\}$

> $f(x)$ is undefined when the denominator is zero.

$f(0) = \dfrac{0-2}{3(0)+4} = \dfrac{-2}{4}$ or $-\dfrac{1}{2}$

The y-intercept is $-\dfrac{1}{2}$.

> To determine the y-intercept, let $x = 0$.

$f(x) = 0$ when $\dfrac{x-2}{3x+4} = 0.$

$\qquad\qquad x - 2 = 0$

$\qquad\qquad\qquad x = 2$

The x-intercept is 2.

> To determine the x-intercept, let $y = 0$. Any rational function equals zero when its numerator equals zero.

The line $x = -\dfrac{4}{3}$ is a vertical asymptote.

> This is the value that makes $f(x)$ undefined.

The line $y = \dfrac{1}{3}$ is a horizontal asymptote.

> The ratio of the leading coefficients of the numerator and denominator is $\dfrac{1}{3}$.

Examine the signs of the numerator and denominator, and their quotient, to determine the positive/negative intervals.

	$x < -\dfrac{4}{3}$	$-\dfrac{4}{3} < x < 2$	$x > 2$
$x - 2$	$-$	$-$	$+$
$3x + 4$	$-$	$+$	$+$
$\dfrac{x-2}{3x-4}$	$\dfrac{-}{-} = +$	$\dfrac{-}{+} = -$	$\dfrac{+}{+} = +$

> The vertical asymptote and the x-intercept divide the set of real numbers into three intervals: $\left(-\infty, -\dfrac{4}{3}\right), \left(-\dfrac{4}{3}, 2\right),$ and $(2, \infty)$. Choose numbers in each interval to evaluate the sign of each expression.

$f(x)$ is positive when $x \in \left(-\infty, -\dfrac{4}{3}\right)$ and when $x \in (2, \infty)$.

$f(x)$ is negative when $x \in \left(-\dfrac{4}{3}, 2\right)$.

ii)

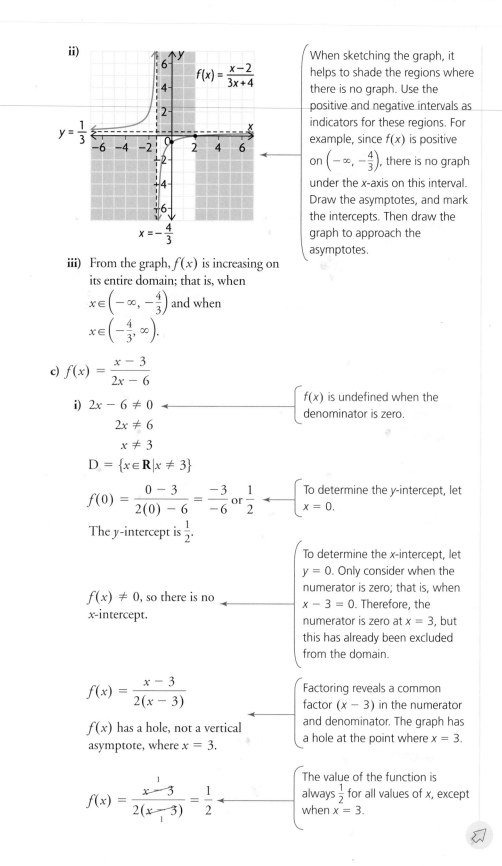

$$f(x) = \frac{x-2}{3x+4}$$

$$y = \frac{1}{3}$$

$$x = -\frac{4}{3}$$

When sketching the graph, it helps to shade the regions where there is no graph. Use the positive and negative intervals as indicators for these regions. For example, since $f(x)$ is positive on $\left(-\infty, -\frac{4}{3}\right)$, there is no graph under the x-axis on this interval. Draw the asymptotes, and mark the intercepts. Then draw the graph to approach the asymptotes.

iii) From the graph, $f(x)$ is increasing on its entire domain; that is, when $x \in \left(-\infty, -\frac{4}{3}\right)$ and when $x \in \left(-\frac{4}{3}, \infty\right)$.

c) $f(x) = \dfrac{x-3}{2x-6}$

i) $2x - 6 \neq 0$

$2x \neq 6$

$x \neq 3$

$D = \{x \in \mathbf{R} | x \neq 3\}$

$f(0) = \dfrac{0-3}{2(0)-6} = \dfrac{-3}{-6} \text{ or } \dfrac{1}{2}$

The y-intercept is $\dfrac{1}{2}$.

$f(x)$ is undefined when the denominator is zero.

To determine the y-intercept, let $x = 0$.

$f(x) \neq 0$, so there is no x-intercept.

To determine the x-intercept, let $y = 0$. Only consider when the numerator is zero; that is, when $x - 3 = 0$. Therefore, the numerator is zero at $x = 3$, but this has already been excluded from the domain.

$f(x) = \dfrac{x-3}{2(x-3)}$

$f(x)$ has a hole, not a vertical asymptote, where $x = 3$.

Factoring reveals a common factor $(x - 3)$ in the numerator and denominator. The graph has a hole at the point where $x = 3$.

$f(x) = \dfrac{\overset{1}{\cancel{x-3}}}{2(\underset{1}{\cancel{x-3}})} = \dfrac{1}{2}$

The value of the function is always $\dfrac{1}{2}$ for all values of x, except when $x = 3$.

$f(x)$ is positive at all points in its domain.

> $f(x)$ has no vertical asymptote or x-intercept. There is only one interval to consider: $(-\infty, \infty)$. For any value of x, $f(x) = \frac{1}{2}$.

ii) The graph is a horizontal line with the equation $y = \frac{1}{2}$. There is a hole at $x = 3$.

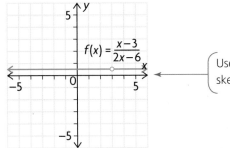

$$f(x) = \frac{x-3}{2x-6}$$

> Use the information in part i) to sketch the graph.

iii) The function is neither increasing nor decreasing. It is constant on its entire domain.

EXAMPLE **3**	Solving a problem by graphing a rational function

The function $P(t) = \dfrac{30(7t + 9)}{3t + 2}$ models the population, in thousands, of a town t years since 1990. Describe the population of the town over the next 20 years.

Solution

$$P(t) = \frac{30(7t + 9)}{3t + 2}$$

> Use the equation to help you decide on the window settings. For the given context, $t \geq 0$ and $P(t) > 0$.

Determine the initial population in 1990, when $t = 0$.

$$P(0) = \frac{30(7(0) + 9)}{3(0) + 2} = 135$$

```
WINDOW
 Xmin=0
 Xmax=20
 Xscl=2
 Ymin=0
 Ymax=150
 Yscl=10
 Xres=1
```

Graph $P(t)$ to show the population for the 20 years after 1990.

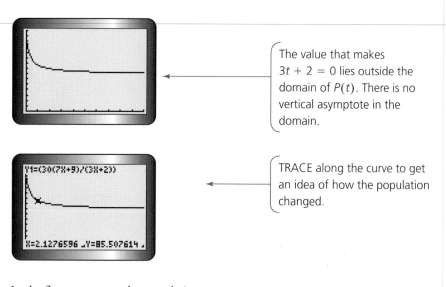

The value that makes $3t + 2 = 0$ lies outside the domain of $P(t)$. There is no vertical asymptote in the domain.

TRACE along the curve to get an idea of how the population changed.

In the first two years, the population dropped by about 50 000 people. Then it began to level off and approach a steady value.

There is a horizontal asymptote at $P = \dfrac{30(7)}{3} = 70$.

Use the function equation to determine the equation of the horizontal asymptote. For large values of t, $P(t) \doteq \dfrac{30(7t)}{3t}$. Therefore, the leading coefficients in the numerator and denominator define the equation of the horizontal asymptote.

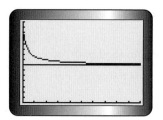

The population of the town has been decreasing since 1990. It was 135 000 in 1990, but dropped by about 50 000 in the next two years. Since then, the population has begun to level off and, according to the model, will approach a steady value of 70 000 people by 2010.

Multiply the values of the function by 1000, since the population is given in thousands.

In Summary

Key Ideas

- The graphs of most rational functions of the form $f(x) = \dfrac{b}{cx + d}$ and $f(x) = \dfrac{ax + b}{cx + d}$ have both a vertical asymptote and a horizontal asymptote.
- You can determine the equation of the vertical asymptote directly from the equation of the function by finding the zero of the denominator.
- You can determine the equation of the horizontal asymptote directly from the equation of the function by examining the ratio of the leading coefficients in the numerator and the denominator. This gives you the end behaviours of the function.
- To sketch the graph of a rational function, you can use the domain, intercepts, equations of asymptotes, and positive/negative intervals.

Need to Know

- Rational functions of the form $f(x) = \dfrac{b}{cx + d}$ have a vertical asymptote defined by $x = -\dfrac{d}{c}$ and a horizontal asymptote defined by $y = 0$. For example, see the graph of $f(x) = \dfrac{2}{x - 3}$.

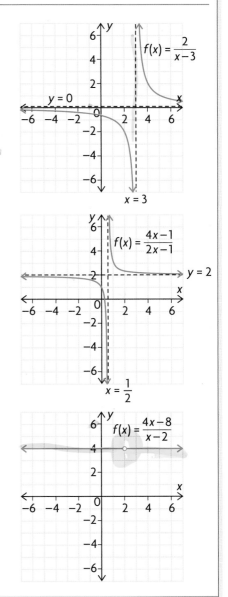

- Most rational functions of the form $f(x) = \dfrac{ax + b}{cx + d}$ have a vertical asymptote defined by $x = -\dfrac{d}{c}$ and a horizontal asymptote defined by $y = \dfrac{a}{c}$. For example, see the graph of $f(x) = \dfrac{4x - 1}{2x - 1}$.

  The exception occurs when the numerator and the denominator both contain a common linear factor. This results in a graph of a horizontal line that has a hole where the zero of the common factor occurs. As a result, the graph has no asymptotes. For example, see the graph of $f(x) = \dfrac{4x - 8}{x - 2} = \dfrac{4(x - 2)}{(x - 2)}$.

CHECK Your Understanding

1. Match each function with its graph.

   a) $h(x) = \dfrac{x + 4}{2x + 5}$

   c) $f(x) = \dfrac{3}{x - 1}$

   b) $m(x) = \dfrac{2x - 4}{x - 2}$

   d) $g(x) = \dfrac{2x - 3}{x + 2}$

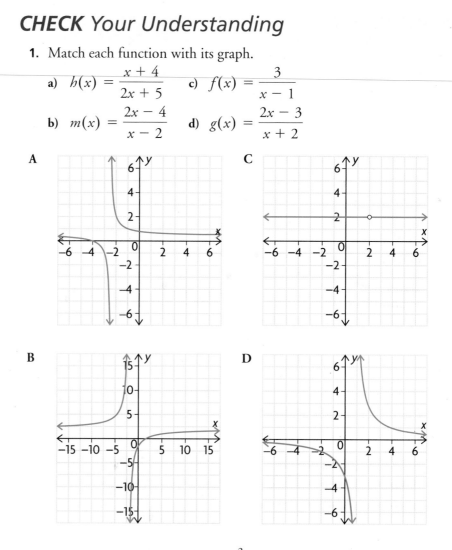

A

B

C

D

2. Consider the function $f(x) = \dfrac{3}{x - 2}$.
   a) State the equation of the vertical asymptote.
   b) Use a table of values to determine the behaviour(s) of the function near its vertical asymptote.
   c) State the equation of the horizontal asymptote.
   d) Use a table of values to determine the end behaviours of the function near its horizontal asymptote.
   e) Determine the domain and range.
   f) Determine the positive and negative intervals.
   g) Sketch the graph.

3. Repeat question 2 for the rational function $f(x) = \dfrac{4x - 3}{x + 1}$.

PRACTISING

4. State the equation of the vertical asymptote of each function. Then choose a strategy to determine how the graph of the function approaches its vertical asymptote.

a) $y = \dfrac{2}{x + 3}$

c) $y = \dfrac{2x + 1}{2x - 1}$

b) $y = \dfrac{x - 1}{x - 5}$

d) $y = \dfrac{3x + 9}{4x + 1}$

5. For each function, determine the domain, intercepts, asymptotes, and positive/negative intervals. Use these characteristics to sketch the graph of the function. Then describe where the function is increasing or decreasing.

a) $f(x) = \dfrac{3}{x + 5}$

c) $f(x) = \dfrac{x + 5}{4x - 1}$

b) $f(x) = \dfrac{10}{2x - 5}$

d) $f(x) = \dfrac{x + 2}{5(x + 2)}$

6. Read each set of conditions. State the equation of a rational function of the form $f(x) = \dfrac{ax + b}{cx + d}$ that meets these conditions, and sketch the graph.

a) vertical asymptote at $x = -2$, horizontal asymptote at $y = 0$; negative when $x \in (-\infty, -2)$, positive when $x \in (-2, \infty)$; always decreasing

b) vertical asymptote at $x = -2$, horizontal asymptote at $y = 1$; x-intercept $= 0$, y-intercept $= 0$; positive when $x \in (-\infty, -2)$ or $(0, \infty)$, negative when $x \in (-2, 0)$

c) hole at $x = 3$; no vertical asymptotes; y-intercept $= (0, 0.5)$

d) vertical asymptotes at $x = -2$ and $x = 6$, horizontal asymptote at $y = 0$; positive when $x \in (-\infty, -2)$ or $(6, \infty)$, negative when $x \in (-2, 6)$; increasing when $x \in (-\infty, 2)$, decreasing when $x \in (2, \infty)$

7. a) Use a graphing calculator to investigate the similarities and differences in the graphs of rational functions of the form

$$f(x) = \dfrac{8x}{nx + 1}, \text{ for } n = 1, 2, 4, \text{ and } 8.$$

b) Use your answer for part a) to make a conjecture about how the function changes as the values of n approach infinity.

c) If n is negative, how does the function change as the value of n approaches negative infinity? Choose your own values, and use them as examples to support your conclusions.

8. Without using a graphing calculator, compare the graphs of the rational functions $f(x) = \dfrac{3x + 4}{x - 1}$ and $g(x) = \dfrac{x - 1}{2x + 3}$.

9. The function $I(t) = \dfrac{15t + 25}{t}$ gives the value of an investment, in thousands of dollars, over t years.
   a) What is the value of the investment after 2 years?
   b) What is the value of the investment after 1 year?
   c) What is the value of the investment after 6 months?
   d) There is an asymptote on the graph of the function at $t = 0$. Does this make sense? Explain why or why not.
   e) Choose a very small value of t (a value near zero). Calculate the value of the investment at this time. Do you think that the function is accurate at this time? Why or why not?
   f) As time passes, what will the value of the investment approach?

10. An amount of chlorine is added to a swimming pool that contains
   A pure water. The concentration of chlorine, c, in the pool at t hours is given by $c(t) = \dfrac{2t}{2 + t}$, where c is measured in milligrams per litre. What happens to the concentration of chlorine in the pool during the 24 h period after the chlorine is added?

11. Describe the key characteristics of the graphs of rational functions of
   C the form $f(x) = \dfrac{ax + b}{cx + d}$. Explain how you can determine these characteristics using the equations of the functions. In what ways are the graphs of all the functions in this family alike? In what ways are they different? Use examples in your comparison.

Extending

12. Not all asymptotes are horizontal or vertical. Find a rational function that has an asymptote that is neither horizontal nor vertical, but slanted or oblique.

13. Use long division to rewrite $f(x) = \dfrac{2x^3 - 7x^2 + 8x - 5}{x - 1}$ in the form $f(x) = ax^2 + bx + c + \dfrac{k}{x - 1}$. What does this tell you about the end behaviour of the function? Graph the function. Include all asymptotes in your graph. Write the equations of the asymptotes.

14. Let $f(x) = \dfrac{3x - 1}{x^2 - 2x - 3}$, $g(x) = \dfrac{x^3 + 8}{x^2 + 9}$, $h(x) = \dfrac{x^3 - 3x}{x + 1}$, and $m(x) = \dfrac{x^2 + x - 12}{x^2 - 4}$.
   a) Which of these rational functions has a horizontal asymptote?
   b) Which has an oblique asymptote?
   c) Which has no vertical asymptote?
   d) Graph $y = m(x)$, showing the asymptotes and intercepts.

FREQUENTLY ASKED Questions

Q: **How can you use the graph of a linear or quadratic function to graph its reciprocal function?**

A: If you have the graph of a linear or quadratic function, you can draw the graph of its reciprocal function as follows:

1. Draw a vertical asymptote for the reciprocal function at each zero of the original function. The x-axis is a horizontal asymptote for the reciprocal function, unless the original function is a constant function.

2. The reciprocal function has the same positive/negative intervals that the original function has, so you can shade the regions where there will be no graph.

3. Mark any points where the y-value of the original function is 1 or -1. The reciprocal function also goes through these points.

4. The y-intercept of the reciprocal function is the reciprocal of the y-intercept of the original function. Determine and mark the y-intercept of the reciprocal function.

5. If the original function is quadratic, the reciprocal function has a local maximum/minimum at the same x-value as the vertex of the quadratic function. The y-value of this local maximum/minimum is the reciprocal of the y-value of the vertex. Determine and mark the local maximum/minimum point.

6. Draw the pieces of the graph of the reciprocal function through the marked points, approaching the asymptotes.

> **Study | Aid**
> - See Lesson 5.1, Examples 1 and 2.
> - Try Mid-Chapter Review Questions 1 and 2.

Q: **What are rational functions, and what are the characteristics of their graphs?**

A: Rational functions are quotients of polynomial functions. Their equations have the form $f(x) = \dfrac{p(x)}{q(x)}$, where $p(x)$ and $q(x)$ are polynomial functions and $q(x) \neq 0$. Graphs of rational functions may have vertical, horizontal, or oblique asymptotes. Some rational functions have holes in their graphs.

> **Study | Aid**
> - See Lesson 5.2.
> - Try Mid-Chapter Review Question 3.

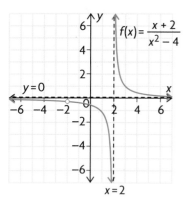

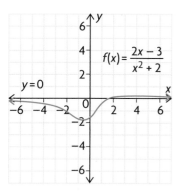

Q: **Most rational functions have one or more discontinuities. Where and why do these discontinuities occur? When is a rational function continuous?**

A: If the polynomial function in the denominator of a rational function has one or more zeros, the rational function will be discontinuous at these points. If a value of x can be zero in both the numerator and the denominator of a rational function (that is, if the numerator and denominator have a common linear factor), the result is a hole. This type of discontinuity is called a point discontinuity.

If a zero in the denominator does not correspond to a zero in the numerator, there will be a vertical asymptote at the x-value. This is called an infinite discontinuity.

For example, $f(x) = \dfrac{x+2}{x^2-4} = \dfrac{x+2}{(x-2)(x+2)}$ has a point

discontinuity where $x = -2$ because -2 is a zero of both the denominator, $q(x) = x^2 - 4$, and the numerator, $p(x) = x + 2$. The graph of $f(x)$ has an infinite discontinuity where $x = 2$ because 2 is a zero of $q(x)$ but not of $p(x)$. The graph also has a hole at $x = -2$ and a vertical asymptote at $x = 2$. Note that $\dfrac{p(-2)}{q(-2)} = \dfrac{0}{0}$,

but $\dfrac{p(2)}{q(2)} = \dfrac{4}{0}$.

If the polynomial function in the denominator of a rational function does not have any zeros, the rational function is continuous. Its graph is a smooth curve, with no breaks.

For example, $f(x) = \dfrac{2x-3}{x^2+2}$ is a continuous rational function with a horizontal asymptote at $y = 0$.

Q: **How do you determine the equations of the vertical and horizontal asymptotes of a rational function of the form**
$$f(x) = \frac{b}{cx+d} \text{ and } f(x) = \frac{ax+b}{cx+d}?$$

A: You can determine the equations of the vertical and horizontal asymptotes directly from the equation of a rational function of the form $f(x) = \dfrac{b}{cx+d}$ or $f(x) = \dfrac{ax+b}{cx+d}$. The vertical asymptote occurs at the zero of the function in the denominator. The equation of the vertical asymptote is $x = -\dfrac{d}{c}$. The horizontal asymptote describes the end behaviour of the function when $x \to \pm\infty$.

All rational functions of the form $f(x) = \dfrac{ax+b}{cx+d}$ have $y = \dfrac{a}{c}$ as a horizontal asymptote.

All rational functions of the form $f(x) = \dfrac{b}{cx+d}$ have $y = 0$ (the x-axis) as a horizontal asymptote.

PRACTICE Questions

Lesson 5.1

1. State the reciprocal of each function, and determine the locations of any vertical asymptotes.
   a) $f(x) = x - 3$
   b) $f(q) = -4q + 6$
   c) $f(z) = z^2 + 4z - 5$
   d) $f(d) = 6d^2 + 7d - 3$

2. For each function, determine the domain and range, intercepts, positive/negative intervals, and intervals of increase/decrease. Use this information to sketch the graphs of the function and its reciprocal.
   a) $f(x) = 4x + 6$
   b) $f(x) = x^2 - 4$
   c) $f(x) = x^2 + 6$
   d) $f(x) = -2x - 4$

Lesson 5.2

3. Different characteristics of the graph of a rational function are created by different characteristics of the function. List at least four characteristics of a graph and the characteristic of the function that causes each one. Make sure that you include a characteristic of a continuous rational function in your list.

4. For each function, determine the equations of any vertical asymptotes, the locations of any holes, and the existence of any horizontal asymptotes (other than the x-axis) or oblique asymptotes.
   a) $y = \dfrac{x}{x - 2}$
   b) $y = \dfrac{x - 1}{3x - 3}$
   c) $y = \dfrac{-7x}{4x + 2}$
   d) $y = \dfrac{x^2 + 2}{x - 6}$
   e) $y = \dfrac{1}{x^2 + 2x - 15}$

Lesson 5.3

5. List the functions that had a horizontal asymptote in question 4, and give the equation of the horizontal asymptote.

6. For each function, determine the domain, intercepts, asymptotes, and positive/negative intervals. Use these characteristics to sketch the graph of the function. Then describe where the function is increasing or decreasing.
   a) $f(x) = \dfrac{5}{x - 6}$
   b) $f(x) = \dfrac{3x}{x + 4}$
   c) $f(x) = \dfrac{5x + 10}{x + 2}$
   d) $f(x) = \dfrac{x - 2}{2x - 1}$

7. Kevin is trying to develop a reciprocal function to model some data that he has. He wants the horizontal asymptote to be $y = 7$. He also wants the graph to decrease and approach $y = 7$ as x approaches infinity, so he chooses the equation $y = \dfrac{7x + 6}{x}$. Then he decides that he needs the vertical asymptote to be $x = -1$, so he changes the equation to $y = \dfrac{7x + 6}{x + 1}$. What happened to the graph of Kevin's function? Did it give him the result he wanted? Explain why or why not.

8. For the function $f(x) = \dfrac{7x - m}{2 - nx}$, find the values of m and n such that the vertical asymptote is at $x = 6$ and the x-intercept is 5.

9. Create a rational function that has a domain of $\{x \in \mathbf{R} \mid x \neq -2\}$ and no vertical asymptote. Describe the graph of this function.

Solving Rational Equations

GOAL

Connect the solution to a rational equation with the graph of a rational function.

LEARN ABOUT the Math

When they work together, Stuart and Lucy can deliver flyers to all the homes in their neighbourhood in 42 min. When Lucy works alone, she can finish the deliveries in 13 min less time than Stuart can when he works alone.

? When Stuart works alone, how long does he take to deliver the flyers?

EXAMPLE 1   Selecting a strategy to solve a rational equation

Determine the time that Stuart takes to deliver the flyers when he works alone.

Solution A: Creating an equation and solving it using algebra

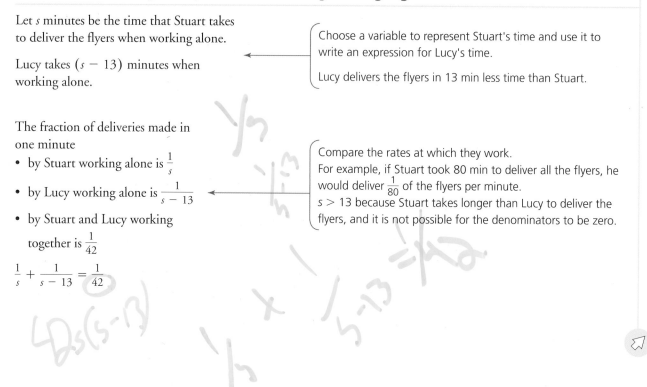

Let s minutes be the time that Stuart takes to deliver the flyers when working alone.

Lucy takes $(s - 13)$ minutes when working alone.

> Choose a variable to represent Stuart's time and use it to write an expression for Lucy's time.
>
> Lucy delivers the flyers in 13 min less time than Stuart.

The fraction of deliveries made in one minute

- by Stuart working alone is $\frac{1}{s}$

- by Lucy working alone is $\frac{1}{s - 13}$

- by Stuart and Lucy working together is $\frac{1}{42}$

$$\frac{1}{s} + \frac{1}{s - 13} = \frac{1}{42}$$

> Compare the rates at which they work.
> For example, if Stuart took 80 min to deliver all the flyers, he would deliver $\frac{1}{80}$ of the flyers per minute.
> $s > 13$ because Stuart takes longer than Lucy to deliver the flyers, and it is not possible for the denominators to be zero.

Multiply by the LCD.

$$42s(s-13)\left(\frac{1}{s}+\frac{1}{s-13}\right)=42s(s-13)\left(\frac{1}{42}\right)$$

$$\frac{42s(s-13)}{s}+\frac{42s(s-13)}{s-13}=\frac{42s(s-13)}{42}$$

There are no common factors in the denominators, so the LCD (lowest common denominator) is the product of the three denominators $42s(s-13)$. Multiply each term by the LCD, and then simplify the resulting rational expressions to remove all the denominators.

$$\frac{\overset{1}{42s}(s-13)}{\underset{1}{\cancel{s}}}+\frac{42s\cancel{(s-13)}}{\cancel{s-13}}=\frac{\overset{1}{42s}(s-13)}{\underset{1}{42}}$$

$$42(s-13)+42s=s(s-13)$$

$$42s-546+42s=s^2-13s$$
$$0=s^2-97s+546$$
$$0=(s-91)(s-6)$$
$$s=6 \text{ or } 91$$

Solve the quadratic equation by factoring or by using the quadratic formula.

$s>13$ so 6 is not an admissible solution.

Remember to look for inadmissible solutions by carefully considering both the context and the information given in the problem.

$$LS=\frac{1}{s}+\frac{1}{s-13}$$
$$=\frac{1}{91}+\frac{1}{91-13}$$
$$=\frac{1}{91}+\frac{1}{78}$$
$$=\frac{78+91}{7098}$$
$$=\frac{169}{7098}$$
$$=\frac{1}{42}$$
$$RS=\frac{1}{42}$$

Check the solution, $s=91$, by substituting it into the original equation.

Since LS = RS, $s=91$ is the solution.

It will take Stuart 91 min to deliver the flyers when working alone.

Solution B: Using the graph of a rational function to solve a rational equation

The equation that models the problem is $\frac{1}{s} + \frac{1}{s-13} = \frac{1}{42}$, where s represents the time, in minutes, that Stuart takes to deliver the flyers when working alone.

$$\frac{1}{s} + \frac{1}{s-13} - \frac{1}{42} = 0 \leftarrow$$

Subtract $\frac{1}{42}$ from each side.

To solve the equation, find the zeros of the function $f(s) = \frac{1}{s} + \frac{1}{s-13} - \frac{1}{42}$.

Graph $f(s) = \frac{1}{s} + \frac{1}{s-13} - \frac{1}{42}$. $\leftarrow$

Use the zero operation to determine the zeros.

From the equation, you can expect the graph to have vertical asymptotes at $s = 0$ and $s = 13$.

Since you are only interested in finding the zeros, you can limit the y-values to those close to zero.

Tech | **Support**

For help determining the zeros on a graphing calculator, see Technical Appendix, T-8.

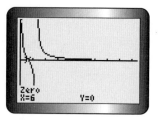

The first zero for $f(s)$ is $s = 6$.
Reject this solution since $s > 13$. $\leftarrow$

Determine the other zero.

You know that Lucy takes 13 min less time than Stuart takes, so Stuart must take longer than 13 min.

The solution $s = 6$ is inadmissible.

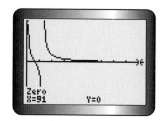

The solution is $s = 91$.

Stuart takes 91 min to deliver the flyers when working alone.

Reflecting

A. In Solution A, explain how a rational equation was created using the times given in the problem.

B. In Solution B, explain how finding the zeros of a rational function provided the solution to the problem.

C. Where did the inadmissible root obtained in Solution A show up in the graphical solution in Solution B? How was this root dealt with?

APPLY the Math

EXAMPLE **2**	Using an algebraic strategy to solve simple rational equations

Solve each rational equation.

a) $\dfrac{x-2}{x-3}=0$ **b)** $\dfrac{x+3}{x-4}=\dfrac{x-1}{x+2}$

Solution

a)

$$\dfrac{x-2}{x-3}=0,\, x\neq 3 \quad \longleftarrow \quad \left.\begin{array}{l}\text{Determine any restrictions on the}\\ \text{value of } x.\end{array}\right.$$

$$\cancel{(x-3)}^{1}\dfrac{(x-2)}{\cancel{(x-3)}_{1}}=0(x-3)$$

$$x-2=0 \quad \longleftarrow$$

$$x=2$$

$\left.\begin{array}{l}\text{Multiply both sides of the}\\ \text{equation by the LCD, } (x-3).\\[4pt]\text{Add 2 to each side.}\end{array}\right.$

To verify, graph $f(x)=\dfrac{x-2}{x-3}$ and use the zero operation to determine the zero.

$\left.\begin{array}{l}\text{From the equation, the graph}\\ \text{will have a vertical asymptote at}\\ x=3 \text{ and a horizontal}\\ \text{asymptote at } y=1.\end{array}\right.$

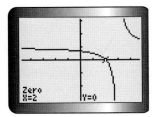

Zero
X=2   Y=0

The solution is $x=2$.

b) $\dfrac{x+3}{x-4} = \dfrac{x-1}{x+2}, x \neq -2, 4$ ← ⎤ Note the restrictions.

$(x-4)(x+2)\left(\dfrac{x+3}{x-4}\right) = (x-4)(x+2)\left(\dfrac{x-1}{x+2}\right)$ ← ⎡ Multiply each side
of the equation
by the LCD,
$(x-4)(x+2)$.

$\overset{1}{\cancel{(x-4)}}(x+2)\left(\dfrac{x+3}{\cancel{x-4}}\right) = (x-4)\overset{1}{\cancel{(x+2)}}\left(\dfrac{x-1}{\cancel{x+2}}\right)$ ← ⎤ Simplify.

$\underset{1}{(x+2)}(x+3) = (x-4)\underset{1}{(x-1)}$ ← ⎡ Expand. Subtract x^2, and
add $5x$ to both sides.

$x^2 + 5x + 6 = x^2 - 5x + 4$

$10x + 6 = 4$ ← ⎤ Solve the resulting linear
equation.

$10x = -2$

$x = -0.2$

To verify, graph $f(x) = \dfrac{x+3}{x-4} - \dfrac{x-1}{x+2}$

and use the zero operation to determine the zero.

⎡ Adjust the window
settings so you can
view enough of the
graph to see all the
possible zeros.

```
Zero
X=-.2          Y=0
```

```
WINDOW
Xmin=-9.4
Xmax=9.4
Xscl=1
Ymin=-10
Ymax=10
Yscl=1
Xres=1
```

The solution is $x = -0.2$.

EXAMPLE 3 **Connecting the solution to a problem with the zeros of a rational function**

Salt water is flowing into a large tank that contains pure water. The concentration of salt, c, in the tank at t minutes is given by $c(t) = \dfrac{10t}{25+t}$, where c is measured in grams per litre. When does the salt concentration in the tank reach 3.75 g/L?

Solution

If the salt concentration is 3.75, $c(t) = 3.75$.

$\dfrac{10t}{25+t} = 3.75$

⎡ Set the function expression
equal to 3.75. $25 + t \neq 0$,
and because t measures the
time since the salt water
started flowing, $t \geq 0$.

$(25+t)\left(\dfrac{10t}{25+t}\right) = 3.75(25+t)$

$\overset{1}{\cancel{(25+t)}}\dfrac{10t}{\underset{1}{\cancel{(25+t)}}} = 3.75(25+t)$ ← ⎡ Multiply both sides of the
equation by the LCD, $(25+t)$,
and solve the resulting linear
equation.

$10t = 93.75 + 3.75t$

$$10t - 3.75t = 93.75$$
$$6.25t = 93.75$$
$$\frac{6.25t}{6.25} = \frac{93.75}{6.25}$$
$$t = 15$$

> Use inverse operations to solve for t.

It takes 15 min for the salt concentration to reach 3.75 g/L.

To verify, graph $f(t) = \dfrac{10t}{25 + t}$ and $g(t) = 3.75$, and determine where the functions intersect.

> Use an appropriate window setting, based on the domain, $t \geq 0$.

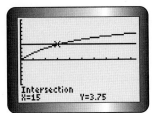

```
WINDOW
Xmin=0
Xmax=47
Xscl=5
Ymin=-10
Ymax=10
Yscl=1
Xres=1
```

Tech | Support

For help determining the point of intersection between two functions, see Technical Appendix, T-12.

Intersection
X=15   Y=3.75

> Use the intersect operation.

The salt concentration reaches 3.75 g/L after 15 min.

EXAMPLE 4   Using a rational function to model and solve a problem

Rima bought a case of concert T-shirts for $450. She kept two T-shirts for herself and sold the rest for $560, making a profit of $10 on each T-shirt. How many T-shirts were in the case?

Solution

Let the number of T-shirts in the case be x.

Buying price per T-shirt $= \dfrac{450}{x}$

Selling price per T-shirt $= \dfrac{560}{x - 2}$

> Rima paid $450 for x T-shirts, so each T-shirt cost her $\$\dfrac{450}{x}$.
>
> She kept two for herself, which left $x - 2$ T-shirts for her to sell.
>
> Rima sold $x - 2$ T-shirts for $560, so she charged $\$\dfrac{560}{x - 2}$ for each one.

$$\frac{560}{x-2} - \frac{450}{x} = 10$$

She made a profit of $10 on each T-shirt, so the difference between the selling price and the buying price was $10.

$$x(x-2)\left(\frac{560}{x-2} - \frac{450}{x}\right) = 10x(x-2)$$

Multiply both sides of the equation by the LCD, $x(x-2)$.

$$\frac{560x\cancel{(x-2)}^{\,1}}{\cancel{x-2}^{\,1}} - \frac{450\cancel{x}^{\,1}(x-2)}{\cancel{x}^{\,1}} = 10x(x-2)$$

$$560x - 450(x-2) = 10x(x-2)$$

Expand and collect all terms to one side of the equation.

$$560x - 450x + 900 = 10x^2 - 20x$$

$$0 = 10x^2 - 130x - 900$$

$$0 = 10(x^2 - 13x - 90)$$

Solve the resulting quadratic equation by factoring.

$$0 = 10(x-18)(x+5)$$

$$x = 18 \text{ or } -5$$

-5 is inadmissible since $x \geq 0$.
There were 18 T-shirts in the case.

You cannot have a negative number of T-shirts in the case.

To verify, graph $f(x) = \dfrac{560}{x-2} - \dfrac{450}{x} - 10$ and determine the zeros using the zero operation.

If $\dfrac{560}{x-2} - \dfrac{450}{x} = 10$, then $\dfrac{560}{x-2} - \dfrac{450}{x} - 10 = 0$.
Zeros for $f(x)$ are possible solutions to the problem.

Use an appropriate window setting, based on the domain, $x \geq 0$.

```
WINDOW
 Xmin=0
 Xmax=47
 Xscl=5
 Ymin=-10
 Ymax=10
 Yscl=1
 Xres=1
```

The zero occurs when $x = 18$.
Zoom out to check that there are no other zeros in the domain.

The other zero is for a negative value of x, which is inadmissible in the context of this problem.

There is no other zero in the domain.
There were 18 T-shirts in the case.

In Summary

Key Ideas

- You can solve a rational equation algebraically by multiplying each term in the equation by the lowest common denominator and solving the resulting polynomial equation.

- The root of the equation $\frac{ax + b}{cx + d} = 0$ is the zero (x-intercept) of the function $f(x) = \frac{ax + b}{cx + d}$.

- You can use graphing technology to solve a rational equation or verify the solution. Determine the zeros of the corresponding rational function, or determine the intersection of two functions.

Need to Know

- The zeros of a rational function are the zeros of the function in the numerator.

- Reciprocal functions do not have zeros. All functions of the form $f(x) = \frac{1}{g(x)}$ have the x-axis as a horizontal asymptote. They do not intersect the x-axis.

- When solving contextual problems, it is important to check for inadmissible solutions that are outside the domain determined by the context.

- When using a graphing calculator to determine a zero or intersection point, you can avoid inadmissible roots by matching the window settings to the domain of the function in the context of the problem.

CHECK Your Understanding

1. Are $x = 3$ and $x = -2$ solutions to the equation $\frac{2}{x} = \frac{x-1}{3}$? Explain how you know. _Both are right because it makes both sides equal._

2. Solve each equation algebraically. Then verify your solution using graphing technology.

   a) $\frac{x + 3}{x - 1} = 0$

   b) $\frac{x + 3}{x - 1} = 2$

   c) $\frac{x + 3}{x - 1} = 2x + 1$

   d) $\frac{3}{3x + 2} = \frac{6}{5x}$

3. For each rational equation, write a function whose zeros are the solutions.

   a) $\frac{x - 3}{x + 3} = 2$

   b) $\frac{3x - 1}{x} = \frac{5}{2}$

   c) $\frac{x - 1}{x} = \frac{x + 1}{x + 3}$

   d) $\frac{x - 2}{x + 3} = \frac{x - 4}{x + 5}$

4. Solve each equation in question 3 algebraically, and verify your solution using a graphing calculator.

PRACTISING

5. Solve each equation algebraically.

a) $\dfrac{2}{x} + \dfrac{5}{3} = \dfrac{7}{x}$

d) $\dfrac{2}{x+1} + \dfrac{1}{x+1} = 3$

b) $\dfrac{10}{x+3} + \dfrac{10}{3} = 6$

e) $\dfrac{2}{2x+1} = \dfrac{5}{4-x}$

c) $\dfrac{2x}{x-3} = 1 - \dfrac{6}{x-3}$

f) $\dfrac{5}{x-2} = \dfrac{4}{x+3}$

6. Solve each equation algebraically.

a) $\dfrac{2x}{2x+1} = \dfrac{5}{4-x}$

d) $x + \dfrac{x}{x-2} = 0$

b) $\dfrac{3}{x} + \dfrac{4}{x+1} = 2$

e) $\dfrac{1}{x+2} + \dfrac{24}{x+3} = 13$

c) $\dfrac{2x}{5} = \dfrac{x^2 - 5x}{5x}$

f) $\dfrac{-2}{x-1} = \dfrac{x-8}{x+1}$

7. Solve each equation using graphing technology. Round your answers to two decimal places, if necessary.

a) $\dfrac{2}{x+2} = \dfrac{3}{x+6}$

d) $\dfrac{1}{x} - \dfrac{1}{45} = \dfrac{1}{2x-3}$

b) $\dfrac{2x-5}{x+10} = \dfrac{1}{x-6}$

e) $\dfrac{2x+3}{3x-1} = \dfrac{x+2}{4}$

c) $\dfrac{1}{x-3} = \dfrac{x+2}{7x+14}$

f) $\dfrac{1}{x} = \dfrac{2}{x} + 1 + \dfrac{1}{1-x}$

8. **a)** Use algebra to solve $\dfrac{x+1}{x-2} = \dfrac{x+3}{x-4}$. Explain your steps.

   b) Verify your answer in part a) using substitution.

   c) Verify your answer in part a) using a graphing calculator.

9. The Greek mathematician Pythagoras is credited with the discovery of the Golden Rectangle. This is considered to be the rectangle with the dimensions that are the most visually appealing. In a Golden Rectangle, the length and width are related by the proportion $\dfrac{l}{w} = \dfrac{w}{l-w}$. A billboard with a length of 15 m is going to be built. What must its width be to form a Golden Rectangle?

10. The Turtledove Chocolate factory has two chocolate machines. Machine A takes s minutes to fill a case with chocolates, and machine B takes $s + 10$ minutes to fill a case. Working together, the two machines take 15 min to fill a case. Approximately how long does each machine take to fill a case?

11. Tayla purchased a large box of comic books for $300. She gave 15 of the comic books to her brother and then sold the rest on an Internet website for $330, making a profit of $1.50 on each one. How many comic books were in the box? What was the original price of each comic book?

12. Polluted water flows into a pond. The concentration of pollutant,
A c, in the pond at time t minutes is modelled by the equation
$c(t) = 9 - 90\,000\left(\dfrac{1}{10\,000 + 3t}\right)$, where c is measured in kilograms per cubic metre.

   a) When will the concentration of pollutant in the pond reach $6\ \text{kg/m}^3$?

   b) What will happen to the concentration of pollutant over time?

13. Three employees work at a shipping warehouse. Tom can fill an order in
T s minutes. Paco can fill an order in $s - 2$ minutes. Carl can fill an order in $s + 1$ minutes. When Tom and Paco work together, they take about 1 minute and 20 seconds to fill an order. When Paco and Carl work together, they take about 1 minute and 30 seconds to fill an order.

   a) How long does each person take to fill an order?

   b) How long would all three of them, working together, take to fill an order?

14. Compare and contrast the different methods you can use to
C solve a rational equation. Make a list of the advantages and disadvantages of each method.

Extending

15. Solve $\dfrac{x^2 - 6x + 5}{x^2 - 2x - 3} = \dfrac{2 - 3x}{x^2 + 3x + 3}$ correct to two decimal places.

16. Objects A and B move along a straight line. Their positions, s, with respect to an origin, at t seconds, are modelled by the following functions:

Object A: $s(t) = \dfrac{7t}{t^2 + 1}$

Object B: $s(t) = t + \dfrac{5}{t + 2}$

   a) When are the objects at the same position?

   b) When is object A closer to the origin than object B?

5.5 Solving Rational Inequalities

YOU WILL NEED

- graphing calculator

GOAL

GOAL

Solve rational inequalities using algebraic and graphical approaches.

LEARN ABOUT the Math

rational inequality

a statement that one rational expression is less than or greater than another rational expression $\left(\text{e.g.,} \frac{2x}{x+3} > \frac{x-1}{5x} \right)$

The function $P(t) = \frac{20t}{t+1}$ models the population, in thousands, of Nickelford, t years after 1997. The population, in thousands, of nearby New Ironfield is modelled by $Q(t) = \frac{240}{t+8}$.

❓ How can you determine the time period when the population of New Ironfield exceeded the population of Nickelford?

EXAMPLE 1 | Selecting a strategy to solve a problem

Determine the interval(s) of t where the values of $Q(t)$ are greater than the values of $P(t)$.

Solution A: Using an algebraic strategy to solve an inequality

$$\frac{240}{t+8} > \frac{20t}{t+1} \longleftarrow$$

The population of New Ironfield exceeds the population of Nickelford when $Q(t) > P(t)$.

$t \geq 0$ in the context of this problem. There are no other restrictions on the expressions in the **rational inequality** since the values that make both expressions undefined are negative numbers.

$$(t + 8)(t + 1)\left(\frac{240}{t + 8}\right) > (t + 8)(t + 1)\left(\frac{20t}{t + 1}\right)$$

$$\overset{1}{\cancel{(t+8)}}(t + 1)\left(\frac{240}{\underset{1}{\cancel{t+8}}}\right) > (t + 8)\overset{1}{\cancel{(t+1)}}\left(\frac{20t}{\underset{1}{\cancel{t+1}}}\right)$$

| | Multiply both sides of the inequality by the LCD. The value of the LCD is always positive, since $t \geq 0$, so the inequality sign is unchanged.

$$240(t + 1) > 20t(t + 8)$$
$$240t + 240 > 20t^2 + 160t$$
$$0 > 20t^2 + 160t - 240t - 240$$
$$0 > 20t^2 - 80t - 240$$
$$0 > 20(t^2 - 4t - 12)$$
$$0 > 20(t - 6)(t + 2)$$

Expand and simplify both sides. Then subtract $240t$ and 240 from both sides.

Factor the resulting quadratic expression.

Examine the sign of the factored polynomial expression on the right side of the inequality.

	$t < -2$	$-2 < t < 6$	$t > 6$
$20(t - 6)$	$-$	$-$	$+$
$t + 2$	$-$	$+$	$+$
$20(t - 6)(t + 2)$	$(-)(-) = +$	$(-)(+) = -$	$(+)(+) = +$

The inequality $0 > 20(t - 6)(t + 2)$ is true when $-2 < t < 6$.

The inequality $0 > 20(t - 6)(t + 2)$ is true when the expression on the right side is negative. The sign of the factored quadratic expression changes when $t = -2$ and when $t = 6$, because the expression is zero at these values. Use a table to determine when the sign of the expression is negative on each side of these values.

The population of New Ironfield exceeded the population of Nickelford for six years after 1997, until 2003.

Since the domain is $t \geq 0$, however, numbers that are negative cannot be included. Therefore, the solution is $0 \leq t < 6$.

Solution B: Solving a rational inequality by graphing two rational functions

To solve $Q(t) > P(t)$, graph $Q(t) = \frac{240}{t + 8}$ and $P(t) = \frac{20t}{t + 1}$ using graphing technology, and determine the value of t at the intersection point(s).

It helps to bold the graph of $Q(t)$ so you can remember which graph is which. Use window settings that reflect the domain of the functions.

There is only one intersection within the domain of the functions.

From the graphs, $Q(t) > P(t)$ for $0 \le t < 6$.
The population of New Ironfield exceeded the
population of Nickelford until 2003.

If $Q(t) > P(t)$, the graph of $Q(t)$
lies above the graph of $P(t)$.
Looking at the graphs, this is true
for the parts of the graph of $Q(t)$
up to the intersection point at $t = 6$.
The graphs will not intersect again
because each graph is approaching
a different horizontal asymptote.
From the defining equations, the
graph of $Q(t)$ is approaching the
line $Q = 0$ while the graph of $P(t)$ is
approaching the line $P = 20$.

Solution C: Solving a rational inequality by determining the zeros of a combined function

When $Q(t) > P(t)$, $Q(t) - P(t) > 0$.

Graph $f(t) = Q(t) - P(t) = \dfrac{240}{t + 8} - \dfrac{20t}{t + 1}$ and use the
zero operation to locate the zero.

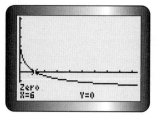

Combine the two population
functions into a single function,
$f(t) = Q(t) - P(t)$. When
$Q(t) > P(t)$, $f(t)$ will have
positive values.

When a function has positive values,
its graph lies above the x-axis.

The graph is above the x-axis for $0 \le t < 6$.

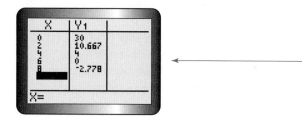

By examining the values of $f(t)$
in a table, you can verify that the
function continues to decrease
but remains positive when
$0 \le t < 6$.

$f(t)$ has positive values for $0 \le t < 6$.
For the six years after 1997, the population of New Ironfield
exceeded the population of Nickelford.

Reflecting

A. How is the solution to an inequality different from the solution to an equation?

B. In Solution A, how was the rational inequality manipulated to obtain a simpler quadratic inequality?

C. In Solution B, how were the graphs of the related rational functions used to find the solution to an inequality?

D. In Solution C, how did creating a new function help to solve the inequality?

APPLY the Math

EXAMPLE **2**	Selecting a strategy to solve an inequality that involves a linear function and a reciprocal function

Solve $x - 2 < \dfrac{8}{x}$.

Solution A: Using an algebraic strategy and a sign chart

$$x - 2 < \frac{8}{x}, x \neq 0$$

$$x - 2 - \frac{8}{x} < 0$$

$$\frac{x^2}{x} - \frac{2x}{x} - \frac{8}{x} < 0$$

$$\frac{x^2 - 2x - 8}{x} < 0$$

$$\frac{(x - 4)(x + 2)}{x} < 0$$

Determine any restrictions on x.
Subtract $\frac{8}{x}$ from both sides.

x is the LCD and it can be positive or negative. Multiplying both sides by x would require that two cases be considered, since the inequality sign must be reversed when multiplying by a negative. The alternative is to create an expression with a common denominator, x.

Combine the terms to create a single rational expression.

Factor the numerator.

Examine the sign of the rational expression.

	$x < -2$	$-2 < x < 0$	$0 < x < 4$	$x > 4$
$x - 4$	$-$	$-$	$-$	$+$
$x + 2$	$-$	$+$	$+$	$+$
x	$-$	$-$	$+$	$+$
$\dfrac{(x-4)(x+2)}{x}$	$\dfrac{(-)(-)}{-} = -$	$\dfrac{(-)(+)}{-} = +$	$\dfrac{(-)(+)}{+} = -$	$\dfrac{(+)(+)}{+} = +$

> The sign of a rational expression changes each time the sign of one of its factors changes. Choose a test value in each interval to determine the sign of each part of the expression. Then determine the intervals where the overall expression is negative.

The overall expression is negative when $x < -2$ or when $0 < x < 4$.

The inequality is true when $x \in (-\infty, -2)$ or $x \in (0, 4)$.

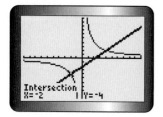

> Write the solution in interval or set notation, and draw the solution set on a number line.

Solution B: Using graphing technology

$$x - 2 < \frac{8}{x}, x \neq 0$$

Let $f(x) = x - 2$ and $g(x) = \dfrac{8}{x}$.

The solution set for the inequality will be all x-values for which $f(x) < g(x)$.

> Write each side of the inequality as its own function. Enter both functions in the equation editor, using a bold line for $f(x)$.

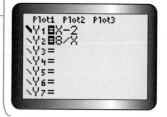

Graph $f(x)$ and $g(x)$ on the same axes, and use the intersect operation to determine the intersection points.

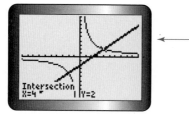

> $f(x) < g(x)$ where the bold graph of $f(x)$ lies beneath the graph of $g(x)$. Notice that the bold linear function is above the reciprocal function on the left side and close to the vertical asymptote, $x = 0$. It is below the reciprocal function on the right side and close to this asymptote.

$f(x) < g(x)$ when $x < -2$ or when $0 < x < 4$.

The solution set is $\{x \in \mathbf{R} \mid x < -2 \text{ or } 0 < x < 4\}$.

> You can also use interval notation or a number line to describe the solution set, as in Solution A.

EXAMPLE 3	Determining the solution set for an inequality that involves two rational functions

Determine the solution set for the inequality $\frac{x+3}{x+1} \geq \frac{x-2}{x-3}$.

Solution A: Using algebra and a sign chart

Rewrite $\frac{x+3}{x+1} \geq \frac{x-2}{x-3}$, $x \neq -1, 3$,

as $\frac{x+3}{x+1} - \frac{x-2}{x-3} \geq 0$.

$$\frac{(x-3)(x+3)}{(x-3)(x+1)} - \frac{(x-2)(x+1)}{(x-3)(x+1)} \geq 0$$

$$\frac{x^2 - 9 - (x^2 - x - 2)}{(x-3)(x+1)} \geq 0$$

$$\frac{x^2 - 9 - x^2 + x + 2}{(x-3)(x+1)} \geq 0$$

$$\frac{x-7}{(x-3)(x+1)} \geq 0$$

> Note the restrictions on x.
> Subtract $\frac{x-2}{x-3}$ from both sides to create an inequality with zero on the right side.
>
> Subtract the rational expressions on the left side using a common denominator.
>
> Expand and simplify the numerator.
>
> A rational expression is zero when its numerator is zero.

The rational expression is equal to zero when $x = 7$, so 7 is included in the solution set.

Examine the sign of the simplified rational expression on the intervals shown to determine where the rational expression is greater than zero.

	$x < -1$	$-1 < x < 3$	$3 < x < 7$	$x > 7$
$x - 7$	$-$	$-$	$-$	$+$
$x - 3$	$-$	$-$	$+$	$+$
$x + 1$	$-$	$+$	$+$	$+$
$\dfrac{(x-7)}{(x-3)(x+1)}$	$\dfrac{-}{(-)(-)} = -$	$\dfrac{-}{(-)(+)} = +$	$\dfrac{-}{(+)(+)} = -$	$\dfrac{+}{(+)(+)} = +$

> The expression is undefined at $x = -1$ and $x = 3$. It is equal to 0 at $x = 7$. These numbers create four intervals to consider. Choose a test value in each interval to determine the sign of each part of the expression. Then determine the intervals where the overall expression is positive.

The solution set is $\{x \in \mathbf{R} \mid -1 < x < 3 \text{ or } x \geq 7\}$.

Solution B: Using graphing technology

$$\frac{x+3}{x+1} \geq \frac{x-2}{x-3}, x \neq -1, 3$$

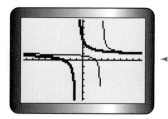

Use each side of the inequality to define a function. Graph $f(x) = \frac{x+3}{x+1}$ with a bold line and $g(x) = \frac{x-2}{x-3}$ with a regular line.

The graph of $f(x)$ has a vertical asymptote at $x = -1$.
The graph for $g(x)$ has a vertical asymptote at $x = 3$.
Both graphs have $y = 1$ as a horizontal asymptote.

Determine the equations of the asymptotes from the equations of the functions.

Use the intersect operation to locate any intersection points.

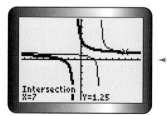

It looks as though the graphs might intersect on the left side of the screen, as well as on the right side. No matter how far you trace along the left branches, however, you never reach a point where the y-value is the same on both curves.

The functions are equal when $x = 7$.

$f(x) > g(x)$ between the asymptotes at $x = -1$ and $x = 3$, and for $x > 7$.

$f(x) = g(x)$ when $x = 7$.

The bold graph of $f(x)$ is above the graph of $g(x)$ between the two vertical asymptotes and then after the intersection point.

The solution set for $\frac{x+3}{x+1} \geq \frac{x-2}{x-3}$ is

In Summary

Key Ideas

- Solving an inequality means finding all the possible values of the variable that satisfy the inequality.
- To solve a rational inequality algebraically, rearrange the inequality so that one side is zero. Combine the expressions on the no-zero side using a common denominator. Make a table to examine the sign of each factor and the sign of the entire expression on the intervals created by the zeros of the numerator and the denominator.
- Only when you are certain that each denominator is positive can you multiply both sides by the lowest common denominator to make the inequality easier to solve.
- You can always solve a rational inequality using graphing technology.

Need to Know

- When multiplying or dividing both sides of an inequality by a negative it is necessary to reverse the inequality sign to maintain equivalence.
- You can solve an inequality using graphing technology by graphing the functions on each side of the inequality sign and then identifying all the intervals created by the vertical asymptotes and points of intersection. For x-values that satisfy $f(x) > g(x)$, identify the specific intervals where the graph of $f(x)$ is above the graph of $g(x)$. For x-values that satisfy $f(x) < g(x)$, identify the specific intervals where the graph of $f(x)$ is below the graph of $g(x)$.
  Consider the following graph:

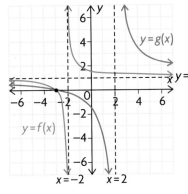

In this graph, there are four intervals to consider: $(-\infty, -3)$, $(-3, -2)$, $(-2, 2)$ and $(2, \infty)$. In these intervals, $f(x) > g(x)$ when $x \in (-\infty, -3)$ or $(-2, 2)$, and $f(x) < g(x)$ when $x \in (-3, -2)$ or $(2, \infty)$.

- You can also solve an inequality using graphing technology by creating an equivalent inequality with zero on one side and then identifying the intervals created by the zeros on the graph of the new function. Finding where the graph lies above the x-axis (where $f(x) > 0$) or below the x-axis (where $f(x) < 0$) defines the solutions to the inequality.

CHECK Your Understanding

1. Use the graph shown to determine the solution set for each of the following inequalities.

   a) $\dfrac{x + 5}{x - 1} < 4$

   b) $4x - 1 > \dfrac{x + 5}{x - 1}$

2. a) Show that the inequality $\dfrac{6x}{x + 3} \leq 4$ is equivalent to the inequality $\dfrac{2(x - 6)}{(x + 3)} \leq 0$.

   b) Sketch the solution on a number line.

   c) Write the solution using interval notation.

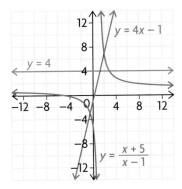

3. a) Show that the inequality $x + 2 > \dfrac{15}{x}$ is equivalent to the inequality $\dfrac{(x + 5)(x - 3)}{x} > 0$.

b) Use a table to determine the positive/negative intervals for
$$f(x) = \dfrac{(x + 5)(x - 3)}{x}.$$

c) State the solution to the inequality using both set notation and interval notation.

PRACTISING

4. Use algebra to find the solution set for each inequality. Verify your answer using graphing technology.

a) $\dfrac{1}{x + 5} > 2$

b) $\dfrac{1}{2x + 10} < \dfrac{1}{x + 3}$

c) $\dfrac{3}{x - 2} < \dfrac{4}{x}$

d) $\dfrac{7}{x - 3} \geq \dfrac{2}{x + 4}$

e) $\dfrac{-6}{x + 1} > \dfrac{1}{x}$

f) $\dfrac{-5}{x - 4} < \dfrac{3}{x + 1}$

5. Use algebra to obtain a factorable expression from each inequality, if necessary. Then use a table to determine interval(s) in which the inequality is true.

a) $\dfrac{t^2 - t - 12}{t - 1} < 0$

b) $\dfrac{t^2 + t - 6}{t - 4} \geq 0$

c) $\dfrac{6t^2 - 5t + 1}{2t + 1} > 0$

d) $t - 1 < \dfrac{30}{5t}$

e) $\dfrac{2t - 10}{t} > t + 5$

f) $\dfrac{-t}{4t - 1} \geq \dfrac{2}{t - 9}$

6. Use graphing technology to solve each inequality.

a) $\dfrac{x + 3}{x - 4} \geq \dfrac{x - 1}{x + 6}$

b) $x + 5 < \dfrac{x}{2x + 6}$

c) $\dfrac{x}{x + 4} \leq \dfrac{1}{x + 1}$

d) $\dfrac{x}{x + 9} \geq \dfrac{1}{x + 1}$

e) $\dfrac{x - 8}{x} > 3 - x$

f) $\dfrac{x^2 - 16}{(x - 1)^2} \geq 0$

7. a) Find all the values of x that make the following inequality true:
$$\dfrac{3x - 8}{2x - 1} > \dfrac{x - 4}{x + 1}$$

b) Graph the solution set on a number line. Write the solution set using interval notation and set notation.

8. a) Use an algebraic strategy to solve the inequality $\dfrac{-6t}{t-2} < \dfrac{-30}{t-2}$.

 b) Graph both inequalities to verify your solution.

 c) Can these rational expressions be used to model a real-world situation? Explain.

9. The equation $f(t) = \dfrac{5t}{t^2 + 3t + 2}$ models the bacteria count, in thousands, for a sample of tap water that is left to sit over time, t, in days. The equation $g(t) = \dfrac{15t}{t^2 + 9}$ models the bacteria count, in thousands, for a sample of pond water that is also left to sit over several days. In both models, $t > 0$. Will the bacteria count for the tap water sample ever exceed the bacteria count for the pond water? Justify your answer.

10. Consider the inequality $0.5x - 2 < \dfrac{5}{2x}$.

 a) Rewrite the inequality so that there is a single, simplified expression on one side and a zero on the other side.

 b) List all the factors of the rational expression in a table, and determine on which intervals the inequality is true.

11. An economist for a sporting goods company estimates the revenue and cost functions for the production of a new snowboard. These functions are $R(x) = -x^2 + 10x$ and $C(x) = 4x + 5$, respectively, where x is the number of snowboards produced, in thousands. The average profit is defined by the function $AP(x) = \dfrac{P(x)}{x}$, where $P(x)$ is the profit function. Determine the production levels that make $AP(x) > 0$.

12. a) Explain why the inequalities $\dfrac{x+1}{x-1} < \dfrac{x+3}{x+2}$ and $\dfrac{x+5}{(x-1)(x+2)} < 0$ are equivalent.

 b) Describe how you would use a graphing calculator to solve these inequalities.

 c) Explain how you would use a table to solve these inequalities.

Extending

13. Solve $\left| \dfrac{x}{x-4} \right| \geq 1$.

14. Solve $\dfrac{1}{\sin x} < 4,\ 0° \leq x \leq 360°$.

15. Solve $\dfrac{\cos(x)}{x} > 0.5,\ 0° < x < 90°$.

5.6 Rates of Change in Rational Functions

GOAL

Determine average rates of change, and estimate instantaneous rates of change for rational functions.

LEARN ABOUT the Math

The instantaneous rate of change at a point on a revenue function is called the *marginal revenue*. It is a measure of the estimated additional revenue from selling one more item.

For example, the demand equation for a toothbrush is $p(x) = \dfrac{5}{2 + x}$, where x is the number of toothbrushes sold, in thousands, and p is the price, in dollars.

> ❓ **What is the marginal revenue when 1500 toothbrushes are sold? When is the marginal revenue the greatest? When is it the least?**

EXAMPLE 1 | **Selecting a strategy to determine instantaneous rates of change**

Determine the marginal revenue when 1500 toothbrushes are sold and when it is the greatest and the least.

Solution A: Calculating the average rate of change by squeezing centred intervals around $x = 1.5$

$$
\begin{aligned}
\text{Revenue } R(x) &= xp(x) \\
&= \frac{5x}{2 + x}
\end{aligned}
$$

← (Revenue = Number of items sold × Price)

The average rate of change close to $x = 1.5$ is shown in the following table.

Centred Intervals	Average Rate of Change $\dfrac{R(x_2) - R(x_1)}{x_2 - x_1}$
$1.4 \le x \le 1.6$	0.817
$1.45 \le x \le 1.55$	0.816
$1.49 \le x \le 1.51$	0.816
$1.499 \le x \le 1.501$	0.816

(x is measured in thousands, so when 1500 toothbrushes are sold, $x = 1.5$.
The average rate of change from $(x_1, R(x_1))$ to $(x_2, R(x_2))$ is the slope of the secant that joins each pair of endpoints.)

The average rate of change approaches 0.816. The marginal revenue when 1500 toothbrushes are sold is $0.82 per toothbrush.

> When x_1 and x_2 are very close to each other, the slope of the secant is approximately the same as the slope of the tangent. The slopes of the secants near the point where $x = 1.5$ approach 0.816.

Sketch the graph of $R(x) = \dfrac{5x}{2 + x}$.

The graph starts at $(0, 0)$ and has a horizontal asymptote at $y = 5$.

> The vertical asymptote at $x = -2$ is not in the domain of $R(x)$, since $x \geq 0$, so it can be ignored.

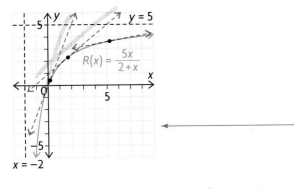

> In the context of the problem, x and $R(x)$ have only positive values. Examine the slope of the tangent lines at various points along the domain of the revenue graph. The slope is the greatest at the beginning of the graph and then decreases as x increases.

The marginal revenue is the greatest when $x = 0$ and then decreases from there, approaching zero, as the graph gets closer to the horizontal asymptote.

Solution B: Using the difference quotient and graphing technology to analyze the revenue function

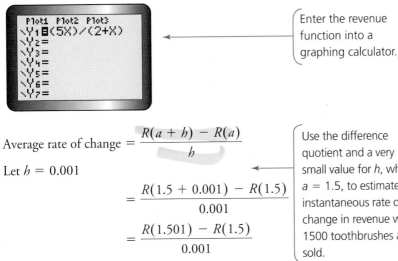

> Enter the revenue function into a graphing calculator.

Average rate of change $= \dfrac{R(a + h) - R(a)}{h}$

Let $h = 0.001$

> Use the difference quotient and a very small value for h, where $a = 1.5$, to estimate the instantaneous rate of change in revenue when 1500 toothbrushes are sold.

$$= \frac{R(1.5 + 0.001) - R(1.5)}{0.001}$$

$$= \frac{R(1.501) - R(1.5)}{0.001}$$

Enter the rate of change expression into the graphing calculator to determine its value, using the equation entered into Y1.

The average rate of change is about 0.816. The marginal revenue when 1500 toothbrushes are sold is $0.82 per toothbrush.

To verify, graph the revenue function $R(x) = xp(x) = \dfrac{5x}{2 + x}$ and draw a tangent line at $x = 1.5$.

Since x and $R(x)$ only have positive values, graph the function in the first quadrant.

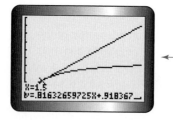

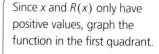

When 1500 toothbrushes are sold, the marginal revenue is $0.82 per toothbrush.

Use the DRAW feature of the graphing calculator to draw a tangent line where $x = 1.5$.

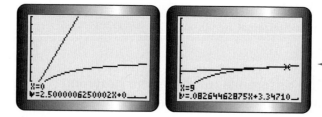

The tangent lines to this curve are steepest at the beginning of the curve. Their slopes decrease as x increases.

The marginal revenue is the greatest when $x = 0$.

The marginal revenue decreases to very small values as x increases.

Reflecting

A. In Solution A, how were average rates of change used to estimate the instantaneous rate of change at a point?

B. In Solutions A and B, how were graphs used to estimate the instantaneous rate of change at a point?

C. In each solution, how was it determined where the marginal revenue was the greatest? Why was it not possible to determine the least marginal revenue?

D. What are the advantages and disadvantages of each method to determine the instantaneous rate of change?

APPLY the Math

EXAMPLE 2 Connecting the instantaneous rate of change to the slope of a tangent

a) Estimate the slope of the tangent to the graph of $f(x) = \dfrac{x}{x+3}$ at the point where $x = -5$.

b) Why can there not be a tangent line where $x = -3$?

Solution

a) $f(x) = \dfrac{x}{x+3}$

average rate of change $= \dfrac{f(a+h) - f(a)}{h}$

Let $h = 0.001$

$$= \dfrac{f(-5 + 0.001) - f(-5)}{0.001}$$

$$= \dfrac{f(-4.999) - f(-5)}{0.001}$$

$$= \dfrac{\left(\dfrac{-4.999}{-4.999+3}\right) - \left(\dfrac{-5}{-5+3}\right)}{0.001}$$

$$= \dfrac{2.500\,750\,375 - 2.5}{0.001}$$

$$\doteq 0.7504$$

> Use the difference quotient and a very small value for h close to $a = -5$ to estimate the slope of the tangent where $x = -5$.

The slope of the tangent at $x = -5$ is 0.75.

b) The value -3 is not in the domain of $f(x)$, so no tangent line is possible there. The graph of $f(x)$ has a vertical asymptote at $x = -3$.

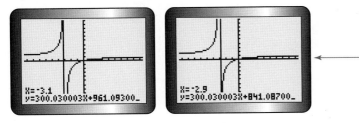

X=-3.1
y=300.030003X+961.09300_

X=-2.9
y=300.030003X+841.08700_

> As x approaches -3 from the left and from the right, the tangent lines are very steep. The tangent lines approach a vertical line, but are never actually vertical. There is no point on the graph with an x-coordinate of -3, so there is no tangent line there.

EXAMPLE **3**

Selecting a graphing strategy to solve a problem that involves average and instantaneous rates of change

The snowshoe hare population in a newly created conservation area can be predicted over time by the model $p(t) = 50 + \dfrac{2500t^2}{25 + t^2}$, where p represents the population size and t is the time in years since the opening of the conservation area. Determine when the hare population will increase most rapidly, and estimate the instantaneous rate of change in population at this time.

Solution

Graph $p(t) = 50 + \dfrac{2500t^2}{25 + t^2}$ for $0 \le t \le 20$.

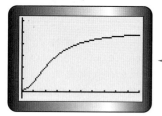

$p(t) \ge 0$, but you can set the minimum y-value to a negative number to allow some space for displayed values.

The slopes of the tangent lines increase slowly at the beginning of the graph. The slopes start to increase more rapidly around $t = 2$. They begin to decrease after $t = 3$.

Draw tangent lines between 2 and 3, and look for the tangent line that has the greatest slope.

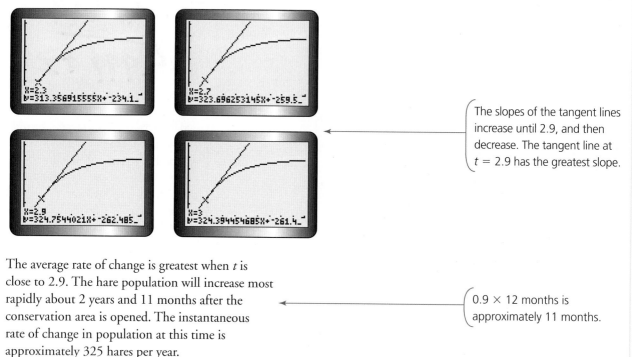

The slopes of the tangent lines increase until 2.9, and then decrease. The tangent line at $t = 2.9$ has the greatest slope.

The average rate of change is greatest when t is close to 2.9. The hare population will increase most rapidly about 2 years and 11 months after the conservation area is opened. The instantaneous rate of change in population at this time is approximately 325 hares per year.

0.9×12 months is approximately 11 months.

In Summary

Key Ideas

- The methods that were previously used to calculate the average rate of change and estimate the instantaneous rate of change can be used for rational functions.
- You cannot determine the average and instantaneous rates of change of a rational function at a point where the graph is discontinuous (that is, where there is a hole or a vertical asymptote).

Need to Know

- The average rate of change of a rational function, $y = f(x)$, on the interval from $x_1 \leq x \leq x_2$ is $\frac{f(x_2) - f(x_1)}{x_2 - x_1}$. Graphically, this is equivalent to the slope of the secant line that passes through the points (x_1, y_1) and (x_2, y_2) on the graph of $y = f(x)$.
- The instantaneous rate of change of a rational function, $y = f(x)$, at $x = a$ can be approximated using the difference quotient $\frac{f(a + h) - f(a)}{h}$ and a very small value of h. Graphically, this is equivalent to estimating the slope of the tangent line that passes through the point $(a, f(a))$ on the graph of $y = f(x)$.
- The instantaneous rate of change at a vertical asymptote is undefined. The instantaneous rates of change at points that are approaching a vertical asymptote become very large positive or very large negative values. The instantaneous rate of change near a horizontal asymptote approaches zero.

CHECK Your Understanding

1. The graph of a rational function is shown.
   a) Determine the average rate of change of the function over the interval $2 \leq x \leq 7$.
   b) Copy the graph, and draw a tangent line at the point where $x = 2$. Determine the slope of the tangent line to estimate the instantaneous rate of change at this point.

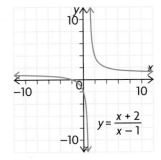

$$y = \frac{x + 2}{x - 1}$$

2. Estimate the instantaneous rate of change of the function in question 1 at $x = 2$ by determining the slope of a secant line from the point where $x = 2$ to the point where $x = 2.01$. Compare your answer with your answer for question 1, part b).

3. Use graphing technology to estimate the instantaneous rate of change of the function in question 1 at $x = 2$.

PRACTISING

4. Estimate the instantaneous rate of change of $f(x) = \frac{x}{x - 4}$ at the point $(2, -1)$.

5. Select a strategy to estimate the instantaneous rate of change of each
K function at the given point.

a) $y = \dfrac{1}{25 - x}$, where $x = 13$

b) $y = \dfrac{17x + 3}{x^2 + 6}$, where $x = -5$

c) $y = \dfrac{x + 3}{x - 2}$, where $x = 4$

d) $y = \dfrac{-3x^2 + 5x + 6}{x + 6}$, where $x = -3$

6. Determine the slope of the line that is tangent to the graph of each
function at the given point. Then determine the value of x at which
there is no tangent line.

a) $f(x) = \dfrac{-5x}{2x + 3}$, where $x = 2$

b) $f(x) = \dfrac{x - 6}{x + 5}$, where $x = -7$

c) $f(x) = \dfrac{2x^2 - 6x}{3x + 5}$, where $x = -2$

d) $f(x) = \dfrac{5}{x - 6}$, where $x = 4$

7. When polluted water begins to flow into an unpolluted pond, the
A concentration of pollutant, c, in the pond at t minutes is modelled by
$c(t) = \dfrac{27t}{10\,000 + 3t}$, where c is measured in kilograms per cubic metre.
Determine the rate at which the concentration is changing after

a) 1 h

b) one week

8. The demand function for snack cakes at a large bakery is given by the
function $p(x) = \dfrac{15}{2x^2 + 11x + 5}$. The x-units are given in thousands of
cakes, and the price per snack cake, $p(x)$, is in dollars.

a) Find the revenue function for the cakes.

b) Estimate the marginal revenue for $x = 0.75$. What is the marginal
revenue for $x = 2.00$?

9. At a small clothing company, the estimated average cost function for
producing a new line of T-shirts is $C(x) = \dfrac{x^2 - 4x + 20}{x}$, where x is
the number of T-shirts produced, in thousands. $C(x)$ is measured in
dollars.

a) Calculate the average cost of a T-shirt at a production level of
3000 pairs.

b) Estimate the rate at which the average cost is changing at a
production level of 3000 T-shirts.

10. Suppose that the number of houses in a new subdivision after t months of development is modelled by $N(t) = \dfrac{100t^3}{100 + t^3}$, where N is the number of houses and $0 \le t \le 12$.

  a) Calculate the average rate of change in the number of houses built over the first 6 months.

  b) Calculate the instantaneous rate of change in the number of houses built at the end of the first year.

  c) Graph the function using a graphing calculator. Discuss what happens to the rate at which houses were built in this subdivision during the first year of development.

11. Given the function $f(x) = \dfrac{x - 2}{x - 5}$, determine an interval and a point where the average rate of change and the instantaneous rate of change are equal.

[T]

12. **a)** The position of an object that is moving along a straight line at t seconds is given by $s(t) = \dfrac{3t}{t + 4}$, where s is measured in metres. Explain how you would determine the average rate of change of $s(t)$ over the first 6 s.

[C]

  b) What does the average rate of change mean in this context?

  c) Compare two ways that you could determine the instantaneous rate of change when $t = 6$. Which method is easier? Explain. Which method is more accurate? Explain.

  d) What does the instantaneous rate of change mean in this context?

Extending

13. The graph of the rational function $f(x) = \dfrac{4x}{x^2 + 1}$ has been given the name Newton's Serpentine. Determine the equations for the tangents at the points where $x = -\sqrt{3}$, 0, and $\sqrt{3}$.

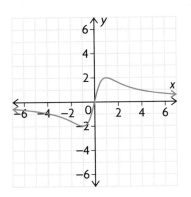

14. Determine the instantaneous rate of change of Newton's Serpentine at points around the point $(0, 0)$. Then determine the instantaneous rate of change of this instantaneous rate of change.

FREQUENTLY ASKED Questions

Q: **How do you solve and verify a rational equation such as** $\dfrac{3x - 8}{2x - 1} = \dfrac{x - 4}{x + 1}$**?**

A: You can solve a simple rational equation algebraically by multiplying each term in the equation by the lowest common denominator and then solving the resulting polynomial equation.

For example, to solve $\dfrac{3x - 8}{2x - 1} = \dfrac{x - 4}{x + 1}$, multiply the equation by $(2x - 1)(x + 1)$, where $x \neq -1$ or $\dfrac{1}{2}$. Then solve the resulting polynomial equation.

To verify your solutions, you can graph the corresponding function, $f(x) = \dfrac{3x - 8}{2x - 1} - \dfrac{x - 4}{x + 1}$, using graphing technology and determine the zeros of f.

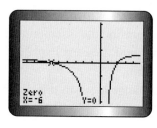 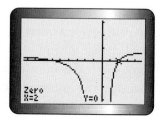

The zeros are -6 and 2, so the solution to the equation is $x = -6$ or 2.

Q: **How do you solve a rational inequality, such as** $\dfrac{x - 2}{x + 1} > \dfrac{x - 6}{x - 2}$**?**

A1: You can solve a rational inequality algebraically by creating and solving an equivalent linear or polynomial inequality with zero on one side. For factorable polynomial inequalities of degree 2 or more, use a table to identify the positive/negative intervals created by the zeros and vertical asymptotes of the rational expression.

A2: You can use graphing technology to graph the functions on both sides of the inequality, determine their intersection and the locations of all vertical asymptotes, and then note the intervals of x that satisfy the inequality.

Q: How do you determine the average or instantaneous rate of change of a rational function?

A: You can determine average and instantaneous rates of change of a rational function at points within the domain of the function using the same methods that are used for polynomial functions.

Study Aid

- See Lesson 5.6, Examples 1, 2, and 3.
- Try Chapter Review Questions 12, 13, and 14.

Q: When is it not possible to determine the average or instantaneous rate of change of a rational function?

A: You cannot determine the average and instantaneous rates of change of a rational function at a point where the graph has a hole or a vertical asymptote. You can only calculate the instantaneous rate of change at a point where the rational function is defined and where a tangent line can be drawn. A rational function is not defined at a point where there is a hole or a vertical asymptote. For example, $f(x) = \dfrac{x + 1}{x - 3}$ and $g(x) = \dfrac{x^2 - 9}{x - 3}$ are rational functions that are not defined at $x = 3$.

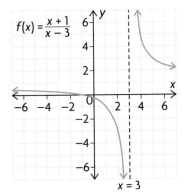

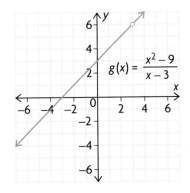

The graph of $f(x)$ has a vertical asymptote at $x = 3$.

The graph of $g(x)$ has a hole at $x = 3$.

You cannot draw a tangent line on either graph at $x = 3$, so you cannot determine an instantaneous rate of change at this point.

PRACTICE Questions

Lesson 5.1

1. For each function, determine the domain and range, intercepts, positive/negative intervals, and increasing and decreasing intervals. Use this information to sketch a graph of the reciprocal function.

   a) $f(x) = 3x + 2$

   b) $f(x) = 2x^2 + 7x - 4$

   c) $f(x) = 2x^2 + 2$

2. Given the graphs of $f(x)$ below, sketch the graphs of $y = \dfrac{1}{f(x)}$.

   a)

   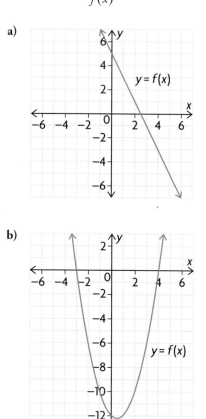

   b)

Lesson 5.2

3. For each function, determine the equations of any vertical asymptotes, the locations of any holes, and the existence of any horizontal or oblique asymptotes.

   a) $y = \dfrac{1}{x + 17}$

   b) $y = \dfrac{2x}{5x + 3}$

   c) $y = \dfrac{3x + 33}{-4x^2 - 42x + 22}$

   d) $y = \dfrac{3x^2 - 2}{x - 1}$

Lesson 5.3

4. The population of locusts in a Prairie a town over the last 50 years is modelled by the function $f(x) = \dfrac{75x}{x^2 + 3x + 2}$. The locust population is given in hundreds of thousands. Describe the locust population in the town over time, where x is time in years.

5. For each function, determine the domain, intercepts, asymptotes, and positive/negative intervals. Use these characteristics to sketch the graph of the function. Then describe where the function is increasing or decreasing.

   a) $f(x) = \dfrac{2}{x + 5}$

   b) $f(x) = \dfrac{4x - 8}{x - 2}$

   c) $f(x) = \dfrac{x - 6}{3x - 18}$

   d) $f(x) = \dfrac{4x}{2x + 1}$

6. Describe how you can determine the behaviour of the values of a rational function on either side of a vertical asymptote.

Lesson 5.4

7. Solve each equation algebraically, and verify your solution using a graphing calculator.

a) $\dfrac{x-6}{x+2} = 0$

b) $15x + 7 = \dfrac{2}{x}$

c) $\dfrac{2x}{x-12} = \dfrac{-2}{x+3}$

d) $\dfrac{x+3}{-4x} = \dfrac{x-1}{-4}$

8. A group of students have volunteered for the student council car wash. Janet can wash a car in m minutes. Rodriguez can wash a car in $m - 5$ minutes, while Nick needs the same amount of time as Janet. If they all work together, they can wash a car in about 3.23 minutes. How long does Janet take to wash a car?

9. The concentration of a toxic chemical in a spring-fed lake is given by the equation $c(x) = \dfrac{50x}{x^2 + 3x + 6}$, where c is given in grams per litre and x is the time in days. Determine when the concentration of the chemical is 6.16 g/L.

Lesson 5.5

10. Use an algebraic process to find the solution set of each inequality. Verify your answers using graphing technology.

a) $-x + 5 < \dfrac{1}{x+3}$

b) $\dfrac{55}{x+16} > -x$

c) $\dfrac{2x}{3x+4} > \dfrac{x}{x+1}$

d) $\dfrac{x}{6x-9} \le \dfrac{1}{x}$

11. A biologist predicted that the population of tadpoles in a pond could be modelled by the function $f(t) = \dfrac{40t}{t^2 + 1}$, where t is given in days. The function that actually models the tadpole population is $g(t) = \dfrac{45t}{t^2 + 8t + 7}$. Determine where $g(t) > f(t)$.

Lesson 5.6

12. Estimate the slope of the line that is tangent to each function at the given point. At what point(s) is it not possible to draw a tangent line?

a) $f(x) = \dfrac{x+3}{x-3}$, where $x = 4$

b) $f(x) = \dfrac{2x-1}{x^2 + 3x + 2}$, where $x = 1$

13. The concentration, c, of a drug in the bloodstream t hours after the drug was taken orally is given by $c(t) = \dfrac{5t}{t^2 + 7}$, where c is measured in milligrams per litre.

a) Calculate the average rate of change in the drug's concentration during the first 2 h since ingestion.

b) Estimate the rate at which the concentration of the drug is changing after exactly 3 h.

c) Graph $c(t)$ on a graphing calculator. When is the concentration of the drug increasing the fastest in the bloodstream? Explain.

14. Given the function $f(x) = \dfrac{2x}{x-4}$, determine the coordinates of a point on $f(x)$ where the slope of the tangent line equals the slope of the secant line that passes through $A(5, 10)$ and $B(8, 4)$.

15. Describe what happens to the slope of a tangent line on the graph of a rational function as the x-coordinate of the point of tangency

a) gets closer and closer to the vertical asymptote.

b) grows larger in both the positive and negative direction.

1. Match each graph with the equation of its corresponding function.

a)

b)

$$\text{A } y = \frac{5x + 2}{x - 1} \qquad\qquad \text{B } y = \frac{1}{2x - 1}$$

2. Suppose that n is a constant and that $f(x)$ is a linear or quadratic function defined when $x = n$. Complete the following sentences.

   a) If $f(n)$ is large, then $\dfrac{1}{f(n)}$ is....

   b) If $f(n)$ is small, then $\dfrac{1}{f(n)}$ is....

   c) If $f(n) = 0$, then $\dfrac{1}{f(n)}$ is....

   d) If $f(n)$ is positive, then $\dfrac{1}{f(n)}$ is....

3. Without using graphing technology, sketch the graph of $y = \dfrac{2x + 6}{x - 2}$.

4. A company purchases x kilograms of steel for \$2249.52. The company processes the steel and turns it into parts that can be used in other factories. After this process, the total mass of the steel has dropped by 25 kg (due to trimmings, scrap, and so on), but the value of the steel has increased to \$10 838.52. The company has made a profit of \$2/kg. What was the original mass of the steel? What is the original cost per kilogram?

5. Select a strategy to solve each of the following.

   a) $\dfrac{-x}{x - 1} = \dfrac{-3}{x + 7}$

   b) $\dfrac{2}{x + 5} > \dfrac{3x}{x + 10}$

6. If you are given the equation of a rational function of the form $f(x) = \dfrac{ax + b}{cx + d}$, explain

   a) how you can determine the equations of all vertical and horizontal asymptotes without graphing the function

   b) when this type of function would have a hole instead of a vertical asymptote

A New School

Researchers at a school board have developed models to predict population changes in the three areas they service. The models are $A(t) = \dfrac{360}{t + 6}$ for area A, $B(t) = \dfrac{30t}{t + 1}$ for area B, and $C(t) = \dfrac{50}{41 - 2t}$ for area C, where the population is measured in thousands and t is the time, in years, since 2007. The existing schools are full, and the board has agreed that a new school should be built.

? In which area should the new school be built, and when will the new school be needed?

A. Graph each population function for the 20 years following 2007. Use your graphs to describe the population trends in each area between 2007 and 2027.

B. Describe the intervals of increase or decrease for each function.

C. Determine which area will have the greatest population in 2010, 2017, 2022, and 2027.

D. Determine the intervals over which
- the population of area A is greater than the population of area B
- the population of area A is greater than the population of area C
- the population of area B is greater than the population of area C

E. Determine when the population of area B will be increasing most rapidly and when the population of area C will be increasing most rapidly.

F. What will happen to the population in each area over time?

G. Decide where and when the school should be built. Compile your results into a recommendation letter to the school board.

> **Task | Checklist**
> - ✔ Did you show all your steps?
> - ✔ Did you draw and label your graphs accurately?
> - ✔ Did you support your choice of location for the school?
> - ✔ Did you explain your thinking clearly?

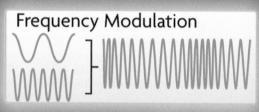

Frequency Modulation

Trigonometric Functions

▶ GOALS

You will be able to

- Understand radian measure and its relationship to degree measure

- Use radian measure with trigonometric functions

- Make connections between trigonometric ratios and the graphs of the primary and reciprocal trigonometric functions

- Pose, model, and solve problems that involve trigonometric functions

- Solve problems that involve rates of change in trigonometric functions

? FM radio stations and many other wireless technologies (such as the sound portion of a television signal, cordless phones, and cell phones) transmit information using sine waves. The equations that are used to model these sine waves, however, do not use angles that are measured in degrees. What is an alternative way to measure angles, and how does this affect the graphs of trigonometric functions?

SKILLS AND CONCEPTS *You Need*

Study Aid

- For help, see the Review of Essential Skills found at the Nelson Advanced Functions website.

Question	Appendix
1, 2, 3, 4	R-10
5	R-11
6, 7	R-12

1. For angle θ, determine
   a) the size of the **related acute angle**
   b) the size of the **principal angle**

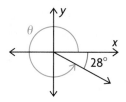

2. Point $P(3, -4)$ lies on the terminal arm of an angle in standard position.
   a) Sketch the angle, and determine the values of the primary and reciprocal ratios.
   b) Determine the measure of the principal angle, to the nearest degree.

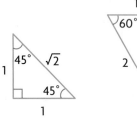

3. Draw each angle in standard position. Then, using the **special triangles** as required, determine the exact value of the trigonometric ratio.
   a) $\sin 60°$
   b) $\tan 180°$
   c) $\sin 120°$
   d) $\cos 300°$
   e) $\sec 135°$
   f) $\csc 270°$

4. Determine the value(s) of θ, if $0° \leq \theta \leq 360°$.
   a) $\cos \theta = \dfrac{1}{2}$
   b) $\tan \theta = \dfrac{1}{\sqrt{3}}$
   c) $\tan \theta = 1$
   d) $\cos \theta = -1$
   e) $\cot \theta = -1$
   f) $\sin \theta = 1$

5. For each of the following, state the **period, amplitude, equation of the axis**, and range of the function. Then sketch its graph.
   a) $y = \sin \theta$, where $-360° \leq \theta \leq 360°$.
   b) $y = \cos \theta$, where $-360° \leq \theta \leq 360°$.

6. State the period, equation of the axis, horizontal shift, and amplitude of each function. Then sketch one cycle.
   a) $y = 2 \sin (3(x + 45°))$ b) $y = -\sin \left(\dfrac{1}{2}(x - 60°)\right) - 1$

7. Identify the transformation that is associated with each of the parameters (a, k, d, and c) in the graphs defined by $y = a \sin (k(x - d)) + c$ and $y = a \cos (k(x - d)) + c$. Discuss which graphical feature (period, amplitude, equation of the axis, or horizontal shift) is associated with each parameter.

APPLYING *What You Know*

Using a Sinusoidal Model

A Ferris wheel has a diameter of 20 m, and its axle is located 15 m above the ground. Once the riders are loaded, the Ferris wheel accelerates to a steady speed and rotates 10 times in 4 min. The height, h metres, of a rider above the ground during a ride on this Ferris wheel can be modelled by a sinusoidal function of the form $h(t) = a \sin (k(t - d)) + c$, where t is the time in seconds.

The height of a rider begins to be tracked when the rider is level with the axis of the Ferris wheel on the first rotation.

YOU WILL NEED
- graph paper

? What does the graph of the rider's height versus time, for three complete revolutions, look like? What equation can be used to describe this graph?

A. Determine the maximum and minimum heights of a rider above the ground during the ride.

B. How many seconds does one complete revolution take? What part of the graph represents this?

C. On graph paper, sketch a graph of the rider's height above the ground versus time for three revolutions of the Ferris wheel.

D. What type of curve does your graph resemble?

E. Is this function a periodic function? Explain.

F. What is the amplitude of this function?

G. What is the period of this function?

H. What is the equation of the axis of this function?

I. Assign appropriate values to each parameter in $h(t)$ for this situation.

J. Write the equation of a sine function that describes the graph you sketched in part C.

Radian Measure

Use radian measurement to represent the size of an angle.

LEARN ABOUT the Math

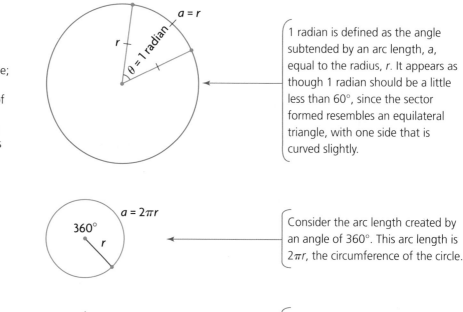

Angles are commonly measured in degrees. In mathematics and physics, however, there are many applications in which expressing the size of an angle as a pure number, without units, is more convenient than using degrees. In these applications, the size of an angle is expressed in terms of the length of an arc, a, that subtends the angle, θ, at the centre of a circle with radius r. In this situation, a is proportional to r and also to θ, where $\theta = \frac{a}{r}$. The unit of measure is the radian.

? How are radians and degrees related to each other?

EXAMPLE 1 | **Connecting radians and degrees**

How many degrees is 1 radian?

Solution

radian

the size of an angle that is subtended at the centre of a circle by an arc with a length equal to the radius of the circle; both the arc length and the radius are measured in units of length (such as centimetres) and, as a result, the angle is a real number without any units

$$\theta = \frac{a}{r} = \frac{r}{r} = 1$$

1 radian is defined as the angle subtended by an arc length, a, equal to the radius, r. It appears as though 1 radian should be a little less than 60°, since the sector formed resembles an equilateral triangle, with one side that is curved slightly.

Consider the arc length created by an angle of 360°. This arc length is $2\pi r$, the circumference of the circle.

$$\theta = \frac{2\pi \overset{1}{\cancel{r}}}{\underset{1}{\cancel{r}}} = 2\pi \text{ radians}$$

Using the relationship $\theta = \frac{a}{r}$, the size of the angle can be expressed in radians.

$$\theta = 360° \longleftarrow$$
θ is also 360°, the size of the central angle with an arc length of $2\pi r$.

$$2\pi \text{ radians} = 360°$$
$$\pi \text{ radians} = 180° \longleftarrow$$
Equating the measures of θ gives an expression relating degrees and radians.

Dividing both sides by 2 gives a simpler relationship between degrees and radians.

$$\frac{\pi \text{ radians}}{\pi} = \frac{180°}{\pi} \longleftarrow$$
$$1 \text{ radian} = \frac{180°}{\pi} \doteq 57.3°$$
Dividing both sides by π gives the value of 1 radian in degree measure.

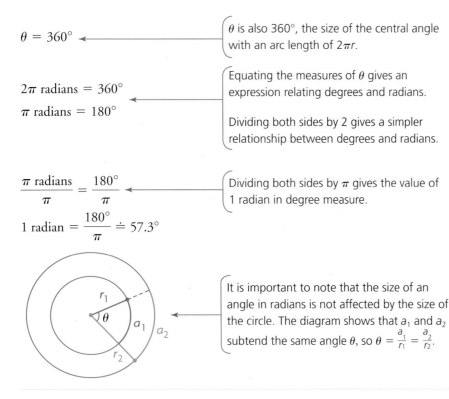

It is important to note that the size of an angle in radians is not affected by the size of the circle. The diagram shows that a_1 and a_2 subtend the same angle θ, so $\theta = \frac{a_1}{r_1} = \frac{a_2}{r_2}$.

The relationship π radians $= 180°$ can be used to convert between degrees and radians.

| EXAMPLE 2 | Reasoning how to convert degrees to radians |

Convert each of the following angles to radians.
a) 20°   **b)** 225°

Solution

a) π radians $= 180° \longleftarrow$
Divide both sides by 180° to get an equivalent expression that is equal to 1.

$$\frac{\pi}{180°} = 1 \longleftarrow$$
Multiplying by 1 creates an equivalent expression, so multiply by $\frac{\pi}{180°}$ to convert degrees to radians.

$$20° = (20°)\left(\frac{\pi}{180°}\right) \longleftarrow$$
Simplify by dividing by the common factor of 20. Notice that the units cancel out.

$$= \frac{\pi}{9}$$
$$\doteq 0.35 \longleftarrow$$
Express the answer as an exact value in terms of π or as an approximate decimal value, as required.

b) $225° = (225°)\left(\dfrac{\pi}{180°}\right)$ ← ⎛Multiply by $\dfrac{\pi}{180°}$ to convert degrees to radians.⎞

$\quad\quad = \dfrac{225°\pi}{180°} \div \dfrac{45}{45}$ ← ⎛Simplify by dividing by the common factor of 45. (Note that the degree symbols cancel.)⎞

$\quad\quad = \dfrac{5\pi}{4}$

EXAMPLE 3 | **Reasoning how to convert radians to degrees**

Convert each radian measure to degrees.

a) $\dfrac{5\pi}{6}$ **b)** 1.75 radians

Solution

a) π radians $= 180°$

$\quad\quad \dfrac{5\pi}{6} = \dfrac{5(180°)}{6}$ ← ⎛Substitute $180°$ for π.⎞

$\quad\quad\quad = 5(30°)$ ← ⎛Evaluate.⎞

$\quad\quad\quad = 150°$

b) π radians $= 180°$

$\quad\quad 1 = \dfrac{180°}{\pi \text{ radians}}$ ← ⎛Divide both sides by π radians to get an equivalent expression that is equal to 1.⎞

$1.75 \text{ radians} = 1.75 \; \overset{1}{\cancel{\text{radians}}} \times \dfrac{180°}{\underset{1}{\cancel{\pi \text{ radians}}}}$ ← ⎛Multiplying by 1 creates an equivalent expression, so multiply by $\dfrac{180°}{\pi \text{ radians}}$ to convert radians to degrees.⎞

$\quad\quad\quad \doteq 100.3°$

Reflecting

A. Consider the formula $\theta = \dfrac{a}{r}$. Explain why angles can be described as having no unit when they are measured in radians.

B. Explain how to convert any angle measure that is given in degrees to radians.

C. Explain how to convert any angle measure that is given in radians to degrees.

APPLY the Math

EXAMPLE 4 | Solving a problem that involves radians

The London Eye Ferris wheel has a diameter of 135 m and completes one revolution in 30 min.
a) Determine the angular velocity, ω, in radians per second.
b) How far has a rider travelled at 10 min into the ride?

Solution

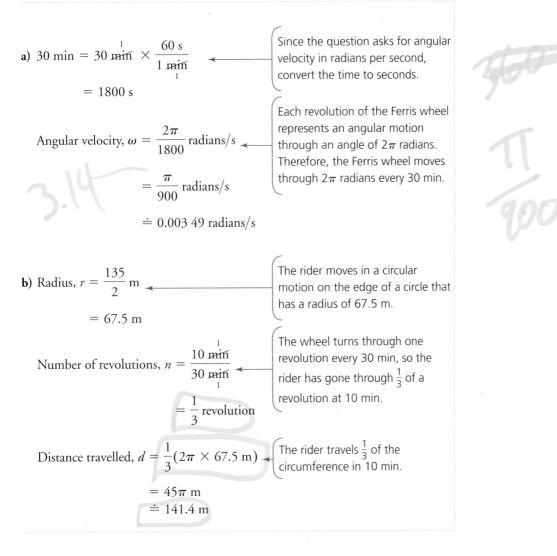

a) $30 \text{ min} = 30 \overset{1}{\cancel{\text{min}}} \times \dfrac{60 \text{ s}}{\underset{1}{\cancel{1 \text{ min}}}}$

      $= 1800 \text{ s}$

> Since the question asks for angular velocity in radians per second, convert the time to seconds.

Angular velocity, $\omega = \dfrac{2\pi}{1800} \text{ radians/s}$

> Each revolution of the Ferris wheel represents an angular motion through an angle of 2π radians. Therefore, the Ferris wheel moves through 2π radians every 30 min.

      $= \dfrac{\pi}{900} \text{ radians/s}$

      $\doteq 0.003\,49 \text{ radians/s}$

b) Radius, $r = \dfrac{135}{2} \text{ m}$

      $= 67.5 \text{ m}$

> The rider moves in a circular motion on the edge of a circle that has a radius of 67.5 m.

Number of revolutions, $n = \dfrac{\overset{1}{\cancel{10 \text{ min}}}}{\underset{1}{\cancel{30 \text{ min}}}}$

> The wheel turns through one revolution every 30 min, so the rider has gone through $\frac{1}{3}$ of a revolution at 10 min.

      $= \dfrac{1}{3} \text{ revolution}$

Distance travelled, $d = \dfrac{1}{3}(2\pi \times 67.5 \text{ m})$

> The rider travels $\frac{1}{3}$ of the circumference in 10 min.

      $= 45\pi \text{ m}$

      $\doteq 141.4 \text{ m}$

In Summary

Key Ideas

- The radian is an alternative way to represent the size of an angle. The arc length, a, of a circle is proportional to its radius, r, and the central angle that it subtends, θ, by the formula $\theta = \dfrac{a}{r}$.

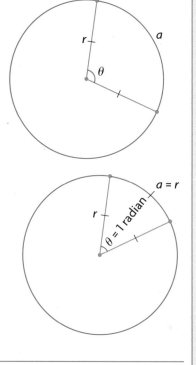

- One radian is defined as the angle subtended by an arc that is the same length as the radius. $\theta = \dfrac{a}{r} = \dfrac{r}{r} = 1$. 1 radian is about $57.3°$.

Need to Know

- Using radians enables you to express the size of an angle as a real number without any units, often in terms of π. It is related to degree measure by the following conversion factor: π radians $= 180°$.
- To convert from degree measure to radians, multiply by $\dfrac{\pi}{180°}$.
- To convert from radians to degrees, multiply by $\dfrac{180°}{\pi}$.

CHECK Your Understanding

Communication | Tip

Recall that counterclockwise rotation is represented using positive angles, while clockwise rotation is represented using **negative angles**.

1. A point is rotated about a circle of radius 1. Its start and finish are shown. State the rotation in radian measure and in degree measure.

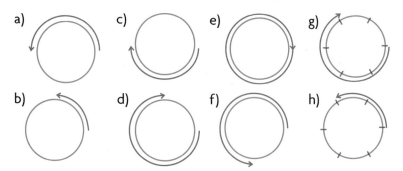

a)

b)

c)

d)

e)

f)

g)

h)

2. Sketch each rotation about a circle of radius 1.

a) π
c) $\dfrac{2\pi}{3}$
e) $\dfrac{5\pi}{3}$
g) $-\dfrac{\pi}{2}$

b) $\dfrac{\pi}{3}$
d) $\dfrac{4\pi}{3}$
f) $-\pi$
h) $-\dfrac{\pi}{4}$

3. Convert each angle from degrees to radians, in exact form.
a) $75°$
b) $200°$
c) $400°$
d) $320°$

4. Convert each angle from radians to degrees. Express the measure correct to two decimal places, if necessary.

a) $\dfrac{5\pi}{3}$
b) 0.3π
c) 3
d) $\dfrac{11\pi}{4}$

PRACTISING

5. a) Determine the measure of the central angle that is formed by an arc length of 5 cm in a circle with a radius of 2.5 cm. Express the measure in both radians and degrees, correct to one decimal place.

b) Determine the arc length of the circle in part a) if the central angle is $200°$.

6. Determine the arc length of a circle with a radius of 8 cm if
a) the central angle is 3.5
b) the central angle is $300°$

7. Convert to radian measure.

a) $90°$
c) $-180°$
e) $-135°$
g) $240°$
b) $270°$
d) $45°$
f) $60°$
h) $-120°$

8. Convert to degree measure.

a) $\dfrac{2\pi}{3}$
c) $\dfrac{\pi}{4}$
e) $\dfrac{7\pi}{6}$
g) $\dfrac{11\pi}{6}$

b) $-\dfrac{5\pi}{3}$
d) $-\dfrac{3\pi}{4}$
f) $-\dfrac{3\pi}{2}$
h) $-\dfrac{9\pi}{2}$

9. If a circle has a radius of 65 m, determine the arc length for each of the following central angles.

a) $\dfrac{19\pi}{20}$
b) 1.25
c) $150°$

10. Given $\angle DCE = \dfrac{\pi}{12}$ radians and $CE = 4.5$ cm, determine the size of θ and x.

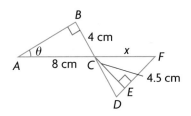

11. A wind turbine has three blades, each measuring 3 m from centre to tip. At a particular time, the turbine is rotating four times a minute.
    a) Determine the angular velocity of the turbine in radians/second.
    b) How far has the tip of a blade travelled after 5 min?

12. A wheel is rotating at an angular velocity of 1.2π radians/s, while a point on the circumference of the wheel travels 9.6π m in 10 s.
    a) How many revolutions does the wheel make in 1 min?
    b) What is the radius of the wheel?

13. Two pieces of mud are stuck to the spoke of a bicycle wheel. Piece A is
    T closer to the circumference of the tire, while piece B is closer to the centre of the wheel.
    a) Is the angular velocity at which piece A is travelling greater than, less than, or equal to the angular velocity at which piece B is travelling?
    b) Is the velocity at which piece A is travelling greater than, less than, or equal to the velocity at which piece B is travelling?
    c) If the angular velocity of the bicycle wheel increased, would the velocity at which piece A is travelling as a percent of the velocity at which piece B is travelling increase, decrease, or stay the same?

14. In your notebook, sketch the diagram shown and label each angle, in
    C degrees, for one revolution. Then express each of these angles in exact radian measure.

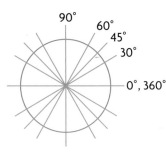

Extending

15. Circle A has a radius of 15 cm and a central angle of $\frac{\pi}{6}$ radians, circle B has a radius of 17 cm and a central angle of $\frac{\pi}{7}$ radians, and circle C has a radius of 14 cm and a central angle of $\frac{\pi}{5}$ radians. Put the circles in order, from smallest to largest, based on the lengths of the arcs subtending the central angles.

16. The members of a high-school basketball team are driving from Calgary to Vancouver, which is a distance of 675 km. Each tire on their van has a radius of 32 cm. If the team members drive at a constant speed and cover the distance from Calgary to Vancouver in 6 h 45 min, what is the angular velocity, in radians/second, of each tire during the drive?

Radian Measure and Angles on the Cartesian Plane

Use the Cartesian plane to evaluate the trigonometric ratios for angles between 0 and 2π.

LEARN ABOUT the Math

Recall that the special triangles shown can be used to determine the exact values of the primary and reciprocal trigonometric ratios for some angles measured in degrees.

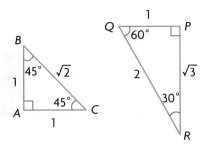

? How can these special triangles be used to determine the exact values of the trigonometric ratios for angles expressed in radians?

EXAMPLE 1 Connecting radians and the special triangles

Determine the radian measures of the angles in the special triangles, and calculate their primary trigonometric ratios.

Solution

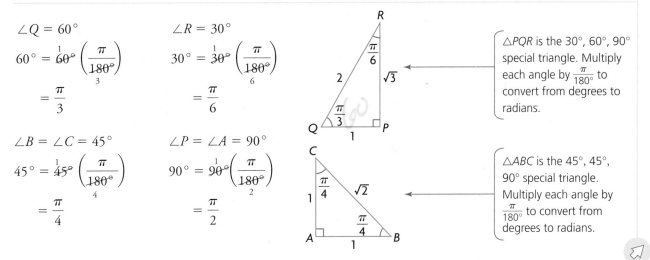

$\angle Q = 60°$

$60° = \overset{1}{\cancel{60°}}\left(\dfrac{\pi}{\cancel{180°}_{3}}\right)$

$= \dfrac{\pi}{3}$

$\angle R = 30°$

$30° = \overset{1}{\cancel{30°}}\left(\dfrac{\pi}{\cancel{180°}_{6}}\right)$

$= \dfrac{\pi}{6}$

△PQR is the 30°, 60°, 90° special triangle. Multiply each angle by $\dfrac{\pi}{180°}$ to convert from degrees to radians.

$\angle B = \angle C = 45°$

$45° = \overset{1}{\cancel{45°}}\left(\dfrac{\pi}{\cancel{180°}_{4}}\right)$

$= \dfrac{\pi}{4}$

$\angle P = \angle A = 90°$

$90° = \overset{1}{\cancel{90°}}\left(\dfrac{\pi}{\cancel{180°}_{2}}\right)$

$= \dfrac{\pi}{2}$

△ABC is the 45°, 45°, 90° special triangle. Multiply each angle by $\dfrac{\pi}{180°}$ to convert from degrees to radians.

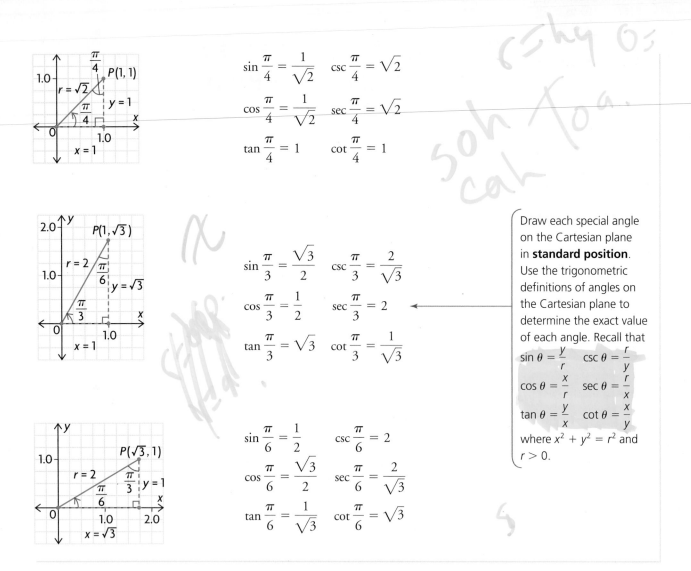

$$\sin \frac{\pi}{4} = \frac{1}{\sqrt{2}} \qquad \csc \frac{\pi}{4} = \sqrt{2}$$

$$\cos \frac{\pi}{4} = \frac{1}{\sqrt{2}} \qquad \sec \frac{\pi}{4} = \sqrt{2}$$

$$\tan \frac{\pi}{4} = 1 \qquad \cot \frac{\pi}{4} = 1$$

$$\sin \frac{\pi}{3} = \frac{\sqrt{3}}{2} \qquad \csc \frac{\pi}{3} = \frac{2}{\sqrt{3}}$$

$$\cos \frac{\pi}{3} = \frac{1}{2} \qquad \sec \frac{\pi}{3} = 2$$

$$\tan \frac{\pi}{3} = \sqrt{3} \qquad \cot \frac{\pi}{3} = \frac{1}{\sqrt{3}}$$

$$\sin \frac{\pi}{6} = \frac{1}{2} \qquad \csc \frac{\pi}{6} = 2$$

$$\cos \frac{\pi}{6} = \frac{\sqrt{3}}{2} \qquad \sec \frac{\pi}{6} = \frac{2}{\sqrt{3}}$$

$$\tan \frac{\pi}{6} = \frac{1}{\sqrt{3}} \qquad \cot \frac{\pi}{6} = \sqrt{3}$$

Draw each special angle on the Cartesian plane in **standard position**. Use the trigonometric definitions of angles on the Cartesian plane to determine the exact value of each angle. Recall that

$$\sin \theta = \frac{y}{r} \qquad \csc \theta = \frac{r}{y}$$

$$\cos \theta = \frac{x}{r} \qquad \sec \theta = \frac{r}{x}$$

$$\tan \theta = \frac{y}{x} \qquad \cot \theta = \frac{x}{y}$$

where $x^2 + y^2 = r^2$ and $r > 0$.

Reflecting

A. Compare the exact values of the trigonometric ratios in each special triangle when the angles are given in radians and when the angles are given in degrees.

B. Explain why the strategy that is used to determine the value of a trigonometric ratio for a given angle on the Cartesian plane is the same when the angle is expressed in radians and when the angle is expressed in degrees.

APPLY the Math

EXAMPLE 2   Selecting a strategy to determine the exact value of a trigonometric ratio

Determine the exact value of each trigonometric ratio.

a) $\sin\left(\dfrac{\pi}{2}\right)$ **b)** $\cot\left(\dfrac{3\pi}{2}\right)$

Solution

a)

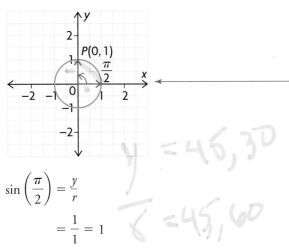

$\dfrac{\pi}{2}$ is one-quarter of a full revolution, and the point $P(0, 1)$ lies on the unit circle, as shown. Draw the angle in standard position with its terminal arm on the positive y-axis. From the drawing, $x = 0, y = 1$, and $r = 1$.

$\sin\left(\dfrac{\pi}{2}\right) = \dfrac{y}{r}$

$= \dfrac{1}{1} = 1$

b)

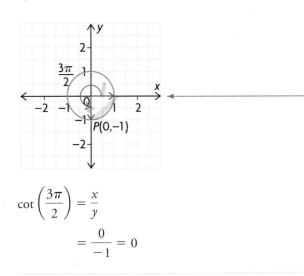

$\dfrac{3\pi}{2}$ is three-quarters of a full revolution, and the point $P(0, -1)$ lies on the unit circle, as shown. Draw the angle in standard position with its terminal arm on the negative y-axis. From the drawing, $x = 0, y = -1$ and $r = 1$.

$\cot\left(\dfrac{3\pi}{2}\right) = \dfrac{x}{y}$

$= \dfrac{0}{-1} = 0$

The relationships between the principal angle, its related acute angle, and the trigonometric ratios for angles in standard position are the same when the angles are measured in radians and degrees.

EXAMPLE **3**	Selecting a strategy to determine the exact value of a trigonometric ratio

Determine the exact value of each trigonometric ratio.

a) $\cos\left(\dfrac{5\pi}{4}\right)$ **b)** $\csc\left(\dfrac{11\pi}{6}\right)$

Solution A: Using the special angles

a)

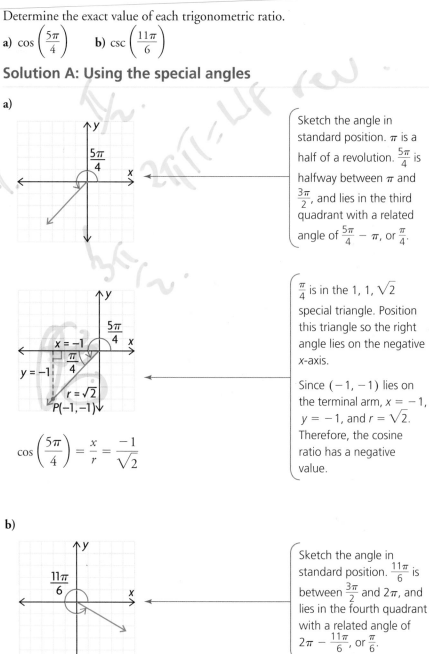

Sketch the angle in standard position. π is a half of a revolution. $\dfrac{5\pi}{4}$ is halfway between π and $\dfrac{3\pi}{2}$, and lies in the third quadrant with a related angle of $\dfrac{5\pi}{4} - \pi$, or $\dfrac{\pi}{4}$.

$\dfrac{\pi}{4}$ is in the 1, 1, $\sqrt{2}$ special triangle. Position this triangle so the right angle lies on the negative x-axis.

Since $(-1, -1)$ lies on the terminal arm, $x = -1$, $y = -1$, and $r = \sqrt{2}$. Therefore, the cosine ratio has a negative value.

$$\cos\left(\frac{5\pi}{4}\right) = \frac{x}{r} = \frac{-1}{\sqrt{2}}$$

b)

Sketch the angle in standard position. $\dfrac{11\pi}{6}$ is between $\dfrac{3\pi}{2}$ and 2π, and lies in the fourth quadrant with a related angle of $2\pi - \dfrac{11\pi}{6}$, or $\dfrac{\pi}{6}$.

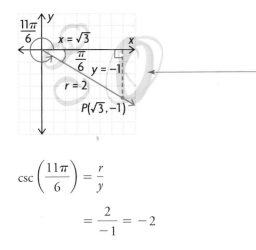

$\frac{\pi}{6}$ is in the 1, $\sqrt{3}$, 2 special triangle. Position it so that the right angle lies on the positive x-axis. Since the point $(\sqrt{3}, -1)$ lies on the terminal arm, $x = \sqrt{3}$, $y = -1$, and $r = 2$. Therefore, the csc ratio has a negative value.

$$\csc\left(\frac{11\pi}{6}\right) = \frac{r}{y}$$

$$= \frac{2}{-1} = -2$$

Solution B: Using a calculator

a)

Set the calculator to radian mode. Enter the expression.

The result is a decimal. Entering $-\frac{1}{\sqrt{2}}$ confirms that the answer is equivalent to this decimal.

$$\cos\left(\frac{5\pi}{4}\right) = \frac{-1}{\sqrt{2}}$$

Tech | Support

To put a graphing calculator in radian mode, press the (MODE) key, scroll to Radian, and press (ENTER).

b)

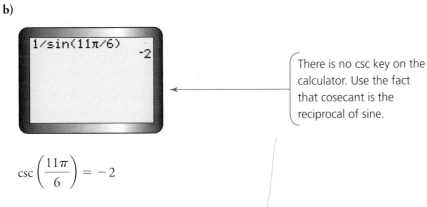

There is no csc key on the calculator. Use the fact that cosecant is the reciprocal of sine.

$$\csc\left(\frac{11\pi}{6}\right) = -2$$

EXAMPLE **4**

EXAMPLE 4 | Solving a trigonometric equation that involves radians

If $\tan \theta = -\frac{7}{24}$, where $0 \leq \theta \leq 2\pi$, evaluate θ to the nearest hundredth.

Solution

$$\tan \theta = -\frac{7}{24} = \frac{y}{x}$$

There are two possibilities to consider:
$x = 24, y = -7$ and
$x = -24, y = 7$.

P(24, −7)

For the ordered pair $(24, -7)$, the terminal arm of the angle θ lies in the fourth quadrant.
$\frac{3\pi}{2} < \theta < 2\pi$

tan⁻¹(7/24)
            .2837941092

Use a calculator to determine the related acute angle by calculating the inverse tan of $\frac{7}{24}$. The related angle is 0.28, rounded to two decimal places. Subtract 0.28 from 2π to determine one measure of θ.

$2\pi - 0.28 \doteq 6.00$

In the fourth quadrant, θ is about 6.00.

P(−24, 7)

For the ordered pair $(-24, 7)$, the terminal arm of θ lies in the second quadrant, $\frac{\pi}{2} < \theta < \pi$, and also has a related angle of 0.28. Subtract 0.28 from π to determine the other measure of θ.

$\pi - 0.28 \doteq 2.86$

In the second quadrant, θ is about 2.86.

In Summary

Key Ideas

- The angles in the special triangles can be expressed in radians, as well as in degrees. The radian measures can be used to determine the exact values of the trigonometric ratios for multiples of these angles between 0 and 2π.
- The strategies that are used to determine the values of the trigonometric ratios when an angle is expressed in degrees on the Cartesian plane can also be used when the angle is expressed in radians.

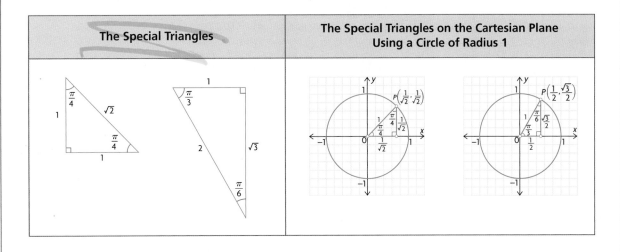

The Special Triangles	The Special Triangles on the Cartesian Plane Using a Circle of Radius 1

Need to Know

- The trigonometric ratios for any principal angle, θ, in standard position can be determined by finding the related acute angle, β, using coordinates of any point that lies on the terminal arm of the angle.

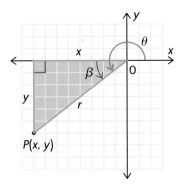

From the Pythagorean theorem, $r^2 = x^2 + y^2$, if $r > 0$.

$$\sin \theta = \frac{y}{r} \qquad \cos \theta = \frac{x}{r} \qquad \tan \theta = \frac{y}{x}$$

$$\csc \theta = \frac{r}{y} \qquad \sec \theta = \frac{r}{x} \qquad \cot \theta = \frac{x}{y}$$

- The CAST rule is an easy way to remember which primary trigonometric ratios are positive in which quadrant. Since r is always positive, the sign of each primary ratio depends on the signs of the coordinates of the point.
  - In quadrant 1, **A**ll (A) ratios are positive because both x and y are positive.
  - In quadrant 2, only **S**ine (S) is positive, since x is negative and y is positive.
  - In quadrant 3, only **T**angent (T) is positive because both x and y are negative.
  - In quadrant 4, only **C**osine (C) is positive, since x is positive and y is negative.

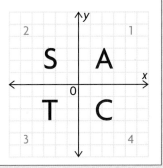

CHECK Your Understanding

1. For each trigonometric ratio, use a sketch to determine in which quadrant the terminal arm of the principal angle lies, the value of the related acute angle, and the sign of the ratio.

a) $\sin \dfrac{3\pi}{4}$ d) $\sec \dfrac{5\pi}{6}$

b) $\cos \dfrac{5\pi}{3}$ e) $\cos \dfrac{2\pi}{3}$

c) $\tan \dfrac{4\pi}{3}$ f) $\cot \dfrac{7\pi}{4}$

2. Each of the following points lies on the terminal arm of an angle in standard position.
   i) Sketch each angle.
   ii) Determine the value of r.
   iii) Determine the primary trigonometric ratios for the angle.
   iv) Calculate the radian value of θ, to the nearest hundredth, where $0 \le \theta \le 2\pi$.

a) $(6, 8)$ c) $(4, -3)$

b) $(-12, -5)$ d) $(0, 5)$

3. Determine the primary trigonometric ratios for each angle.

a) $-\dfrac{\pi}{2}$ c) $\dfrac{7\pi}{4}$

b) $-\pi$ d) $-\dfrac{\pi}{6}$

4. State an equivalent expression in terms of the related acute angle.

a) $\sin \dfrac{5\pi}{6}$ c) $\cot \left(-\dfrac{\pi}{4}\right)$

b) $\cos \dfrac{5\pi}{3}$ d) $\sec \dfrac{7\pi}{6}$

PRACTISING

5. Determine the exact value of each trigonometric ratio.
   K

a) $\sin \dfrac{2\pi}{3}$ c) $\tan \dfrac{11\pi}{6}$ e) $\csc \dfrac{5\pi}{6}$

b) $\cos \dfrac{5\pi}{4}$ d) $\sin \dfrac{7\pi}{4}$ f) $\sec \dfrac{5\pi}{3}$

6. For each of the following values of cos θ, determine the radian value of θ if $\pi \leq \theta \leq 2\pi$.

   a) $-\dfrac{1}{2}$ c) $-\dfrac{\sqrt{2}}{2}$ e) 0

   b) $\dfrac{\sqrt{3}}{2}$ d) $-\dfrac{\sqrt{3}}{2}$ f) -1

7. The terminal arm of an angle in standard position passes through each of the following points. Find the radian value of the angle in the interval $[0, 2\pi]$, to the nearest hundredth.

   a) $(-7, 8)$ c) $(3, 11)$ e) $(9, 10)$
   b) $(12, 2)$ d) $(-4, -2)$ f) $(6, -1)$

8. State an equivalent expression in terms of the related acute angle.

   a) $\cos \dfrac{3\pi}{4}$ c) $\csc\left(-\dfrac{\pi}{3}\right)$ e) $\sin \dfrac{-\pi}{6}$

   b) $\tan \dfrac{11\pi}{6}$ d) $\cot \dfrac{2\pi}{3}$ f) $\sec \dfrac{7\pi}{4}$

9. **A** A leaning flagpole, 5 m long, makes an obtuse angle with the ground. If the distance from the tip of the flagpole to the ground is 3.4 m, determine the radian measure of the obtuse angle, to the nearest hundredth.

10. The needle of a compass makes an angle of 4 radians with the line pointing east from the centre of the compass. The tip of the needle is 4.2 cm below the line pointing west from the centre of the compass. How long is the needle, to the nearest hundredth of a centimetre?

11. **T** A clock is showing the time as exactly 3:00 p.m. and 25 s. Because a full minute has not passed since 3:00, the hour hand is pointing directly at the 3 and the minute hand is pointing directly at the 12. If the tip of the second hand is directly below the tip of the hour hand, and if the length of the second hand is 9 cm, what is the length of the hour hand?

12. **C** If you are given an angle, θ, that lies in the interval $\theta \in \left[\dfrac{\pi}{2}, 2\pi\right]$, how would you determine the values of the primary trigonometric ratios for this angle?

13. You are given $\cos \theta = -\dfrac{5}{13}$, where $0 \leq \theta \leq 2\pi$.
    a) In which quadrant(s) could the terminal arm of θ lie?
    b) Determine all the possible trigonometric ratios for θ.
    c) State all the possible radian values of θ, to the nearest hundredth.

14. Use special triangles to show that the equation
$\cos\left(\dfrac{5\pi}{6}\right) = \cos\left(-150°\right)$ is true.

15. Show that $2\sin^2\theta - 1 = \sin^2\theta - \cos^2\theta$ for $\dfrac{11\pi}{6}$.

16. Determine the length of AB. Find the sine, cosine, and tangent ratios of $\angle D$, given $AC = CD = 8$ cm.

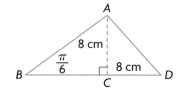

17. Given that x is an acute angle, draw a diagram of both angles (in standard position) in each of the following equalities. For each angle, indicate the related acute angle as well as the principal angle. Then, referring to your drawings, explain why each equality is true.
    a) $\sin x = \sin\left(\pi - x\right)$ c) $\cos x = -\cos\left(\pi - x\right)$
    b) $\sin x = -\sin\left(2\pi - x\right)$ d) $\tan x = \tan\left(\pi + x\right)$

Extending

18. Find the sine of the angle formed by two rays that start at the origin of the Cartesian plane if one ray passes through the point $(3\sqrt{3}, 3)$ and the other ray passes through the point $(-4, 4\sqrt{3})$. Round your answer to the nearest hundredth, if necessary.

19. Find the cosine of the angle formed by two rays that start at the origin of the Cartesian plane if one ray passes through the point $(6\sqrt{2}, 6\sqrt{2})$ and the other ray passes through the point $(-7\sqrt{3}, 7)$. Round your answer to the nearest hundredth, if necessary.

20. Julie noticed that the ranges of the sine and cosine functions go from -1 to 1, inclusive. She then began to wonder about the reciprocals of these functions—that is, the cosecant and secant functions. What do you think the ranges of these functions are? Why?

21. The terminal arm of θ is in the fourth quadrant. If $\cot\theta = -\sqrt{3}$, then calculate $\sin\theta\cot\theta - \cos^2\theta$.

Exploring Graphs of the Primary Trigonometric Functions

Use radians to graph the primary trigonometric functions.

YOU WILL NEED
- graph paper
- graphing calculator

EXPLORE the Math

The unit circle is a circle that is centred at the origin and has a radius of 1 unit. On the unit circle, the sine and cosine functions take a particularly simple form: $\sin \theta = \frac{y}{1} = y$ and $\cos \theta = \frac{x}{1} = x$. The value of $\sin \theta$ is the y-coordinate of each point on the circle, and the value of $\cos \theta$ is the x-coordinate. As a result, each point on the circle can be represented by the ordered pair $(x, y) = (\cos \theta, \sin \theta)$, where θ is the angle formed between the positive x-axis and the terminal arm of the angle that passes through each point. For example, the point $\left(\cos \frac{\pi}{6}, \sin \frac{\pi}{6}\right)$ lies on the terminal arm of the angle $\frac{\pi}{6}$. Evaluating each trigonometric expression using the special triangles results in the ordered pair $\left(\frac{\sqrt{3}}{2}, \frac{1}{2}\right)$. Repeating this process for other angles between 0 and 2π results in the following diagram:

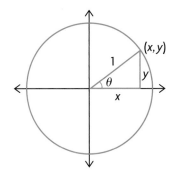

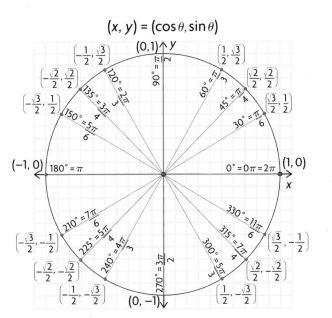

$(x, y) = (\cos \theta, \sin \theta)$

? What do the graphs of the primary trigonometric functions look like when θ is expressed in radians?

A. Copy the following table. Complete the table using a calculator and the unit circle shown to approximate each value to two decimal places.

θ	0	$\dfrac{\pi}{6}$	$\dfrac{\pi}{4}$	$\dfrac{\pi}{3}$	$\dfrac{\pi}{2}$	$\dfrac{2\pi}{3}$	$\dfrac{3\pi}{4}$	$\dfrac{5\pi}{6}$	π
$\sin\theta$									
$\cos\theta$									

θ	$\dfrac{7\pi}{6}$	$\dfrac{5\pi}{4}$	$\dfrac{4\pi}{3}$	$\dfrac{3\pi}{2}$	$\dfrac{5\pi}{3}$	$\dfrac{7\pi}{4}$	$\dfrac{11\pi}{6}$	2π
$\sin\theta$								
$\cos\theta$								

B. Plot the ordered pairs $(\theta, \sin\theta)$, and sketch the graph of the function $y = \sin\theta$. On the same pair of axes, plot the ordered pairs $(\theta, \cos\theta)$ and sketch the graph of the function $y = \cos\theta$.

C. State the domain, range, amplitude, equation of the axis, and period of each function.

D. Recall that $\tan\theta = \dfrac{\sin\theta}{\cos\theta}$. Use the values from your table for part A to calculate the value of $\tan\theta$. Use a calculator to confirm your results, to two decimal places.

θ	0	$\dfrac{\pi}{6}$	$\dfrac{\pi}{4}$	$\dfrac{\pi}{3}$	$\dfrac{\pi}{2}$	$\dfrac{2\pi}{3}$	$\dfrac{3\pi}{4}$	$\dfrac{5\pi}{6}$	π
$\dfrac{\sin\theta}{\cos\theta}$									

θ	$\dfrac{7\pi}{6}$	$\dfrac{5\pi}{4}$	$\dfrac{4\pi}{3}$	$\dfrac{3\pi}{2}$	$\dfrac{5\pi}{3}$	$\dfrac{7\pi}{4}$	$\dfrac{11\pi}{6}$	2π
$\dfrac{\sin\theta}{\cos\theta}$								

E. What do you notice about the value of the tangent ratio when $\cos\theta = 0$? What do you notice about its value when $\sin\theta = 0$?

F. Based on your observations in part E, what characteristics does this imply for the graph of $y = \tan\theta$?

G. What do you notice about the value of the tangent ratio when $\theta = \pm\dfrac{\pi}{4}, \pm\dfrac{3\pi}{4}, \pm\dfrac{5\pi}{4}$, and $\pm\dfrac{7\pi}{4}$? Why does this occur?

H. On a new pair of axes, plot the ordered pairs $(\theta, \tan \theta)$ and sketch the graph of the function $y = \tan \theta$, where $0 \le \theta \le 2\pi$.

I. Determine the domain, range, amplitude, equation of the axis, and period of this function, if possible.

Reflecting

J. The tangent function is directly related to the slope of the line segment that joins the origin to each point on the unit circle. Explain why.

K. Where are the vertical asymptotes for the tangent graph located when $0 \le \theta \le 2\pi$, and what are their equations? Explain why they are found at these locations.

L. How does the period of the tangent function compare with the period of the sine and cosine functions?

In Summary

Key Idea

- The graphs of the primary trigonometric functions can be summarized as follows:

Key points when
$0 \le \theta \le 2\pi$

θ	$y = \sin(\theta)$
0	0
$\dfrac{\pi}{2}$	1
π	0
$\dfrac{3\pi}{2}$	-1
2π	0

Period $= 2\pi$
Axis: $y = 0$
Amplitude $= 1$
Maximum value $= 1$
Minimum value $= -1$

$D = \{\theta \in \mathbf{R}\}$
$R = \{y \in \mathbf{R} \mid -1 \le y \le 1\}$

Key points when
$0 \le \theta \le 2\pi$

θ	$y = \cos(\theta)$
0	1
$\dfrac{\pi}{2}$	0
π	-1
$\dfrac{3\pi}{2}$	0
2π	1

Period $= 2\pi$
Axis: $y = 0$
Amplitude $= 1$
Maximum value $= 1$
Minimum value $= -1$

$D = \{\theta \in \mathbf{R}\}$
$R = \{y \in \mathbf{R} \mid -1 \le y \le 1\}$

(continued)

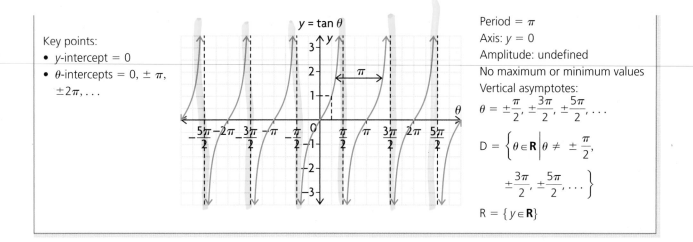

Key points:
- y-intercept $= 0$
- θ-intercepts $= 0, \pm\,\pi,$
  $\pm 2\pi, \ldots$

$y = \tan\theta$

Period $= \pi$
Axis: $y = 0$
Amplitude: undefined
No maximum or minimum values
Vertical asymptotes:
$$\theta = \pm\frac{\pi}{2}, \pm\frac{3\pi}{2}, \pm\frac{5\pi}{2}, \ldots$$
$$D = \left\{\theta \in \mathbf{R}\,\middle|\,\theta \neq \pm\frac{\pi}{2},\right.$$
$$\left.\pm\frac{3\pi}{2}, \pm\frac{5\pi}{2}, \ldots\right\}$$
$$R = \{y \in \mathbf{R}\}$$

FURTHER Your Understanding

1. **a)** Examine the graphs of $y = \sin\theta$ and $y = \cos\theta$. Create a table to compare their similarities and differences.
   b) Repeat part a) using the graphs of $y = \sin\theta$ and $y = \tan\theta$.

2. **a)** Use a graphing calculator, in radian mode, to create the graphs of the trigonometric functions $y = \sin\theta$ and $y = \cos\theta$ on the interval $-2\pi \le \theta \le 2\pi$. To do this, enter the functions $Y1 = \sin\theta$ and $Y2 = \cos\theta$ in the equation editor, and use the window settings shown.
   b) Determine the values of θ where the functions intersect.
   c) The equation $t_n = a + (n - 1)d$ can be used to represent the general term of any arithmetic sequence, where a is the first term and d is the common difference. Use this equation to find an expression that describes the location of each of the following values for $y = \sin\theta$, where $n \in \mathbf{I}$ and θ is in radians.
   i) θ-intercepts
   ii) maximum values
   iii) minimum values

3. Find an expression that describes the location of each of the following values for $y = \cos\theta$, where $n \in \mathbf{I}$ and θ is in radians.
   a) θ-intercepts   **b)** maximum values   **c)** minimum values

4. Graph $y = \dfrac{\sin\theta}{\cos\theta}$ using a graphing calculator in radian mode. Compare your graph with the graph of $y = \tan\theta$.

5. Find an expression that describes the location of each of the following values for $y = \tan\theta$, where $n \in \mathbf{I}$ and θ is in radians.
   a) θ-intercepts   **b)** vertical asymptotes

Transformations of Trigonometric Functions

YOU WILL NEED

- graph paper
- graphing calculator

GOAL

Use transformations to sketch the graphs of the primary trigonometric functions in radians.

LEARN ABOUT the Math

The following transformations are applied to the graph of $y = \sin x$, where $0 \leq x \leq 2\pi$:

- a vertical stretch by a factor of 3
- a horizontal compression by a factor of $\frac{1}{2}$
- a horizontal translation $\frac{\pi}{6}$ to the left
- a vertical translation 1 down

? **What is the equation of the transformed function, and what does its graph look like?**

EXAMPLE **1**	Selecting a strategy to apply transformations and graph a sine function

Use the transformations above to sketch the graph of the transformed function in the interval $0 \leq x \leq 2\pi$.

Solution A: Applying the transformation to the key points of the parent function

$y = \sin x$ is the parent function.

x	y = sin (x)
0	0
$\frac{\pi}{2}$	1
π	0
$\frac{3\pi}{2}$	-1
2π	0

One cycle of the parent function can be described with five key points. By applying the relevant transformations to these points, a complete cycle of the transformed function can be graphed.

$y = 3 \sin \left(2\left(x + \frac{\pi}{6}\right)\right) - 1$ is the equation of the transformed function.

Recall that, in the general function $y = af(k(x - d)) + c$, each parameter is associated with a specific transformation. In this case,

$a = 3$ (vertical stretch)

$k = \frac{1}{\frac{1}{2}} = 2$ (horizontal compression)

$d = -\frac{\pi}{6}$ (translation left)

$c = -1$ (translation down)

$$(x, y) \rightarrow \left(\frac{1}{2}x, 3y\right)$$

Parent Function, $y = \sin x$	Stretched/Compressed Function, $y = 3 \sin (2x)$
$(0, 0)$	$\left(\frac{1}{2}(0), 3(0)\right) = (0, 0)$
$\left(\frac{\pi}{2}, 1\right)$	$\left(\frac{1}{2}\left(\frac{\pi}{2}\right), 3(1)\right) = \left(\frac{\pi}{4}, 3\right)$
$(\pi, 0)$	$\left(\frac{1}{2}(\pi), 3(0)\right) = \left(\frac{\pi}{2}, 0\right)$
$\left(\frac{3\pi}{2}, -1\right)$	$\left(\frac{1}{2}\left(\frac{3\pi}{2}\right), 3(-1)\right) = \left(\frac{3\pi}{4}, -3\right)$
$(2\pi, 0)$	$\left(\frac{1}{2}(2\pi), 3(0)\right) = (\pi, 0)$

The parameters k and d affect the x-coordinates of each point on the parent function, and the parameters a and c affect the y-coordinates. All stretches/compressions and reflections must be applied before any translations. In this example, each x-coordinate of the five key points is multiplied by $\frac{1}{2}$, and each y-coordinate is multiplied by 3.

Plot the key points of the parent function and the key points of the transformed function, and draw smooth curves through them. Extend the red curve for one more cycle.

$$\left(\frac{1}{2}x, 3y\right) \rightarrow \left(\frac{1}{2}x - \frac{\pi}{6}, 3y - 1\right)$$

Stretched/Compressed Function, $y = 3 \sin (2x)$	Final Transformed Function, $y = 3 \sin \left(2\left(x + \frac{\pi}{6}\right)\right) - 1$
$(0, 0)$	$\left(0 - \frac{\pi}{6}, 0 - 1\right) = \left(-\frac{\pi}{6}, -1\right)$
$\left(\frac{\pi}{4}, 3\right)$	$\left(\frac{\pi}{4} - \frac{\pi}{6}, 3 - 1\right) = \left(\frac{\pi}{12}, 2\right)$
$\left(\frac{\pi}{2}, 0\right)$	$\left(\frac{\pi}{2} - \frac{\pi}{6}, 0 - 1\right) = \left(\frac{\pi}{3}, -1\right)$
$\left(\frac{3\pi}{4}, -3\right)$	$\left(\frac{3\pi}{4} - \frac{\pi}{6}, -3 - 1\right) = \left(\frac{7\pi}{12}, -4\right)$
$(\pi, 0)$	$\left(\pi - \frac{\pi}{6}, 0 - 1\right) = \left(\frac{5\pi}{6}, -1\right)$

Each x-coordinate of the key points on the previous function now has $\frac{\pi}{6}$ subtracted from it, and each y-coordinate has 1 subtracted from it.

These five points represent one complete cycle of the graph. To extend the graph to 2π, copy this cycle by adding the period of π to each x-coordinate in the table of the transformed key points.

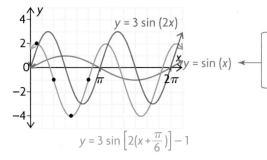

$$y = 3 \sin \left[2\left(x + \frac{\pi}{6}\right) \right] - 1$$

Plot the key points of the final transformed function, and draw a smooth curve through them.

Note that the vertical stretch and translation cause corresponding changes in the range of the parent function. The range of the parent function is $-1 \le y \le 1$, and the range of the transformed function is $-4 \le y \le 2$.

Solution B: Using the features of the transformed function

$y = 3 \sin \left(2\left(x + \frac{\pi}{6}\right) \right) - 1$ is the equation of the transformed function. It has the following characteristics:

Amplitude $= 3$

Period $= \dfrac{2\pi}{2} = \pi$

Equation of the axis: $y = -1$

Recall that each parameter in the general function $y = af(k(x - d)) + c$ is associated with a specific transformation. For the transformations applied to $f(x) = \sin x$,

$a = 3$ (vertical stretch)

$k = \dfrac{1}{\frac{1}{2}} = 2$ (horizontal compression)

$d = -\dfrac{\pi}{6}$ (translation left)

$c = -1$ (translation down)

Sketch the graph of $y = 3 \sin (2x) - 1$ by plotting its axis, points on its axis, and maximum and minimum values.

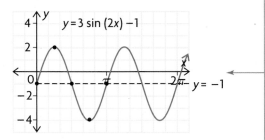

Since the axis is $y = -1$ and the amplitude is 3, the graph has a maximum at 2 and a minimum at -4. Since this is a sine function with a period of π, the maximum occurs at $x = \dfrac{\pi}{4}$, and the minimum occurs at $x = \dfrac{3\pi}{4}$. The graph has points on the axis when $x = 0$, $x = \dfrac{\pi}{2}$, and $x = \pi$.

Since the given domain is $0 \le \theta \le 2\pi$, add the period π to each point that was plotted for the first cycle and draw a smooth curve.

$y = 3 \sin\left(2\left(x + \dfrac{\pi}{6}\right)\right) - 1$ is the function

$y = 3 \sin(2x) - 1$ translated $\dfrac{\pi}{6}$ to the left.

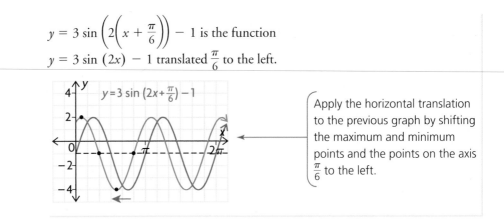

Apply the horizontal translation to the previous graph by shifting the maximum and minimum points and the points on the axis $\dfrac{\pi}{6}$ to the left.

Reflecting

A. What transformations affect each of the following characteristics of a sinusoidal function?

   i) period   ii) amplitude   iii) equation of the axis

B. In both solutions, it was necessary to extend the graphs after the final transformed points were plotted. Explain how this was done.

C. Which strategy for graphing sinusoidal functions do you prefer? Explain why.

APPLY the Math

> **EXAMPLE 2**   **Using the graph of a sinusoidal function to solve a problem**

A mass on a spring is pulled toward the floor and released, causing it to move up and down. Its height, in centimetres, above the floor after t seconds is given by the function $h(t) = 10 \sin(2\pi t + 1.5\pi) + 15$, $0 \le t \le 3$. Sketch a graph of height versus time. Then use your graph to predict when the mass will be 18 cm above the floor as it travels in an upward direction.

Solution

$h(t) = 10 \sin(2\pi t + 1.5\pi) + 15$

$h(t) = 10 \sin(2\pi(t + 0.75)) + 15$

For this function, the amplitude is 10 and the period is 1. The equation of the axis is $h = 15$. The function undergoes a horizontal translation 0.75 to the left.

Determine the characteristics that define the graph of this function. To do so, divide out the common factor from the **argument**. Then determine the values of the parameters a, k, d, and c.

$a = 10$

$k = 2\pi$, so the period is $\dfrac{2\pi}{2\pi} = 1$

$d = -0.75$

$c = 15$

argument

the expression on which a function operates; in Example 2, sin is the function and it operates on the expression $2\pi t + 1.5\pi$; so $2\pi t + 1.5\pi$ is the argument

Sketch the graph of $h(t) = 10 \sin (2\pi t) + 15$ over one cycle using the axis, amplitude, and period.

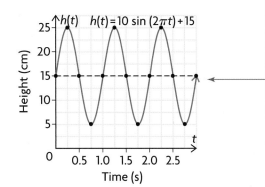

Since the axis is $h(t) = 15$ and the amplitude is 10, the graph will have a maximum at 25 and a minimum at 5. Since this is a sine function with a period of 1, these points will occur at $t = \frac{1}{4}$ and $t = \frac{3}{4}$. The graph has points on the axis when $t = 0$, $t = \frac{1}{2}$, and $t = 1$.

Since the given domain is $0 \le t \le 3$, add the period 1 to each point that was plotted for the first cycle. Repeat using the points on the second cycle to get three complete cycles. Then draw a smooth curve.

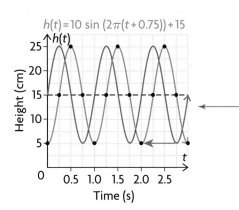

Apply the horizontal translation to the previous graph by shifting the maximum and minimum points and the points on the axis 0.75 to the left.

The spring is on its way up on the parts of the graph where the height is increasing.

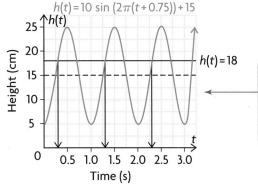

Use the graph to estimate when the spring will be 18 cm above the floor on the intervals $t \in [0, 0.5]$, $[1.0, 1.5]$, and $[2.0, 2.5]$.

On its way up, the spring is at a height of 18 cm at about 0.3 s, 1.3 s, and 2.3 s.

If you are given a graph of a sinusoidal function, then characteristics of its graph can be used to determine the equation of the function.

EXAMPLE 3

Connecting the features of the graph of a sinusoidal function to its equation

The following graph shows the temperature in Nellie's dorm room over a 24 h period.

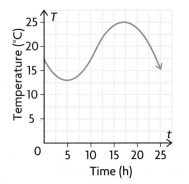

Determine the equation of this sinusoidal function.

Solution

Use the graph to determine the values of the parameters a, k, d, and c, and write the equation.

> The graph resembles the cosine function, so its equation is of the form $y = a \cos (k(x - d)) + c$.

The axis is $c = \dfrac{13 + 25}{2} = 19$.

> The value of c indicates the horizontal axis of the function. The horizontal axis is the mean of the maximum and minimum values.

$a = \dfrac{25 - 13}{2} = 6$

> The value of a indicates the amplitude of the function. The amplitude is half the difference between the maximum and minimum values.

$\text{Period} = \dfrac{2\pi}{k}$, so $24 = \dfrac{2\pi}{k}$

$24k = 2\pi$

$k = \dfrac{\pi}{12}$

> The value of k is related to the period of the function.
>
> If you assume that this cycle repeats itself over several days, then the period is 1 day, or 24 h.

> Let us use a cosine function. The parent function has a maximum value at $t = 0$.

$d = 17$

The equation is $T(t) = 6 \cos \left(\dfrac{\pi}{12}(t - 17) \right) + 19$.

> This graph has a maximum value at $t = 17$. Therefore, we translate the function 17 units to the right.

In Summary

Key Idea

- The graphs of functions of the form $f(x) = a \sin (k(x - d)) + c$ and $f(x) = a \cos (k(x - d)) + c$ are transformations of the parent functions $y = \sin (x)$ and $y = \cos (x)$, respectively.

  To sketch these functions, you can use a variety of strategies. Two of these strategies are given below:
  1. Begin with the key points in one cycle of the parent function and apply any stretches/compressions and reflections to these points: $(x, y) \rightarrow \left(\frac{x}{k}, ay \right)$. Take each of the new points, and apply any translations: $\left(\frac{x}{k}, ay \right) \rightarrow \left(\frac{x}{k} + d, ay + c \right)$.

     To graph more cycles, as required by the given domain, add multiples of the period to the x-coordinates of these transformed points and draw a smooth curve.
  2. Using the given equation, determine the equation of the axis, amplitude, and period of the function. Use this information to determine the location of the maximum and minimum points and the points that lie on the axis for one cycle. Plot these points, and then apply the horizontal translation to these points. To graph more cycles, as required by the domain, add multiples of the period to the x-coordinates of these points and draw a smooth curve.

Need to Know

- The parameters in the equations $f(x) = a \sin (k(x - d)) + c$ and $f(x) = a \cos (k(x - d)) + c$ give useful information about transformations and characteristics of the function.

Transformations of the Parent Function	Characteristics of the Transformed Function
$\|a\|$ gives the vertical stretch/compression factor. If $a < 0$, there is also a reflection in the x-axis.	$\|a\|$ gives the amplitude.
$\left\| \frac{1}{k} \right\|$ gives the horizontal stretch/compression factor. If $k < 0$, there is also a reflection in the y-axis.	$\frac{2\pi}{\|k\|}$ gives the period.
d gives the horizontal translation.	d gives the horizontal translation.
c gives the vertical translation.	$y = c$ gives the equation of the axis.

- If the independent variable has a coefficient other than $+1$, the argument must be factored to separate the values of k and c. For example,
  $y = 3 \cos (2x + \pi)$ should be changed to $y = 3 \cos \left(2\left(x + \frac{\pi}{2} \right) \right)$.

CHECK *Your Understanding*

1. State the period, amplitude, horizontal translation, and equation of the axis for each of the following trigonometric functions.

   a) $y = 0.5 \cos (4x)$

   b) $y = \sin \left(x - \frac{\pi}{4} \right) + 3$

   c) $y = 2 \sin (3x) - 1$

   d) $y = 5 \cos \left(-2x + \frac{\pi}{3} \right) - 2$

```
WINDOW
Xmin=0
Xmax=6.2831853…
Xscl=.52359877…
Ymin=-4
Ymax=4
Yscl=1
Xres=1
```

2. Suppose the trigonometric functions in question 1 are graphed using a graphing calculator in radian mode and the window settings shown. Which functions produce a graph that is not cut off on the top or bottom and that displays at least one cycle?

3. Identify the key characteristics of $y = -2 \cos(4x + \pi) + 4$, and sketch its graph. Check your graph with a graphing calculator.

PRACTISING

4. The following trigonometric functions have the parent function $f(x) = \sin x$. They have undergone no horizontal translations and no reflections in either axis. Determine the equation of each function.

   a) The graph of this trigonometric function has a period of π and an amplitude of 25. The equation of the axis is $y = -4$.

   b) The graph of this trigonometric function has a period of 10 and an amplitude of $\frac{2}{5}$. The equation of the axis is $y = \frac{1}{15}$.

   c) The graph of this trigonometric function has a period of 6π and an amplitude of 80. The equation of the axis is $y = -\frac{9}{10}$.

   d) The graph of this trigonometric function has a period of $\frac{1}{2}$ and an amplitude of 11. The equation of the axis is $y = 0$.

5. State the period, amplitude, and equation of the axis of the
K trigonometric function that produces each of the following tables of values. Then use this information to write the equation of the function.

a)

x	0	$\frac{\pi}{2}$	π	$\frac{3\pi}{2}$	2π
y	0	18	0	-18	0

b)

x	0	π	2π	3π	4π
y	-2	4	-2	-8	-2

c)

x	0	3π	6π	9π	12π
y	4	9	4	9	4

d)

x	0	2π	4π	6π	8π
y	-3	1	-3	1	-3

6. State the transformations that were applied to the parent function $f(x) = \sin x$ to obtain each of the following transformed functions. Then graph the transformed functions.

a) $f(x) = 4 \sin x + 3$

b) $f(x) = -\sin\left(\dfrac{1}{4}x\right)$

c) $f(x) = \sin(x - \pi) - 1$

d) $f(x) = \sin\left(4x + \dfrac{2\pi}{3}\right)$

7. The trigonometric function $f(x) = \cos x$ has undergone the following sets of transformations. For each set of transformations, determine the equation of the resulting function and sketch its graph.

a) vertical compression by a factor of $\dfrac{1}{2}$, vertical translation 3 units up

b) horizontal stretch by a factor of 2, reflection in the y-axis

c) vertical stretch by a factor of 3, horizontal translation $\dfrac{\pi}{2}$ to the right

d) horizontal compression by a factor of $\dfrac{1}{2}$, horizontal translation $\dfrac{\pi}{2}$ to the left

8. Sketch each graph for $0 \leq x \leq 2\pi$. Verify your sketch using graphing technology.

a) $y = 3 \sin\left(2\left(x - \dfrac{\pi}{6}\right)\right) + 1$

b) $y = 5 \cos\left(x + \dfrac{\pi}{4}\right) - 2$

c) $y = -2 \sin\left(2\left(x + \dfrac{\pi}{4}\right)\right) + 2$

d) $y = -\cos\left(0.5x - \dfrac{\pi}{6}\right) + 3$

e) $y = 0.5 \sin\left(\dfrac{x}{4} - \dfrac{\pi}{16}\right) - 5$

f) $y = \dfrac{1}{2} \cos\left(\dfrac{x}{2} - \dfrac{\pi}{12}\right) - 3$

9. **A** Each person's blood pressure is different, but there is a range of blood pressure values that is considered healthy. The function

$$P(t) = -20 \cos \dfrac{5\pi}{3}t + 100$$ models the blood pressure, p, in

millimetres of mercury, at time t, in seconds, of a person at rest.

a) What is the period of the function? What does the period represent for an individual?

b) How many times does this person's heart beat each minute?

c) Sketch the graph of $y = P(t)$ for $0 \leq t \leq 6$.

d) What is the range of the function? Explain the meaning of the range in terms of a person's blood pressure.

10. A pendulum swings back and forth 10 times in 8 s. It swings through a total horizontal distance of 40 cm.

a) Sketch a graph of this motion for two cycles, beginning with the pendulum at the end of its swing.

b) Describe the transformations necessary to transform $y = \sin x$ into the function you graphed in part a).

c) Write the equation that models this situation.

11. A rung on a hamster wheel, with a radius of 25 cm, is travelling at a
constant speed. It makes one complete revolution in 3 s. The axle of
the hamster wheel is 27 cm above the ground.

    a) Sketch a graph of the height of the rung above the ground during
two complete revolutions, beginning when the rung is closest to
the ground.

    b) Describe the transformations necessary to transform $y = \cos x$
into the function you graphed in part a).

    c) Write the equation that models this situation.

12. The graph of a sinusoidal function has been horizontally compressed
and horizontally translated to the left. It has maximums at the points
$\left(-\dfrac{5\pi}{7}, 1\right)$ and $\left(-\dfrac{3\pi}{7}, 1\right)$, and it has a minimum at $\left(-\dfrac{4\pi}{7}, -1\right)$.
If the x-axis is in radians, what is the period of the function?

13. The graph of a sinusoidal function has been vertically stretched, vertically
translated up, and horizontally translated to the right. The graph has a
maximum at $\left(\dfrac{\pi}{13}, 13\right)$, and the equation of the axis is $y = 9$. If
the x-axis is in radians, list one point where the graph has a minimum.

14. Determine a sinusodial equation for each of the following graphs.

a)

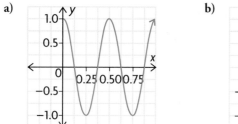

b)

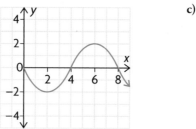

c)

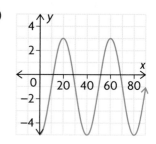

15. Create a flow chart that summarises how you would use transformations
to sketch the graph of $f(x) = -2 \sin\left(0.5\left(x - \dfrac{\pi}{4}\right)\right) + 3$.

Extending

16. The graph shows the distance from a light pole to a car racing around a
circular track. The track is located north of the light pole.

    a) Determine the distance from the light pole to the edge of the track.

    b) Determine the distance from the light pole to the centre of the track.

    c) Determine the radius of the track.

    d) Detemine the time that the car takes to complete one lap of the track.

    e) Determine the speed of the car in metres per second.

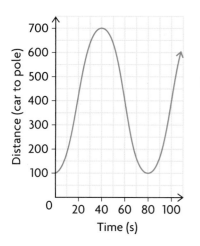

FREQUENTLY ASKED Questions

Q: How are radians and degrees related?

A: Radians are determined by the relationship $\theta = \frac{a}{r}$, where θ is the angle subtended by arc length a in a circle with radius r. One revolution creates an angle of $360°$, or 2π radians. Since $360° = 2\pi$ radians, it follows that $180° = \pi$ radians. This relationship can be used to convert between the two measures.

- To convert from degrees to radians, multiply by $\frac{\pi}{180°}$.

- To convert from radians to degrees, either substitute $180°$ for π or multiply by $\frac{180°}{\pi}$.

Here are three examples:

$$75° = 75° \times \frac{\pi}{180°} \qquad \frac{5\pi}{4} = \frac{5(180°)}{4} \qquad 3 \text{ radians} = \frac{3(180°)}{\pi}$$

$$= \frac{5\pi}{12} \qquad\qquad = 225° \qquad\qquad \doteq 171.887°$$

Study | Aid

- See Lesson 6.1, Examples 1, 2, and 3.
- Try Mid-Chapter Review Questions 1, 2, and 3.

Q: How do you determine exact values of trigonometric ratios for multiples of special angles expressed in radians?

A: An angle on the Cartesian plane is determined by rotating the terminal arm in either a clockwise or counterclockwise direction. The special triangles can be used to determine the coordinates of a point that lies on the terminal arm of the angle. Then, using the x, y, r trigonometric definitions and the related angle, the exact values of the trigonometric ratios can be evaluated for multiples of angles $\frac{\pi}{3}$, $\frac{\pi}{4}$, and $\frac{\pi}{6}$.

For example, to determine the exact value of $\sec \frac{5\pi}{4}$, sketch the angle in standard position. Determine the related angle. Since the terminal arm of $\frac{5\pi}{4}$ lies in the third quadrant, the related angle is $\frac{5\pi}{4} - \pi = \frac{\pi}{4}$.

Study | Aid

- See Lesson 6.2, Example 3.
- Try Mid-Chapter Review Questions 4 and 6.

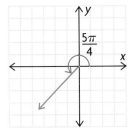

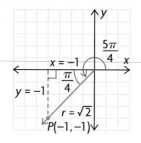

Sketch the 1, 1, $\sqrt{2}$ special triangle by drawing a vertical line from the point $(-1, -1)$ on the terminal arm to the negative x- axis. Use the values of x, y, and r and the appropriate ratio to determine the value.

$$\sec \frac{5\pi}{4} = \frac{r}{x}$$
$$= \frac{\sqrt{2}}{-1}$$
$$= -\sqrt{2}$$

Study | *Aid*

• See Lesson 6.4, Example 3.
• Try Mid-Chapter Review Questions 8 and 9.

Q: How can transformations be used to graph sinusoidal functions?

A: The graphs of functions of the form $f(x) = a \sin (k(x - d)) + c$ and $f(x) = a \cos (k(x - d)) + c$ are transformations of the parent functions $y = \sin (x)$ and $y = \cos (x)$, respectively.

In sinusoidal functions, the parameters a, k, d, and c give the transformations to be applied, as well as the key characteristics of the graph.

- $|a|$ gives the vertical stretch/compression factor and the amplitude of the function.

- $\left|\frac{1}{k}\right|$ determines the horizontal stretch/compression factor, and $\left|\frac{2\pi}{k}\right|$ gives the period of the function.

- When a is negative, the function is reflected in the x-axis. When k is negative, the function is reflected in the y-axis.

- d gives the horizontal translation.

- c gives the vertical translation, and $y = c$ gives the equation of the horizontal axis of the function.

To sketch these functions, begin with the key points of the parent function. Apply any stretches/compressions and reflections first, and then follow them with any translations.

Alternatively, use the equation of the axis, amplitude, and period to sketch a graph of the form $f(x) = a \sin (x) + c$ or $f(x) = a \cos (x) + c$. Then apply the horizontal translation to the points of this graph, if necessary.

PRACTICE Questions

Lesson 6.1

1. Convert each angle from radians to degrees. Express your answer to one decimal place, if necessary.

   a) $\dfrac{\pi}{8}$　　　　　c) 5

   b) 4π　　　　　d) $\dfrac{11\pi}{12}$

2. Convert each angle from degrees to radians. Express your answer to one decimal place, if necessary.

   a) $125°$　　　　　d) $330°$

   b) $450°$　　　　　e) $215°$

   c) $5°$　　　　　f) $-140°$

3. A tire with a diameter of 38 cm rotates 10 times in 5 s.

   a) What is the angle that the tire rotates through, in radians, from 0 s to 5 s?

   b) Determine the angular velocity of the tire.

   c) Determine the distance travelled by a pebble that is trapped in the tread of the tire.

Lesson 6.2

4. Sketch each angle in standard position, and then determine the exact value of the trigonometric ratio.

   a) $\sin \dfrac{3\pi}{4}$　　　　d) $\tan \dfrac{5\pi}{6}$

   b) $\sin \dfrac{11\pi}{6}$　　　　e) $\cos \dfrac{3\pi}{2}$

   c) $\tan \dfrac{5\pi}{3}$　　　　f) $\cos \dfrac{4\pi}{3}$

5. The terminal arms of angles in standard position pass through the following points. Find the measure of each angle in radians, to the nearest hundredth.

   a) $(-3, 14)$　　　　d) $(-5, -18)$

   b) $(6, 7)$　　　　e) $(2, 3)$

   c) $(1, 9)$　　　　f) $(4, -20)$

6. State an equivalent expression for each of the following expressions, in terms of the related acute angle.

   a) $\sin\left(-\dfrac{7\pi}{6}\right)$　　　c) $\sec\left(-\dfrac{\pi}{2}\right)$

   b) $\cot \dfrac{7\pi}{4}$　　　　d) $\cos\left(-\dfrac{5\pi}{6}\right)$

Lesson 6.3

7. State the x-intercepts and y-intercepts of the graph of each of the following functions.

   a) $y = \sin x$

   b) $y = \cos x$

   c) $y = \tan x$

Lesson 6.4

8. Sketch the graph of each function on the interval $-2\pi \leq x \leq 2\pi$.

   a) $y = \tan (x)$

   b) $y = 2 \sin (-x) - 1$

   c) $y = \dfrac{5}{2} \cos \left(2\left(x + \dfrac{\pi}{4}\right)\right) + 3$

   d) $y = -\dfrac{1}{2} \cos \left(\dfrac{1}{2}x - \dfrac{\pi}{6}\right)$

   e) $y = 2 \sin \left(-3\left(x - \dfrac{\pi}{2}\right)\right) + 4$

   f) $y = 0.4 \sin (\pi - 2x) - 2.5$

9. The graph of the function $y = \sin x$ is transformed by vertically compressing it by a factor of $\dfrac{1}{3}$, reflecting it in the y-axis, horizontally compressing it by a factor of $\dfrac{1}{3}$, horizontally translating it $\dfrac{\pi}{8}$ units to the left, and vertically translating it 23 units down. Write the equation of the resulting graph.

Exploring Graphs of the Reciprocal Trigonometric Functions

YOU WILL NEED

- graph paper
- graphing calculator

GOAL

Graph the reciprocal trigonometric functions and determine their key characteristics.

EXPLORE the Math

Recall that the characteristics of the graph of a reciprocal function of a linear or quadratic function are directly related to the characteristics of the original function. Therefore, the key characteristics of the graph of a linear or quadratic function can be used to graph the related reciprocal function. The same strategies can be used to graph the reciprocal of a trigonometric function.

? What do the graphs of the reciprocal trigonometric functions $y = \csc x$, $y = \sec x$, and $y = \cot x$ look like, and what are their key characteristics?

A. Here is the graph of $y = \sin x$.

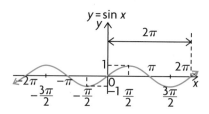

Use this graph to predict where each of the following characteristics of the graph of $y = \dfrac{1}{\sin x}$ will occur.

a) vertical asymptotes
b) maximum and minimum values
c) positive and negative intervals
d) intervals of increase and decrease
e) points of intersection for $y = \sin x$ and $y = \dfrac{1}{\sin x}$

B. Use your predictions in part A to sketch the graph of $y = \dfrac{1}{\sin x}$ (that is, $y = \csc x$). Verify your sketch by entering $y = \sin x$ into Y1 and $y = \dfrac{1}{\sin x}$ into Y2 of a graphing calculator, using the window settings shown. Compare the period and amplitude of each function.

```
WINDOW
Xmin=-9.4
Xmax=9.4
Xscl=1
Ymin=-3.1
Ymax=3.1
Yscl=1
Xres=1
```

C. Predict what will happen if the period of $y = \sin x$ changes from 2π to π. Change Y1 to $y = \sin(2x)$ and Y2 to $y = \dfrac{1}{\sin(2x)}$ and discuss the results.

D. Here is the graph of $y = \cos x$.

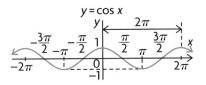

Repeat parts A to C using the cosine function and its reciprocal $y = \dfrac{1}{\cos x}$ (that is, $y = \sec x$).

E. Here is the graph of $y = \tan x$. Recall that $\tan x = \dfrac{\sin x}{\cos x}$.

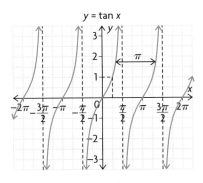

Repeat parts A to C using this form of the tangent function and its reciprocal $y = \dfrac{\cos x}{\sin x}$ (that is, $y = \cot x$).

Reflecting

F. Do the primary trigonometric functions and their reciprocal functions have the same kind of relationship that linear and quadratic functions and their reciprocal functions have? Explain.

G. Which x-values of the reciprocal function, in the interval $-2\pi \leq x \leq 2\pi$, result in vertical asymptotes? Why does this happen?

H. What is the relationship between the positive and negative intervals of the primary trigonometric functions and the positive and negative intervals of their reciprocal functions?

I. Where do the points of intersection occur for the primary trigonometric functions and their reciprocal functions?

In Summary

Key Idea

- Each of the primary trigonometric graphs has a corresponding reciprocal function.

Cosecant	Secant	Cotangent
$y = \csc \theta$	$y = \sec \theta$	$y = \cot \theta$
$y = \dfrac{1}{\sin \theta}$	$y = \dfrac{1}{\cos \theta}$	$y = \dfrac{1}{\tan \theta} = \dfrac{\cos \theta}{\sin \theta}$

Need to Know

- The graph of a reciprocal trigonometric function is related to the graph of its corresponding primary trigonometric function in the following ways:
  - The graph of the reciprocal function has a vertical asymptote at each zero of the corresponding primary trigonometric function.
  - The reciprocal function has the same positive/negative intervals as the corresponding primary trigonometric function.
  - Intervals of increase on the primary trigonometric function are intervals of decrease on the corresponding reciprocal function. Intervals of decrease on the primary trigonometric function are intervals of increase on the corresponding reciprocal function.
  - The ranges of the primary trigonometric functions include 1 and -1, so a reciprocal function intersects its corresponding primary function at points where the y-coordinate is 1 or -1.
  - If the primary trigonometric function has a local minimum point, the corresponding reciprocal function has a local maximum point at the same θ value. If the primary trigonometric function has a local maximum point, the corresponding reciprocal function has a local minimum point at the same θ value.

Cosecant	**Secant**	**Cotangent**

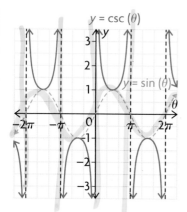 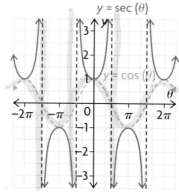 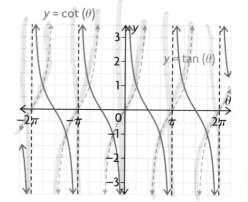

- has vertical asymptotes at the points where $\sin \theta = 0$
- has the same period (2π) as $y = \sin \theta$
- has the domain $\{x \in \mathbf{R} \,|\, \theta \neq n\pi, n \in \mathbf{I}\}$
- has the range $\{y \in \mathbf{R} \,|\, |y| \geq 1\}$

- has vertical asymptotes at the points where $\cos \theta = 0$
- has the same period (2π) as $y = \cos \theta$
- has the domain $\{x \in \mathbf{R} \,|\, \theta \neq (2n-1)\dfrac{\pi}{2}, n \in \mathbf{I}\}$
- has the range $\{y \in \mathbf{R} \,|\, |y| \geq 1\}$

- has vertical asymptotes at the points where $\tan \theta = 0$
- has zeros at the points where $y = \tan \theta$ has asymptotes
- has the same period (π) as $y = \tan \theta$
- has the domain $\{x \in \mathbf{R} \,|\, \theta \neq n\pi, n \in \mathbf{I}\}$
- has the range $\{y \in \mathbf{R}\}$

FURTHER Your Understanding

1. The equation $t_n = a + (n - 1)\,d$ can be used to represent the general term of any arithmetic sequence, where a is the first term and d is the common difference. Use this equation to find an expression that describes the location of each of the following values for $y = \csc x$, where $n \in \mathbf{I}$ and x is in radians.
   a) vertical asymptotes
   b) maximum values
   c) minimum values

2. Find an expression that describes the location of each of the following values for $y = \sec x$, where $n \in \mathbf{I}$ and x is in radians.
   a) vertical asymptotes
   b) maximum values
   c) minimum values

3. Find an expression that describes the location of each of the following values for $y = \cot x$, where $n \in \mathbf{I}$ and x is in radians.
   a) vertical asymptotes
   b) x-intercepts

4. Use graphing technology to graph $y = \csc x$ and $y = \sec x$. For which values of the independent variable do the graphs intersect? Compare these values with the intersections of $y = \sin x$ and $y = \cos x$. Explain.

5. The graphs of the functions $y = \sin x$ and $y = \cos x$ are congruent, related by a translation of $\frac{\pi}{2}$ where $\sin \left(x + \frac{\pi}{2} \right) = \cos x$. Does this relationship hold for $y = \csc x$ and $y = \sec x$? Verify your conjecture using graphing technology.

6. Two successive transformations can be applied to the graph of $y = \tan x$ to obtain the graph of $y = \cot x$. There is more than one way to apply these transformations, however. Describe one of these compound transformations.

7. Use transformations to sketch the graph of each function. Then state the period of the function.
   a) $y = \cot \left(\dfrac{x}{2} \right)$
   b) $y = \csc \left(2 \left(x + \dfrac{\pi}{2} \right) \right)$
   c) $y = \sec x - 1$
   d) $y = \csc \left(0.5x + \pi \right)$

Modelling with Trigonometric Functions

YOU WILL NEED

- graphing calculator or graphing software

GOAL

Model and solve problems that involve trigonometric functions and radian measurement.

LEARN ABOUT the Math

The tides at Cape Capstan, New Brunswick, change the depth of the water in the harbour. On one day in October, the tides have a high point of approximately 10 m at 2 p.m. and a low point of approximately 1.2 m at 8:15 p.m. A particular sailboat has a *draft* of 2 m. This means it can only move in water that is at least 2 m deep. The captain of the sailboat plans to exit the harbour at 6:30 p.m.

? Can the captain exit the harbour safely in the sailboat at 6 p.m.?

EXAMPLE 1 Modelling the problem using a sinusoidal equation

Create a sinusoidal function to model the problem, and use it to determine whether the sailboat can exit the harbour safely at 6 p.m.

Solution

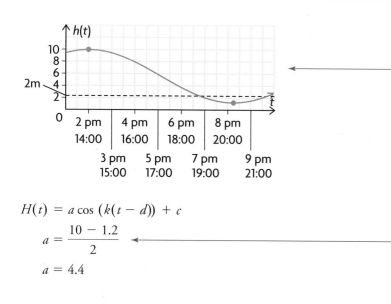

A sinusoidal function can be used to model the height of the water versus time. Draw a sketch to get an idea of when the captain needs to leave. It appears that the captain will have enough depth at 6:30 p.m., but you cannot be sure from a rough sketch.

$$H(t) = a \cos (k(t - d)) + c$$

$$a = \frac{10 - 1.2}{2}$$

$$a = 4.4$$

Choose the cosine function to model the problem, since the graph starts at a maximum value. The amplitude, period, horizontal translation, and equation of the axis need to be determined.

Use the maximum and minimum measurements of the tides to calculate the amplitude of the function. This gives the value of *a* in the equation.

$$\text{Period} = \frac{2\pi}{k}$$

$$12.5 = \frac{2\pi}{k}$$

$$12.5k = 2\pi$$

$$k = \frac{2\pi}{12.5} = \frac{4\pi}{25}$$

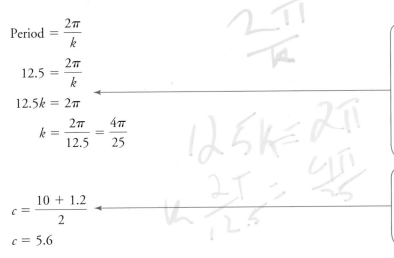

In a sinusoidal function, the horizontal distance between the maximum and minimum points represents half of one cycle.

Since a maximum tide and a minimum tide occur 6 h 15 min apart, the period must be 12.5 h. The period can be used to determine the value of k in the equation.

$$c = \frac{10 + 1.2}{2}$$

$$c = 5.6$$

The equation of the axis is the mean of the maximum and minimum points. This can be used to determine the value of c in the equation.

A function that models the tides at Cape Capstan is

$$H(t) = 4.4 \cos\left(\frac{4\pi}{25}(t - 2)\right) + 5.6.$$

The parent cosine function starts at a maximum point.
If we let $t = 0$ represent noon, then our function needs a maximum at $t = 2$ (or 2 p.m.). We use a horizontal translation right 2 units. Therefore $d = 2$.

$$H(18) = 4.4 \cos\left(\frac{4\pi}{25}(6.5 - 2)\right) + 5.6$$

$$= 4.4 \cos\left(\frac{18\pi}{25}\right) + 5.6$$

$$\doteq 2.80 \text{ m}$$

To determine the water level at 6:30 p.m., let $t = 6.5$.

Since the depth of the water is greater than 2 m at 6:30 p.m., the sailboat can safely exit the harbour.

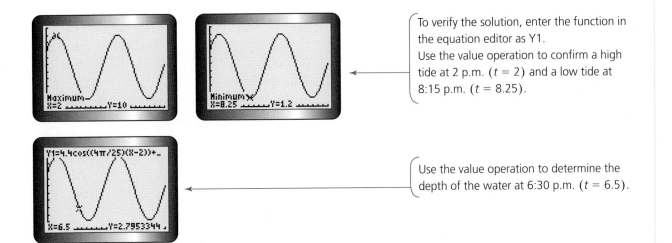

To verify the solution, enter the function in the equation editor as Y1.
Use the value operation to confirm a high tide at 2 p.m. ($t = 2$) and a low tide at 8:15 p.m. ($t = 8.25$).

Use the value operation to determine the depth of the water at 6:30 p.m. ($t = 6.5$).

Reflecting

A. What characteristics of your model would change if you used a sine function to model the problem?

B. What role did the maximum value play in determining the required horizontal translation?

C. If $t = 0$ was set at 2 p.m. instead of noon, how would the equation change? Would this make a difference to your final answer?

APPLY the Math

EXAMPLE 2   Representing a situation described by data using a sinusoidal equation

The following table shows the average monthly means of the daily (24 h) temperatures in Hamilton, Ontario. Each month's average temperature is represented by the day in the middle of the month.

Month	Jan.	Feb.	Mar.	Apr.	May	June	July	Aug.	Sep.	Oct.	Nov.	Dec.
Day of Year	15	45	75	106	136	167	197	228	259	289	320	350
°C	−4.8	−4.8	−0.2	6.6	12.7	18.6	21.9	20.7	16.4	10.5	3.6	−2.3

a) Plot the temperature data for Hamilton, and fit a sinusoidal curve to the points.
b) Estimate the average daily temperature in Hamilton on the 200th day of the year.

Solution A: Using the data and reasoning about the characteristics of the graph

a)

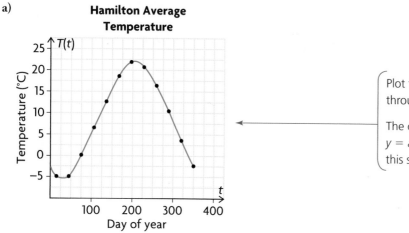

Plot the data, and sketch a smooth curve through the points.

The curve appears to be sinusoidal, so use $y = a \sin (k(t - d)) + c$ as the model for this situation.

$$a = \frac{\text{maximum} - \text{minimum}}{2}$$

$$a = \frac{21.9 - (-4.8)}{2}$$

$$a = 13.35$$

Estimate the maximum and minimum temperatures for the year from the graph. Use these temperatures to calculate the values of a and c. The value of a gives the amplitude. The sine function has been stretched vertically by a factor of 13.35.

$$c = \frac{\text{maximum} + \text{minimum}}{2}$$

$$c = \frac{21.9 + (-4.8)}{2}$$

$$c = 8.55$$

The value of c gives the horizontal axis. The sine function has been vertically translated by 8.55 units on the Temperature axis. Lightly draw a horizontal line through your graph at this value.

$$\text{Period} = \frac{2\pi}{k}, \text{ so } k = \frac{2\pi}{\text{period}}$$

$$k = \frac{2\pi}{365}$$

The value of k in the equation is determined by the period. Assume that the cycle repeats itself every year (365 days).

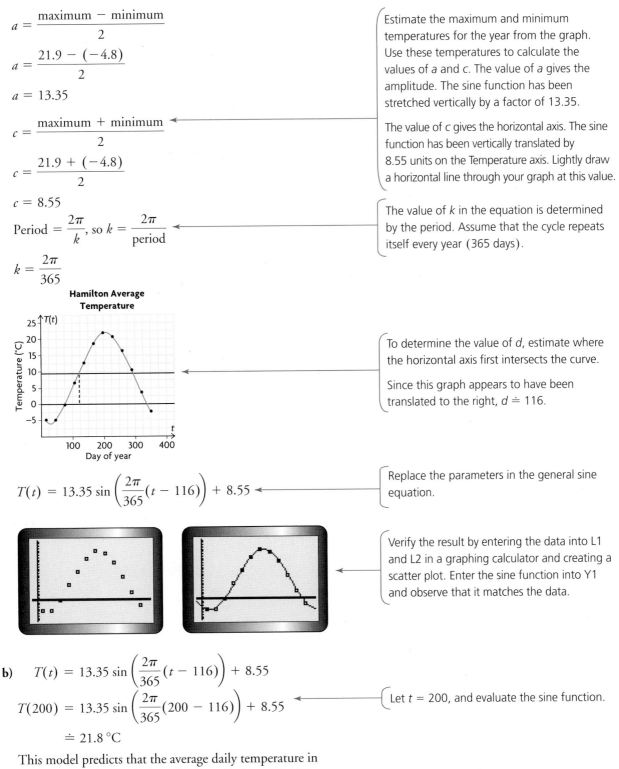

Hamilton Average Temperature

To determine the value of d, estimate where the horizontal axis first intersects the curve.

Since this graph appears to have been translated to the right, $d \doteq 116$.

$$T(t) = 13.35 \sin\left(\frac{2\pi}{365}(t - 116)\right) + 8.55$$

Replace the parameters in the general sine equation.

Verify the result by entering the data into L1 and L2 in a graphing calculator and creating a scatter plot. Enter the sine function into Y1 and observe that it matches the data.

b)
$$T(t) = 13.35 \sin\left(\frac{2\pi}{365}(t - 116)\right) + 8.55$$

$$T(200) = 13.35 \sin\left(\frac{2\pi}{365}(200 - 116)\right) + 8.55$$

$$\doteq 21.8\,^\circ C$$

Let $t = 200$, and evaluate the sine function.

This model predicts that the average daily temperature in Hamilton on the 200th day of the year is about 21.8 °C.

Since sinusoidal functions are periodic, they can be used (where appropriate) to make educated predictions.

EXAMPLE **3**

Analyzing a situation that involves sinusoidal models

The population size, O, of owls (predators) in a certain region can be modelled by the function $O(t) = 1000 + 100 \sin\left(\frac{\pi t}{12}\right)$, where t represents the time in months and $t = 0$ represents January. The population size, m, of mice (prey) in the same region is given by the function $m(t) = 20\,000 + 4000 \cos\left(\frac{\pi t}{12}\right)$.

a) Sketch the graphs of these functions.
b) Compare the graphs, and discuss the relationships between the two populations.
c) How does the mice-to-owls ratio change over time?
d) When is there the most food per owl? When is it safest for the mice?

Solution

a) Graph the prey function.

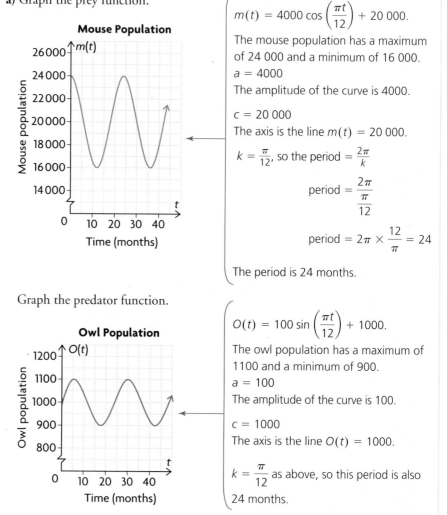

Mouse Population

$m(t) = 4000 \cos\left(\frac{\pi t}{12}\right) + 20\,000.$

The mouse population has a maximum of 24 000 and a minimum of 16 000.
$a = 4000$
The amplitude of the curve is 4000.

$c = 20\,000$
The axis is the line $m(t) = 20\,000$.

$k = \frac{\pi}{12}$, so the period $= \frac{2\pi}{k}$

$$\text{period} = \frac{2\pi}{\frac{\pi}{12}}$$

$$\text{period} = 2\pi \times \frac{12}{\pi} = 24$$

The period is 24 months.

Graph the predator function.

Owl Population

$O(t) = 100 \sin\left(\frac{\pi t}{12}\right) + 1000.$

The owl population has a maximum of 1100 and a minimum of 900.
$a = 100$
The amplitude of the curve is 100.

$c = 1000$
The axis is the line $O(t) = 1000$.

$k = \frac{\pi}{12}$ as above, so this period is also 24 months.

b)

Mouse Population

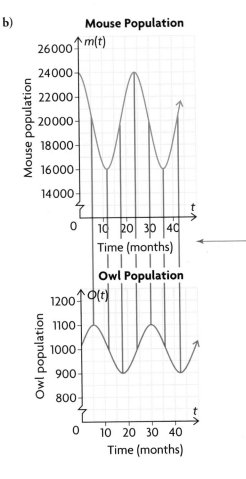

The graphs can be compared, since the same scale was used on both horizontal axes. As the owl population begins to increase, the mouse population begins to decrease. The mouse population continues to decrease, and this has an impact on the owl population, since its food supply dwindles. The owl population peaks and then also starts to decrease. The mouse population reaches a minimum and begins to rise as there are fewer owls to eat the mice. As the mouse population increases, food becomes more plentiful for the owls. So their population begins to rise again. Since both graphs have the same period, this pattern repeats every 24 months.

c) The following table shows the ratio of mice to owls at key points in the first four years.

Time	Mice	Owls	Mice-to-Owl Ratio
0	24 000	1000	24
6	20 000	1100	18.2
12	16 000	1000	16
18	20 000	900	22.2
24	24 000	1000	24

There seems to be a pattern. Enter the mouse function into Y1 of the equation editor of a graphing calculator, and enter the owl function into Y2. Turn off each function, and enter Y3 = Y1/Y2.

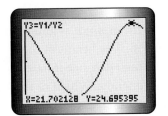

The resulting graph is shown. The ratio of mice to owls is also sinusoidal.

d) The most food per owl occurs when the ratio of mice to owls is the highest (there are more mice per owl).

The safest time for the mice occurs at the same time, when the ratio of mice to owls is the highest (there are fewer owls per mouse).

This occurs near the end of the 21st month of the two-year cycle.

In Summary

Key Ideas

- The graphs of $y = \sin x$ and $y = \cos x$ can model periodic phenomena when they are transformed to fit a given situation. The transformed functions are of the form $y = a \sin (k(x - d)) + c$ and $y = a \cos (k(x - d)) + c$, where
  - $|a|$ is the amplitude and $a = \dfrac{max - min}{2}$
  - $|k|$ is the number of cycles in 2π radians, when the period $= \dfrac{2\pi}{k}$
  - d gives the horizontal translation
  - c is the vertical translation and $y = c$ is the horizontal axis

Need to Know

- Tables of values, graphs, and equations of sinusoidal functions can be used as mathematical models when solving problems. Determining the equation of the appropriate sine or cosine function from the data or graph provided is the most efficient strategy, however, since accurate calculations can be made using the equation.

CHECK *Your Understanding*

1. A cosine curve has an amplitude of 3 units and a period of 3π radians. The equation of the axis is $y = 2$, and a horizontal shift of $\dfrac{\pi}{4}$ radians to the left has been applied. Write the equation of this function.

2. Determine the value of the function in question 1 if $x = \dfrac{\pi}{2}, \dfrac{3\pi}{4}$, and $\dfrac{11\pi}{6}$.

3. Sketch a graph of the function in question 1. Use your graph to estimate the x-value(s) in the domain $0 < x < 2$, where $y = 2.5$, to one decimal place.

PRACTISING

4. The height of a patch on a bicycle tire above the ground, as a function of time, is modelled by one sinusoidal function. The height of the patch above the ground, as a function of the total distance it has travelled, is modelled by another sinusoidal function. Which of the following characteristics do the two sinusoidal functions share: amplitude, period, equation of the axis?

5. Mike is waving a sparkler in a circular motion at a constant speed.
K The tip of the sparkler is moving in a plane that is perpendicular to the ground. The height of the tip of the sparkler above the ground, as a function of time, can be modelled by a sinusoidal function. At $t = 0$, the sparkler is at its highest point above the ground.

a) What does the amplitude of the sinusoidal function represent in this situation?

b) What does the period of the sinusoidal function represent in this situation?

c) What does the equation of the axis of the sinusoidal function represent in this situation?

d) If no horizontal translations are required to model this situation, should a sine or cosine function be used?

6. To test the resistance of a new product to temperature changes, the
A product is placed in a controlled environment. The temperature in this environment, as a function of time, can be described by a sine function. The maximum temperature is $120\,°C$, the minimum temperature is $-60\,°C$, and the temperature at $t = 0$ is $30\,°C$. It takes 12 h for the temperature to change from the maximum to the minimum. If the temperature is initially increasing, what is the equation of the sine function that describes the temperature in this environment?

7. A person who was listening to a siren reported that the frequency of the sound fluctuated with time, measured in seconds. The minimum frequency that the person heard was 500 Hz, and the maximum frequency was 1000 Hz. The maximum frequency occurred at $t = 0$ and $t = 15$. The person also reported that, in 15, she heard the maximum frequency 6 times (including the times at $t = 0$ and $t = 15$). What is the equation of the cosine function that describes the frequency of this siren?

8. A contestant on a game show spins a wheel that is located on a plane perpendicular to the floor. He grabs the only red peg on the circumference of the wheel, which is 1.5 m above the floor, and pushes it downward. The red peg reaches a minimum height of 0.25 m above the floor and a maximum height of 2.75 m above the floor. Sketch two cycles of the graph that represents the height of the red peg above the floor, as a function of the total distance it moved. Then determine the equation of the sine function that describes the graph.

9. At one time, Maple Leaf Village (which no longer exists) had North America's largest Ferris wheel. The Ferris wheel had a diameter of 56 m, and one revolution took 2.5 min to complete. Riders could see Niagara Falls if they were higher than 50 m above the ground. Sketch three cycles of a graph that represents the height of a rider above the ground, as a function of time, if the rider gets on at a height of 0.5 m at $t = 0$ min. Then determine the time intervals when the rider could see Niagara Falls.

10. The number of hours of daylight in Vancouver can be modelled by a sinusoidal function of time, in days. The longest day of the year is June 21, with 15.7 h of daylight. The shortest day of the year is December 21, with 8.3 h of daylight.
    a) Find an equation for $n(t)$, the number of hours of daylight on the nth day of the year.
    b) Use your equation to predict the number of hours of daylight in Vancouver on January 30th.

11. The city of Thunder Bay, Ontario, has average monthly temperatures that vary between $-14.8\,°C$ and $17.6\,°C$. The following table gives the average monthly temperatures, averaged over many years. Determine the equation of the sine function that describes the data, and use your equation to determine the times that the temperature is below $0\,°C$.

Month	Jan.	Feb.	Mar.	Apr.	May	June	July	Aug.	Sep.	Oct.	Nov.	Dec.
Average Temperature (°C)	−14.8	−12.7	−5.9	2.5	8.7	13.9	17.6	16.5	11.2	5.6	−2.7	−11.1

12. A nail is stuck in the tire of a car. If a student wanted to graph a sine function to model the height of the nail above the ground during a trip from Kingston, Ontario, to Hamilton, Ontario, should the student graph the distance of the nail above the ground as a function of time or as a function of the total distance travelled by the nail? Explain your reasoning.

Extending

13. A clock is hanging on a wall, with the centre of the clock 3 m above the floor. Both the minute hand and the second hand are 15 cm long. The hour hand is 8 cm long. For each hand, determine the equation of the cosine function that describes the distance of the tip of the hand above the floor as a function of time. Assume that the time, t, is in minutes and that the distance, $D(t)$, is in centimetres. Also assume that $t = 0$ is midnight.

6.7 Rates of Change in Trigonometric Functions

GOAL

Examine average and instantaneous rates of change in trigonometric functions.

LEARN ABOUT the Math

Melissa used a motion detector to measure the horizontal distance between her and a child on a swing. She stood in front of the child and recorded the distance, $d(t)$, in metres over a period of time, t, in seconds. The data she collected are given in the following tables and are shown on the graph below.

Time (s)	0	0.1	0.2	0.3	0.4	0.5	0.6	0.7	0.8	0.9	1	1.1
Distance (m)	3.8	3.68	3.33	2.81	2.2	1.59	1.07	0.72	0.6	0.72	1.07	1.59

Time (s)	1.2	1.3	1.4	1.5	1.6	1.7	1.8	1.9	2.0	2.1	2.2	2.3	2.4
Distance (m)	2.2	2.81	3.33	3.68	3.8	3.68	3.33	2.81	2.2	1.59	1.07	0.72	0.6

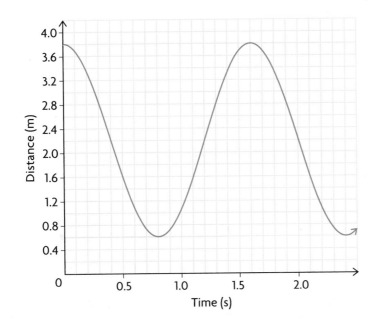

? How did the speed of the child change as the child swung back and forth?

EXAMPLE **1**   Using the data and the graph to analyze the situation

Use the data and the graph to discuss how the speed of the child changed as the child swung back and forth.

Solution

Analyze the motion.

Melissa began recording the motion when the child was the farthest distance from the motion detector, which was 3.8 m. The child's closest distance to the motion detector was 0.6 m and occurred at 0.8 s. The child was moving toward the motion detector between 0 s and 0.8 s and away from the motion detector between 0.8 s and 1.6 s.

> Looking at the graph, the maximum value was 3.8 and occurred at 0 s and 1.6 s. It took 1.6 s for the child to swing one complete cycle.
>
> Looking at the data and the graph, the distances between the child and the motion detector were decreasing between 0 s and 0.8 s, and increasing between 0.8 s and 1.6 s. This pattern repeated itself every multiple of 1.6 s.

Analyze the instantaneous velocity by drawing tangent lines at various points over one swing cycle.

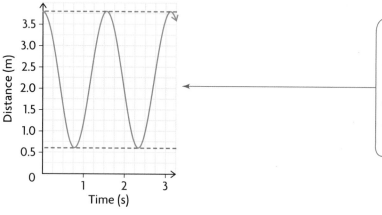

> The slope of a tangent line on any distance versus time graph gives the instantaneous velocity, which is the instantaneous rate of change in distance with respect to time.
>
> When the child was at the farthest point and closest point from the motion detector, the instantaneous velocity was 0.

Between 0 s and about 0.4 s, the child's speed was increasing.

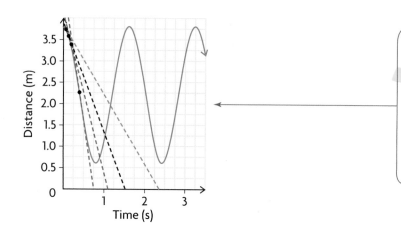

> On this interval, the tangent lines become steeper as time increases.
>
> $\text{Speed} = |\text{velocity}| = \left| \dfrac{\Delta \text{distance}}{\Delta \text{time}} \right|$. This means the magnitudes of the slopes are increasing. The tangent lines have negative slopes, which means the distance between the child and the motion detector continues to decrease.

Between 0.4 s and about 0.8 s, the child's speed was decreasing.

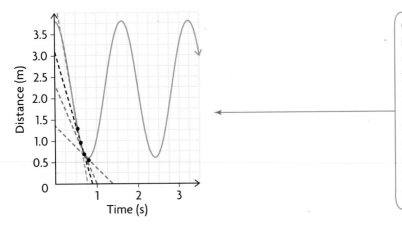

On this interval, the tangent lines are getting less steep as time increases. This means the magnitudes of the slopes are decreasing. The tangent lines still have negative slopes, which means the distance between the child and the motion detector is still decreasing. The child is slowing down as the swing approaches the point where a change in direction occurs. The slopes indicate a change in the child's position from toward the detector to away from the detector.

Between 0.8 s and about 1.2 s, the child's speed was increasing.

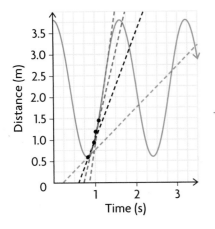

On this interval, the tangent lines are getting steeper as time increases. This means the magnitudes of the slopes are increasing. The tangent lines have positive slopes, which means the distance between the child and the motion detector is increasing. Therefore, the motion is away from the detector.

Between 1.2 s and about 1.6 s, the child's speed was decreasing.

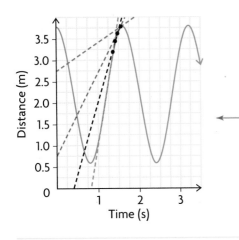

On this interval, the tangent lines are getting less steep as time increases. This means the magnitudes of the slopes are decreasing. The tangent lines still have positive slopes, which means the distance between the child and the motion detector is still increasing. The child is slowing down as the swing approaches the point where there is a change in direction from away from the detector to toward the detector.

Reflecting

A. Explain how the data in the table indicates the direction in which the child swung.

B. Explain how the sign of the slope of each tangent line indicates the direction in which the child swung.

C. How can you tell, from the graph, when the speed of the child was 0 m/s?

D. If someone began to push the child after 2.4 s, describe what effect this would have on the distance versus time graph.

APPLY the Math

EXAMPLE 2   Using the slopes of secant lines to calculate average rate of change

Calculate the child's average speed over the intervals of time as the child swung toward and away from the motion detector on the first swing.

Solution

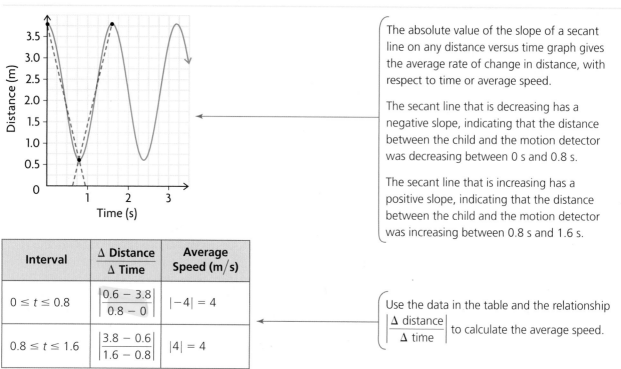

The absolute value of the slope of a secant line on any distance versus time graph gives the average rate of change in distance, with respect to time or average speed.

The secant line that is decreasing has a negative slope, indicating that the distance between the child and the motion detector was decreasing between 0 s and 0.8 s.

The secant line that is increasing has a positive slope, indicating that the distance between the child and the motion detector was increasing between 0.8 s and 1.6 s.

Interval	$\dfrac{\Delta \text{ Distance}}{\Delta \text{ Time}}$	Average Speed (m/s)
$0 \le t \le 0.8$	$\left\lvert\dfrac{0.6 - 3.8}{0.8 - 0}\right\rvert$	$\lvert -4 \rvert = 4$
$0.8 \le t \le 1.6$	$\left\lvert\dfrac{3.8 - 0.6}{1.6 - 0.8}\right\rvert$	$\lvert 4 \rvert = 4$

Use the data in the table and the relationship $\left\lvert\dfrac{\Delta \text{ distance}}{\Delta \text{ time}}\right\rvert$ to calculate the average speed.

The child's average speed was the same in both directions as the child swung back and forth.

In Summary

Key Idea

- The average and instantaneous rates of change of a sinusoidal function can be determined using the same strategies that were used for other types of functions.

Need to Know

- The tangent lines at the maximum and minimum values of a sinusoidal function are horizontal. Since the slope of a horizontal line is zero, the instantaneous rate of change at these points is zero.
- In a sinusoidal function, the slope of a tangent line is the least at the point that lies halfway between the maximum and minimum values. The slope is the greatest at the point that lies halfway between the minimum and maximum values. As a result, the instantaneous rate of change at these points is the least and greatest, respectively. The approximate value of the instantaneous rate of change can be determined using one of the strategies below:
  - sketching an approximate tangent line on the graph and estimating its slope using two points that lie on the secant line
  - using two points in the table of values (preferably two points that lie on either side and/or as close as possible to the tangent point) to calculate the slope of the corresponding secant line
  - using the defining equation of the trigonometric function and a very small interval near the point of tangency to calculate the slope of the corresponding secant line

CHECK *Your Understanding*

1. For the following graph of a function, state two intervals in which the function has an average rate of change in $f(x)$ that is
   a) zero
   b) a negative value
   c) a positive value

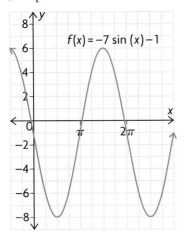

$f(x) = -7 \sin(x) - 1$

2. For this graph of a function, state two points where the function has an instantaneous rate of change in $f(x)$ that is
   a) zero
   b) a negative value
   c) a positive value

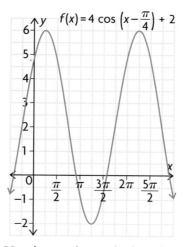

$f(x) = 4 \cos \left(x - \frac{\pi}{4}\right) + 2$

3. Use the graph to calculate the average rate of change in $f(x)$ on the interval $2 \leq x \leq 5$.

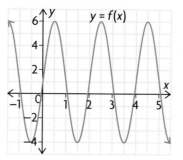

$y = f(x)$

4. Determine the average rate of change of the function
   $y = 2 \cos \left(x - \frac{\pi}{3}\right) + 1$ for each interval.

   a) $0 \leq x \leq \dfrac{\pi}{2}$

   b) $\dfrac{\pi}{6} \leq x \leq \dfrac{\pi}{2}$

   c) $\dfrac{\pi}{3} \leq x \leq \dfrac{\pi}{2}$

   d) $\dfrac{\pi}{2} \leq x \leq \dfrac{5\pi}{4}$

PRACTISING

5. State two intervals where the function $y = 3 \cos (4x) - 4$ has an average rate of change that is
   a) zero
   b) a negative value
   c) a positive value

6. State two points where the function $y = -2 \sin (2\pi x) + 7$ has an instantaneous rate of change that is
   a) zero
   b) a negative value
   c) a positive value

7. State the average rate of change of each of the following functions over the interval $\frac{\pi}{4} \leq x \leq \pi$.
   a) $y = 6 \cos (3x) + 2$

   b) $y = -5 \sin \left(\frac{1}{2}x \right) - 9$

   c) $y = \frac{1}{4} \cos (8x) + 6$

8. **T** The height of the tip of an airplane propeller above the ground once the airplane reaches full speed can be modelled by a sine function. At full speed, the propeller makes 200 revolutions per second. At $t = 0$, the tip of the propeller is at its minimum height above the ground. Determine whether the instantaneous rate of change in height at $t = \frac{1}{300}$ is a negative value, a positive value, or zero.

9. Recall in Section 6.6, Example 3, the situation that modelled the populations of mice and owls in a particular area.

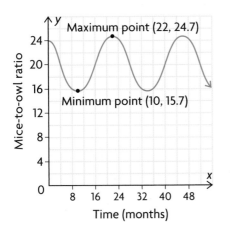

a) Determine an equation for the curve that models the ratio of mice per owl.
b) Use the curve to determine when the ratio of mice per owl has its fastest and slowest instantaneous rates of change.
c) Use the equation you determined in part a) to estimate the instantaneous rate of change in mice per owl when this rate is at its maximum. Use a centred interval of 1 month before to 1 month after the time when the instantaneous rate of change is at its maximum to make your estimate.

10. The number of tons of paper waiting to be recycled at a 24 h recycling plant can be modelled by the equation $P(t) = 0.5 \sin\left(\frac{\pi}{6}t\right) + 4$, where t is the time, in hours, and $P(t)$ is the number of tons waiting to be recycled.

a) Use the equation to estimate the instantaneous rate of change in tons of paper waiting to be recycled when this rate is at its maximum. To make your estimate, use each of the following centred intervals:

   i) 1 h before to 1 h after the time when the instantaneous rate of change is at its maximum

   ii) 0.5 h before to 0.5 h after the time when the instantaneous rate of change is at its maximum

   iii) 0.25 h before to 0.25 h after the time when the instantaneous rate of change is at its maximum

b) Which estimate is the most accurate? What is the relationship between the size of the interval and the accuracy of the estimate?

11. A strobe photography camera takes photos at regular intervals to capture the motion of a pendulum as it swings from right to left. A student takes measurements from the photo below to analyze the motion.

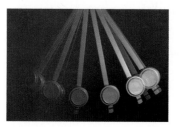

Time (s)	0	0.1	0.2	0.3	0.4	0.5	0.6	0.7	0.8	0.9	1
Horizontal Distance from Rest Position* (cm)	7.2	6.85	5.8	4.25	2.2	0.0	−2.2	−4.25	−5.8	−6.85	−7.2

*negative is left of rest position

a) Plot the data, and draw a smooth curve through the points.

b) What portion of one cycle is represented by the curve?

c) Select the endpoints, and determine the average rate of change in horizontal distance on this interval of time.

d) Can you tell, from the photo, when the pendulum bob is moving the fastest? Explain.

e) Explain how your answer to part d) relates to the rate of change as it is represented on the graph.

12. A ship that is docked in a harbour rises and falls with the waves. The

A function $h(t) = \sin\left(\frac{\pi}{5}t\right)$ models the vertical movement of the ship, h in metres, at t seconds.
   a) Determine the average rate of change in the height of the ship over the first 5 s.
   b) Estimate the instantaneous rate of change in the height of the ship at $t = 6$.

13. For a certain pendulum, the angle θ shown is given by the equation
   $\theta = \frac{1}{5}\sin\left(\frac{1}{2}\pi t\right)$ where t is in seconds and θ is in radians.
   a) Sketch a graph of the function given by the equation.
   b) Calculate the average rate of change in the angle the pendulum swings through in the interval $t \in [0, 1]$.
   c) Estimate the instantaneous rate of change in the angle the pendulum swings through at $t = 1.5$ s.
   d) On the interval $t \in [0, 8]$, estimate the times when the pendulum's speed is greatest.

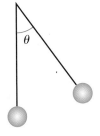

14. Compare the instantaneous rates of change of $f(x) = \sin x$ and
   C $f(x) = 3 \sin x$ for the same values of x. What can you conclude? Are there values of x for which the instantaneous rates of change of the two functions are the same?

Extending

15. In calculus, the derivative of a function is a function that yields the instantaneous rate of change of a function at any given point.
   a) Estimate the instantaneous rate of change of the function $f(x) = \sin x$ for the following values of x: $-\pi, -\frac{\pi}{2}, 0, \frac{\pi}{2}$, and π.
   b) Plot the points that represent the instantaneous rate of change, and draw a sinusoidal curve through them. What function have you graphed? Based on this information, what is the derivative of $f(x) = \sin x$?

16. a) Estimate the instantaneous rate of change of the function $f(x) = \cos x$ for the following values of x: $-\pi, -\frac{\pi}{2}, 0, \frac{\pi}{2}$, and π.
   b) Plot the points that represent the instantaneous rate of change, and draw a sinusoidal curve through them. What function have you graphed? Based on this information, what is the derivative of $f(x) = \cos x$?

FREQUENTLY ASKED Questions

Study Aid

• See Lesson 6.5.
• Try Chapter Review Question 13.

Q: What do the graphs of the reciprocal trigonometric functions look like, and what are their defining characteristics?

A: Each of the primary trigonometric graphs has a corresponding reciprocal function:

Cosecant

$y = \csc x$

$y = \dfrac{1}{\sin x}$

Secant

$y = \sec x$

$y = \dfrac{1}{\cos x}$

Cotangent

$y = \cot x$

$y = \dfrac{1}{\tan x}$

$y = \cot(x)$

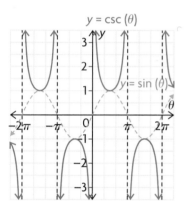

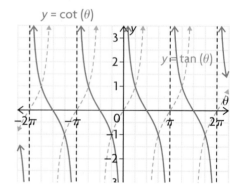

• has vertical asymptotes at the points where $\sin x = 0$
• has a period of 2π radians, the same period as $y = \sin x$
• has the domain $\{x \in \mathbf{R} \mid x \neq n\pi, n \in \mathbf{I}\}$
• has the range $\{y \in \mathbf{R} \mid |y| \geq 1\}$

• has vertical asymptotes at the points where $\cos x = 0$
• has a period of 2π radians, the same period as $y = \cos x$
• has the domain $\{x \in \mathbf{R} \mid x \neq (2n-1)\dfrac{\pi}{2}, n \in \mathbf{I}\}$
• has the range $\{y \in \mathbf{R} \mid |y| \geq 1\}$

• has vertical asymptotes at the points where $y = \tan x$ crosses the x-axis
• has zeros at the points where $y = \tan x$ has asymptotes
• has a period of π, the same period as $y = \tan x$
• has the domain $\{x \in \mathbf{R} \mid x \neq n\pi, n \in \mathbf{I}\}$
• has the range $\{y \in \mathbf{R}\}$

Study Aid

• See Lesson 6.6, Example 1.
• Try Chapter Review Questions 14, 15, and 16.

Q: How can you use a sinusoidal function to model a periodic situation?

A: If you are given a description of a periodic situation, draw a rough sketch of one cycle. If you are given data, create a scatter plot. Based on the graph, decide whether you will use a sine model or a cosine model. Use these graphs to determine the equation of the axis, the vertical translation, c, and the amplitude, a, of the function.

Use the period to help you determine k. Determine the horizontal translation, d, that must be applied to a key point on the parent function to map its corresponding location on the model. Use the parameters you found to write the equation in the form $y = a \sin (k(x - d)) + c$ or $y = a \cos (k(x - d)) + c$.

Q: **Does the average rate of change of a sinusoidal function have any unique characteristics?**

A:

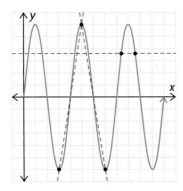

Study Aid
• See Lesson 6.7, Example 2.
• Try Chapter Review Questions 17 and 19.

For a sinusoidal function,
• the average rate of change is zero on any interval where the values of the function are the same
• the absolute value of the average rate of change on the intervals between a maximum and a minimum and between a minimum and a maximum are equal

Q: **Do the instantaneous rates of change of a sinusoidal function have any unique characteristics?**

A:

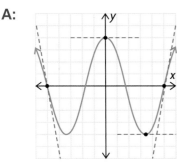

Study Aid
• See Lesson 6.7, Examples 1 and 3.
• Try Chapter Review Question 18.

For a sinusoidal function, the instantaneous rate of change is
• zero at any maximum or minimum
• at its least value halfway between a maximum and a minimum
• at its greatest value halfway between a minimum and a maximum

PRACTICE Questions

Lesson 6.1

1. An arc 33 m long subtends a central angle of a circle with a radius of 16 m. Determine the measure of the central angle in radians.

2. A circle has a radius of 75 cm and a central angle of $\dfrac{14\pi}{15}$. Determine the arc length.

3. Convert each of the following to exact radian measure and then evaluate to one decimal.
   a) $20°$ c) $160°$
   b) $-50°$ d) $420°$

4. Convert each of the following to degree measure.
   a) $\dfrac{\pi}{4}$ c) $\dfrac{8\pi}{3}$
   b) $-\dfrac{5\pi}{4}$ d) $-\dfrac{2\pi}{3}$

Lesson 6.2

5. For each of the following values of $\sin\theta$, determine the measure of θ if $\dfrac{\pi}{2} \le \theta \le \dfrac{3\pi}{2}$.
   a) $\dfrac{1}{2}$ c) $\dfrac{\sqrt{2}}{2}$
   b) $-\dfrac{\sqrt{3}}{2}$ d) $-\dfrac{1}{2}$

6. If $\cos\theta = \dfrac{-5}{13}$ and $0 \le \theta \le 2\pi$, determine
   a) $\tan\theta$
   b) $\sec\theta$
   c) the possible values of θ to the nearest tenth

7. A tower that is 65 m high makes an obtuse angle with the ground. The vertical distance from the top of the tower to the ground is 59 m. What obtuse angle does the tower make with the ground, to the nearest hundredth of a radian?

Lesson 6.3

8. State the period of the graph of each function, in radians.
   a) $y = \sin x$ c) $y = \tan x$
   b) $y = \cos x$

Lesson 6.4

9. The following graph is a sine curve. Determine the equation of the graph.

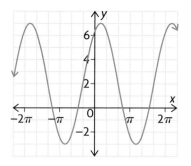

10. The following graph is a cosine curve. Determine the equation of the graph.

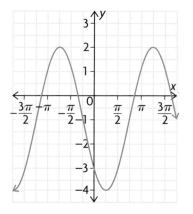

11. State the transformations that have been applied to $f(x) = \cos x$ to obtain each of the following functions.
   a) $f(x) = -19\cos x - 9$
   b) $f(x) = \cos\left(10\left(x + \dfrac{\pi}{12}\right)\right)$
   c) $f(x) = \dfrac{10}{11}\cos\left(x - \dfrac{\pi}{9}\right) + 3$
   d) $f(x) = -\cos(-x + \pi)$

12. The current, I, in amperes, of an electric circuit is given by the function $I(t) = 4.5 \sin(120\pi t)$, where t is the time in seconds.
   a) Draw a graph that shows one cycle.
   b) What is the singular period?
   c) At what value of t is the current a maximum in the first cycle?
   d) When is the current a minimum in the first cycle?

Lesson 6.5

13. State the period of the graph of each function, in radians.
   a) $y = \csc x$ c) $y = \cot x$
   b) $y = \sec x$

Lesson 6.6

14. A bumblebee is flying in a circular motion within a vertical plane, at a constant speed. The height of the bumblebee above the ground, as a function of time, can be modelled by a sinusoidal function. At $t = 0$, the bumblebee is at its lowest point above the ground.
   a) What does the amplitude of the sinusoidal function represent in this situation?
   b) What does the period of the sinusoidal function represent in this situation?
   c) What does the equation of the axis of the sinusoidal function represent in this situation?
   d) If a reflection in the horizontal axis was applied to the sinusoidal function, was the sine function or the cosine function used?

15. The population of a ski-resort town, as a function of the number of months into the year, can be described by a cosine function. The maximum population of the town is about 15 000 people, and the minimum population is about 500 people. At the beginning of the year, the population is at its greatest. After six months, the population reaches its lowest number of people. What is the equation of the cosine function that describes the population of this town?

16. A weight is bobbing up and down on a spring attached to a ceiling. The data in the following table give the height of the weight above the floor as it bobs. Determine the sine function that models this situation.

t (s)	0.0	0.2	0.4	0.6	0.8	1.0	1.2	1.4	1.6	1.8	2.0	2.2
h(t) (cm)	120	136	165	180	166	133	120	135	164	179	165	133

Lesson 6.7

17. State two intervals in which the function $y = 7 \sin\left(\frac{1}{5}x\right) + 2$ has an average rate of change that is
   a) zero
   b) a negative value
   c) a positive value

18. State two points where the function $y = \frac{1}{4}\cos(4\pi x) - 3$ has an instantaneous rate of change that is
   a) zero
   b) a negative value
   c) a positive value

19. A person's blood pressure, $P(t)$, in millimetres of mercury (mm Hg), is modelled by the function $P(t) = 100 - 20\cos\left(\frac{8\pi}{3}t\right)$, where t is the time in seconds.
   a) What is the period of the function?
   b) What does the value of the period mean in this situation?
   c) Calculate the average rate of change in a person's blood pressure on the interval $t \in [0.2, 0.3]$.
   d) Estimate the instantaneous rate of change in a person's blood pressure at $t = 0.5$.

1. Which trigonometric function has an asymptote at $x = \dfrac{5\pi}{2}$?

2. Which expression does not have the same value as all the other expressions?

$$\sin \dfrac{3\pi}{2}, \ \cos \pi, \ \tan \dfrac{7\pi}{4}, \ \csc \dfrac{3\pi}{2}, \ \sec 2\pi, \ \cot \dfrac{3\pi}{4}$$

3. The function $y = \cos x$ is reflected in the x-axis, vertically stretched by a factor of 12, horizontally compressed by a factor of $\dfrac{3}{5}$, horizontally translated $\dfrac{\pi}{6}$ units to the left, and vertically translated 100 units up. Determine the value of the new function, to the nearest tenth, when $x = \dfrac{5\pi}{4}$.

4. The daily high temperature of a city, in degrees Celsius, as a function of the number of days into the year, can be described by the function $T(d) = -20 \cos \left(\dfrac{2\pi}{365}(d - 10) \right) + 25$. What is the average rate of change, in degrees Celsius per day, of the daily high temperature of the city from February 21 to May 8?

5. Arrange the following angles in order, from smallest to largest:
$$\dfrac{5\pi}{8}, \ 113°, \ \dfrac{2\pi}{3}, \ 110°, \ \dfrac{3\pi}{5}$$

6. Write an equivalent sine function for $y = \cos \left(x + \dfrac{\pi}{8} \right)$.

7. The point $(5, y)$ lies on the terminal arm of an angle in standard position. If the angle measures 4.8775 radians, what is the value of y to the nearest unit?

8. The temperature, T, in degrees Celsius, of the surface water in a swimming pool varies according to the following graph, where t is the number of hours since sunrise at 6 a.m.
   a) Find a possible equation for the temperature of the surface water as a function of time.
   b) Calculate the average rate of change in water temperature from sunrise to noon.
   c) Estimate the instantaneous rate of change in water temperature at 6 p.m.

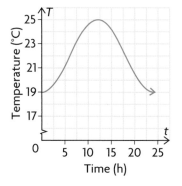

Investigating Changes in Temperature

The following table gives the mean monthly temperatures for Sudbury and Windsor, two cities in Ontario. Each month is represented by the day of the year in the middle of the month.

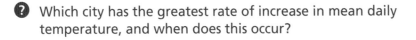

Month	Jan.	Feb.	Mar.	Apr.	May	June	July	Aug.	Sep.	Oct.	Nov.	Dec.
Day of Year	15	45	75	106	136	167	197	228	259	289	320	350
Temperature for Sudbury (°C)	−13.7	−11.9	−5.9	3.0	10.6	15.8	18.9	17.4	12.2	6.2	−1.2	−10.1
Temperature for Windsor (°C)	−4.7	−3.8	2.3	8.7	14.6	20.2	22.6	22.0	17.9	11.5	4.8	−1.2

❓ Which city has the greatest rate of increase in mean daily temperature, and when does this occur?

A. Make a conjecture about which city has the greatest rate of increase in mean daily temperature. Provide reasons for your conjecture.

B. Create a scatter plot of mean monthly temperature versus day of the year for each city.

C. Draw the curve of best fit for each graph.

D. Use your graphs to estimate when the mean daily temperature increases the fastest in both cities. Explain how you determined these values.

E. Use your graphs to estimate the rate at which the mean daily temperature is increasing at the times you estimated in part D.

F. Determine an equation of a sinusoidal function to model the data for each city.

G. Use the equations you found in part F to estimate the fastest rate at which the mean daily temperature is increasing.

Task | *Checklist*

✔ Did you provide reasons for your conjecture?

✔ Did you draw and label your graphs accurately?

✔ Did you determine when the mean daily temperature is increasing the fastest in both cities?

✔ Did you show all the steps in your calculations of rates of change and clearly explain your thinking?

Multiple Choice

1. What are the solutions of
$x^4 + 3x^3 = 4x^2 + 12x$?
a) $-2, 0, 3, 2$ c) $-3, 0, 4$
b) $-4, -3, 0$ d) $-3, -2, 0, 2$

2. Which cubic function has zeros at $-1, 1,$ and 4 and passes through $(2, 36)$?
a) $f(x) = 2(x - 1)(x + 1)(x + 4)$
b) $f(x) = -6x^3 + 24x^2 + 6x - 24$
c) $f(x) = 36x^3 - 144x^2 - 6x + 144$
d) $f(x) = 6(x + 1)(x - 1)(x - 4)$

3. Which value is *not* a solution of
$2 - 3x < x - 5$?
a) -2 b) 2 c) 3 d) 5

4. What is the solution of $-10 \le 3x + 5 \le 8$?
a) $-5 \le x \le \dfrac{13}{3}$ c) $-5 \le x \le 1$

b) $x \in (-5, 1)$ d) $x \in \left[-\dfrac{5}{3}, 1\right]$

5. On which interval is $f(x) < g(x)$?

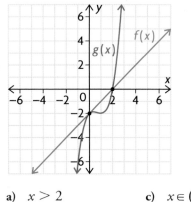

a) $x > 2$ c) $x \in (-\infty, 0)$
b) $x < 0$ and $x > 2$ d) $x \in (0, 2)$

6. The height in metres of a diver above the pool's surface is given by $h(t) = -5t^2 + 3.5t + 10$, where t is in seconds. When is the diver more than 10.0 m above the pool?
a) $t < 1.5$ c) $t \in (0, 1)$
b) $t \in (0, 0.7)$ d) $0.7 < t < 1$

7. The instantaneous rate of change of a cubic function is positive for $x < 0$, negative for $0 < x < 2$, and positive for $x > 2$. Which is *not* a possible set of zeros for the function?
a) $x = 0, x = 1$
b) $x = -0.73, x = 1, x = 2.73$
c) $x = -3$
d) $x = -0.73, x = 2$

8. Which value is the best estimate of the instantaneous rate of change of the function $f(x) = 2x^3 - 4x^2 + 6x$ at the point $(0, 0)$?
a) -6.5 b) 0 c) 6.2 d) 5.5

9. Which is the graph of $y = \dfrac{1}{x^2 - 3x}$?

a)

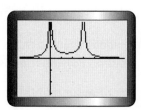

b)

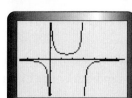

c)

d)

10. What type of asymptote(s) does
$f(x) = \dfrac{1}{x^2 + 3x - 10}$ have?

a) only vertical
b) only horizontal
c) both vertical and horizontal
d) only oblique

11. Which function has a vertical asymptote at $x = 3$ and an oblique asymptote?

a) $f(x) = \dfrac{x - 3}{x^2 - 9}$
c) $h(x) = \dfrac{x + 3}{x - 3}$

b) $g(x) = \dfrac{x^2 - 9}{x - 3}$
d) $j(x) = \dfrac{x^2 + 9}{x - 3}$

12. Which function has domain $\{x \in \mathbf{R} \,|\, x \neq 3\}$ and is positive on $\{x \in \mathbf{R} \,|\, -2 < x < 3\}$?

a) $f(x) = \dfrac{x + 2}{3 - x}$
c) $h(x) = \dfrac{x - 2}{x + 3}$

b) $g(x) = \dfrac{x + 2}{x - 3}$
d) $j(x) = \dfrac{2 - x}{x + 3}$

13. How does the function $f(x) = \dfrac{2 - 3x}{5x - 3}$ behave as x approaches $\dfrac{3}{5}$ from the left?

a) $f(x) \to \infty$
c) $f(x) \to \dfrac{1}{5}$

b) $f(x) \to 0$
d) $f(x) \to -\infty$

14. What is the solution of $\dfrac{3 - 2x}{x + 2} = 3x$?

a) $x = 0, x = 1.5$
c) $x = -3, x = \dfrac{1}{3}$

b) $x = -2, x = 0$
d) $x = -\dfrac{1}{3}, x = 3$

15. When solving a rational equation such as $\dfrac{2 - 3x}{5x - 3} = \dfrac{x + 2}{5x}$, what is a possible first step?

a) Graph each side as a function.
b) Determine the zeros of the denominators.
c) Multiply all terms by the lowest common denominator.
d) any of the above

16. The inequality $2x - 3 \leq \dfrac{2}{x}$ is equivalent to

a) $\dfrac{(2x + 1)(x - 2)}{x} \leq 0$

b) $\dfrac{x(2x - 3)}{2} \leq 1$

c) $\dfrac{(2x - 1)(x + 2)}{x} \leq 0$

d) $\dfrac{(2x + 1)(x - 2)}{2} \leq 0$

17. For which interval(s) is the inequality $x - 3 > \dfrac{6}{x - 2}$ true?

a) $x \in (-\infty, 0)$ or $x \in (2, 5)$
b) $x \in (0, 5)$
c) $x < 0$ or $x > 5$
d) $0 < x < 2$ or $x > 5$

18. What is the slope of the line tangent to $y = \dfrac{3 - x}{2x}$ at $x = 1$?

a) $m = \dfrac{3}{2}$
c) $m = 3$

b) $m = -\dfrac{3}{2}$
d) $m = -3$

19. The position of an object moving along a straight line at time t seconds is given by $s(t) = \dfrac{2t + 1}{t - 4}$, where s is measured in metres. Which is the best estimate for the rate of change of s at $t = 3$ s?

a) -12 m/s
c) -9.6 m/s

b) -9 m/s
d) -7 m/s

20. A sector of a circle with a radius of 3 m has a central angle of $\dfrac{5\pi}{12}$. What is the perimeter of the sector?

a) $6\dfrac{5}{24}$ m
c) $\dfrac{5\pi}{2} + 6$ m

b) $\dfrac{5\pi}{4} + 6$ m
d) $\dfrac{5\pi}{4}$ m

21. Which of the following pairs of angles are equivalent?

a) $20°$ and $\dfrac{\pi}{9}$ c) $-270°$ and $-\dfrac{3\pi}{2}$

b) $135°$ and $\dfrac{3\pi}{4}$ d) all of the above

22. The point $(-4, 7)$ lies on the terminal arm of angle θ. What is the measure of θ in radians?

a) 4.19 b) 119.74 c) 2.09 d) 2.62

23. If $\sin \theta = -\dfrac{\sqrt{3}}{2}$, what are possible values of $\cos \theta$ and $\tan \theta$?

a) $\cos \theta = \dfrac{1}{2}$, $\tan \theta = -\sqrt{3}$

b) $\cos \theta = -\dfrac{1}{2}$, $\tan \theta = -\sqrt{3}$

c) $\cos \theta = -\dfrac{1}{2}$, $\tan \theta = -\dfrac{1}{\sqrt{3}}$

d) $\cos \theta = -\dfrac{1}{2}$, $\tan \theta = \dfrac{1}{\sqrt{3}}$

24. Which of the following values of x, where $x \in [0, 2\pi]$, satisfy $\sin x = 0.5$?

a) $\dfrac{\pi}{6}$ and $\dfrac{7\pi}{6}$ c) $\dfrac{\pi}{6}$ and $\dfrac{11\pi}{6}$

b) $\dfrac{\pi}{3}$ and $\dfrac{5\pi}{3}$ d) $\dfrac{\pi}{6}$ and $\dfrac{5\pi}{6}$

25. What is the equation of this transformation of the graph of $y = \sin x$?

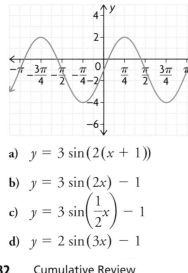

a) $y = 3 \sin(2(x + 1))$

b) $y = 3 \sin(2x) - 1$

c) $y = 3 \sin\left(\dfrac{1}{2}x\right) - 1$

d) $y = 2 \sin(3x) - 1$

26. What transformations are needed to transform $y = \cos x$ into $y = \cos\left(\dfrac{1}{3}(x + 2\pi)\right)$?

a) horizontal compression by a factor of $\dfrac{1}{3}$, horizontal translation 2π units left

b) horizontal stretch by a factor of 3, horizontal translation 2π units left

c) vertical compression by a factor of $\dfrac{1}{3}$, vertical translation 2 units up

d) horizontal stretch by a factor of 3, horizontal translation 2π units left

27. One blade of a wind turbine is at an angle of $-\dfrac{\pi}{4}$ to the upward vertical at time $t = 0$, and rotates counterclockwise one revolution every 2 seconds. The tip of the blade varies between 5 m and 41 m above the ground. Which equation is a model for the height, h, of the blade tip?

a) $h = 18 \cos\left(\pi t + \dfrac{\pi}{4}\right) + 23$

b) $h = 41 \cos\left(2\left(t + \dfrac{\pi}{4}\right)\right) - 5$

c) $h = 18 \cos\left(\pi t - \dfrac{\pi}{4}\right) - 23$

d) $h = 41 \cos\left(\pi\left(t + \dfrac{\pi}{4}\right)\right) - 36$

28. The instantaneous rate of change of $y = 2 \sin(3x - \pi)$ is negative on which of the following intervals?

a) $\dfrac{\pi}{2} < x < \dfrac{5\pi}{6}$ c) both a) and b)

b) $\dfrac{\pi}{2} < x < \dfrac{3\pi}{2}$ d) neither a) nor b)

29. The population of blackflies at a lake in northern Ontario can be modelled by the function $P(t) = 23.7 \cos\left(\dfrac{\pi}{6}(t - 7)\right) + 24.1$, where P is in millions and t is in months. Over which time interval is the average rate of change in the blackfly population the greatest?

a) $0 \leq t \leq 4$ c) $7 \leq t \leq 16$

b) $1 \leq t \leq 7$ d) $10 \leq t \leq 18$

Investigations

The Greatest Volume

30. An open top box is made by cutting corners out of a 50 cm by 40 cm piece of cardboard.

a) Determine a mathematical model that represents the volume of the box.

b) Determine the length of the sides of each square that must be cut that will result in a box with a volume of 6000 cm³.

c) Determine the length of the sides of each square that must be cut that will result in a box with maximum volume.

d) Determine a range of sizes of the squares that can be cut from each corner that will result in a box with a volume of at least 1008 cm³.

Combining Functions

31. Consider the polynomial functions
$f(x) = x^2 - 5x + 6$ and $g(x) = x - 3$. Determine

a) the zeros of $f(x)$, $g(x)$, $\dfrac{f(x)}{g(x)}$, and $\dfrac{g(x)}{f(x)}$

b) the holes and asymptotes of $\dfrac{f(x)}{g(x)}$ and $\dfrac{g(x)}{f(x)}$, if any

c) any x-coordinate(s) where the tangents of $\dfrac{f(x)}{g(x)}$ and $\dfrac{g(x)}{f(x)}$ are perpendicular, and the equation(s) of the tangent(s) at such coordinates

Transformations of Trigonometric Functions

32. a) Investigate the effect of various types of transformations (i.e., stretches/compressions, reflections, and translations) of $y = \sin x$ on its zeros, maximum and minimum values, and instantaneous rates of change.

b) Repeat part a) for $y = \cos x$ and $y = \tan x$.

Chapter

7

Trigonometric Identities and Equations

▶ GOALS

You will be able to

- Recognize equivalent trigonometric relationships

- Use compound angle formulas to determine the exact values of trigonometric ratios that involve sums, differences, and products of special angles

- Prove trigonometric identities using a variety of strategies

- Solve trigonometric equations using a variety of strategies

❓ Global temperatures have increased by an average of 1 °C in the past 100 years. Ocean levels are rising by 1 cm to 2 cm every year. How do temperatures vary from month to month? How do ocean levels in a harbour vary from hour to hour? What types of functions model these types of variation?

Study | Aid

- For help, see the Review of Essential Skills found at the Nelson Advanced Functions website.

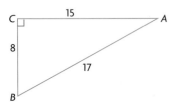

Question	Appendix/Lesson
1	R-6
3	R-10
4, 5, 6	6.2
7	R-14
8	R-12

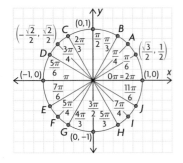

SKILLS AND CONCEPTS You Need

1. Solve each equation to two decimal places where necessary.

   a) $3x - 7 = 5 - 9x$

   b) $2(x + 3) - \dfrac{x}{4} = \dfrac{1}{2}$

   c) $x^2 - 5x - 24 = 0$

   d) $6x^2 + 11x = 10$

   e) $x^2 + 2x - 1 = 0$

   f) $3x^2 = 3x + 1$

2. Show that the line segment from $A(1, 0)$ to $B\left(2, \dfrac{1}{2}\right)$ is the same length as the line segment from $C\left(-\dfrac{1}{2}, 5\right)$ to $D(0, 6)$.

3. Given $\triangle ABC$ shown,

   a) state the six trigonometric ratios for $\angle A$

   b) determine the measure of $\angle A$ in **radians**, to one decimal place

   c) determine the measure of $\angle B$ in **degrees**, to one decimal place

4. $P(-2, 2)$ lies on the terminal arm of an angle in **standard position**.

   a) Sketch the **principal angle**, θ.

   b) Determine the value of the **related acute angle** in radians.

   c) Determine the value of θ in radians.

5. a) Determine the coordinates of each missing point on the unit circle shown.

   b) Determine:

      i) $\cos\left(\dfrac{3\pi}{4}\right)$ ii) $\sin\left(\dfrac{11\pi}{6}\right)$ iii) $\cos(\pi)$ iv) $\csc\left(\dfrac{\pi}{6}\right)$

6. Given $\tan x = -\dfrac{3}{4}$, where $0 \le x \le 2\pi$,

   a) state the other five trigonometric ratios as fractions

   b) determine the value(s) of x, to one decimal place

7. State whether each relationship is true or false.

   a) $\tan\theta = \dfrac{\sin\theta}{\cos\theta}, \cos\theta \ne 0$

   b) $\sin^2\theta + \cos^2\theta = 1$

   c) $\sec\theta = \dfrac{1}{\sin\theta}, \sin\theta \ne 0$

   d) $\cos^2\theta = \sin^2\theta - 1$

   e) $1 + \tan^2\theta = \sec^2\theta$

   f) $\cot\theta = \dfrac{\cos\theta}{\sin\theta}, \sin\theta \ne 0$

8. Create a flow chart that shows how transformations can be used to sketch the graph of a sinusoidal function in the form $y = a\sin(k(x - d)) + c$.

APPLYING *What You Know*

Going for a Run

YOU WILL NEED

• graph paper

Julie goes for a daily run in her local park. She parks her bike at point *A* and runs five times around the playing field, in a counterclockwise direction. The radius of the path that she runs is 200 m. This morning, she ran one-third of the way around the field, to point *B*, before realizing that she had left her heart-rate monitor on her bike. She ran in a straight line across the field, back to her bike, to get her monitor.

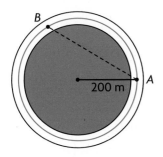

? How far did Julie run when she went across the field, back to her bike?

A. Draw a circle (centred at the origin) on graph paper, as shown, to represent the path that Julie runs. Write the coordinates of point *A*.

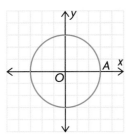

B. Mark point *B* one-third of the way around the circle from point *A*. What is the radian measure of $\angle AOB$? Write the coordinates $(r\cos\theta, r\sin\theta)$ of point *B* in terms of this angle.

C. Use the distance formula, $d = \sqrt{(x_2 - x_1)^2 + (y_2 - y_1)^2}$, to calculate the distance from *A* to *B*.

D. What kind of triangle is $\triangle AOB$? What are the lengths of *AO* and *BO*?

E. Verify your answer in part C using the cosine law.

F. How far did Julie run when she went across the field, back to her bike, to get her heart-rate monitor?

7.1 Exploring Equivalent Trigonometric Functions

YOU WILL NEED

• graphing calculator or graphing software

GOAL

Identify equivalent trigonometric relationships.

EXPLORE the Math

What is a possible equation for the function shown?

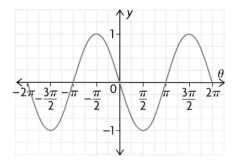

Craig, Erin, Robin, and Sarah are comparing their answers to the question shown above.

Craig's function: $f(\theta) = -\sin \theta$

Erin's function: $g(\theta) = \sin (\theta + \pi)$

Robin's function: $h(\theta) = \sin (\theta - \pi)$

Sarah's function: $j(\theta) = \cos \left(\theta + \dfrac{\pi}{2}\right)$

Their teacher explains that they are all correct because they have written equivalent trigonometric functions.

? How can you verify that these equations are equivalent and identify other equivalent trigonometric expressions?

A. Enter each student's function into Y1 to Y4 in the equation editor of a graphing calculator, using the settings shown. Use radian mode, and graph using the Zoom 7:Ztrig command. What do you notice?

B. Examine the table of values for each function. Are you convinced that the four functions are equivalent? Explain.

Creating equivalent expressions using the period of a function

C. Clear all functions from the calculator, and graph $f(\theta) = \sin \theta$. Using transformations, explain why $\sin (\theta + 2\pi) = \sin \theta$. Write a similar statement for $\cos \theta$ and another similar statement for $\tan \theta$.

D. Verify that your statements for part C are equivalent by graphing the corresponding pair of functions. Write similar statements for the reciprocal trigonometric functions, and verify them by graphing.

Tech | **Support**

Scroll to the left of Y2, Y3, and Y4. Press Enter until the required graphing option appears.

Creating equivalent expressions by classifying a function as odd or even

E. $f(\theta) = \cos\theta$ is an **even function** because its graph is symmetrical in the y-axis. Use transformations to explain why $\cos(-\theta) = \cos\theta$, and then verify by graphing.

F. $f(\theta) = \sin\theta$ is an **odd function** because its graph has rotational symmetry about the origin. Use transformations to explain why $\sin(-\theta) = -\sin\theta$, and then verify by graphing.

G. Classify the tangent functions as even or odd. Based on your classification, write the corresponding pair of equivalent expressions.

Creating equivalent expressions using complementary angles

H. Determine the exact values of the six trigonometric ratios for each acute angle in the triangle shown. Record the values in a table like the one below. Describe any relationships that you see.

$\sin\left(\dfrac{\pi}{3}\right) =$	$\csc\left(\dfrac{\pi}{3}\right) =$	$\sin\left(\dfrac{\pi}{6}\right) =$	$\csc\left(\dfrac{\pi}{6}\right) =$
$\cos\left(\dfrac{\pi}{3}\right) =$	$\sec\left(\dfrac{\pi}{3}\right) =$	$\cos\left(\dfrac{\pi}{6}\right) =$	$\sec\left(\dfrac{\pi}{6}\right) =$
$\tan\left(\dfrac{\pi}{3}\right) =$	$\cot\left(\dfrac{\pi}{3}\right) =$	$\tan\left(\dfrac{\pi}{6}\right) =$	$\cot\left(\dfrac{\pi}{6}\right) =$

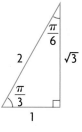

I. Repeat part H for a right triangle in which one acute angle is $\dfrac{\pi}{8}$ and the other acute angle is $\dfrac{3\pi}{8}$. Use a calculator to determine the approximate values of the six trigonometric ratios for each of these acute angles. Record the values in a table like the one above. How do the relationships in this table compare with the relationships in the table you completed for part H?

J. Any right triangle, where θ is the measure of one of the acute angles, has a complementary angle of $\left(\dfrac{\pi}{2} - \theta\right)$ for the other angle. Explain how you know that the cofunction **identity** $\sin\theta = \cos\left(\dfrac{\pi}{2} - \theta\right)$ is true.

K. Write all the other cofunction identities between θ and $\left(\dfrac{\pi}{2} - \theta\right)$ based on the relationships in parts H and I. Verify each identity by graphing the corresponding functions on the graphing calculator.

Creating equivalent expressions using the principal and related angles

L. Explain how you can tell, from this diagram of a unit circle, that
  i) $\sin(\pi - \theta) = \sin\theta$
  ii) $\cos(\pi - \theta) = -\cos\theta$
  iii) $\tan(\pi - \theta) = -\tan\theta$

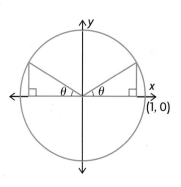

M. Write similar statements for the following diagrams.

i)

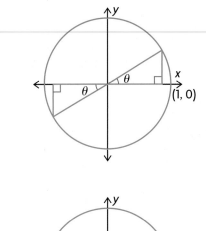

ii)

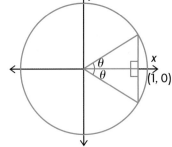

N. Summarize the strategies you used to identify and verify equivalent trigonometric expressions. Make a list of all the equivalent expressions you found.

Reflecting

O. How does a graphing calculator help you investigate the possible equivalence of two trigonometric expressions?

P. How can transformations be used to identify and confirm equivalent trigonometric expressions?

Q. How can the relationship between the acute angles in a right triangle be used to identify and confirm equivalent trigonometric expressions?

R. How can the relationship between a principal angle in standard position and the related acute angle be used to identify and confirm equivalent trigonometric expressions?

In Summary

Key Ideas

- Because of their periodic nature, there are many equivalent trigonometric expressions.
- Two expressions may be equivalent if the graphs created by a graphing calculator of their corresponding functions coincide, producing only one visible graph over the entire domain of both functions. To demonstrate equivalency requires additional reasoning about the properties of both graphs.

Need to Know

- Horizontal translations that involve multiples of the period of a trigonometric function can be used to obtain two equivalent functions with the same graph. For example, the sine function has a period of 2π, so the graphs of $f(\theta) = \sin \theta$ and $f(\theta) = \sin(\theta + 2\pi)$ are the same. Therefore, $\sin \theta = \sin(\theta + 2\pi)$.

- Horizontal translations of $\frac{\pi}{2}$ that involve both a sine function and a cosine function can be used to obtain two equivalent functions with the same graph. Translating the cosine function $\frac{\pi}{2}$ to the right $\left(f(\theta) = \cos\left(\theta - \frac{\pi}{2}\right)\right)$ results in the graph of the sine function, $f(\theta) = \sin \theta$.

  Similarly, translating the sine function $\frac{\pi}{2}$ to the left $\left(f(\theta) = \sin\left(\theta + \frac{\pi}{2}\right)\right)$ results in the graph of the cosine function, $f(\theta) = \cos \theta$.

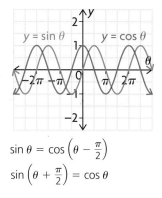

$$\sin \theta = \cos\left(\theta - \frac{\pi}{2}\right)$$
$$\sin\left(\theta + \frac{\pi}{2}\right) = \cos \theta$$

- Since $f(\theta) = \cos \theta$ is an even function, reflecting its graph across the y-axis results in two equivalent functions with the same graph.

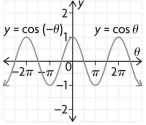

$$\cos \theta = \cos(-\theta)$$

- $f(\theta) = \sin \theta$ and $f(\theta) = \tan \theta$ are odd and have the property of rotational symmetry about the origin. Reflecting these functions across both the x-axis and the y-axis produces the same effect as rotating the function through $180°$ about the origin. Thus, the same graph is produced.

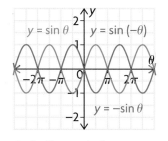

$$\sin(-\theta) = -\sin \theta$$

$$\tan(-\theta) = -\tan \theta$$

(continued)

- The cofunction identities describe trigonometric relationships between the complementary angles θ and $\left(\dfrac{\pi}{2} - \theta\right)$ in a right triangle.

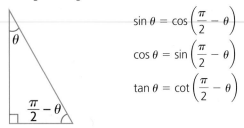

$$\sin\theta = \cos\left(\frac{\pi}{2} - \theta\right)$$

$$\cos\theta = \sin\left(\frac{\pi}{2} - \theta\right)$$

$$\tan\theta = \cot\left(\frac{\pi}{2} - \theta\right)$$

- You can identify equivalent trigonometric expressions by comparing principal angles drawn in standard position in quadrants II, III, and IV with their related acute angle, θ, in quadrant I.

Principal Angle in Quadrant II	Principal Angle in Quadrant III	Principal Angle in Quadrant IV
$\sin(\pi - \theta) = \sin\theta$	$\sin(\pi + \theta) = -\sin\theta$	$\sin(2\pi - \theta) = -\sin\theta$
$\cos(\pi - \theta) = -\cos\theta$	$\cos(\pi + \theta) = -\cos\theta$	$\cos(2\pi - \theta) = \cos\theta$
$\tan(\pi - \theta) = -\tan\theta$	$\tan(\pi + \theta) = \tan\theta$	$\tan(2\pi - \theta) = -\tan\theta$

FURTHER *Your Understanding*

1. **a)** Use transformations and the cosine function to write three equivalent expressions for the following graph.

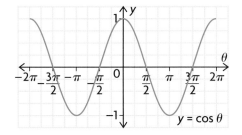

   b) Use transformations and a different trigonometric function to write three equivalent expressions for the graph.

2. **a)** Classify the reciprocal trigonometric functions as odd or even, and then write the corresponding equation.
   b) Use transformations to explain why each equation is true.

3. Use the cofunction identities to write an expression that is equivalent to each of the following expressions.

   a) $\sin\dfrac{\pi}{6}$

   b) $\cos\dfrac{5\pi}{12}$

   c) $\tan\dfrac{3\pi}{8}$

   d) $\cos\dfrac{5\pi}{16}$

   e) $\sin\dfrac{\pi}{8}$

   f) $\tan\dfrac{\pi}{6}$

4. a) Write the cofunction identities for the reciprocal trigonometric functions.

b) Use transformations to explain why each identity is true.

5. Write an expression that is equivalent to each of the following expressions, using the related acute angle.

a) $\sin \dfrac{7\pi}{8}$

c) $\tan \dfrac{5\pi}{4}$

e) $\sin \dfrac{13\pi}{8}$

b) $\cos \dfrac{13\pi}{12}$

d) $\cos \dfrac{11\pi}{6}$

f) $\tan \dfrac{5\pi}{3}$

6. Show that each equation is true, using the given diagram.

a) $\cos \left(\dfrac{\pi}{2} - \theta \right) = \sin \theta$

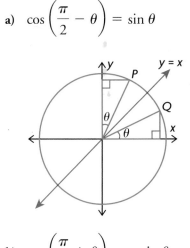

b) $\cos \left(\dfrac{\pi}{2} + \theta \right) = -\sin \theta$

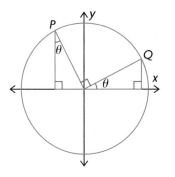

7. State whether each of the following are true or false. For those that are false, justify your decision.

a) $\cos (\theta + 2\pi) = \cos \theta$

d) $\tan (\pi - \theta) = \tan \theta$

b) $\sin (\pi - \theta) = -\sin \theta$

e) $\cot \left(\dfrac{\pi}{2} + \theta \right) = \tan \theta$

c) $\cos \theta = -\cos (\theta + 4\pi)$

f) $\sin (\theta + 2\pi) = \sin (-\theta)$

Compound Angle Formulas

Verify and use compound angle formulas.

INVESTIGATE *the Math*

compound angle

an angle that is created by adding or subtracting two or more angles

The cosine of the compound angle $(a - b)$ can be expressed in terms of the sines and cosines of a and b. Consider the following unit circle diagram:

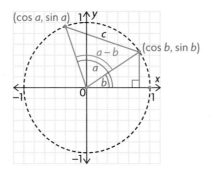

By the cosine law, $c^2 = 1^2 + 1^2 - 2(1)(1)\cos(a - b)$

① $c^2 = 2 - 2\cos(a - b)$

However, c has endpoints of $(\cos a, \sin a)$ and $(\cos b, \sin b)$.
By the distance formula, $c = \sqrt{(\sin a - \sin b)^2 + (\cos a - \cos b)^2}$
Squaring both sides,
$c^2 = (\sin a - \sin b)^2 + (\cos a - \cos b)^2$
$c^2 = \sin^2 a - 2\sin a \sin b + \sin^2 b + \cos^2 a - 2\cos a \cos b + \cos^2 b$
$c^2 = \sin^2 a + \cos^2 a - 2\sin a \sin b - 2\cos a \cos b + \sin^2 b + \cos^2 b$
$c^2 = 1 - 2\sin a \sin b - 2\cos a \cos b + 1$

② $c^2 = 2 - 2\sin a \sin b - 2\cos a \cos b$

Equating ① and ②,
$2 - 2\cos(a - b) = 2 - 2\sin a \sin b - 2\cos a \cos b$
Solving for $\cos(a - b)$,
$\cos(a - b) = \sin a \sin b + \cos a \cos b$

? How can other formulas be developed to relate the primary trigonometric ratios of a compound angle to the trigonometric ratios of each angle in the compound angle?

A. Use a calculator and the special triangles to verify that the subtraction formula for cosine works if $a = 45°$ and $b = 30°$. Repeat for $a = \frac{\pi}{3}$ and $b = \frac{\pi}{6}$.

B. Use the subtraction formula for cosine to obtain an addition formula for cosine, $\cos(a + b)$, as follows:
 i) Rewrite the compound angle equation for $\cos(a - b)$.
 ii) Replace b with $(-b)$, and derive an equation for $\cos(a + b)$.
 iii) Simplify this equation, using your knowledge of even and odd functions, to write $\sin(-b)$ in terms of $\sin b$, and $\cos(-b)$ in terms of $\cos b$.

C. Use a calculator and the special triangles to verify your addition formula for cosine if $a = \frac{\pi}{3}$ and $b = \frac{\pi}{4}$.

D. To find an addition formula for sine, $\sin(a + b)$, use the cofunction identity $\sin\theta = \cos\left(\frac{\pi}{2} - \theta\right)$.
 i) Write $\sin(a + b) = \cos\left(\frac{\pi}{2} - (a + b)\right) = \cos\left(\left(\frac{\pi}{2} - a\right) - b\right)$.
 ii) Use the subtraction formula for cosine to expand and simplify this formula.

E. Use a calculator and the special triangles to verify your addition formula for sine by substituting $a = \frac{\pi}{3}$ and $b = \frac{\pi}{4}$.

F. Determine and verify a subtraction formula for sine, $\sin(a - b)$, using the addition formula you found in part D and the strategy you used in part B.

G. Recall that $\tan\theta = \frac{\sin\theta}{\cos\theta}$. Use this identity to determine addition and subtraction formulas for $\tan(a + b)$ and $\tan(a - b)$. Use a calculator and the special triangles to verify your formulas if $a = \frac{\pi}{6}$ and $b = \frac{\pi}{4}$.

H. Make a list of all the compound angle formulas that you determined.

Reflecting

I. How did you use equivalent trigonometric expressions to simplify formulas in parts B, D, F, and G?

J. How did you use the special triangles to verify the addition and subtraction formulas you determined?

APPLY the Math

Selecting a strategy to determine the exact value of a trigonometric ratio

Determine the exact value of

a) $\cos(15°)$ **b)** $\tan\left(-\dfrac{5\pi}{12}\right)$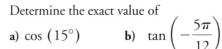

Solution

a) $\cos(15°)$

$\quad = (\cos 45° - 30°)$ ⟵ 15° = 45° − 30°, so 15° can be expressed as the compound angle (45° − 30°).

$\cos(a - b)$
$= (\cos a)(\cos b) + (\sin a)(\sin b)$
$= (\cos 45°)(\cos 30°) + (\sin 45°)(\sin 30°)$ ⟵ Use the subtraction formula for cosine to expand this expression where $a = 45°$ and $b = 30°$. Then use the special triangles to evaluate it.
$= \left(\dfrac{1}{\sqrt{2}}\right)\left(\dfrac{\sqrt{3}}{2}\right) + \left(\dfrac{1}{\sqrt{2}}\right)\left(\dfrac{1}{2}\right)$
$= \dfrac{\sqrt{3} + 1}{2\sqrt{2}}$

b) $\tan\left(-\dfrac{5\pi}{12}\right)$

$-\dfrac{5\pi}{12} = \dfrac{-5(180°)}{12} = -75°$
$-75° = -45° - 30°$

So $-\dfrac{5\pi}{12}$ can be expressed as the compound angle $\left(-\dfrac{\pi}{4} - \dfrac{\pi}{6}\right)$.

$\quad = \tan\left(-\dfrac{\pi}{4} - \dfrac{\pi}{6}\right)$ ⟵

$\tan(a - b)$
$= \dfrac{\tan a - \tan b}{1 + \tan a \tan b}$

$= \dfrac{\tan\left(-\dfrac{\pi}{4}\right) - \tan\left(\dfrac{\pi}{6}\right)}{1 + \tan\left(-\dfrac{\pi}{4}\right)\tan\left(\dfrac{\pi}{6}\right)}$ ⟵ Use the subtraction formula for tangent to expand this expression where $a = -\dfrac{\pi}{4}$ and $b = \dfrac{\pi}{6}$. Then use the special triangles to evaluate it.

$= \dfrac{-1 - \dfrac{1}{\sqrt{3}}}{1 + (-1)\left(\dfrac{1}{\sqrt{3}}\right)}$ ⟵ Simplify.

$= \dfrac{\dfrac{-\sqrt{3} - 1}{\sqrt{3}}}{\dfrac{\sqrt{3} - 1}{\sqrt{3}}}$ ⟵ Divide by multiplying by the reciprocal.

$= \dfrac{-\sqrt{3} - 1}{\sqrt{3} - 1}$

Compound angle formulas can be used, both forward and backward, to evaluate and simplify trigonometric expressions.

EXAMPLE 2 Using compound angle formulas to simplify trigonometric expressions

Simplify each expression.

a) $\cos \dfrac{7\pi}{12} \cos \dfrac{5\pi}{12} + \sin \dfrac{7\pi}{12} \sin \dfrac{5\pi}{12}$

b) $\sin 2x \cos x - \cos 2x \sin x$

Solution

a) $\cos(a - b)$

$= (\cos a)(\cos b) + (\sin a)(\sin b)$ ← The expression given is the right side of the subtraction formula for cosine, where $a = \dfrac{7\pi}{12}$ and $b = \dfrac{5\pi}{12}$.

$\cos \dfrac{7\pi}{12} \cos \dfrac{5\pi}{12} + \sin \dfrac{7\pi}{12} \sin \dfrac{5\pi}{12}$

$= \cos\left(\dfrac{7\pi}{12} - \dfrac{5\pi}{12}\right)$

$\dfrac{7\pi}{12} - \dfrac{5\pi}{12} = \dfrac{2\pi}{12}$

$= \cos \dfrac{\pi}{6}$ ←

$= \dfrac{\pi}{6}$

Use a special triangle to evaluate $\cos \dfrac{\pi}{6}$.

$= \dfrac{\sqrt{3}}{2}$

b) $\sin(a - b)$

$= (\sin a)(\cos b) - (\cos a)(\sin b)$ ← The expression given is the right side of the subtraction formula for sine, where $a = 2x$ and $b = x$.

$\sin 2x \cos x - \cos 2x \sin x$

$= \sin(2x - x)$

$= \sin x$

By expressing an angle as a sum or difference of angles in the special triangles, exact values of other angles can be determined.

EXAMPLE 3   Calculating trigonometric ratios of compound angles

Evaluate $\sin (a + b)$, where a and b are obtuse angles; $\sin a = \frac{3}{5}$ and $\sin b = \frac{5}{13}$.

Solution

$$\sin a = \frac{3}{5} = \frac{y}{r} \qquad \text{and} \quad \sin b = \frac{5}{13} = \frac{y}{r}$$

$x^2 + y^2 = r^2$	$x^2 + y^2 = r^2$
$x^2 + 3^2 = 5^2$	$x^2 + 5^2 = 13^2$
$x^2 = 25 - 9$	$x^2 = 169 - 25$
$x = \pm\sqrt{16}$	$x = \pm\sqrt{144}$
$x = -4$	$x = -12$

> Use the Pythagorean theorem to determine the x-coordinate of each point on the terminal arm. Since a and b are obtuse angles, their terminal arms lie in the second quadrant, where $\frac{\pi}{2} < a < \pi$ and $\frac{\pi}{2} < b < \pi$. In the second quadrant, x must be negative.

Sketch each angle in standard position.

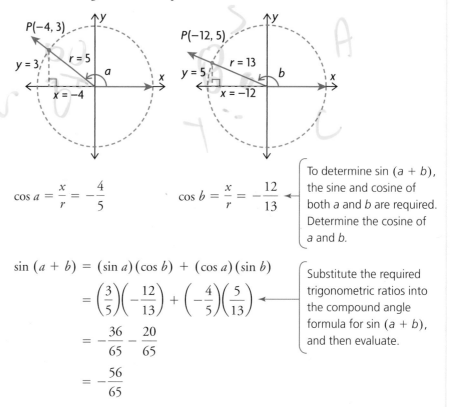

$$\cos a = \frac{x}{r} = -\frac{4}{5} \qquad\qquad \cos b = \frac{x}{r} = -\frac{12}{13}$$

> To determine $\sin (a + b)$, the sine and cosine of both a and b are required. Determine the cosine of a and b.

$$\sin (a + b) = (\sin a)(\cos b) + (\cos a)(\sin b)$$

$$= \left(\frac{3}{5}\right)\left(-\frac{12}{13}\right) + \left(-\frac{4}{5}\right)\left(\frac{5}{13}\right)$$

$$= -\frac{36}{65} - \frac{20}{65}$$

$$= -\frac{56}{65}$$

> Substitute the required trigonometric ratios into the compound angle formula for $\sin (a + b)$, and then evaluate.

Compound angle formulas can also be used to prove the equivalence of trigonometric expressions.

EXAMPLE **4**   Identifying equivalent trigonometric
expressions using compound angle formulas

Use compound angle formulas to show that $\sin(x - \pi)$, $\sin(x + \pi)$, and
$\cos\left(x + \dfrac{\pi}{2}\right)$ are equivalent trigonometric expressions.

Solution

$$\sin(x - \pi) = (\sin x)(\cos \pi) - (\cos x)(\sin \pi) \quad\longleftarrow$$
$$= (\sin x)(-1) - (\cos x)(0)$$
$$= -\sin x$$

| Use the subtraction formula for sine. |

$$\sin(x + \pi) = (\sin x)(\cos \pi) + (\cos x)(\sin \pi) \quad\longleftarrow$$
$$= (\sin x)(-1) + (\cos x)(0)$$
$$= -\sin x$$

| Use the addition formula for sine. |

$$\cos\left(x + \frac{\pi}{2}\right) = (\cos x)\left(\cos \frac{\pi}{2}\right) - (\sin x)\left(\sin \frac{\pi}{2}\right) \quad\longleftarrow$$
$$= (\cos x)(0) - (\sin x)(1)$$
$$= -\sin x$$

| Use the addition formula for cosine. |

$$\sin(x - \pi) = \sin(x + \pi) = \cos\left(x + \frac{\pi}{2}\right) \quad\longleftarrow$$

| They are all equivalent to the same expression, $-\sin x$. |

In Summary

Key Idea

- The trigonometric ratios of compound angles are related to the trigonometric ratios of their component angles by the following compound angle formulas.

Addition Formulas	**Subtraction Formulas**
$\sin(a + b) = \sin a \cos b + \cos a \sin b$	$\sin(a - b) = \sin a \cos b - \cos a \sin b$
$\cos(a + b) = \cos a \cos b - \sin a \sin b$	$\cos(a - b) = \cos a \cos b + \sin a \sin b$
$\tan(a + b) = \dfrac{\tan a + \tan b}{1 - \tan a \tan b}$	$\tan(a - b) = \dfrac{\tan a - \tan b}{1 + \tan a \tan b}$

Need to Know

- You can use compound angle formulas to obtain exact values for trigonometric ratios.
- You can use compound angle formulas to show that some trigonometric expressions are equivalent.

CHECK Your Understanding

1. Rewrite each expression as a single trigonometric ratio.
   a) $\sin a \cos 2a + \cos a \sin 2a$
   b) $\cos 4x \cos 3x - \sin 4x \sin 3x$

2. Rewrite each expression as a single trigonometric ratio, and then evaluate the ratio.
   a) $\dfrac{\tan 170° - \tan 110°}{1 + \tan 170° \tan 110°}$
   b) $\cos \dfrac{5\pi}{12} \cos \dfrac{\pi}{12} + \sin \dfrac{5\pi}{12} \sin \dfrac{\pi}{12}$

3. Express each angle as a compound angle, using a pair of angles from the special triangles.
   a) $75°$
   c) $-\dfrac{\pi}{6}$
   e) $105°$
   b) $-15°$
   d) $\dfrac{\pi}{12}$
   f) $\dfrac{5\pi}{6}$

4. Determine the exact value of each trigonometric ratio.
   a) $\sin 75°$
   c) $\tan \dfrac{5\pi}{12}$
   e) $\cos 105°$
   b) $\cos 15°$
   d) $\sin \left(-\dfrac{\pi}{12}\right)$
   f) $\tan \dfrac{23\pi}{12}$

PRACTISING

5. Use the appropriate compound angle formula to determine the exact value of each expression.
   a) $\sin \left(\pi + \dfrac{\pi}{6}\right)$
   c) $\tan \left(\dfrac{\pi}{4} + \pi\right)$
   e) $\tan \left(\dfrac{\pi}{3} - \dfrac{\pi}{6}\right)$
   b) $\cos \left(\pi - \dfrac{\pi}{4}\right)$
   d) $\sin \left(-\dfrac{\pi}{2} + \dfrac{\pi}{3}\right)$
   f) $\cos \left(\dfrac{\pi}{2} + \dfrac{\pi}{3}\right)$

6. Use the appropriate compound angle formula to create an equivalent expression.
   a) $\sin (\pi + x)$
   c) $\cos \left(x + \dfrac{\pi}{2}\right)$
   e) $\sin (x - \pi)$
   b) $\cos \left(x + \dfrac{3\pi}{2}\right)$
   d) $\tan (x + \pi)$
   f) $\tan (2\pi - x)$

7. Use transformations to explain why each expression you created in question 6 is equivalent to the given expression.

8. Determine the exact value of each trigonometric ratio.

a) $\cos 75°$

b) $\tan (-15°)$

c) $\cos \dfrac{11\pi}{12}$

d) $\sin \dfrac{13\pi}{12}$

e) $\tan \dfrac{7\pi}{12}$

f) $\tan \dfrac{-5\pi}{12}$

9. If $\sin x = \dfrac{4}{5}$ and $\sin y = -\dfrac{12}{13}$, $0 < x < \dfrac{\pi}{2}$, $\dfrac{3\pi}{2} < y < 2\pi$, evaluate

a) $\cos (x + y)$

b) $\sin (x + y)$

c) $\cos (x - y)$

d) $\sin (x - y)$

e) $\tan (x + y)$

f) $\tan (x - y)$

10. **A** α and β are acute angles in quadrant I, with $\sin \alpha = \dfrac{7}{25}$ and $\cos \beta = \dfrac{5}{13}$. Without using a calculator, determine the values of $\sin (\alpha + \beta)$ and $\tan (\alpha + \beta)$.

11. Use compound angle formulas to verify each of the following cofunction identities.

a) $\sin x = \cos \left(\dfrac{\pi}{2} - x \right)$

b) $\cos x = \sin \left(\dfrac{\pi}{2} - x \right)$

12. Simplify each expression.

a) $\sin (\pi + x) + \sin (\pi - x)$

b) $\cos \left(x + \dfrac{\pi}{3} \right) - \sin \left(x + \dfrac{\pi}{6} \right)$

13. **T** Simplify $\dfrac{\sin (f + g) + \sin (f - g)}{\cos (f + g) + \cos (f - g)}$.

14. **C** Create a flow chart to show how you would evaluate $\cos (a + b)$, given the values of $\sin a$ and $\sin b$, if both a and $b \in \left[0, \dfrac{\pi}{2} \right]$.

15. List the compound angle formulas you used in this lesson, and look for similarities and differences. Explain how you can use these similarities and differences to help you remember the formulas.

Extending

16. Prove $\sin C + \sin D = 2 \sin \left(\dfrac{C + D}{2} \right) \cos \left(\dfrac{C - D}{2} \right)$.

17. Determine $\cot (x + y)$ in terms of $\cot x$ and $\cot y$.

18. Prove $\cos C + \cos D = 2 \cos \left(\dfrac{C + D}{2} \right) \cos \left(\dfrac{C - D}{2} \right)$.

19. Prove $\cos C - \cos D = -2 \sin \left(\dfrac{C + D}{2} \right) \sin \left(\dfrac{C - D}{2} \right)$.

7.3 Double Angle Formulas

YOU WILL NEED

• graphing calculator

GOAL

Develop and use double angle formulas.

INVESTIGATE the Math

From your work with graphs of trigonometric functions, you already know that $f(\theta) = \sin 2\theta$ is not the same as $f(\theta) = 2 \sin \theta$.

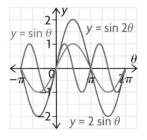

$f(\theta) = \sin 2\theta$ is the graph of $y = \sin \theta$ compressed horizontally by a factor of $\frac{1}{2}$.

$f(\theta) = 2 \sin \theta$ is the graph of $y = \sin \theta$ stretched vertically by a factor of 2.

? How are the trigonometric ratios of an angle that has been doubled to 2θ related to the trigonometric ratios of the original angle θ?

A. Given $\sin 2\theta = \sin (\theta + \theta)$, use the appropriate compound angle formula to expand $\sin (\theta + \theta)$. Simplify both sides to develop a formula for $\sin 2\theta$.

B. Verify your double angle formula for sine by graphing each side as a function on a graphing calculator and examining the tables of values.

C. Verify that your double angle formula for sine works by evaluating both sides of the formula for $\theta = 45°$. Repeat for $\theta = \frac{\pi}{6}$.

D. Repeat parts A to C to develop a double angle formula for $\cos 2\theta$.

E. Use the identity $\sin^2 \theta + \cos^2 \theta = 1$ to eliminate $\sin \theta$ from the right side of your formula in part D. Verify that your new formula is correct by graphing and by substitution, as before.

F. Repeat part E, but this time eliminate $\cos \theta$ on the right side to develop an equivalent expression in terms of $\sin \theta$.

G. Repeat parts A to C to develop a double angle formula for $\tan 2\theta$.

H. Make a list of all the double angle formulas you developed.

Reflecting

I. How did you use compound angle formulas to develop double angle formulas?

J. Why were you able to develop three different formulas for $\cos 2\theta$?

K. How might you develop formulas for $\sin \dfrac{\theta}{2}$ and $\cos \dfrac{\theta}{2}$?

APPLY the Math

EXAMPLE **1**	Using double angle formulas to simplify and evaluate expressions

Simplify each of the following expressions and then evaluate.

a) $2 \sin \dfrac{\pi}{8} \cos \dfrac{\pi}{8}$

b) $\dfrac{2 \tan \dfrac{\pi}{6}}{1 - \tan^2 \dfrac{\pi}{6}}$

Solution

a) $2 \sin x \cos x = \sin 2x$

$$2 \sin \dfrac{\pi}{8} \cos \dfrac{\pi}{8} = \sin 2\left(\dfrac{\pi}{8}\right)$$

$$= \sin \dfrac{\pi}{4}$$

$$= \dfrac{1}{\sqrt{2}}$$

> This expression is the right side of the double angle formula for sine.
> In this expression, $x = \dfrac{\pi}{8}$.
> Use the special triangles to evaluate.

b) $\dfrac{2 \tan x}{1 - \tan^2 x} = \tan 2x$, where $\tan x \neq \pm 1$

$$\dfrac{2 \tan \dfrac{\pi}{6}}{1 - \tan^2 \dfrac{\pi}{6}} = \tan 2\left(\dfrac{\pi}{6}\right)$$

$$= \tan \dfrac{\pi}{3}$$

$$= \sqrt{3}$$

> This expression is similar to the right side of the double angle formula for tangent. In this expression, $x = \dfrac{\pi}{6}$.

> Use the special triangles to evaluate $\tan \dfrac{\pi}{3}$.

If you know one of the primary trigonometric ratios for any angle, then you can determine the other two. You can then determine the primary trigonometric ratios for this angle doubled.

EXAMPLE **2**

Selecting a strategy to determine the value of trigonometric ratios for a double angle

If $\cos \theta = -\frac{2}{3}$ and $0 \le \theta \le 2\pi$, determine the value of $\cos 2\theta$ and $\sin 2\theta$.

Solution

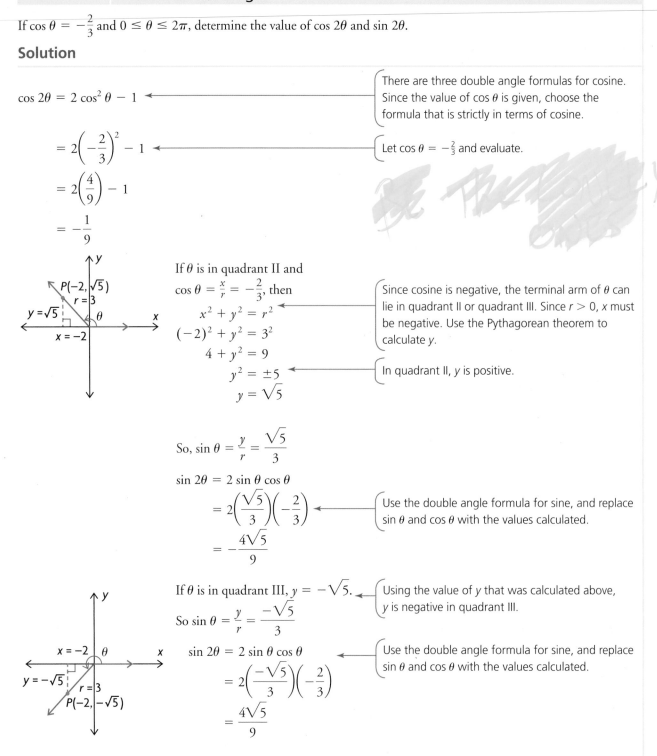

$\cos 2\theta = 2 \cos^2 \theta - 1$ ← There are three double angle formulas for cosine. Since the value of $\cos \theta$ is given, choose the formula that is strictly in terms of cosine.

$= 2\left(-\frac{2}{3}\right)^2 - 1$ ← Let $\cos \theta = -\frac{2}{3}$ and evaluate.

$= 2\left(\frac{4}{9}\right) - 1$

$= -\frac{1}{9}$

If θ is in quadrant II and $\cos \theta = \frac{x}{r} = -\frac{2}{3}$, then

$x^2 + y^2 = r^2$ ← Since cosine is negative, the terminal arm of θ can lie in quadrant II or quadrant III. Since $r > 0$, x must be negative. Use the Pythagorean theorem to calculate y.

$(-2)^2 + y^2 = 3^2$

$4 + y^2 = 9$

$y^2 = \pm 5$ ← In quadrant II, y is positive.

$y = \sqrt{5}$

So, $\sin \theta = \frac{y}{r} = \frac{\sqrt{5}}{3}$

$\sin 2\theta = 2 \sin \theta \cos \theta$

$= 2\left(\frac{\sqrt{5}}{3}\right)\left(-\frac{2}{3}\right)$ ← Use the double angle formula for sine, and replace $\sin \theta$ and $\cos \theta$ with the values calculated.

$= -\frac{4\sqrt{5}}{9}$

If θ is in quadrant III, $y = -\sqrt{5}$. ← Using the value of y that was calculated above, y is negative in quadrant III.

So $\sin \theta = \frac{y}{r} = \frac{-\sqrt{5}}{3}$

$\sin 2\theta = 2 \sin \theta \cos \theta$ ← Use the double angle formula for sine, and replace $\sin \theta$ and $\cos \theta$ with the values calculated.

$= 2\left(\frac{-\sqrt{5}}{3}\right)\left(-\frac{2}{3}\right)$

$= \frac{4\sqrt{5}}{9}$

EXAMPLE 3 Selecting a strategy to determine the primary trigonometric ratios for a double angle

Given $\tan \theta = -\frac{3}{4}$, where $\frac{3\pi}{2} \le \theta \le 2\pi$, calculate the value of $\cos 2\theta$.

Solution

$$\tan \theta = \frac{y}{x} = \frac{-3}{4}$$

$$x^2 + y^2 = r^2$$

$$4^2 + (-3)^2 = r^2$$

$$16 + 9 = r^2$$

$$\pm\sqrt{25} = r$$

$$5 = r$$

Since $\frac{3\pi}{2} \le \theta \le 2\pi$, the terminal arm of the angle lies in quadrant IV. Therefore, x is positive and y is negative. Use the Pythagorean theorem to determine r.

Since r is always positive, $r > 0$.

Draw θ in standard position.

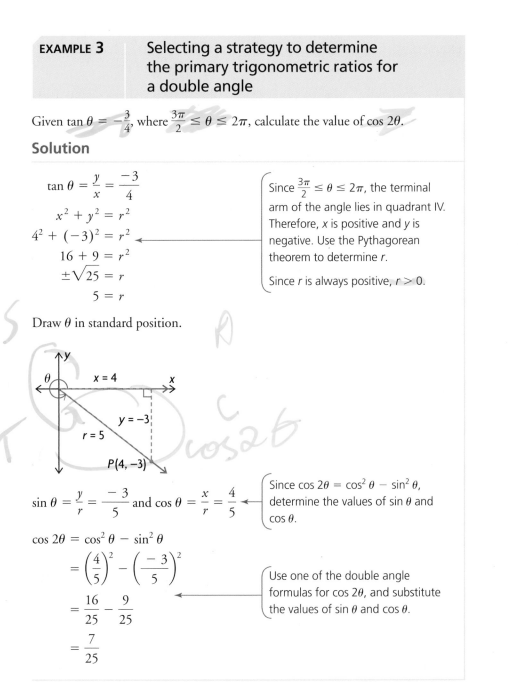

$$\sin \theta = \frac{y}{r} = \frac{-3}{5} \text{ and } \cos \theta = \frac{x}{r} = \frac{4}{5}$$

Since $\cos 2\theta = \cos^2 \theta - \sin^2 \theta$, determine the values of $\sin \theta$ and $\cos \theta$.

$$\cos 2\theta = \cos^2 \theta - \sin^2 \theta$$

$$= \left(\frac{4}{5}\right)^2 - \left(\frac{-3}{5}\right)^2$$

$$= \frac{16}{25} - \frac{9}{25}$$

$$= \frac{7}{25}$$

Use one of the double angle formulas for $\cos 2\theta$, and substitute the values of $\sin \theta$ and $\cos \theta$.

The double angle formulas can be used to create other equivalent trigonometric relationships.

| EXAMPLE 4 | Using reasoning to derive other formulas from the double angle formulas |

Develop a formula for $\sin \frac{x}{2}$.

Solution

$$\cos 2x = 1 - 2 \sin^2 x$$

$$\cos 2\left(\frac{x}{2}\right) = 1 - 2 \sin^2 \left(\frac{x}{2}\right)$$

Since $\cos x = \cos 2\left(\frac{x}{2}\right)$, replace x with $\frac{x}{2}$ in the cosine double angle formula that only involves sine.

$$\cos x = 1 - 2 \sin^2 \left(\frac{x}{2}\right)$$

$$2 \sin^2 \left(\frac{x}{2}\right) = 1 - \cos x$$

$$\sin^2 \left(\frac{x}{2}\right) = \frac{1 - \cos x}{2}$$

$$\sin \left(\frac{x}{2}\right) = \pm \sqrt{\frac{1 - \cos x}{2}}$$

Solve for $\sin \left(\frac{x}{2}\right)$ as follows:

- Add $2 \sin^2 \left(\frac{x}{2}\right)$ to both sides.
- Subtract $\cos x$ from both sides.
- Divide both sides by 2.
- Take the square root of both sides.

In Summary

Key Idea

- The double angle formulas show how the trigonometric ratios for a double angle, 2θ, are related to the trigonometric ratios for the original angle, θ.

Double Angle Formula for Sine

$$\sin 2\theta = 2 \sin \theta \cos \theta$$

Double Angle Formulas for Cosine

$$\cos 2\theta = \cos^2 \theta - \sin^2 \theta$$
$$\cos 2\theta = 2 \cos^2 \theta - 1$$
$$\cos 2\theta = 1 - 2 \sin^2 \theta$$

Double Angle Formula for Tangent

$$\tan 2\theta = \frac{2 \tan \theta}{1 - \tan^2 \theta}$$

Need to Know

- The double angle formulas can be derived from the appropriate compound angle formulas.
- You can use the double angle formulas to simplify expressions and to calculate exact values.
- The double angle formulas can be used to develop other equivalent formulas.

CHECK *Your Understanding*

1. Express each of the following as a single trigonometric ratio.

   a) $2 \sin 5x \cos 5x$

   b) $\cos^2 \theta - \sin^2 \theta$

   c) $1 - 2 \sin^2 3x$

   d) $\dfrac{2 \tan 4x}{1 - \tan^2 4x}$

   e) $4 \sin \theta \cos \theta$

   f) $2 \cos^2 \dfrac{\theta}{2} - 1$

2. Express each of the following as a single trigonometric ratio and then evaluate.

   a) $2 \sin 45° \cos 45°$

   b) $\cos^2 30° - \sin^2 30°$

   c) $2 \sin \dfrac{\pi}{12} \cos \dfrac{\pi}{12}$

   d) $\cos^2 \dfrac{\pi}{12} - \sin^2 \dfrac{\pi}{12}$

   e) $1 - 2 \sin^2 \dfrac{3\pi}{8}$

   f) $2 \tan 60° \cos^2 60°$

3. Use a double angle formula to rewrite each trigonometric ratio.

   a) $\sin 4\theta$

   b) $\cos 3x$

   c) $\tan x$

   d) $\cos 6\theta$

   e) $\sin x$

   f) $\tan 5\theta$

PRACTISING

4. **K** Determine the values of $\sin 2\theta$, $\cos 2\theta$, and $\tan 2\theta$, given $\cos \theta = \dfrac{3}{5}$ and $0 \le \theta \le \dfrac{\pi}{2}$.

5. Determine the values of $\sin 2\theta$, $\cos 2\theta$, and $\tan 2\theta$, given $\tan \theta = -\dfrac{7}{24}$ and $\dfrac{\pi}{2} \le \theta \le \pi$.

6. Determine the values of $\sin 2\theta$, $\cos 2\theta$, and $\tan 2\theta$, given $\sin \theta = -\dfrac{12}{13}$ and $\dfrac{3\pi}{2} \le \theta \le 2\pi$.

7. Determine the values of $\sin 2\theta$, $\cos 2\theta$, and $\tan 2\theta$, given $\cos \theta = -\dfrac{4}{5}$ and $\dfrac{\pi}{2} \le \theta \le \pi$.

8. **A** Determine the value of a in the following equation:
   $2 \tan x - \tan 2x + 2a = 1 - \tan 2x \tan^2 x$.

9. Jim needs to find the sine of $\dfrac{\pi}{8}$. If he knows that $\cos \dfrac{\pi}{4} = \dfrac{1}{\sqrt{2}}$, how can he use this fact to find the sine of $\dfrac{\pi}{8}$? What is his answer?

10. Marion needs to find the cosine of $\dfrac{\pi}{12}$. If she knows that $\cos \dfrac{\pi}{6} = \dfrac{\sqrt{3}}{2}$, how can she use this fact to find the cosine of $\dfrac{\pi}{12}$? What is her answer?

11. a) Use a double angle formula to develop a formula for $\sin 4x$ in terms of x.

b) Use the formula you developed in part a) to verify that $\sin \dfrac{2\pi}{3} = \sin \dfrac{8\pi}{3}$.

12. Use the appropriate compound angle formula and double angle formula to develop a formula for

a) $\sin 3\theta$ in terms of $\cos \theta$ and $\sin \theta$

b) $\cos 3\theta$ in terms of $\cos \theta$ and $\sin \theta$

c) $\tan 3\theta$ in terms of $\tan \theta$

13. The angle x lies in the interval $\dfrac{\pi}{2} \le x \le \pi$, and $\sin^2 x = \dfrac{8}{9}$. Without using a calculator, determine the value of

a) $\sin 2x$ **c)** $\cos \dfrac{x}{2}$

b) $\cos 2x$ **d)** $\sin 3x$

14. Create a flow chart to show how you would evaluate $\sin 2a$, given the value of $\sin a$, if $a \in \left[\dfrac{\pi}{2}, \pi\right]$.

15. Describe how you could use your knowledge of double angle formulas to sketch the graph of each function. Include a sketch with your description.

a) $f(x) = \sin x \cos x$

b) $f(x) = 2 \cos^2 x$

c) $f(x) = \dfrac{\tan x}{1 - \tan^2 x}$

Extending

16. Eliminate A from each pair of equations to find an equation that relates x to y.

a) $x = \tan 2A,\ y = \tan A$ **c)** $x = \cos 2A,\ y = \csc A$

b) $x = \cos 2A,\ y = \cos A$ **d)** $x = \sin 2A,\ y = \sec 4A$

17. Solve each equation for values of x in the interval $0 \le x \le 2\pi$.

a) $\cos 2x = \sin x$ **b)** $\sin 2x - 1 = \cos 2x$

18. Express each of the following in terms of $\tan \theta$.

a) $\sin 2\theta$ **c)** $\dfrac{\sin 2\theta}{1 + \cos 2\theta}$

b) $\cos 2\theta$ **d)** $\dfrac{1 - \cos 2\theta}{\sin 2\theta}$

FREQUENTLY ASKED *Questions*

Q: **How can you identify equivalent trigonometric expressions?**

Study | *Aid*
- See Lesson 7.1.
- Try Mid-Chapter Review Questions 1 and 2.

A1: Compare the graphs of the corresponding trigonometric functions on a graphing calculator. If the graphs appear to be identical, then the expressions may be equivalent.

For example, to see if $\sin\left(x + \dfrac{\pi}{6}\right)$ is the same as $\cos\left(x - \dfrac{\pi}{3}\right)$, graph the functions $f(x) = \sin\left(x + \dfrac{\pi}{6}\right)$ and $g(x) = \cos\left(x - \dfrac{\pi}{3}\right)$ on the same screen. If you use a bold line for the second function, you will see it drawing in over the first graph.

Since the graphs appear to coincide, you can make the conjecture that $f(x) = g(x)$. It follows that $\sin\left(x + \dfrac{\pi}{6}\right) = \cos\left(x - \dfrac{\pi}{3}\right)$. This can be confirmed by analyzing both functions. Both functions have a period of 2π. As well, $f(x) = \sin\left(x + \dfrac{\pi}{6}\right)$ is the sine function translated $\dfrac{\pi}{6}$ to the left, while $g(x) = \cos\left(x - \dfrac{\pi}{3}\right)$ is the cosine function translated $\dfrac{\pi}{3}$ to the right. These transformations of the parent functions result in the same function over their entire domains.

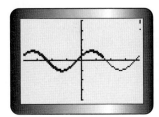

A2: Use some of the following strategies:
- the reflective property of even and odd functions
- translations of a function by an amount that is equal to a multiple of its period
- combinations of other transformations
- the relationship between trigonometric ratios of complementary angles in a right triangle
- the relationship between a principal angle in standard position on the Cartesian plane and its related angles

A3: Use compound angle formulas.

Study | *Aid*
- See Lesson 7.2, Example 4.
- Try Mid-Chapter Review Questions 3 and 4.

For example, to identify a trigonometric expression that is equivalent to $\cos\left(x - \dfrac{\pi}{4}\right)$, use the subtraction formula for cosine.

$$\cos\left(x - \frac{\pi}{4}\right) = \cos x \cos \frac{\pi}{4} + \sin x \sin \frac{\pi}{4}$$

$$= (\cos x)\left(\frac{1}{\sqrt{2}}\right) + (\sin x)\left(\frac{1}{\sqrt{2}}\right)$$

$$= \frac{1}{\sqrt{2}}(\cos x + \sin x)$$

Study | *Aid*

- See Lesson 7.2, Example 1.
- Try Mid-Chapter Review Questions 5 and 6.

Q: **How can you determine the exact values of trigonometric ratios for angles other than the special angles $\frac{\pi}{6}, \frac{\pi}{4}, \frac{\pi}{3}$, and $\frac{\pi}{2}$, and their multiples?**

A: You can combine special angles by adding or subtracting them, and then use compound angle formulas to determine trigonometric ratios for the new angle.

For example, consider $\frac{\pi}{4} + \frac{\pi}{3} = \frac{7\pi}{12}$.

Determine $\sin \frac{7\pi}{12}$ by finding

$$\sin\left(\frac{\pi}{4} + \frac{\pi}{3}\right) = \sin\frac{\pi}{4}\cos\frac{\pi}{3} + \cos\frac{\pi}{4}\sin\frac{\pi}{3}$$

$$= \left(\frac{1}{\sqrt{2}}\right)\left(\frac{1}{2}\right) + \left(\frac{1}{\sqrt{2}}\right)\left(\frac{\sqrt{3}}{2}\right)$$

$$= \frac{1 + \sqrt{3}}{2\sqrt{2}}$$

Study | *Aid*

- See Lesson 7.3, Example 2.
- Try Mid-Chapter Review Questions 8 to 12.

Q: **Given a trigonometric ratio for θ, how would you calculate trigonometric ratios for 2θ?**

A: You can use double angle formulas.

For example, if you know that $\cos \theta = \frac{2}{5}$, you can calculate $\cos 2\theta$ using the formula

$$\cos 2\theta = 2\cos^2\theta - 1$$

$$= 2\left(\frac{2}{5}\right)^2 - 1$$

$$= \frac{8}{25} - 1$$

$$= -\frac{17}{25}$$

To calculate $\sin 2\theta$ and $\tan 2\theta$, you need to consider the quadrant in which θ lies. If $\cos \theta$ is positive, θ can be in quadrant I or quadrant IV. This means you need to calculate two answers for both $\sin 2\theta$ and $\tan 2\theta$.

PRACTICE *Questions*

1. For each of the following trigonometric ratios, state an equivalent trigonometric ratio.

   a) $\cos \dfrac{\pi}{16}$

   b) $\sin \dfrac{7\pi}{9}$

   c) $\tan \dfrac{9\pi}{10}$

   d) $-\cos \dfrac{2\pi}{5}$

   e) $-\sin \dfrac{9\pi}{7}$

   f) $\tan \dfrac{3\pi}{4}$

2. Use the sine function to write an equation that is equivalent to $y = -6 \cos \left(x + \dfrac{\pi}{2}\right) + 4$.

3. Use a compound angle addition formula to determine a trigonometric expression that is equivalent to each of the following expressions.

   a) $\cos \left(x + \dfrac{5\pi}{3}\right)$

   b) $\sin \left(x + \dfrac{5\pi}{6}\right)$

   c) $\tan \left(x + \dfrac{5\pi}{4}\right)$

   d) $\cos \left(x + \dfrac{4\pi}{3}\right)$

4. Use a compound angle subtraction formula to determine a trigonometric expression that is equivalent to each of the following expressions.

   a) $\sin \left(x - \dfrac{11\pi}{6}\right)$

   b) $\tan \left(x - \dfrac{\pi}{3}\right)$

   c) $\cos \left(x - \dfrac{7\pi}{4}\right)$

   d) $\sin \left(x - \dfrac{2\pi}{3}\right)$

5. Evaluate each expression.

   a) $\dfrac{\tan \dfrac{8\pi}{9} - \tan \dfrac{5\pi}{9}}{1 + \tan \dfrac{8\pi}{9} \tan \dfrac{5\pi}{9}}$

   b) $\sin \dfrac{299\pi}{298} \cos \dfrac{\pi}{298} - \cos \dfrac{299\pi}{298} \sin \dfrac{\pi}{298}$

   c) $\sin 50° \cos 20° - \cos 50° \sin 20°$

   d) $\sin \dfrac{3\pi}{8} \cos \dfrac{\pi}{8} + \cos \dfrac{3\pi}{8} \sin \dfrac{\pi}{8}$

6. Simplify each expression.

   a) $\dfrac{2 \tan x}{1 - \tan^2 x}$

   b) $\sin \dfrac{x}{5} \cos \dfrac{4x}{5} + \cos \dfrac{x}{5} \sin \dfrac{4x}{5}$

   c) $\cos \left(\dfrac{\pi}{2} - x\right)$

   d) $\sin \left(\dfrac{\pi}{2} + x\right)$

   e) $\cos \left(\dfrac{\pi}{4} + x\right) + \cos \left(\dfrac{\pi}{4} + x\right)$

   f) $\tan \left(x - \dfrac{\pi}{4}\right)$

7. The expression $a \cos x + b \sin x$ can be expressed in the form $R \cos (x - \alpha)$, where $R = \sqrt{a^2 + b^2}$, $\cos \alpha = \dfrac{a}{R}$, and $\sin \alpha = \dfrac{b}{R}$. Use this information to write an expression that is equivalent to $\sqrt{3} \cos x - 3 \sin x$.

8. Evaluate each expression.

   a) $2 \cos^2 \dfrac{2\pi}{3} - 1$

   b) $2 \sin \dfrac{11\pi}{12} \cos \dfrac{11\pi}{12}$

   c) $\cos^2 \dfrac{7\pi}{8} - \sin^2 \dfrac{7\pi}{8}$

   d) $1 - 2 \sin^2 \left(\dfrac{\pi}{2}\right)$

9. The angle x lies in the interval $\pi \le x \le \dfrac{3\pi}{2}$, and $\cos^2 x = \dfrac{10}{11}$. Without using a calculator, determine the value of each trigonometric ratio.

   a) $\sin x$

   b) $\cos x$

   c) $\sin 2x$

   d) $\cos 2x$

10. Given $\sin x = \dfrac{3}{5}$ and $0 \le x \le \dfrac{\pi}{2}$, find $\sin 2x$ and $\cos 2x$.

11. Given $\sin x = \dfrac{5}{13}$ and $0 \le x \le \dfrac{\pi}{2}$, find $\sin 2x$.

12. Given $\cos x = -\dfrac{4}{5}$ and $\pi \le x \le \dfrac{3\pi}{2}$, find $\tan 2x$.

7.4 Proving Trigonometric Identities

YOU WILL NEED

- graphing calculator

GOAL

Use equivalent trigonometric relationships to prove that an equation is an identity.

LEARN ABOUT the Math

When Alysia graphs the function $f(x) = \dfrac{\sin 2x}{1 + \cos 2x}$ using a graphing calculator, she sees that her graph looks the same as the graph for the tangent function $f(x) = \tan x$.

She makes a conjecture that $\dfrac{\sin 2x}{1 + \cos 2x} = \tan x$ is a trigonometric **identity**. In other words, she predicts that this equation is true for all values of x for which the expressions in the equation are defined.

? How can Alysia prove that her conjecture is true?

EXAMPLE 1   Using reasoning to prove an identity that involves double angles

Prove that $\dfrac{\sin 2x}{1 + \cos 2x} = \tan x.$

Solution

$$LS = \frac{\sin 2x}{1 + \cos 2x}$$

Begin with the left side (LS) because you can use double angle formulas to express the LS, using the same **argument** as the right side (RS).

$$= \frac{2 \sin x \cos x}{1 + 2 \cos^2 x - 1}$$

$$= \frac{2 \sin x \cos x}{2 \cos^2 x}$$

After applying the double angle formulas, simplify the denominator. Then divide the numerator and the denominator by $2 \cos x$.

$$= \frac{\sin x}{\cos x}$$

$$= \tan x = RS$$

Since both sides are equal,

$$\frac{\sin 2x}{1 + \cos 2x} = \tan x \longleftarrow$$

The expressions are equivalent for all real numbers, except where $\cos 2x = -1$ and $\cos x = 0$.

Reflecting

A. Why was the left side of the identity simplified at the beginning of the solution?

B. Which formula for $\cos 2x$ was used, and why? Could another formula have been used instead?

C. If you replaced x with $\frac{\pi}{4}$ in Alysia's conjecture and you showed that both sides result in the same value, could you conclude that the equation is an identity? Explain.

APPLY the Math

EXAMPLE 2   **Proving that an equation is not an identity**

Prove that $\sin x + \sin 2x = \sin 3x$ is not an identity.

Solution

Let $x = \frac{\pi}{2}$.

$$LS = \sin\left(\frac{\pi}{2}\right) + \sin 2\left(\frac{\pi}{2}\right)$$
$$= 1 + 0$$
$$= 1$$

$$RS = \sin 3\left(\frac{\pi}{2}\right)$$
$$= -1$$

Choose any value for which both sides of the equation are defined, and evaluate both sides.

Since there is a value for which the left side does not equal the right side, the equation is not an identity.

$x = \frac{\pi}{2}$ is a **counterexample**—it disproves the equivalence of both sides of the equation.

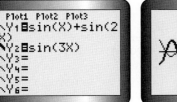

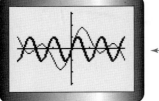

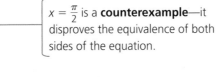

Graphing both sides of the equation results in very different graphs.

EXAMPLE 3   Using reasoning to prove a cofunction identity

Prove that $\cos\left(\dfrac{\pi}{2} + x\right) = -\sin x$.

Solution

$$\text{LS} = \cos\left(\dfrac{\pi}{2} + x\right)$$

Begin with the left side because a compound angle formula can be used to simplify the expression on the left side. Substitute the numerical values of $\cos\left(\dfrac{\pi}{2}\right)$ and $\sin\left(\dfrac{\pi}{2}\right)$.

$$= \cos\left(\dfrac{\pi}{2}\right)\cos x - \sin\left(\dfrac{\pi}{2}\right)\sin x$$

$$= (0)\cos x - (1)\sin x$$

$$= 0 - \sin x$$

$$= -\sin x$$

$$= \text{RS}$$

Since both sides are equal,

$$\cos\left(\dfrac{\pi}{2} + x\right) = -\sin x$$

Because there is no denominator or square root on either side of the equation, the expressions are equivalent for all real numbers.

When you encounter a more complicated identity, you may be able to use several different strategies to prove the equivalence of the expressions.

EXAMPLE 4   Using reasoning to prove an identity that involves rational trigonometric expressions

Prove that $\dfrac{\cos (x - y)}{\cos (x + y)} = \dfrac{1 + \tan x \tan y}{1 - \tan x \tan y}$.

Solution

$$\text{RS} = \dfrac{1 + \tan x \tan y}{1 - \tan x \tan y}$$

Start with the right side. Replace $\tan x$ with $\dfrac{\sin x}{\cos x}$, and replace $\tan y$ with $\dfrac{\sin y}{\cos y}$. Then multiply the expression by $\dfrac{(\cos x)(\cos y)}{(\cos x)(\cos y)}$ (because this equals 1) to get one numerator and one denominator.

$$= \dfrac{1 + \left(\dfrac{\sin x}{\cos x}\right)\left(\dfrac{\sin y}{\cos y}\right)}{1 - \left(\dfrac{\sin x}{\cos x}\right)\left(\dfrac{\sin y}{\cos y}\right)} \times \dfrac{(\cos x)(\cos y)}{(\cos x)(\cos y)}$$

$$= \dfrac{(\cos x)(\cos y) + (\sin x)(\sin y)}{(\cos x)(\cos y) - (\sin x)(\sin y)}$$

Rewrite the expressions in the numerator and the denominator using compound angle formulas.

$$= \dfrac{\cos (x - y)}{\cos (x + y)}$$

$$= \text{LS}$$

Since both sides are equal,

$$\frac{\cos (x - y)}{\cos (x + y)} = \frac{1 + \tan x \tan y}{1 - \tan x \tan y}$$ ← The expressions are equivalent for all real numbers, except where $\cos (x + y) = 0$ and $\tan x \tan y = 1$.

Sometimes, you may need to factor if you want to prove that a given equation is an identity.

| EXAMPLE **5** | Using a factoring strategy to prove an identity |

Prove that $\tan 2x - 2 \tan 2x \sin^2 x = \sin 2x$. $\neq 0$

Solution

$$LS = \tan 2x - 2 \tan 2x \sin^2 x$$

$$= \tan 2x(1 - 2 \sin^2 x)$$

$$= \tan 2x \cos 2x$$

$$= \frac{\sin 2x}{\cos 2x}(\cos 2x)$$

$$= \sin 2x, \cos 2x \neq 0$$

$$= RS$$

Begin with the more complicated side.

Factor $\tan 2x$ out of the two terms.

The expression inside the brackets can be simplified using a double angle formula.

Write $\tan 2x$ as $\frac{\sin 2x}{\cos 2x}$, and simplify the resulting expression.

Since both sides are equal,

$$\tan 2x - 2 \tan 2x \sin^2 x = \sin 2x,$$
$$\cos 2x \neq 0.$$

The expressions are equivalent for all real numbers, except where $\cos 2x = 0$. The left side involves the tangent function, which was expressed as a quotient, so the denominator cannot be 0.

In Summary

Key Ideas

- A trigonometric identity states the equivalence of two trigonometric expressions. It is written as an equation that involves trigonometric ratios, and the solution set is all real numbers for which the expressions on both sides of the equation are defined. As a result, the equation has an infinite number of solutions.
- Some trigonometric identities are the result of a definition, while others are derived from relationships that exist among trigonometric ratios.

Need to Know

- The following trigonometric identities are important for you to remember:

Identities Based on Definitions

Identities Derived from Relationships

Reciprocal Identities

$$\csc x = \frac{1}{\sin x}$$

$$\sec x = \frac{1}{\cos x}$$

$$\cot x = \frac{1}{\tan x}$$

Quotient Identities

$$\tan x = \frac{\sin x}{\cos x}$$

$$\cot x = \frac{\cos x}{\sin x}$$

Pythagorean Identities

$$\sin^2 x + \cos^2 x = 1$$

$$1 + \tan^2 x = \sec^2 x$$

$$1 + \cot^2 x = \csc^2 x$$

Double Angle Formulas

$$\sin 2x = 2 \sin x \cos x$$

$$\cos 2x = \cos^2 x - \sin^2 x$$

$$= 2 \cos^2 x - 1$$

$$= 1 - 2 \sin^2 x$$

$$\tan 2x = \frac{2 \tan x}{1 - \tan^2 x}$$

Addition and Subtraction Formulas

$$\sin (x + y) = \sin x \cos y + \cos x \sin y$$

$$\sin (x - y) = \sin x \cos y - \cos x \sin y$$

$$\cos (x + y) = \cos x \cos y - \sin x \sin y$$

$$\cos (x - y) = \cos x \cos y + \sin x \sin y$$

$$\tan (x + y) = \frac{\tan x + \tan y}{1 - \tan x \tan y}$$

$$\tan (x - y) = \frac{\tan x - \tan y}{1 + \tan x \tan y}$$

- You can verify the truth of a given trigonometric identity by graphing each side separately and showing that the two graphs are the same.
- To prove that a given equation is an identity, the two sides of the equation must be shown to be equivalent. This can be accomplished using a variety of strategies, such as
  - simplifying the more complicated side until it is identical to the other side, or manipulating both sides to get the same expression
  - rewriting expressions using any of the identities stated above
  - using a common denominator or factoring, where possible

CHECK Your Understanding

1. Jared claims that $\sin x = \cos x$ is an identity, since $\sin \frac{\pi}{4} = \cos \frac{\pi}{4} = \frac{\sqrt{2}}{2}$. Use a counterexample to disprove his claim.

2. **a)** Use a graphing calculator to graph $f(x) = \sin x$ and $g(x) = \tan x \cos x$ for $-2\pi \le x \le 2\pi$.
   b) Write a trigonometric identity based on your graphs.
   c) Simplify one side of your identity to prove it is true.
   d) This identity is true for all real numbers, except where $\cos x = 0$. Explain why.

3. Graph the appropriate functions to match each expression on the left with the equivalent expression on the right.
   a) $\sin x \cot x$ **A** $\sin^2 x + \cos^2 x + \tan^2 x$
   b) $1 - 2\sin^2 x$ **B** $1 + 2\sin x \cos x$
   c) $(\sin x + \cos x)^2$ **C** $\cos x$
   d) $\sec^2 x$ **D** $2\cos^2 x - 1$

4. Prove algebraically that the expressions you matched in question 3 are equivalent.

PRACTISING

5. Give a counterexample to show that each equation is not an identity.
   K
   a) $\cos x = \dfrac{1}{\cos x}$ **c)** $\sin(x + y) = \cos x \cos y + \sin x \sin y$
   b) $1 - \tan^2 x = \sec^2 x$ **d)** $\cos 2x = 1 + 2\sin^2 x$

6. Graph the expression $\dfrac{1 - \tan^2 x}{1 + \tan^2 x}$, and make a conjecture about another
   A expression that is equivalent to this expression.

7. Prove your conjecture in question 6.

8. Prove that $\dfrac{1 + \tan x}{1 + \cot x} = \dfrac{1 - \tan x}{\cot x - 1}$.

9. Prove each identity.
   a) $\dfrac{\cos^2 \theta - \sin^2 \theta}{\cos^2 \theta + \sin \theta \cos \theta} = 1 - \tan \theta$
   b) $\tan^2 x - \sin^2 x = \sin^2 x \tan^2 x$
   c) $\tan^2 x - \cos^2 x = \dfrac{1}{\cos^2 x} - 1 - \cos^2 x$
   d) $\dfrac{1}{1 + \cos \theta} + \dfrac{1}{1 - \cos \theta} = \dfrac{2}{\sin^2 \theta}$

10. Prove each identity.

a) $\cos x \tan^3 x = \sin x \tan^2 x$

b) $\sin^2 \theta + \cos^4 \theta = \cos^2 \theta + \sin^4 \theta$

c) $(\sin x + \cos x)\left(\dfrac{\tan^2 x + 1}{\tan x}\right) = \dfrac{1}{\cos x} + \dfrac{1}{\sin x}$

d) $\tan^2 \beta + \cos^2 \beta + \sin^2 \beta = \dfrac{1}{\cos^2 \beta}$

e) $\sin\left(\dfrac{\pi}{4} + x\right) + \sin\left(\dfrac{\pi}{4} - x\right) = \sqrt{2} \cos x$

f) $\sin\left(\dfrac{\pi}{2} - x\right) \cot\left(\dfrac{\pi}{2} + x\right) = -\sin x$

11. Prove each identity.

T

a) $\dfrac{\cos 2x + 1}{\sin 2x} = \cot x$

b) $\dfrac{\sin 2x}{1 - \cos 2x} = \cot x$

c) $(\sin x + \cos x)^2 = 1 + \sin 2x$

d) $\cos^4 \theta - \sin^4 \theta = \cos 2\theta$

e) $\cot \theta - \tan \theta = 2 \cot 2\theta$

f) $\cot \theta + \tan \theta = 2 \csc 2\theta$

g) $\dfrac{1 + \tan x}{1 - \tan x} = \tan\left(x + \dfrac{\pi}{4}\right)$

h) $\csc 2x + \cot 2x = \cot x$

i) $\dfrac{2 \tan x}{1 + \tan^2 x} = \sin 2x$

j) $\sec 2t = \dfrac{\csc t}{\csc t - 2 \sin t}$

k) $\csc 2\theta = \dfrac{1}{2}(\sec \theta)(\csc \theta)$

l) $\sec t = \dfrac{\sin 2t}{\sin t} - \dfrac{\cos 2t}{\cos t}$

12. Graph the expression $\dfrac{\sin x + \sin 2x}{1 + \cos x + \cos 2x}$, and make a conjecture about another expression that is equivalent to this expression.

13. Prove your conjecture in question 12.

14. Copy the chart shown, and complete it to summarize what you know
C about trigonometric identities.

Definition	Methods of Proof
Examples	Non-Examples

Trigonometric Identities

15. Your friend wants to know whether the equation $2 \sin x \cos x = \cos 2x$ is an identity. Explain how she can determine whether it is an identity. If it is an identity, explain how she can prove this. If it is not an identity, explain how she can change one side of the equation to make it an identity.

Extending

16. Each of the following expressions can be written in the form $a \sin 2x + b \cos 2x + c$. Determine the values of a, b, and c.

a) $2 \cos^2 x + 4 \sin x \cos x$ **b)** $-2 \sin x \cos x - 4 \sin^2 x$

17. Express $8 \cos^4 x$ in the form $a \cos 4x + b \cos 2x + c$. State the values of the constants a, b, and c.

7.5 Solving Linear Trigonometric Equations

GOAL

Solve linear trigonometric equations algebraically and graphically.

LEARN ABOUT the Math

In Lesson 7.4, you learned how to prove that a given trigonometric equation is an identity. Not all trigonometric equations are identities, however. To see the difference between an equation that is an identity and an equation that is not, consider the following two equations on the domain $0 \le x \le 2\pi$: $\sin^2 x + \cos^2 x = 1$ and $2 \sin x - 1 = 0$.

The first equation is true for all values of x in the given domain, so it is an identity.

The second equation is true for only some values of x, so it is not an identity.

? How can you solve a trigonometric equation that is not an identity?

EXAMPLE 1 Selecting a strategy to determine the solutions for a linear trigonometric equation

You are given the equation $2 \sin x + 1 = 0$, $0 \le x \le 2\pi$.
a) Determine all the solutions in the specified interval.
b) Verify the solutions using graphing technology.

Solution

a) $2 \sin x + 1 = 0$
$$2 \sin x = -1$$
$$\sin x = -\frac{1}{2}$$

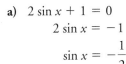

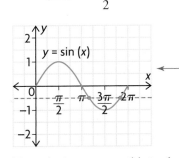

Two solutions are possible in the specified interval, $0 \le x \le 2\pi$, since the sine graph will complete one cycle in this interval.

Rearrange the equation to isolate $\sin x$.
Sketch a graph of the sine function to estimate where its value is $-\frac{1}{2}$.
From the graph, one solution is possible when $\pi \le x \le \frac{3\pi}{2}$ and another solution is possible when $\frac{3\pi}{2} \le x \le 2\pi$. Therefore, the terminal arms of the two angles lie in quadrants III and IV. This makes sense since r is positive and y is negative, so the sine ratio is negative for angles in both of these quadrants. This is confirmed by the CAST rule.

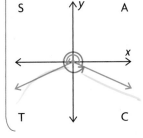

Determine the related acute angle.

$$\sin^{-1}\left(\frac{1}{2}\right) = \frac{\pi}{6}$$

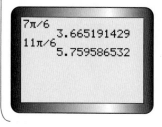

$\frac{\pi}{6}$ is a special angle.

Using the special triangle that contains $\frac{\pi}{6}$ and $\frac{\pi}{3}$, $\sin\frac{\pi}{6} = \frac{1}{2}$.

Use the related angle to determine the required solutions in the given interval.

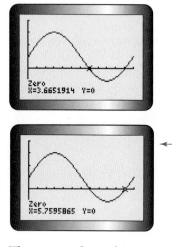

The solution in quadrant III is $\pi + \frac{\pi}{6} = \frac{7\pi}{6}$.

The solution in quadrant IV is $2\pi - \frac{\pi}{6} = \frac{11\pi}{6}$.

b) Graph $f(x) = 2\sin x + 1$ in radian mode, for $0 \le x \le 2\pi$, and determine the zeros.

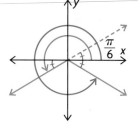

Use the window settings that match the domain for Xmin and Xmax. Use a scale of $\frac{\pi}{6}$.

To verify the solutions found in part a), express the solutions as decimals.

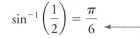

The zeros are located at approximately 3.665 191 4 and 5.759 586 5. These values are very close to $\frac{7\pi}{6}$ and $\frac{11\pi}{6}$.

Reflecting

A. How was solving the equation $2\sin x + 1 = 0$ like solving the equation $2x + 1 = 0$? How was it different?

B. Once $\sin x$ was isolated in Example 1, how was the sign of the trigonometric ratio used to determine the quadrants in which the solutions were located?

C. The interval in Example 1 was $0 \le x \le 2\pi$. If the interval had been $x \in \mathbf{R}$, how many solutions would the equation have had? Explain.

APPLY *the Math*

EXAMPLE 2	Using an algebraic strategy to determine the approximate solutions for a linear trigonometric equation

Solve $3(\tan \theta + 1) = 2$, where $0° \leq \theta \leq 360°$, correct to one decimal place.

Solution

$$3(\tan \theta + 1) = 2$$

$$\tan \theta + 1 = \frac{2}{3}$$

$$\tan \theta = \frac{2}{3} - 1 \leftarrow$$ Rearrange the equation to isolate $\tan \theta$.

$$\tan \theta = -\frac{1}{3}$$

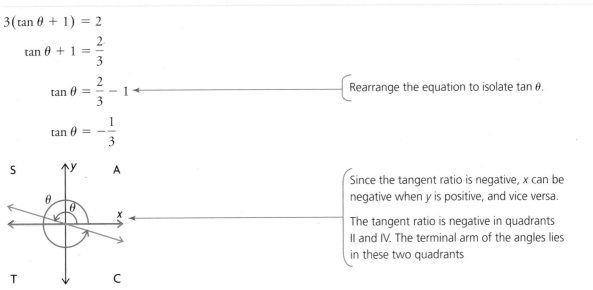

Since the tangent ratio is negative, x can be negative when y is positive, and vice versa.

The tangent ratio is negative in quadrants II and IV. The terminal arm of the angles lies in these two quadrants

There are two solutions for θ in the interval $0° \leq \theta \leq 360°$.

Determine the related acute angle using the inverse tangent function.

Evaluate $\tan^{-1}\left(\frac{1}{3}\right)$ using a calculator in degree mode, and round your answer to one decimal place.

$\tan^{-1}\left(\frac{1}{3}\right) \doteq 18.4°$, so the related acute angle is about $18.4°$.

Subtract $18.4°$ from $180°$ to obtain the solution in quadrant II. $\leftarrow$
$\theta \doteq 180° - 18.4° = 161.6°$

If β is the related angle, the principal angle in quadrant II is $180° - \beta$. The principal angle in quadrant IV is $360° - \beta$.

Subtract $18.4°$ from $360°$ to obtain the solution in quadrant IV.
$\theta \doteq 360° - 18.4° = 341.6°$

θ is about $161.6°$ or $341.6°$.

Verify the solutions by graphing $f(\theta) = 3(\tan\theta + 1) - 2$
in degree mode and determining the zeros in the given domain.

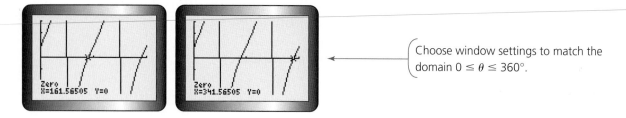

Zero
X=161.56505 Y=0

Zero
X=341.56505 Y=0

Choose window settings to match the
domain $0 \le \theta \le 360°$.

The results confirm the solutions.

EXAMPLE 3   Solving a problem that involves a linear trigonometric equation

Today, the high tide in Matthews Cove, New Brunswick, is at midnight. The water level at high tide is 7.5 m.
The depth, d metres, of the water in the cove at time t hours is modelled by the equation $d(t) = 4 + 3.5 \cos\frac{\pi}{6}t$.
Jenny is planning a day trip to the cove tomorrow, but the water needs to be at least 2 m deep for her to manoeuvre her
sailboat safely. How can Jenny determine the times when it will be safe for her to sail into Matthews Cove?

Solution

Draw a rough sketch of the depth function for at least
the next 24 h, assuming that $t = 0$ is the high tide at
midnight.

For the function $f(x) = a \cos kx + c$,
the amplitude is a, the period is $\frac{2\pi}{k}$,
and the horizontal axis is the line
$y = c$. For the function
$d(t) = 4 + 3.5 \cos\frac{\pi}{6}t$,
$a = 3.5$
$c = 4$

$$\text{period} = \frac{2\pi}{\frac{\pi}{6}} = 2\pi \times \frac{6}{\pi} = 12$$

From the graph, the water level will
be near 2 m around 4 a.m., 8 a.m.,
4 p.m., and 8 p.m.

It looks like the best time for her
to enter the cove is around 8 a.m.,
and she needs to leave the cove
around 4 p.m.

Determine the times when the
water level is above 2 m and the
times when the level equals 2 m.

$$4 + 3.5 \cos\frac{\pi}{6}t = 2$$

$$3.5 \cos\frac{\pi}{6}t = 2 - 4$$

$$\cos\frac{\pi}{6}t = \frac{-2}{3.5}$$

To get a better approximation of the
times, solve the equation for
$d(t) = 2$ to determine the related
acute angle.

Since $4 + 3.5 \cos\frac{\pi}{6}t = 2$ is a linear
trigonometric equation, isolate $\cos\frac{\pi}{6}t$.

Determine the related acute angle.

Using a calculator in radian mode, determine the inverse cosine of $\frac{2}{3.5}$ to find the related acute angle.

$\frac{\pi}{6}t \doteq 0.96$

The related acute angle is about 0.96.

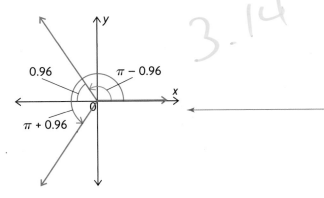

The cosine ratio is negative, so x is negative and r is positive. The terminal arms of $\frac{\pi}{6}t$ must lie in quadrants II and III.

To find the value of $\frac{\pi}{6}t$ in quadrant II, subtract the related acute angle from π.
$\pi - 0.96 = 2.18$

To find the value of $\frac{\pi}{6}t$ in quadrant III, add the related acute angle to π.
$\pi + 0.96 = 4.1$

The value of $\frac{\pi}{6}t$ is about 2.18 in quadrant II and about 4.1 in quadrant III.

To find the approximate times when the depth is 2 m, solve the following equations.

$\frac{\pi}{6}t = 2.18$ or $\frac{\pi}{6}t = 4.1$

Since Jenny is sailing tomorrow, the domain is $0 \le t \le 24$.

$t = \frac{6}{\pi}(2.18)$ $\qquad t = \frac{6}{\pi}(4.1)$

$t \doteq 4.16$ $\qquad\qquad t \doteq 7.83$

$t = 4.16 + 12$ $\qquad t = 7.83 + 12$

$t = 16.16$ $\qquad\qquad t = 19.83$

You can generate more solutions by adding 12, the period of the cosine function.

Jenny can safely sail into the cove when the water level is higher than 2 m. This occurs tomorrow, during the day, between 7:50 a.m. and 4:10 p.m.

Multiply the digits to the right of the decimal by 60 to convert from a fraction of an hour to minutes. Tomorrow, the water level will be 2 m at about 4:10 a.m., 7:50 a.m., 4:10 p.m., and 7:50 p.m.

The water level is higher than 2 m when the tide function graph is above the line $d = 2$.

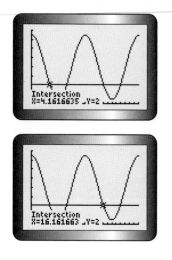

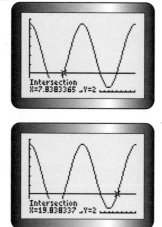

The values of t are very close to the calculated values. Therefore, the solution is reasonable.

To verify the solution, graph $d(t)$ and the horizontal line $d = 2$ for the 24 h following midnight. Then determine the points of intersection.

There is no need to convert the values of t into hours and minutes, since the values on the graph can be compared with the calculated solutions.

EXAMPLE 4

Selecting a strategy to solve a linear trigonometric equation that involves double angles

Solve $2 \sin \theta \cos \theta = \cos 2\theta$ for θ in the interval $0 \leq \theta \leq 2\pi$.

Solution

$$2 \sin \theta \cos \theta = \cos 2\theta$$
$$\sin 2\theta = \cos 2\theta$$

Use the sin 2θ double angle formula to express the equation using the same argument.

$$\frac{\sin 2\theta}{\cos 2\theta} = \frac{\cos 2\theta}{\cos 2\theta}$$
$$\tan 2\theta = 1$$

Divide both sides by cos 2θ to express the equation using a single trigonometric function.

Solve $\tan 2\theta = 1$.

The related acute angle of 2θ is $\tan^{-1}(1) = \frac{\pi}{4}$.

> Determine the related angle for 2θ by evaluating $\tan^{-1}(1)$.
>
> Use the 1, 1, $\sqrt{2}$ special triangle to determine the inverse tangent of 1.

The tangent ratio is positive in quadrants I and III.

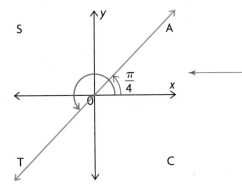

> Since the tangent ratio is positive, x and y must have the same sign. This means that the terminal arm of 2θ lies in quadrant I or quadrant III.

The value of 2θ in quadrant I is $\frac{\pi}{4}$.

The value of 2θ in quadrant III is $\frac{5\pi}{4}$.

To determine θ, solve the following equations.

$$2\theta = \frac{\pi}{4} \quad \text{or} \quad 2\theta = \frac{5\pi}{4}$$

$$\theta = \frac{\pi}{8} \qquad\qquad \theta = \frac{5\pi}{8}$$

> To find the value of 2θ in quadrant III, add the related angle to π.
>
> $$\pi + \frac{\pi}{4} = \frac{5\pi}{4}.$$

$$\theta = \frac{\pi}{8} + \frac{\pi}{2} = \frac{5\pi}{8} \text{ (already determined)}$$

$$\theta = \frac{5\pi}{8} + \frac{\pi}{2} = \frac{9\pi}{8}$$

$$\theta = \frac{9\pi}{8} + \frac{\pi}{2} = \frac{13\pi}{8}$$

> The period of $\tan 2\theta$ is $\frac{\pi}{2}$, so adding this to the two solutions will generate the other solutions in the given domain, $0 \le \theta \le 2\pi$.

Solutions for θ are $\frac{\pi}{8}, \frac{5\pi}{8}, \frac{9\pi}{8}$, or $\frac{13\pi}{8}$.

In Summary

Key Idea

- The same strategies can be used to solve linear trigonometric equations when the variable is measured in degrees or radians.

Need to Know

- Because of their periodic nature, trigonometric equations have an infinite number of solutions. When we use a trigonometric model, we usually want solutions within a specified interval.
- To solve a linear trigonometric equation, use special triangles, a calculator, a sketch of the graph, and/or the CAST rule.
- A scientific or graphing calculator provides very accurate estimates of the value for an inverse trigonometric function. The inverse trigonometric function of a positive ratio yields the related angle. Use the related acute angle and the period of the corresponding function to determine all the solutions in the given interval.
- You can use a graphing calculator to verify the solutions for a linear trigonometric equation by
  - graphing the appropriate functions on the graphing calculator and determining the points of intersection
  - graphing an equivalent single function and determining its zeros

CHECK Your Understanding

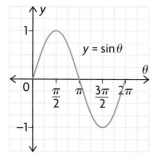

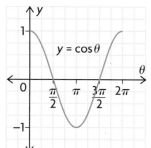

1. Use the graph of $y = \sin \theta$ to estimate the value(s) of θ in the interval $0 \le \theta \le 2\pi$.

   a) $\sin \theta = 1$ c) $\sin \theta = 0.5$ e) $\sin \theta = 0$

   b) $\sin \theta = -1$ d) $\sin \theta = -0.5$ f) $\sin \theta = \dfrac{\sqrt{3}}{2}$

2. Use the graph of $y = \cos \theta$ to estimate the value(s) of θ in the interval $0 \le \theta \le 2\pi$.

   a) $\cos \theta = 1$ c) $\cos \theta = 0.5$ e) $\cos \theta = 0$

   b) $\cos \theta = -1$ d) $\cos \theta = -0.5$ f) $\cos \theta = \dfrac{\sqrt{3}}{2}$

3. Solve $\sin x = \dfrac{\sqrt{3}}{2}$, where $0 \le x \le 2\pi$.

   a) How many solutions are possible?
   b) In which quadrants would you find the solutions?
   c) Determine the related acute angle for the equation.
   d) Determine all the solutions for the equation.

4. Solve $\cos x = -0.8667$, where $0° \leq x \leq 360°$.
   a) How many solutions are possible?
   b) In which quadrants would you find the solutions?
   c) Determine the related angle for the equation, to the nearest degree.
   d) Determine all the solutions for the equation, to the nearest degree.

5. Solve $\tan \theta = 2.7553$, where $0 \leq \theta \leq 2\pi$.
   a) How many solutions are possible?
   b) In which quadrants would you find the solutions?
   c) Determine the related angle for the equation, to the nearest hundredth.
   d) Determine all the solutions for the equation, to the nearest hundredth.

PRACTISING

6. Determine the solutions for each equation, where $0 \leq \theta \leq 2\pi$.
   K

   a) $\tan \theta = 1$
   c) $\cos \theta = \dfrac{\sqrt{3}}{2}$
   e) $\cos \theta = -\dfrac{1}{\sqrt{2}}$

   b) $\sin \theta = \dfrac{1}{\sqrt{2}}$
   d) $\sin \theta = -\dfrac{\sqrt{3}}{2}$
   f) $\tan \theta = \sqrt{3}$

7. Using a calculator, determine the solutions for each equation on the interval $0° \leq \theta \leq 360°$. Express your answers to one decimal place.
   a) $2 \sin \theta = -1$
   d) $-3 \sin \theta - 1 = 1$
   b) $3 \cos \theta = -2$
   e) $-5 \cos \theta + 3 = 2$
   c) $2 \tan \theta = 3$
   f) $8 - \tan \theta = 10$

8. Using a calculator, determine the solutions for each equation, to two decimal places, on the interval $0 \leq x \leq 2\pi$.
   a) $3 \sin x = \sin x + 1$
   c) $\cos x - 1 = -\cos x$
   b) $5 \cos x - \sqrt{3} = 3 \cos x$
   d) $5 \sin x + 1 = 3 \sin x$

9. Using a calculator, determine the solutions for each equation, to two decimal places, on the interval $0 \leq x \leq 2\pi$.
   a) $2 - 2 \cot x = 0$
   d) $2 \csc x + 17 = 15 + \csc x$
   b) $\csc x - 2 = 0$
   e) $2 \sec x + 1 = 6$
   c) $7 \sec x = 7$
   f) $8 + 4 \cot x = 10$

10. Using a calculator, determine the solutions for each equation, to two decimal places, on the interval $0 \leq x \leq 2\pi$.

    a) $\sin 2x = \dfrac{1}{\sqrt{2}}$
    c) $\sin 3x = -\dfrac{\sqrt{3}}{2}$
    e) $\cos 2x = -\dfrac{1}{2}$

    b) $\sin 4x = \dfrac{1}{2}$
    d) $\cos 4x = -\dfrac{1}{\sqrt{2}}$
    f) $\cos \dfrac{x}{2} = \dfrac{\sqrt{3}}{2}$

11. A city's daily high temperature, in degrees Celsius, can be modelled by
A the function $t(d) = -28 \cos \frac{2\pi}{365} d + 10$, where d is the day of the
year and $1 =$ January 1. On days when the temperature is
approximately 32 °C or above, the air conditioners at city hall are
turned on. During what days of the year are the air conditioners
running at city hall?

12. The height, in metres, of a nail in a water wheel above the surface of
the water, as a function of time, can be modelled by the function
$h(t) = -4 \sin \frac{\pi}{4}(t - 1) + 2.5$, where t is the time in seconds.
During what periods of time is the nail below the water in the first
24 s that the wheel is rotating?

13. Solve $\sin \left(x + \frac{\pi}{4} \right) = \sqrt{2} \cos x$ for $0 \leq x \leq 2\pi$.
T

14. Sketch the graph of $y = \sin 2\theta$ for $0 \leq \theta \leq 2\pi$. On the graph,
C clearly indicate all the solutions for the trigonometric equation
$\sin 2\theta = -\frac{1}{\sqrt{2}}$.

15. Explain why the value of the function $f(x) = 25 \sin \frac{\pi}{50}(x + 20) - 55$
at $x = 3$ is the same as the value of the function at $x = 7$.

16. Create a table like the one below to compare the algebraic and
graphical strategies for solving a trigonometric equation. In what ways
are the strategies similar, and in what ways are they different? Use
examples in your comparison.

	Method for Solving	
	Algebraic Strategy	**Graphical Strategy**
Similarities		
Differences		

Extending

17. Solve the trigonometric equation $2 \sin x \cos x + \sin x = 0$. (*Hint:* You
may find it helpful to factor the left side of the equation.)

18. Solve each equation for $0 \leq x \leq 2\pi$.
    a) $\sin 2x - 2 \cos^2 x = 0$ **b)** $3 \sin x + \cos 2x = 2$

7.6 Solving Quadratic Trigonometric Equations

YOU WILL NEED
- graphing calculator

GOAL

Solve quadratic trigonometric equations using graphs and algebra.

LEARN ABOUT the Math

A polarizing material is used in camera lens filters, LCD televisions, and sunglasses to reduce glare. In these examples, two polarizers are used to reduce the intensity of the light that enters your eyes.

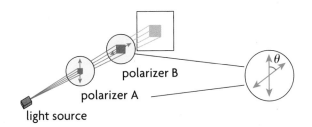

The amount of the reduction in light intensity, I, depends on θ, the acute angle formed between the axis of polarizer A and the axis of polarizer B. Malus's law states that $I = I_0 \cos^2 \theta$, where I_0 is the intensity of the initial beam of light and I is the intensity of the light emerging from the polarizing material.

? At what angle to the axis of polarizer A should polarizer B be placed to reduce the light intensity by 97%?

EXAMPLE 1   Solving a quadratic trigonometric equation using an algebraic strategy

Use Malus's law to determine the angle between polarizer A and polarizer B that will reduce the light intensity by 97%.

Solution

Malus's law is $I = I_0 \cos^2 \theta$.
Solve the equation $0.03\, I_0 = I_0 \cos^2 \theta$.

> If the light intensity is reduced by 97%, then it is $1 - 0.97$ or 0.03 of the initial intensity. Therefore, $I = 0.03 I_0$.

$$\frac{0.03I_0}{I_0} = \frac{I_0 \cos^2 \theta}{I_0}$$

Divide both sides by I_0 to isolate $\cos \theta$.

$$0.03 = \cos^2 \theta$$
$$\pm\sqrt{0.03} = \sqrt{\cos^2 \theta}$$
$$\pm 0.1732 = \cos \theta$$
$$\cos \theta = 0.1732 \text{ or } \cos \theta = -0.1732$$

Take the square root of both sides.

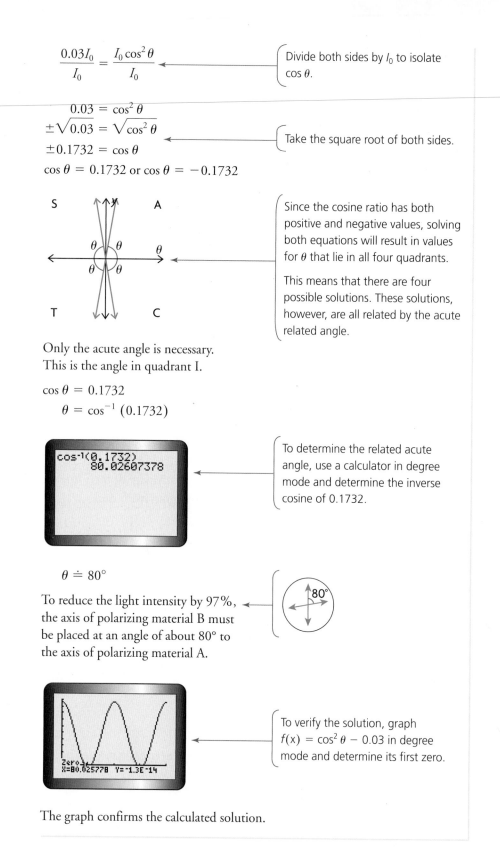

Since the cosine ratio has both positive and negative values, solving both equations will result in values for θ that lie in all four quadrants.

This means that there are four possible solutions. These solutions, however, are all related by the acute related angle.

Only the acute angle is necessary. This is the angle in quadrant I.

$$\cos \theta = 0.1732$$
$$\theta = \cos^{-1}(0.1732)$$

To determine the related acute angle, use a calculator in degree mode and determine the inverse cosine of 0.1732.

$$\theta \doteq 80°$$

To reduce the light intensity by 97%, the axis of polarizing material B must be placed at an angle of about 80° to the axis of polarizing material A.

To verify the solution, graph $f(x) = \cos^2 \theta - 0.03$ in degree mode and determine its first zero.

The graph confirms the calculated solution.

Reflecting

A. Compare the number of solutions between 0° and 360° for the equation $\cos^2 x = 0.03$ with the number of solutions for a linear trigonometric equation, such as $\cos x = 0.03$. Explain the difference, using both graphical and algebraic analyses.

B. Why were some of the solutions for the trigonometric equation $\cos^2 x = 0.03$ omitted in the context of Example 1?

C. How would the equation change if the intensity of light in an LCD television was reduced by 25%? What angle would be needed between the axis of polarizer A and the axis of polarizer B for this situation?

APPLY the Math

| EXAMPLE **2** | Selecting a factoring strategy to solve quadratic trigonometric equations |

Solve each equation for x in the interval $0 \le x \le 2\pi$. Verify your solutions by graphing.

a) $\sin^2 x - \sin x = 2$ **b)** $2 \sin^2 x - 3 \sin x + 1 = 0$

Solution

a)
$$\sin^2 x - \sin x = 2$$
$$\sin^2 x - \sin x - 2 = 0$$
$$(\sin x - 2)(\sin x + 1) = 0$$
$$\sin x = 2 \text{ or } \sin x = -1$$

Subtract 2, so you have 0 on the right side. This is a quadratic equation in sin x. Factor.

Solve both of these equations.

The equation $\sin x = 2$ has no solutions.

Since the graph of $y = \sin x$ has the range $\{y \in \mathbf{R} \mid -1 \le y \le 1\}$, the values of sin x cannot exceed 1.

The equation $\sin x = -1$ has only one solution in the interval $0 \le x \le 2\pi$.

Since $\sin x = \frac{y}{r} = \frac{-1}{1}$, the point $(0, -1)$ lies on the terminal arm of angle x.

The solution is $x = \dfrac{3\pi}{2}$.

Tech | **Support**

For help using the graphing
calculator to determine points
of intersection, see Technical
Appendix, T-12.

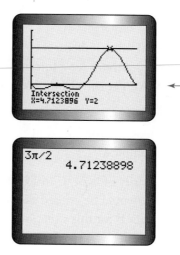

To verify the solution, graph
$f(x) = \sin^2 x - \sin x$ and $g(x) = 2$
in the required interval. Then
determine the points of intersection.

```
WINDOW
Xmin=0
Xmax=6.2831853...
Xscl=1.5707963...
Ymin=-1
Ymax=3
Yscl=.5
Xres=1
```

You can see that there is only one
solution in the interval $0 \le x \le 2\pi$.

Since $\dfrac{3\pi}{2} \doteq 4.712\,388\,98$, this verifies

the previous solution.

b) $\quad 2\sin^2 x - 3\sin x + 1 = 0$

$\quad (2\sin x - 1)(\sin x - 1) = 0$ ⟵ Factor the left side.

$\quad \sin x = \dfrac{1}{2}$ or $\sin x = 1$

$\sin x = \dfrac{1}{2}$ has two solutions in

$0 \le x \le 2\pi$. ⟵

Use the 1, 2, $\sqrt{3}$ special triangle
to determine that $\sin\dfrac{\pi}{6} = \dfrac{1}{2}$.

$\sin^{-1}\left(\dfrac{1}{2}\right) = \dfrac{\pi}{6}$ is the solution in

quadrant I and is also the related acute angle.

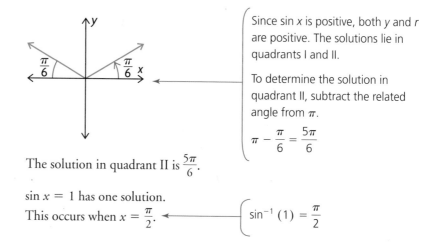

Since $\sin x$ is positive, both y and r
are positive. The solutions lie in
quadrants I and II.

To determine the solution in
quadrant II, subtract the related
angle from π.

$\pi - \dfrac{\pi}{6} = \dfrac{5\pi}{6}$

The solution in quadrant II is $\dfrac{5\pi}{6}$.

$\sin x = 1$ has one solution.

This occurs when $x = \dfrac{\pi}{2}$. ⟵

$\sin^{-1}(1) = \dfrac{\pi}{2}$

Graph $f(x) = 2 \sin^2 x - 3 \sin x + 1$, and determine the zeros to verify the solutions.

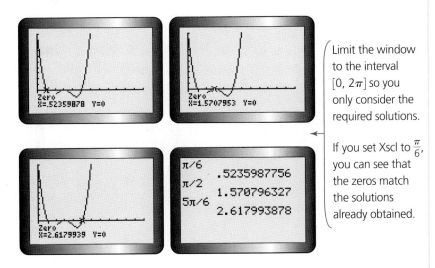

Limit the window to the interval $[0, 2\pi]$ so you only consider the required solutions.

If you set Xscl to $\frac{\pi}{6}$, you can see that the zeros match the solutions already obtained.

The solutions match those obtained algebraically.

EXAMPLE 3 | Selecting a strategy using identities to solve quadratic trigonometric equations

For each equation, use a trigonometric identity to create a quadratic equation. Then solve the equation for x in the interval $[0, 2\pi]$.

a) $2 \sec^2 x - 3 + \tan x = 0$ **b)** $3 \sin x + 3 \cos 2x = 2$

Solution

a)
$$2 \sec^2 x - 3 + \tan x = 0$$
$$2(1 + \tan^2 x) - 3 + \tan x = 0$$

Use the Pythagorean identity $1 + \tan^2 x = \sec^2 x$ to create an equation with only $\tan x$ and $\tan^2 x$ in it.

$$2 + 2 \tan^2 x - 3 + \tan x = 0$$
$$2 \tan^2 x + \tan x - 1 = 0$$

Expand and combine terms. Factor.

$$(2 \tan x - 1)(\tan x + 1) = 0$$
$$2 \tan x - 1 = 0 \text{ or } \tan x + 1 = 0$$

Set each factor equal to 0 to solve the equations.

$$\tan x = \frac{1}{2} \quad \text{or} \quad \tan x = -1$$

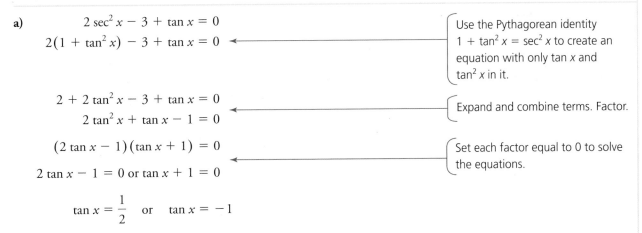

$\tan x = \frac{1}{2}$ has solutions in quadrants I and III.

$\tan^{-1}\left(\frac{1}{2}\right) \doteq 0.46$

This is the solution in quadrant I and is also the related angle.

The solution in quadrant III is
$\pi + 0.46 \doteq 3.60$

$\tan x = -1$ has solutions in quadrants II and IV.

$\tan^{-1}(1) = \frac{\pi}{4}$

The related angle is $\frac{\pi}{4}$.

The solution in quadrant II is $\pi - \frac{\pi}{4} = \frac{3\pi}{4}$.

The solution in quadrant IV is $2\pi - \frac{\pi}{4} = \frac{7\pi}{4}$.

> Use the CAST rule to help determine the solutions in the required interval, $0 \le x \le 2\pi$.

Solutions to the equation are $x \doteq 0.46, \frac{3\pi}{4}, 3.60,$ or $\frac{7\pi}{4}$ radians, rounded to two decimal places where not exact.

> Round answers that are not exact.

b)
$$3 \sin x + 3 \cos 2x = 2$$
$$3 \sin x + 3(1 - 2\sin^2 x) = 2$$
$$3 \sin x + 3 - 6 \sin^2 x = 2$$
$$0 = 2 - 3 \sin x - 3 + 6 \sin^2 x$$
$$0 = 6 \sin^2 x - 3 \sin x - 1$$

> To create a single trigonometric function (such as sin x) with the same argument, use the double angle formula $\cos 2x = 1 - 2\sin^2 x$. Rearrange the equation so that one side equals 0.

$$0 = 6a^2 - 3a - 1$$
$$a = \frac{-(-3) \pm \sqrt{(-3)^2 - 4(6)(-1)}}{2(6)}$$
$$a = \frac{3 \pm \sqrt{33}}{12}$$
$$a \doteq 0.73 \text{ or } a \doteq -0.23$$
$$\sin x = 0.73 \text{ or } \sin x = -0.23$$

> This is not factorable, so substitute $a = \sin x$ and use the quadratic formula.
> $$x = \frac{-b \pm \sqrt{b^2 - 4ac}}{2a},$$
> where $a = 6$, $b = -3$, and $c = -1$.

$\sin x = 0.73$ has solutions in quadrants I and II.

$\sin^{-1}(0.73) \doteq 0.82$

This is the solution in quadrant I and is also the related angle.

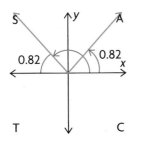

The other solution is $\pi - 0.82 = 2.32$.

$\sin x = -0.23$ has solutions in quadrants III and IV.

$\sin^{-1}(0.23) \doteq 0.23$. The related angle is 0.23.

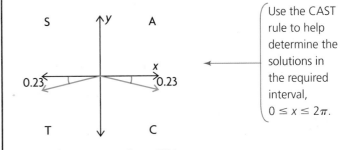

Use the CAST rule to help determine the solutions in the required interval, $0 \leq x \leq 2\pi$.

The solution in quadrant III is $\pi + 0.23 = 3.37$.

The solution in quadrant IV is $2\pi - 0.23 = 6.05$.

The solutions are approximately 0.82, 2.32, 3.37, or 6.05.

In Summary

Key Ideas

- In some applications, the formula contains a square of a trigonometric ratio. This leads to a quadratic trigonometric equation that can be solved algebraically or graphically.
- A quadratic trigonometric equation may have multiple solutions in the interval $0 \leq x \leq 2\pi$. Some of the solutions may be inadmissible, however, in the context of the problem.

Need to Know

- You can often factor a quadratic trigonometric equation and then solve the resulting two linear trigonometric equations. In cases where the equation cannot be factored, use the quadratic formula and then solve the resulting linear trigonometric equations.

  Note: The solutions to $ax^2 + bx + c = 0$ are determined by $x = \dfrac{-b \pm \sqrt{b^2 - 4ac}}{2a}$.

- You may need to use a Pythagorean identity, compound angle formula, or double angle formula to create a quadratic equation that contains only a single trigonometric function whose arguments all match.

CHECK *Your Understanding*

1. Factor each expression.
   a) $\sin^2 \theta - \sin \theta$
   b) $\cos^2 \theta - 2\cos \theta + 1$
   c) $3\sin^2 \theta - \sin \theta - 2$
   d) $4\cos^2 \theta - 1$
   e) $24\sin^2 x - 2\sin x - 2$
   f) $49\tan^2 x - 64$

2. Solve the first equation in each pair of equations for y and/or z. Then use the same strategy to solve the second equation for x in the interval $0 \le x \le 2\pi$.

a) $y^2 = \dfrac{1}{3}$, $\tan^2 x = \dfrac{1}{3}$

b) $y^2 + y = 0$, $\sin^2 x + \sin x = 0$

c) $y - 2yz = 0$, $\cos x - 2 \cos x \sin x = 0$

d) $yz = y$, $\tan x \sec x = \tan x$

3. a) Solve the equation $6y^2 - y - 1 = 0$.
   b) Solve $6 \cos^2 x - \cos x - 1 = 0$ for $0 \le x \le 2\pi$.

PRACTISING

4. Solve for θ, to the nearest degree, in the interval $0° \le \theta \le 360°$.

K

a) $\sin^2 \theta = 1$

b) $\cos^2 \theta = 1$

c) $\tan^2 \theta = 1$

d) $4 \cos^2 \theta = 1$

e) $3 \tan^2 \theta = 1$

f) $2 \sin^2 \theta = 1$

5. Solve each equation for x, where $0° \le x \le 360°$.

a) $\sin x \cos x = 0$

b) $\sin x (\cos x - 1) = 0$

c) $(\sin x + 1) \cos x = 0$

d) $\cos x (2 \sin x - \sqrt{3}) = 0$

e) $(\sqrt{2} \sin x - 1)(\sqrt{2} \sin x + 1) = 0$

f) $(\sin x - 1)(\cos x + 1) = 0$

6. Solve each equation for x, where $0 \le x \le 2\pi$.

a) $(2 \sin x - 1) \cos x = 0$

b) $(\sin x + 1)^2 = 0$

c) $(2 \cos x + \sqrt{3}) \sin x = 0$

d) $(2 \cos x - 1)(2 \sin x + \sqrt{3}) = 0$

e) $(\sqrt{2} \cos x - 1)(\sqrt{2} \cos x + 1) = 0$

f) $(\sin x + 1)(\cos x - 1) = 0$

7. Solve for θ to the nearest hundredth, where $0 \le \theta \le 2\pi$.

a) $2 \cos^2 \theta + \cos \theta - 1 = 0$

b) $2 \sin^2 \theta = 1 - \sin \theta$

c) $\cos^2 \theta = 2 + \cos \theta$

d) $2 \sin^2 \theta + 5 \sin \theta - 3 = 0$

e) $3 \tan^2 \theta - 2 \tan \theta = 1$

f) $12 \sin^2 \theta + \sin \theta - 6 = 0$

8. Solve each equation for x, where $0 \le x \le 2\pi$.

a) $\sec x \csc x - 2 \csc x = 0$

b) $3 \sec^2 x - 4 = 0$

c) $2 \sin x \sec x - 2\sqrt{3} \sin x = 0$

d) $2 \cot x + \sec^2 x = 0$

e) $\cot x \csc^2 x = 2 \cot x$

f) $3 \tan^3 x - \tan x = 0$

9. Solve each equation in the interval $0 \le x \le 2\pi$. Round to two decimal places, if necessary.
   a) $5 \cos 2x - \cos x + 3 = 0$
   c) $4 \cos 2x + 10 \sin x - 7 = 0$
   b) $10 \cos 2x - 8 \cos x + 1 = 0$
   d) $-2 \cos 2x = 2 \sin x$

10. Solve the equation $8 \sin^2 x - 8 \sin x + 1 = 0$ in the interval $0 \le x \le 2\pi$.

11. The quadratic trigonometric equation $\cot^2 x - b \cot x + c = 0$ has the solutions $\frac{\pi}{6}, \frac{\pi}{4}, \frac{7\pi}{6}$, and $\frac{5\pi}{4}$ in the interval $0 \le x \le 2\pi$. What are the values of b and c?

12. The graph of the quadratic trigonometric equation $\sin^2 x - c = 0$ is shown. What is the value of c?

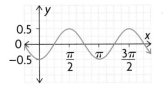

13. **A** Natasha is a marathon runner, and she likes to train on a 2π km stretch of rolling hills. The height, in kilometres, of the hills above sea level, relative to her home, can be modelled by the function $h(d) = 4 \cos^2 d - 1$, where d is the distance travelled in kilometres. At what intervals in the stretch of rolling hills is the height above sea level, relative to Natasha's home, less than zero?

14. **T** Solve the equation $6 \sin^2 x = 17 \cos x + 11$ for x in the interval $0 \le x \le 2\pi$.

15. a) Solve the equation $\sin^2 x - \sqrt{2} \cos x = \cos^2 x + \sqrt{2} \cos x + 2$ for x in the interval $0 \le x \le 2\pi$.
    b) Write a general solution for the equation in part a).

16. **C** Explain why it is possible to have different numbers of solutions for quadratic trigonometric equations. Give examples to illustrate your explanation.

Extending

17. Given that $f(x) = \dfrac{\tan x}{1 - \tan x} - \dfrac{\cot x}{1 - \cot x}$, determine all the values of a in the interval $0 \le a \le 2\pi$, such that $f(x) = \tan(x + a)$.

18. Solve the equation $2 \cos 3x + \cos 2x + 1 = 0$.

19. Solve $3 \tan^2 2x = 1, 0° \le x \le 360°$.

20. Solve $\sqrt{2} \sin \theta = \sqrt{3} - \cos \theta, 0 \le \theta \le 2\pi$.

FREQUENTLY ASKED Questions

Study Aid

- See Lesson 7.4, Examples 1 to 5.
- Try Chapter Review Questions 7, 8, and 9.

Q: **What is the difference between a trigonometric equation and a trigonometric identity, and how can you prove that a given equation is an identity?**

A: A trigonometric equation is true for one, several, or many values of the variable it contains. A trigonometric identity is an equation that involves trigonometric ratios and is true for *all* values of the variables for which the expressions on both sides are defined.

To prove that an equation is an identity, you can use algebraic manipulation on one or both sides of the equation until one side is identical to the other side. This often involves a variety of strategies, such as

- rewriting the expressions using known identities
- rewriting the expressions using compound angle formulas and double angle formulas
- using a common denominator or factoring where possible

To prove that an equation is *not* an identity, you can use a counterexample. If any value, when substituted, results in LS ≠ RS, then the equation is *not* an identity.

Study Aid

- See Lesson 7.5, Examples 1 to 4.
- Try Chapter Review Question 10.

Q: **How can you solve a linear trigonometric equation?**

A1: You can solve a linear trigonometric equation algebraically, using special triangles, a calculator, a sketch of the graph of the corresponding function, and/or the CAST rule.

For example, to solve $2(\cos 2x + 1) = 3$ for $0 \le x \le 2\pi$, first rearrange the equation to isolate $\cos 2x$.

$$2 \cos 2x + 2 = 3$$
$$2 \cos 2x = 1$$
$$\cos 2x = \frac{1}{2}$$

Evaluate $\cos^{-1}\left(\frac{1}{2}\right)$ to determine the related acute angle of $2x$.

Using the 1, 2, $\sqrt{3}$ special triangle, the related angle is $\frac{\pi}{3}$.

Cosine is positive in quadrants I and IV.

$2x = \dfrac{\pi}{3}$ in quadrant I, so $x = \dfrac{\pi}{6}$.

$2x = 2\pi - \dfrac{\pi}{3} = \dfrac{5\pi}{3}$ in quadrant IV, so $x = \dfrac{5\pi}{6}$.

$\dfrac{\pi}{6} + \pi = \dfrac{7\pi}{6}$

$\dfrac{5\pi}{6} + \pi = \dfrac{11\pi}{6}$

$x = \dfrac{\pi}{6}, \dfrac{5\pi}{6}, \dfrac{7\pi}{6}, \dfrac{11\pi}{6}$

Cos 2x has a period of π, so add π to these solutions to determine the other solutions in the given domain.

A2: You can solve a linear trigonometric equation, or verify the solutions, using a graphing calculator.

One way to solve the equation $2(\cos 2x + 1) = 3$ is to enter Y1 $= 2(\cos 2x + 1)$ and Y2 $= 3$ and determine the intersection points.

Another way to solve the equation is to enter Y1 $= 2(\cos 2x + 1) - 3$ and determine the zeros.

Q: What strategies can you use to solve a quadratic trigonometric equation?

A1: You can often factor a quadratic trigonometric equation, and then solve the resulting two linear trigonometric equations.

For example, to solve $2\tan^2 x - \tan x - 6 = 0$, factor the left side so that $(2\tan x + 3)(\tan x - 2) = 0$. Solve the two linear equations, $2\tan x + 3 = 0$ and $\tan x - 2 = 0$.

If it is not factorable, you can use the quadratic formula, then solve the resulting two linear equations.

A2: You may need to use a Pythagorean identity, compound angle formula, or double angle formula to create a quadratic equation that contains only a single trigonometric function whose arguments all match.

A3: You can use a graphing calculator to solve or verify the solutions. Graph the functions defined by the two sides of the equation and determine the intersection points. You can also create a single function of the form $f(x) = 0$, graph it, and determine its zeros.

Study *Aid*

- See Lesson 7.6, Examples 1, 2, and 3.
- Try Chapter Review Questions 11, 12, and 13.

PRACTICE Questions

Lesson 7.1

1. State a trigonometric ratio that is equivalent to each of the following trigonometric ratios.

   a) $\sin \dfrac{3\pi}{10}$

   b) $\cos \dfrac{6\pi}{7}$

   c) $-\sin \dfrac{13\pi}{7}$

   d) $-\cos \dfrac{8\pi}{7}$

2. Write an equation that is equivalent to

   $y = -5 \sin \left(x - \dfrac{\pi}{2} \right) - 8$, using the cosine function.

Lesson 7.2

3. Use a compound angle formula to determine a trigonometric expression that is equivalent to each of the following expressions.

   a) $\sin \left(x - \dfrac{4\pi}{3} \right)$

   b) $\cos \left(x + \dfrac{3\pi}{4} \right)$

   c) $\tan \left(x + \dfrac{\pi}{3} \right)$

   d) $\cos \left(x - \dfrac{5\pi}{4} \right)$

4. Evaluate each expression.

   a) $\dfrac{\tan \dfrac{\pi}{12} + \tan \dfrac{7\pi}{4}}{1 - \tan \dfrac{\pi}{12} \tan \dfrac{7\pi}{4}}$

   b) $\cos \dfrac{\pi}{9} \cos \dfrac{19\pi}{18} - \sin \dfrac{\pi}{9} \sin \dfrac{19\pi}{18}$

Lesson 7.3

5. Simplify each expression.

   a) $2 \sin \dfrac{\pi}{12} \cos \dfrac{\pi}{12}$

   b) $\cos^2 \dfrac{\pi}{12} - \sin^2 \dfrac{\pi}{12}$

   c) $1 - 2 \sin^2 \dfrac{3\pi}{8}$

   d) $\dfrac{2 \tan \dfrac{\pi}{6}}{1 - \tan^2 \dfrac{\pi}{6}}$

6. Determine the values of $\sin 2x$, $\cos 2x$, and $\tan 2x$, given

   a) $\sin x = \dfrac{3}{5}$, and x is acute

   b) $\cot x = -\dfrac{7}{24}$, and x is obtuse

   c) $\cos x = \dfrac{12}{13}$, and $\dfrac{3\pi}{2} \le x \le 2\pi$

Lesson 7.4

7. Determine whether each of the following is a trigonometric equation or a trigonometric identity.

   a) $\tan 2x = \dfrac{2 \sin x \cos x}{1 - 2 \sin^2 x}$

   b) $\sec^2 x - \tan^2 x = \cos x$

   c) $\csc^2 x - \cot^2 x = \sin^2 x + \cos^2 x$

   d) $\tan^2 x = 1$

8. Prove that $\dfrac{1 - \sin^2 x}{\cot^2 x} = 1 - \cos^2 x$ is a trigonometric identity.

9. Prove that $\dfrac{2 \sec^2 x - 2 \tan^2 x}{\csc x} = \sin 2x \sec x$ is a trigonometric identity.

Lesson 7.5

10. Solve each trigonometric equation in the interval $0 \le x \le 2\pi$.

   a) $\dfrac{2}{\sin x} + 10 = 6$

   b) $-\dfrac{5 \cot x}{2} + \dfrac{7}{3} = -\dfrac{1}{6}$

   c) $3 + 10 \sec x - 1 = -18$

Lesson 7.6

11. a) Solve the equation $y^2 - 4 = 0$.

    b) Solve $\csc^2 x - 4 = 0$ in the interval $0 \le x \le 2\pi$.

12. Solve each equation for x in the interval $0 \le x \le 2\pi$.

    a) $2 \sin^2 x - \sin x - 1 = 0$

    b) $\tan^2 x \sin x - \dfrac{\sin x}{3} = 0$

    c) $\cos^2 x + \left(\dfrac{1 - \sqrt{2}}{2} \right) \cos x - \dfrac{\sqrt{2}}{4} = 0$

    d) $25 \tan^2 x - 70 \tan x = -49$

13. Solve the equation $\dfrac{1}{1 + \tan^2 x} = -\cos x$ for x in the interval $0 \le x \le 2\pi$.

1. Prove that $\dfrac{1 - 2 \sin^2 x}{\cos x + \sin x} + 2 \sin \dfrac{x}{2} \cos \dfrac{x}{2} = \cos x.$

2. Solve the following equation: $\cos 2x + 2 \sin^2 x - 3 = -2$, where $0 \le x \le 2\pi$.

3. Determine the solution(s) for each of the following equations, where $0 \le x \le 2\pi$.

   a) $\cos x = \dfrac{\sqrt{3}}{2}$ b) $\tan x = -\sqrt{3}$ c) $\sin x = -\dfrac{\sqrt{2}}{2}$

4. The quadratic trigonometric equation $a \cos^2 x + b \cos x - 1 = 0$ has the solutions $\dfrac{\pi}{3}$, π, and $\dfrac{5\pi}{3}$ in the interval $0 \le x \le 2\pi$. What are the values of a and b?

5. The depth of the ocean at a swim buoy can be modelled by the function $d(t) = 4 + 2 \sin\left(\dfrac{\pi}{6} t\right)$, where d is the depth of water in metres and t is the time in hours, if $0 \le t \le 24$. Consider a day when $t = 0$ represents midnight. Determine when the depth of water is 3 m.

6. Nina needs to find the cosine of $\dfrac{11\pi}{4}$. If she knows the sine and cosine of π, as well as the sine and cosine of $\dfrac{7\pi}{4}$, how can she find the cosine of $\dfrac{11\pi}{4}$? What is her answer?

7. Solve $3 \sin x + 2 = 1.5$, where $0 \le x \le 2\pi$.

8. The tangent of the acute angle α is 0.75, and the tangent of the acute angle β is 2.4. Without using a calculator, determine the value of $\sin(\alpha - \beta)$ and $\cos(\alpha + \beta)$.

9. The angle x lies in the interval $\dfrac{\pi}{2} \le x \le \pi$, and $\sin^2 x = \dfrac{4}{9}$. Determine the value of each of the following. Round your answers to four decimal places.

   a) $\sin 2x$ c) $\cos \dfrac{x}{2}$

   b) $\cos 2x$ d) $\sin 3x$

10. Use the graph of $f(x) = \cos x$ to estimate the solution of each of the following trigonometric equations in the interval $-2\pi \le x \le 2\pi$.
    a) $2 - 14 \cos x = -5$
    b) $9 - 22 \cos x - 1 = 19$
    c) $2 + 7.5 \cos x = -5.5$

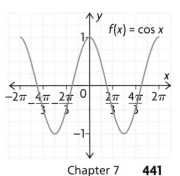

Time to Bloom

The flowering of many commercially grown plants in greenhouses depends on the duration of natural darkness and daylight. Short-day plants, such as chrysanthemums, need 12 or more hours of darkness before they will start to bloom. Long-day plants, such as carnations, need more than 12 h of daylight.

The number of hours of daylight, $h(t)$, varies with the latitude and the time of the year, t, where t is the day of the year.

Month	Day of the Year	Hours of Daylight on the Middle Day of Each Month		
		Ottawa, ON (45° N Lat.)	Regina, SK (50° N Lat.)	Whitehorse, YT (60° N Lat.)
January	15	8.9	8.5	6.6
February	45	10.1	10.1	9.2
March	75	11.6	11.8	11.7
April	106	13.3	13.7	14.5
May	136	14.7	17.1	22.2
June	167	15.4	16.4	18.8
July	197	15.1	15.6	17.5
August	228	13.8	14.6	15.8
September	259	12.2	12.7	13.8
October	289	10.7	10.8	10.2
November	320	9.3	9.1	7.6
December	350	8.6	8.1	5.9

? When will carnations begin to bloom in greenhouses in these parts of Canada?

A. Use the data in the table to estimate when carnations will start to bloom in Ottawa, Regina, and Whitehorse.

B. Plot the data for Regina on a scatter plot, and draw a curve of best fit. Use your graph to determine the amplitude, period, and equation of the horizontal axis.

C. Use your estimate in part A to create an algebraic model for the Regina data. Use sinusoidal regression on a graphing calculator to check your results.

D. Repeat parts B and C for the Ottawa and Whitehorse data.

E. Use the algebraic models you found to calculate
   a) when the hours of daylight first exceed 12 h
   b) the interval in the year when there are more than 12 h of daylight

F. Show your results for part E on the graphs you created for the three cities.

G. Write a report to compare the blooming season for carnations in the three cities. Include the graphs you created in your report.

> ## Task | *Checklist*
> ✔ Did you show all your steps?
>
> ✔ Did you draw and label your graphs accurately?
>
> ✔ Did you support your choice of model?
>
> ✔ Did you explain your thinking clearly?

Chapter

8

Exponential and Logarithmic Functions

▶ **GOALS**

You will be able to

- Relate logarithmic functions to exponential functions
- Describe the characteristics of logarithmic functions and their graphs
- Evaluate logarithms and simplify logarithmic expressions
- Solve exponential and logarithmic equations
- Use exponential and logarithmic functions to solve problems involving exponential growth and decay, and applications of logarithmic scales

 The Richter scale is used to measure earthquake intensity. What type of function do you think the Richter scale might be related to?

\multicolumn{3}{c	}{**Understanding the Richter Scale**}
Richter Magnitude	**Equivalent Kilograms of TNT**	**Extra Information**
0–1	0.6–20 kg of dynamite	We cannot feel these.
2	600 kg of dynamite	Smallest quake people can normally feel.
3	20 000 kg of dynamite	People near the epicentre feel this quake.
4	60 000 kg of dynamite	This will cause damage around the epicentre. It is the same as a small fission bomb.
5	20 000 000 kg of dynamite	Damage done to weak buildings in the area of the epicentre.
6	60 000 000 kg of dynamite	Can cause great damage around the epicentre.
7	20 billion kg of dynamite	Creates enough energy to heat New York City for one year. Can be detected all over the world. Causes serious damage.
8	60 billion kg of dynamite	Causes death and major destruction. Destroyed San Francisco in 1906.
9	20 trillion kg of dynamite	Rare, but would cause unbelievable damage!

SKILLS AND CONCEPTS *You Need*

Study *Aid*

• For help, see the Review of Essential Skills found at the Nelson Advanced Functions website.

Question	Appendix
1, 2, 3	R-1
4, 8	R-7, R-8
6, 7	R-7

1. Rewrite each expression in an equivalent form, and then evaluate.
   a) 5^{-2}
   b) 11^0
   c) $36^{\frac{1}{2}}$
   d) $125^{\frac{1}{3}}$
   e) $-121^{\frac{1}{2}}$
   f) $\left(\dfrac{8}{27}\right)^{-\frac{2}{3}}$

2. Simplify each expression, and then evaluate.
   a) $(3^5)(3^2)$
   b) $(-2)^{12}(-2)^{-10}$
   c) $\dfrac{10^9}{10^6}$
   d) $\dfrac{(7^6)(7^{-3})}{7^{-1}}$
   e) $(8^{\frac{1}{3}})^2$
   f) $\dfrac{(4^{\frac{3}{4}})(4^{\frac{1}{4}})}{4^{\frac{1}{2}}}$

3. Simplify.
   a) $(2m)^3$
   b) $(a^4b^5)^{-2}$
   c) $(16x^6)^{\frac{1}{2}}$
   d) $\dfrac{x^5y^2}{x^2y}$
   e) $(-d^4)\left(\dfrac{c}{d}\right)^2$
   f) $\left((x^3)^{-\frac{1}{3}}\right)^{-1}$

4. Sketch a graph of each of the following exponential functions. State the domain, range, y-intercept, and the equation of the horizontal asymptote of each function.
   a) $y = 2^x$
   b) $y = \left(\dfrac{1}{2}\right)^x$
   c) $y = 3^{2x} - 2$

5. a) Determine the equation of the inverse of each of the following functions.
   i) $f(x) = 3x - 6$
   ii) $f(x) = x^2 - 5$
   iii) $f(x) = 6x^3$
   iv) $f(x) = (x - 4)^2 + 3$
   b) Which of the inverses you found in part a) are also functions?

6. A bacteria culture doubles every 4 h. If there are 100 bacteria in the culture initially, determine how many bacteria there will be after
   a) 12 h
   b) 1 day
   c) 3.5 days
   d) 1 week

7. The population of a town is declining at a rate of 1.2% per year. If the population was 15 000 in 2005, what will the population be in 2020?

8. Use a table like this to compare the graphs of $y = 3(2^x)$ and $y = 3\left(\dfrac{1}{2}\right)^x$.

Similarities	Differences

APPLYING *What You Know*

Underwater Light Intensity

For every metre below the surface of the ocean, the light intensity at the surface is reduced by 2.4%. A particular underwater camera requires at least 40% of the light at the surface of the ocean to operate.

? What is the maximum depth at which the camera can successfully take photographs underwater?

A. Explain why the function $P = 100(0.976)^m$ gives the percent of light remaining at a depth of m metres below the surface of the ocean.

B. Graph P as a function of m.

C. Determine a reasonable domain and range for this function. What restrictions might have to be placed on the domain and range?

D. Determine the light intensity at a depth of 12 m.

E. At what depth is the light intensity reduced to 40% of the intensity at the surface of the ocean? Explain how you determined your answer.

F. The water in the western end of Lake Ontario is murky, and the light intensity is reduced by 3.6%/m. Write the function that represents the percent, P, of light remaining at a depth of m metres below the surface.

G. Graph the function you created in part F.

H. Compare this graph with your graph in part B. How are the graphs alike? How are they different?

I. What is the maximum depth at which the camera could take photographs in the murky water of Lake Ontario?

Exploring the Logarithmic Function

YOU WILL NEED

• graph paper

GOAL

Investigate the inverse of the exponential function.

EXPLORE the Math

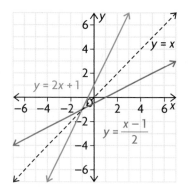

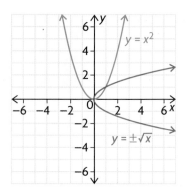

The inverse of a linear function, such as $f(x) = 2x + 1$, is linear.

The inverse of a quadratic function, such as $g(x) = x^2$, has a shape that is congruent to the shape of the original function.

? What does the graph of the inverse of an exponential function like $y = 2^x$ look like, and what are its characteristics?

A. Consider the function $h(x) = 2^x$. Create a table of values, using integer values for the domain $-3 \leq x \leq 4$.

B. On graph paper, graph the exponential function in part A. State the domain and range of this function.

C. Interchange x and y in the equation for h to obtain the equation of the inverse relation. Create a table of values for this inverse relation. How does each y-value of this relation relate to the base, 2, and its corresponding x-value?

D. On the same axes that you used to graph the exponential function in part B, graph the inverse. Is the inverse a function? Explain.

E. Graph the line $y = x$ on the same axes. How do the graphs of the exponential function $h(x) = 2^x$ and the graph of the logarithmic function $h^{-1}(x) = \log_2 x$ relate to this line?

F. Repeat parts A to E, first using $j(x) = 10^x$ and then using $k(x) = \left(\frac{1}{2}\right)^x$.

G. State the domain and range of the inverses of $h(x), j(x),$ and $k(x)$.

H. How is the range of each logarithmic function related to the domain of its corresponding exponential function? How is the domain of the logarithmic function related to the range of the corresponding exponential function?

I. How would you describe these logarithmic functions? Create a summary table that includes information about intercepts, asymptotes, and shapes of the graphs.

logarithmic function

The inverse of the exponential function $y = a^x$ is the function with exponential equation $x = a^y$. We write y as a function of x using the logarithmic form of this equation, $y = \log_a x$. As with the exponential function, $a > 0$ and $a \neq 1$.

Reflecting

J. What point is common to the graphs of all three logarithmic functions?

K. How are the graphs of an exponential function and the logarithmic function with the same base related?

L. How are the graphs of $h(x) = 2^x$ and $k(x) = \left(\frac{1}{2}\right)^x$ related? How are the graphs of $h^{-1}(x) = \log_2 x$ and $k^{-1}(x) = \log_{\frac{1}{2}} x$ related?

M. How does the value of a in $y = a^x$ influence the graph of $y = \log_a x$? How might you have predicted this?

N. The graph of $h^{-1}(x) = \log_2 x$ includes the point $(8,3)$. Therefore, $3 = \log_2 8$. What is the value of $\log_2 16$ What meaning does $\log_2 x$ have? More generally, what meaning does the expression $\log_a x$ have?

In Summary

Key Ideas

- The inverse of the exponential function $y = a^x$ is also a function. It can be written as $x = a^y$. (This is the exponential form of the inverse.) An equivalent form of $x = a^y$ is $y = \log_a x$. (This is the logarithmic form of the inverse and is read as "the **logarithm** of x to the base a.") The function $y = \log_a x$ is called the logarithmic function.
- Since $x = a^y$ and $y = \log_a x$ are equivalent, a logarithm is an exponent. The expression $\log_a x$ means "the exponent that must be applied to base a to get the value of x." For example, $\log_2 8 = 3$ since $2^3 = 8$.

Need to Know

- The general shape of the graph of the logarithmic function depends on the value of the base.

When $a > 1$, the exponential function is an increasing function, and the logarithmic function is also an increasing function.

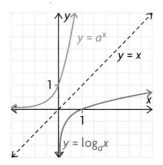

When $0 < a < 1$, the exponential function is a decreasing function and the logarithmic function is also a decreasing function.

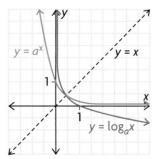

- The y-axis is the vertical asymptote for the logarithmic function. The x-axis is the horizontal asymptote for the exponential function.
- The x-intercept of the logarithmic function is 1, while the y-intercept of the exponential function is 1.
- The domain of the logarithmic function is $\{x \in \mathbf{R} \mid x > 0\}$, since the range of the exponential function is $\{y \in \mathbf{R} \mid y > 0\}$.
- The range of the logarithmic function is $\{y \in \mathbf{R}\}$, since the domain of the exponential function is $\{x \in \mathbf{R}\}$.

FURTHER *Your Understanding*

1. Sketch a graph of the inverse of each exponential function.

   a) $f(x) = 4^x$

   c) $f(x) = \left(\dfrac{1}{3}\right)^x$

   b) $f(x) = 8^x$

   d) $f(x) = \left(\dfrac{1}{5}\right)^x$

2. Write the equation of each inverse function in question 1 in
   i) exponential form
   ii) logarithmic form

3. Compare the key features of the graphs in question 1.

4. Explain how you can use the graph of $y = \log_2 x$ (at right) to help you determine the solution to $2^y = 8$.

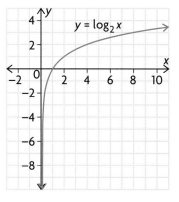

5. Write the equation of the inverse of each exponential function in exponential form.

   a) $y = 3^x$

   c) $y = \left(\dfrac{1}{4}\right)^x$

   b) $y = 10^x$

   d) $y = m^x$

6. Write the equation of the inverse of each exponential function in question 5 in logarithmic form.

7. Write the equation of each of the following logarithmic functions in exponential form.
   a) $y = \log_5 x$
   b) $y = \log_{10} x$
   c) $y = \log_3 x$
   d) $y = \log_{\frac{1}{4}} x$

8. Write the equation of the inverse of each logarithmic function in question 7 in exponential form.

9. Evaluate each of the following:

   a) $\log_2 4$

   c) $\log_4 64$

   e) $\log_2\left(\dfrac{1}{2}\right)$

   b) $\log_3 27$

   d) $\log_5 1$

   f) $\log_3 \sqrt{3}$

10. Why can $\log_3(-9)$ not be evaluated?

11. For each of the following logarithmic functions, write the coordinates of the five points that have y-values of $-2, -1, 0, 1, 2$.
    a) $y = \log_2 x$
    b) $y = \log_{10} x$

8.2 Transformations of Logarithmic Functions

YOU WILL NEED

- graphing calculator

GOAL

Determine the effects of varying the parameters of the graph of $y = a \log_{10}(k(x - d)) + c$.

INVESTIGATE the Math

The function $f(x) = \log_{10}x$ is an example of a logarithmic function. It is the inverse of the exponential function $f(x) = 10^x$.

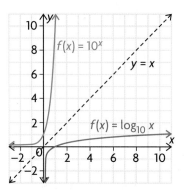

? How does varying the parameters of a function in the form $g(x) = a \log_{10}(k(x - d)) + c$ affect the graph of the parent function, $f(x) = \log_{10}x$?

A. The log button on a graphing calculator represents $\log_{10}x$. Graph $y = \log_{10}x$ on a graphing calculator. Use the window setting shown.

B. Consider the following functions:
- $y = \log_{10}(x - 2)$
- $y = \log_{10}(x - 4)$
- $y = \log_{10}(x + 4)$

Make a conjecture about the type of transformation that must be applied to the graph of $y = \log_{10}x$ to graph each of these functions.

C. Graph the functions in part B along with the graph of $y = \log_{10}x$. Compare each of these graphs with the graph of $y = \log_{10}x$. Was your conjecture correct? Summarize the transformations that are applied to $y = \log_{10}x$ to obtain $y = \log_{10}(x - d)$.

Communication | Tip

If there is no value of a in a logarithmic function ($\log_a x$), the base is understood to be 10; that is, $\log x = \log_{10}x$. Logarithms with base 10 are called common logarithms.

D. Examine the following functions:
- $y = \log_{10}x + 3$
- $y = \log_{10}x - 4$

Make a conjecture about the type of transformation that must be applied to the graph of $y = \log_{10}x$ to graph each of these functions.

E. Delete all but the first function in the equation editor, and enter the functions in part D. Graph the functions. Compare each of these graphs with the graph of $y = \log_{10}x$. Was your conjecture correct? Summarize the transformations that are applied to $y = \log_{10}x$ to obtain $y = \log_{10}x + c$.

F. State the transformations that you would need to apply to $y = \log_{10}x$ to graph the function $y = \log_{10}(x - d) + c$.

G. Make a conjecture about the transformations that you would need to apply to $y = \log_{10}x$ to graph each of the following functions:
- $y = 2\log_{10}x$
- $y = \dfrac{1}{3}\log_{10}x$
- $y = -2\log_{10}x$

H. Delete all but the first function in the equation editor, and enter the functions in part G. Graph the functions. Compare each of these graphs with the graph of $y = \log_{10}x$. Was your conjecture correct? Summarize the transformations that are applied to $y = \log_{10}x$ to obtain $y = a\log_{10}x$.

I. Make a conjecture about the transformations that you would need to apply to $y = \log_{10}x$ to graph each of the following functions:
- $y = \log_{10}(2x)$
- $y = \log_{10}\left(\dfrac{1}{5}x\right)$
- $y = \log_{10}(-2x)$

J. Delete all but the first function in the equation editor, and enter the functions in part I. Graph the functions. Compare each of these graphs with the graph of $y = \log_{10}x$. Was your conjecture correct? Summarize the transformations that are applied to $y = \log_{10}x$ to obtain $y = \log_{10}(kx)$.

K. What transformations must be applied to $y = \log_{10}x$ to graph $y = a\log_{10}(kx)$?

Reflecting

L. Describe the domain and range of $y = \log_{10}(x - d)$, $y = \log_{10}x + c$, $y = \log_{10}(kx)$, and $y = a \log_{10}x$.

M. How do the algebraic representations of the functions resulting from transformations of logarithmic functions compare with the algebraic representations of the functions resulting from transformations of polynomial, trigonometric, and exponential functions?

N. Identify the transformations that are related to the parameters a, k, d, and c in the general logarithmic function
$$y = a\,(\log_{10}k(x - d)) + c.$$

APPLY the Math

EXAMPLE **1**	Connecting transformations of a logarithmic function to key points of $y = \log_{10}x$

Use transformations to sketch the function $y = -2\log_{10}(x - 4)$. State the domain and range.

Solution

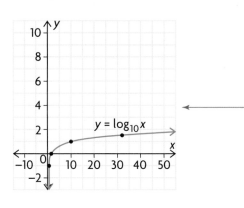

$y = \log_{10}x$

Sketch $y = \log_{10}x$.
Choose some points on the graph, such as $\left(\frac{1}{10}, -1\right)$, $(1, 0)$, $(10, 1)$, and the estimated point $(32, 1.5)$. Use these points as key points to help graph the transformed function. The vertical asymptote is the y-axis, $x = 0$. Apply transformations in the same order used for all functions: stretches/compressions/reflections first, followed by translations.

$$(x, y) \rightarrow (x, -2y)$$

Parent Function $y = \log_{10}x$	Stretched/Reflected Function $y = -2\log_{10}x$
$\left(\frac{1}{10}, -1\right)$	$\left(\frac{1}{10}, -2(-1)\right) = \left(\frac{1}{10}, 2\right)$
$(1, 0)$	$(1, -2(0)) = (1, 0)$
$(10, 1)$	$(10, -2(1)) = (10, -2)$
$(32, 1.5)$	$(32, -2(1.5)) = (32, -3)$

The parent function is changed by multiplying all the y-coordinates by -2, resulting in a vertical stretch of factor 2 and a reflection in the x-axis.

$$(x, -2y) \rightarrow (x + 4, -2y)$$

Stretched/Reflected Function $y = -2 \log_{10} x$	Final Transformed Function $y = -2 \log_{10}(x - 4)$
$\left(\dfrac{1}{10}, 2\right)$	$\left(\dfrac{1}{10} + 4, 2\right) = \left(4\dfrac{1}{10}, 2\right)$
$(1, 0)$	$(1 + 4, 0) = (5, 0)$
$(10, -2)$	$(10 + 4, -2) = (14, -2)$
$(32, -3)$	$(32 + 4, -3) = (36, -3)$

Adding 4 to the x-coordinate of each of the transformed points results in a horizontal translation 4 units to the right.

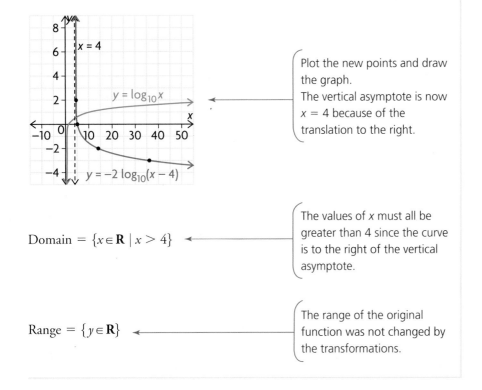

Plot the new points and draw the graph.
The vertical asymptote is now $x = 4$ because of the translation to the right.

$$\text{Domain} = \{x \in \mathbf{R} \mid x > 4\}$$

The values of x must all be greater than 4 since the curve is to the right of the vertical asymptote.

$$\text{Range} = \{y \in \mathbf{R}\}$$

The range of the original function was not changed by the transformations.

EXAMPLE 2

Connecting a geometric description of a function to an algebraic representation

The logarithmic function $y = \log_{10} x$ has been vertically compressed by a factor of $\frac{2}{3}$, horizontally stretched by a factor of 4, and then reflected in the y-axis. It has also been horizontally translated so that the vertical asymptote is $x = -2$ and then vertically translated 3 units down. Write an equation of the transformed function, and state its domain and range.

Solution

$$y = a \log_{10}(k(x - d)) + c$$

Write the general form of the logarithmic equation.

Since the function has been vertically compressed by a factor of $\frac{2}{3}$, $a = \frac{2}{3}$.

Since the function has been horizontally stretched by a factor of 4, $\frac{1}{k} = 4$, so $k = \frac{1}{4}$.

$$y = \frac{2}{3} \log_{10}\left(-\frac{1}{4}(x + 2)\right) - 3$$

The function has been reflected in the y-axis, so k is negative.

The vertical asymptote of the parent function is $x = 0$.

Since the asymptote of the transformed function is $x = -2$, the parent function has been horizontally translated 2 units left, so $d = -2$.

The function has been vertically translated 3 units down, so $c = -3$.

$$\text{Domain} = \{x \in \mathbf{R} \mid x < -2\}$$

The curve is to the left of the vertical asymptote, so the domain is $x < -2$.

$$\text{Range} = \{y \in \mathbf{R}\}$$

The range is the same as the range of the parent function.

In Summary

Key Ideas

- A logarithmic function of the form $f(x) = a \log_{10}(k(x - d)) + c$ can be graphed by applying the appropriate transformations to the parent function, $f(x) = \log_{10}x$.
- To graph a transformed logarithmic function, apply the stretches/compressions/reflections given by parameters a and k first. Then apply the vertical and horizontal translation given by the parameters c and d.

Need to Know

- Consider a logarithmic function of the form $f(x) = a \log_{10}(k(x - d)) + c$.

Transformations of the Parent Function
$\|a\|$ gives the vertical stretch/compression factor. If $a < 0$, there is also a reflection in the x-axis.
$\left\|\frac{1}{k}\right\|$ gives the horizontal stretch/compression factor. If $k < 0$, there is also a reflection in the y-axis.
d gives the horizontal translation.
c gives the vertical translation.

- The vertical asymptote changes when a horizontal translation is applied. The domain of a transformed logarithmic function depends on where the vertical asymptote is located and whether the function is to the left or the right of the vertical asymptote. If the function is to the left of the asymptote $x = d$, the domain is $x < d$. If it is to the right of the asymptote, the domain is $x > d$.
- The range of a transformed logarithmic function is always $\{y \in \mathbf{R}\}$.

CHECK Your Understanding

1. Each of the following functions is a transformation of $f(x) = \log_{10}x$. Describe the transformation that must be applied to $f(x)$ to graph $g(x)$.
   a) $g(x) = 3 \log_{10}x$
   b) $g(x) = \log_{10}(2x)$
   c) $g(x) = \log_{10}x - 5$
   d) $g(x) = \log_{10}(x + 4)$

2. a) State the coordinates of the images of the points $\left(\frac{1}{10}, -1\right)$, $(1, 0)$, and $(10, 1)$ for each of the functions in question 1.
   b) State the domain and range of each transformed function, $g(x)$, in question 1.

3. Given the parent function $f(x) = \log_{10}x$, state the equation of the function that results from each of the following pairs of transformations:
   a) vertical stretch by a factor of 5, vertical translation 3 units up
   b) reflection in the x-axis, horizontal compression by a factor of $\frac{1}{3}$
   c) horizontal translation 4 units left, vertical translation 3 units down
   d) reflection in the x-axis, horizontal translation 4 units right

PRACTISING

4. Let $f(x) = \log_{10}x$. For each function $g(x)$

K **a)** state the transformations that must be applied to f to produce the graph of g.

b) State the coordinates of the points on g that are images of the points $(1, 0)$ and $(10, 1)$ on the graph of f.

c) State the equation of the asymptote.

d) State the domain and range.

i) $g(x) = -4 \log_{10}x + 5$

iv) $g(x) = 2 \log_{10}[-2(x + 2)]$

ii) $g(x) = \dfrac{1}{2} \log_{10}(x - 6) + 3$

v) $g(x) = \log_{10}(2x + 4)$

iii) $g(x) = \log_{10}(3x) - 4$

vi) $g(x) = \log_{10}(-x - 2)$

5. Sketch the graph of each function using transformations. State the domain and range.

a) $f(x) = 3 \log_{10}x + 3$

d) $j(x) = \log_{10}0.5x - 1$

b) $g(x) = -\log_{10}(x - 6)$

e) $k(x) = 4 \log_{10}\left(\dfrac{1}{6}x\right) - 2$

c) $h(x) = \log_{10}2x$

f) $r(x) = \log_{10}(-2x - 4)$

6. Compare the functions $f(x) = 10^{\left(\frac{x}{3}\right)} + 1$ and $g(x) = 3 \log_{10}(x - 1)$.

7. **a)** Describe how the graphs of $f(x) = \log_3x$, $g(x) = \log_3(x + 4)$, and $h(x) = \log_3x + 4$ are similar yet different, without drawing the graphs.

b) Describe how the graphs of $f(x) = \log_3x$, $m(x) = 4 \log_3x$, and $n(x) = \log_34x$ are similar yet different, without drawing the graphs.

8. The function $f(x) = \log_{10}x$ has the point $(10, 1)$ on its graph.

A If $f(x)$ is vertically stretched by a factor of 3, reflected in the x-axis, horizontally stretched by a factor of 2, horizontally translated 5 units to the right, and vertically translated 2 units up, determine

a) the equation of the transformed function

b) the coordinates of the image point transformed from $(10, 1)$

c) the domain and range of the transformed function

9. State the transformations that are needed to turn $y = 4 \log_{10}(x - 4)$

T into $y = -2 \log_{10}(x + 1)$.

10. Describe three characteristics of the function $y = \log_{10}x$ that remain

C unchanged under the following transformations: a vertical stretch by a factor of 4 and a horizontal compression by a factor of 2.

Extending

11. Sketch the graph of $f(x) = \dfrac{-2}{\log_2(x + 2)}$.

8.3 Evaluating Logarithms

GOAL

Evaluate logarithmic expressions, and approximate the logarithm of a number to any base.

LEARN ABOUT *the Math*

Jackson knows that a rumour spreads very quickly. He tells three people a rumour. By the end of the next hour, each of these people has told three more people. Each person who hears the rumour tells three more people in the next hour. Jackson has written an algebraic model, $N(t) = 3^{t+1}$, to represent the number of people who hear the rumour within a particular hour, where $N(t)$ is the number of people told during hour t and $t = 1$ corresponds to the hour during which the first three people heard the rumour and started telling others.

? In which hour will an additional 2187 people hear the rumour?

EXAMPLE 1   Selecting a strategy to solve a problem

Determine the hour in which an additional 2187 people will hear the rumour.

Solution A: Using a guess-and-check strategy to solve an exponential equation

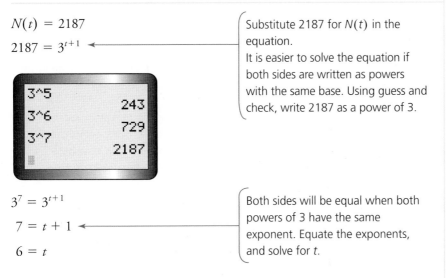

$N(t) = 2187$

$2187 = 3^{t+1}$ ◄————

> Substitute 2187 for $N(t)$ in the equation.
> It is easier to solve the equation if both sides are written as powers with the same base. Using guess and check, write 2187 as a power of 3.

$3^7 = 3^{t+1}$

$7 = t + 1$ ◄————

$6 = t$

> Both sides will be equal when both powers of 3 have the same exponent. Equate the exponents, and solve for t.

Another 2187 students will hear the rumour during the 6th hour.

Solution B: Using a graphing calculator to solve an exponential equation

$N(t) = 2187$

$2187 = 3^{t+1}$ ←——————

A graph can be used to solve the equation.
Enter $y = 3^{x+1}$ in Y1 of the equation editor and $y = 2817$ in Y2. Graph using a window that corresponds to the domain and range in this situation.

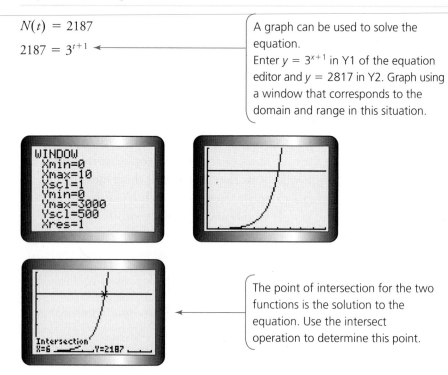

The point of intersection for the two functions is the solution to the equation. Use the intersect operation to determine this point.

Another 2187 students will hear the rumour during the 6th hour.

Solution C: Rewriting an exponential equation in logarithmic form

$N(t) = 2187$

$2187 = 3^{t+1}$ ←——————

Determine the value of the exponent t, when $N(t) = 2187$.
To solve for t, rewrite the equation in logarithmic form.

$t + 1 = \log_3 2187$ ←——————

Since a logarithm is an exponent, evaluate $\log_3 2187$ by determining the exponent to which the base 3 must be raised to get 2187. Use guess and check.

```
3^5
            243
3^6
            729
3^7
            2187
```

$t + 1 = 7$

$\quad t = 6$

Another 2187 students will hear the rumour during the 6th hour.

Reflecting

A. Solutions A and B used the exponential form of the model, but different strategies. Which one of these strategies will only work for some equations? Explain why.

B. Solution C used the logarithmic form of the model. Is there any advantage of rewriting the model in this form? Explain.

C. If you had to solve the equation $3^{t+1} = 1000$, which strategy would you use? Explain your reasons.

APPLY *the Math*

EXAMPLE 2	Using reasoning to evaluate logarithmic expressions

Use the definition of a logarithm to determine the value of each expression.

a) $\log_4 64$

b) $\log_3\left(\dfrac{1}{27}\right)$

c) $\log_2(-4)$

d) $\log_5 \sqrt[3]{25}$

$Log_n x = n^y = x$

Solution

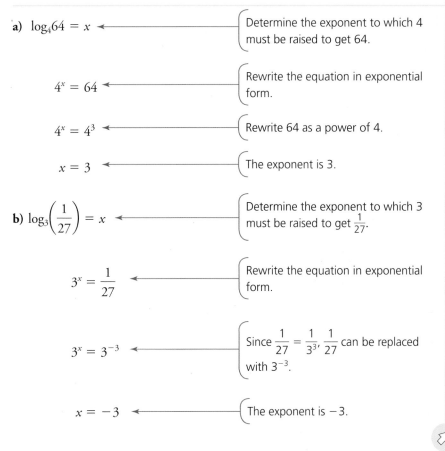

a) $\log_4 64 = x$ ← Determine the exponent to which 4 must be raised to get 64.

$4^x = 64$ ← Rewrite the equation in exponential form.

$4^x = 4^3$ ← Rewrite 64 as a power of 4.

$x = 3$ ← The exponent is 3.

b) $\log_3\left(\dfrac{1}{27}\right) = x$ ← Determine the exponent to which 3 must be raised to get $\frac{1}{27}$.

$3^x = \dfrac{1}{27}$ ← Rewrite the equation in exponential form.

$3^x = 3^{-3}$ ← Since $\dfrac{1}{27} = \dfrac{1}{3^3}$, $\dfrac{1}{27}$ can be replaced with 3^{-3}.

$x = -3$ ← The exponent is -3.

c) $\log_2(-4) = x$ ← Determine the exponent to which 2 must be raised to get -4.

$2^x = -4$ ← Rewrite the equation in exponential form.

There is no solution. ← Since 2 is a positive number, there will never be a negative result when 2 is raised to an exponent. The domain of any logarithmic function is $x > 0$.

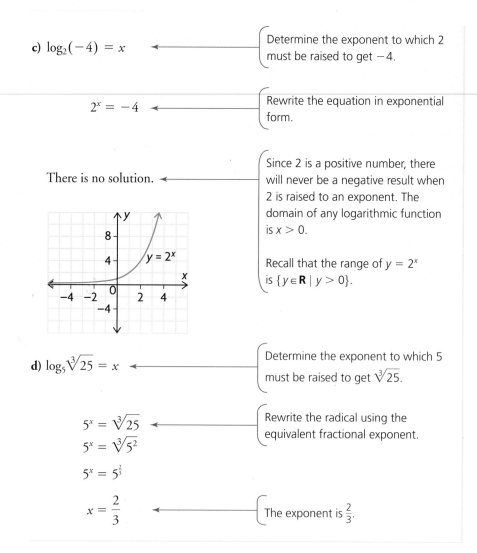

Recall that the range of $y = 2^x$ is $\{y \in \mathbf{R} \mid y > 0\}$.

d) $\log_5 \sqrt[3]{25} = x$ ← Determine the exponent to which 5 must be raised to get $\sqrt[3]{25}$.

$5^x = \sqrt[3]{25}$ ← Rewrite the radical using the equivalent fractional exponent.

$5^x = \sqrt[3]{5^2}$

$5^x = 5^{\frac{2}{3}}$

$x = \dfrac{2}{3}$ ← The exponent is $\frac{2}{3}$.

EXAMPLE 3 **Selecting a strategy to estimate the logarithm of a number**

Determine the approximate value of $\log_5 47$.

Solution A: Using graphing technology

$\log_5 47 = x$ ← Determine the exponent to which 5 must be raised to get 47.

$5^x = 47$ ← Rewrite the equation in exponential form.

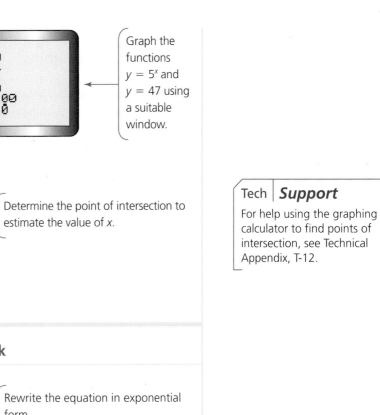

Graph the functions $y = 5^x$ and $y = 47$ using a suitable window.

Determine the point of intersection to estimate the value of x.

Tech | **Support**

For help using the graphing calculator to find points of intersection, see Technical Appendix, T-12.

$x \doteq 2.39$

Solution B: Using guess and check

$\log_5 47 = x$

$5^x = 47$ ← Rewrite the equation in exponential form.

$5^2 = 25$ and $5^3 = 125$ ← The exponent must be between 2 and 3.

$5^{2.5} \doteq 55.9$ ← Try 2.5. The result is too high.

$5^{2.25} \doteq 37.38$ ← Try halfway between 2 and 2.5. The result is too low.

$5^{2.375} \doteq 45.71$ ← Try halfway between 2.25 and 2.5. The result is getting close.

$5^{2.4} \doteq 47.59$ ← Next try 2.4. The result is a little bit too high.

$5^{2.3875} \doteq 46.64$ ← Average 2.4 and 2.375. The result is very close.

$5^{2.39375} \doteq 47.12$ ← Refine the guess by averaging 2.4 and 2.3875.

The value is approximately 2.39.

EXAMPLE 4 Selecting a strategy to evaluate common logarithms

Use the log key on a calculator to evaluate the following logarithms. Explain how the calculator determined the values.

a) log 10   **b)** log 100   **c)** log 500

Solution

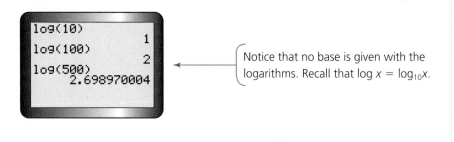

```
log(10)
              1
log(100)
              2
log(500)
     2.698970004
```

Notice that no base is given with the logarithms. Recall that log $x = \log_{10}x$.

a) $\log_{10}10 = x$
$$10^x = 10, \text{ so } x = 1$$

b) $\log_{10}100 = x$
$$10^x = 100, \text{ so } x = 2$$

c) $\log_{10}500 = x$
$$10^x = 500, \text{ so } x \doteq 2.7$$

Let x represent the value of each expression. Rewrite each equation in exponential form.

The calculator determined the exponents that must be applied to base 10 to get 10, 100, and 500.

EXAMPLE 5 Examining some general properties of logarithms

Evaluate each of the following logarithms.

a) $\log_6 1$ **b)** $\log_5 5^x$ **c)** $6^{\log_6 x}$

Solution

a) $\log_6 1 = 0$

The value of the expression is the exponent to which 6 must be raised to get 1. A power equals 1 only when its exponent is 0.

$$\log_6 1 = x$$
$$6^x = 1$$
$$6^x = 6^0$$
$$x = 0$$

To verify, let the expression equal x and rewrite the expression in exponential form.

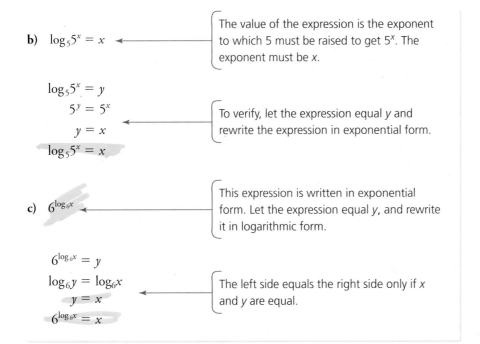

b) $\log_5 5^x = x$ ◀──────── The value of the expression is the exponent to which 5 must be raised to get 5^x. The exponent must be x.

$\log_5 5^x = y$
$5^y = 5^x$ ◀──────── To verify, let the expression equal y and rewrite the expression in exponential form.
$y = x$
$\log_5 5^x = x$

c) $6^{\log_6 x}$ ◀──────── This expression is written in exponential form. Let the expression equal y, and rewrite it in logarithmic form.

$6^{\log_6 x} = y$
$\log_6 y = \log_6 x$ ◀──────── The left side equals the right side only if x and y are equal.
$y = x$
$6^{\log_6 x} = x$

In Summary

Key Ideas

- Simple exponential equations can be solved using a variety of strategies:
  - expressing both sides as powers with a common base and then equating the exponents
  - graphing both sides of the equation using graphing technology and then determining the point of intersection
  - rewriting the equation in logarithmic form and simplifying
- A logarithm is an exponent. The logarithm of a number to a given base is the exponent to which the base must be raised to get the number.

Need to Know

- Logarithms of negative numbers do not exist, because a negative number cannot be written as a power of a positive base.
- A logarithm written with any base can be estimated with a calculator, using graphing technology, or guess and check.
- The expression $\log x$ is called a common logarithm. It means $\log_{10} x$, and it can be evaluated using the log key on a calculator.
- The following are some properties of logarithms, where $a > 0$ and $a \neq 1$:
  - $\log_a 1 = 0$
  - $\log_a a^x = x$
  - $a^{\log_a x} = x$

CHECK *Your Understanding*

1. Express in logarithmic form.

   a) $4^2 = 16$

   b) $3^4 = 81$

   c) $8^0 = 1$

   d) $6^{-2} = \dfrac{1}{36}$

   e) $\left(\dfrac{1}{3}\right)^3 = \dfrac{1}{27}$

   f) $8^{\frac{1}{3}} = 2$

2. Express in exponential form.

   a) $\log_2 8 = 3$

   b) $\log_5 \dfrac{1}{25} = -2$

   c) $\log_3 81 = 4$

   d) $\log_{\frac{1}{6}} 216 = -3$

   e) $\log_6 \sqrt{6} = \dfrac{1}{2}$

   f) $\log_{10} 1 = 0$

3. Evaluate.

   a) $\log_5 5$

   b) $\log_7 1$

   c) $\log_2\left(\dfrac{1}{4}\right)$

   d) $\log_7 \sqrt{7}$

   e) $\log_{\frac{2}{3}}\left(\dfrac{8}{27}\right)$

   f) $\log_2 \sqrt[3]{2}$

PRACTISING

4. Solve for x. Round your answers to two decimal places, if necessary.

   a) $\log\left(\dfrac{1}{10}\right) = x$

   b) $\log 1 = x$

   c) $\log (1\,000\,000) = x$

   d) $\log 25 = x$

   e) $\log x = 0.25$

   f) $\log x = -2$

5. Evaluate.

   a) $\log_6 \sqrt{6}$

   b) $\log_5 125 - \log_5 25$

   c) $\log_3 81 + \log_4 64$

   d) $\log_2 \dfrac{1}{4} - \log_3 1$

   e) $\log_5 \sqrt[3]{5}$

   f) $\log_3 \sqrt{27}$

6. Use your knowledge of logarithms to solve each of the following **K** equations for x.

   a) $\log_5 x = 3$

   b) $\log_x 27 = 3$

   c) $\log_4 \dfrac{1}{64} = x$

   d) $\log_{\frac{1}{4}} x = -2$

   e) $\log_5 x = \dfrac{1}{2}$

   f) $\log_4 x = 1.5$

7. Graph $f(x) = 3^x$. Use your graph to estimate each of the following logarithms.

   a) $\log_3 17$

   b) $\log_3 36$

   c) $\log_3 112$

   d) $\log_3 143$

8. Estimate the value of each of the following logarithms to two decimal places.

   a) $\log_4 32$

   b) $\log_6 115$

   c) $\log_3 212$

   d) $\log_{11} 896$

9. Evaluate.

a) $\log_3 3^5$

c) $4^{\log_4 \frac{1}{16}}$

e) $a^{\log_a b}$

b) $5^{\log_5 25}$

d) $\log_m m^n$

f) $\log_{\frac{1}{10}} 1$

10. Evaluate $\log_2 16^{\frac{1}{3}}$.

11. **A** The number of mold spores in a petri dish increases by a factor of 10 every week. If there are initially 40 spores in the dish, how long will it take for there to be 2000 spores?

12. **Half-life** is the time it takes for half of a sample of a radioactive element to decay. The function $M(t) = P\left(\frac{1}{2}\right)^{\frac{t}{b}}$ can be used to calculate the mass remaining if the half-life is h and the initial mass is P. The half-life of radium is 1620 years.

a) If a laboratory has 5 g of radium, how much will there be in 150 years?

b) How many years will it take until the laboratory has only 4 g of radium?

13. The function $s(d) = 0.159 + 0.118 \log d$ relates the slope, s, of a beach to the average diameter, d, in millimetres, of the sand particles on the beach. Which beach has a steeper slope: beach A, which has very fine sand with $d = 0.0625$, or beach B, which has very coarse sand with $d = 1$? Justify your decision.

14. The function $S(d) = 93 \log d + 65$ relates the speed of the wind, S, in miles per hour, near the centre of a tornado to the distance that the tornado travels, d, in miles.

a) If a tornado travels a distance of about 50 miles, estimate its wind speed near its centre.

b) If a tornado has sustained winds of approximately 250 mph, estimate the distance it can travel.

15. The astronomer Johannes Kepler (1571–1630) determined that the time, D, in days, for a planet to revolve around the Sun is related to the planet's average distance from the Sun, k, in millions of kilometres. This relation is defined by the equation $\log D = \frac{3}{2} \log k - 0.7$. Verify that Kepler's equation gives a good approximation of the time it takes for Earth to revolve around the Sun, if Earth is about 150 000 000 km from the Sun.

16. Use Kepler's equation from question 15 to estimate the period of revolution of each of the following planets about the Sun, given its distance from the Sun.

a) Uranus, 2854 million kilometres

b) Neptune, 4473 million kilometres

17. The doubling function $y = y_0 2^{\frac{t}{D}}$ can be used to model exponential
T growth when the doubling time is D. The bacterium *Escherichia coli*
has a doubling period of 0.32 h. A culture of *E. coli* starts with
100 bacteria.

   a) Determine the equation for the number of bacteria, y, in x hours.

   b) Graph your equation.

   c) Graph the inverse.

   d) Determine the equation of the inverse. What does this equation
represent?

   e) How many hours will it take for there to be 450 bacteria in the
culture? Explain your strategy.

18. To evaluate a logarithm whose base is not 10 you can use the
following relationship (which will be developed in section 8.5):

$$\log_a b = \frac{\log b}{\log a}$$

Use this to evaluate each of the following to four decimal places.

   a) $\log_5 5$ **c)** $\log_5 45$ **e)** $\log_4 0.5$

   b) $\log_2 10$ **d)** $\log_8 92$ **f)** $\log_7 325$

19. Consider the expression $\log_5 a$.
C

   a) For what values of a will this expression yield positive numbers?

   b) For what values of a will this expression yield negative numbers?

   c) For what values of a will this expression be undefined?

Extending

20. Simplify.

   a) $3^{\log_3 27} + 10^{\log_{10} 1000}$ **b)** $5^{\log_5 8} - 3^{\log_3 5 + \log_3 7}$

21. Determine the inverse of each relation.

   a) $y = \sqrt[3]{x}$ **c)** $y = (0.5)^{x+2}$

   b) $y = 3(2)^x$ **d)** $y = 3\log_2(x - 3) + 2$

22. Graph each function and its inverse. State the domain, range, and
asymptote of each. Determine the equation of the inverse.

   a) $y = 3\log(x + 6)$ **d)** $y = 20(8)^x$

   b) $y = -2\log_5 3x$ **e)** $y = 2(3)^{x+2}$

   c) $y = 2 + 3\log x$ **f)** $y = -5^x - 3$

23. For the function $y = \log_{10} x$, where $0 < x < 1000$, how many integer
values of y are possible if $y > -20$?

Laws of Logarithms

Recognize the connection between the laws of exponents and the laws of logarithms, and use the laws of logarithms to simplify expressions.

LEARN ABOUT the Math

Since the logarithm function with base a is the inverse of the exponential function with base a, it makes sense that each exponent law should have a corresponding logarithmic law. You have seen that the exponential property $a^0 = 1$ has the corresponding logarithmic property $\log_a 1 = 0$.

Recall the following exponent laws:
- product law: $a^x \times a^y = a^{x+y}$
- quotient law: $a^x \div a^y = a^{x-y}$
- power law: $(a^x)^y = a^{xy}$

? What are the corresponding laws of logarithms for these exponent laws?

Connecting the product laws

Determine an equivalent expression for $\log_a(mn)$, where a, m, and n are positive numbers and $a \neq 1$.

Solution

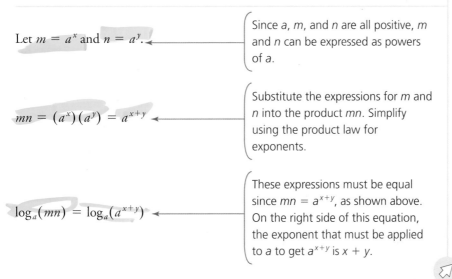

Let $m = a^x$ and $n = a^y$.

Since a, m, and n are all positive, m and n can be expressed as powers of a.

$mn = (a^x)(a^y) = a^{x+y}$

Substitute the expressions for m and n into the product mn. Simplify using the product law for exponents.

$\log_a(mn) = \log_a(a^{x+y})$

These expressions must be equal since $mn = a^{x+y}$, as shown above. On the right side of this equation, the exponent that must be applied to a to get a^{x+y} is $x + y$.

$$\log_a(mn) = x + y$$

$$m = a^x \text{ so } \log_a m = x$$

$$n = a^y \text{ so } \log_a n = y$$

(Write the powers involving m and n in logarithmic form. Substitute the logarithmic expressions into the equation $\log_a(mn) = x + y$.

$$\log_a(mn) = \log_a m + \log_a n$$

(The logarithm of a product is equal to the sum of the logarithms of the factors.

EXAMPLE 2 | Connecting the quotient laws

Determine an equivalent expression for $\log_a\left(\dfrac{m}{n}\right)$, where a, m, and n are positive numbers and $a \neq 1$.

Solution

Let $m = a^x$ and $n = a^y$.

(Since a, m, and n are all positive, m and n can be expressed as powers of a.

$$\frac{m}{n} = \frac{a^x}{a^y} = a^{x-y}$$

(Substitute the expression for m and n into the quotient $\dfrac{m}{n}$. Simplify using the quotient law for exponents.

$$\log_a\left(\frac{m}{n}\right) = \log_a(a^{x-y})$$

$$\log_a\left(\frac{m}{n}\right) = x - y$$

(These expressions must be equal since $\dfrac{m}{n} = a^{x-y}$, as shown above. On the right side of this equation, the exponent that must be applied to a to get a^{x-y} is $x - y$.

$$m = a^x \text{ so } \log_a m = x$$

$$n = a^y \text{ so } \log_a n = y$$

(Write the powers involving m and n in logarithmic form. Substitute the logarithmic expressions into the equation $\log_a\left(\dfrac{m}{n}\right) = x - y$.

$$\log_a\left(\frac{m}{n}\right) = \log_a m - \log_a n$$

(The logarithm of a quotient is equal to the logarithm of the dividend minus the logarithm of the divisor.

| EXAMPLE 3 | Connecting the power laws |

Determine an equivalent expression for $\log_a(m^n)$, where a, m, and n are positive numbers and $a \neq 1$.

Solution

Let $m = a^x$.

> Since a and m are positive, m can be expressed as a power of a.

$m^n = (a^x)^n = a^{nx}$

> Substitute the expression for m into the power m^n. Simplify using the power law for exponents.

$\log_a(m^n) = \log_a(a^{nx})$
$\log_a(m^n) = nx$

> These expressions must be equal since $m^n = a^{nx}$, as shown above. On the right side of this equation, the exponent that must be applied to a to get a^{nx} is nx.

$m = a^x$, so $\log_a m = x$

> Write the power involving m in logarithmic form. Substitute the logarithmic expressions into the equation $\log_a(m^n) = nx$.

$\log_a(m^n) = n \log_a m$

> The logarithm of a power of a number is equal to the exponent multiplied by the logarithm of the number.

Reflecting

A. Which exponent law is related to each logarithm law? How can this be seen in the operations used in each pair of related laws?

B. Why does it make sense that each exponent law has a related logarithm law?

C. Can $\log_2 5 + \log_3 7$ be expressed as a single logarithm using any of the logarithm laws? Explain.

D. Can $\log_6 12 - \log_4 8$ be expressed as a single logarithm using any of the logarithm laws? Explain.

APPLY *the Math*

EXAMPLE 4 | Selecting strategies to simplify logarithmic expressions

Simplify each logarithmic expression.

a) $\log_3 6 + \log_3 4.5$ **b)** $\log_2 48 - \log_2 3$ **c)** $\log_5 \sqrt[3]{25}$

Solution

Communication | Tip

The laws of logarithms are generalizations that simplify the calculation of logarithms with the same base, much like the laws of exponents simplify the calculation of powers with the same base. The laws of logarithms and the laws of exponents can be used both forward and backward to simplify and evaluate expressions.

---

a) $\log_3 6 + \log_3 4.5$

$\qquad$ Since the logarithms have the same base, the sum can be simplified.

$\quad = \log_3 (6 \times 4.5)$

$\qquad$ The sum of the logarithms of two numbers is the logarithm of their product.

$\quad = \log_3 27$

$\qquad$ The exponent that must be applied to 3 to get 27 is 3.

$\quad = 3$

b) $\log_2 48 - \log_2 3$

$\qquad$ These logarithms have the same base, so the difference of the logarithms of the two numbers can be written as the logarithm of their quotient.

$\quad = \log_2 \left(\dfrac{48}{3} \right)$

$\quad = \log_2 16$

$\qquad$ The exponent that must be applied to 2 to get 16 is 4.

$\quad = 4$

c) $\log_5 \sqrt[3]{25}$

$\quad = \log_5 25^{\frac{1}{3}}$

$\qquad$ Change the cube root into a rational exponent.

$\quad = \dfrac{1}{3} \log_5 25$

$\qquad$ The logarithm of a power is the same as the exponent multiplied by the logarithm of the base of the power.

$\quad = \dfrac{1}{3} \times 2$

$\qquad$ Evaluate $\log_5 25$, and then multiply the result by the fraction.

$\quad = \dfrac{2}{3}$

EXAMPLE 5 | Connecting laws of logarithms to graphs of logarithmic functions

Graph the functions $f(x) = \log(1000x)$ and $g(x) = 3 + \log x$. How do the graphs compare? Explain your findings algebraically.

Solution

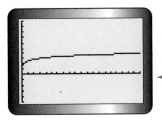

Graph the function $f(x)$ in Y1 with a graphing calculator, using the following window settings.

```
WINDOW
 Xmin=0
 Xmax=5
 Xscl=.25
 Ymin=-5
 Ymax=10
 Yscl=1
 Xres=1
```

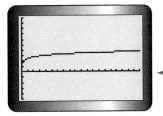

Add the function $g(x)$ in Y2 using the same window. The two graphs are identical on the screen.

```
Plot1 Plot2 Plot3
\Y1◻log(1000X)
\Y2◻3+log(X)
\Y3=
\Y4=
\Y5=
\Y6=
\Y7=
```

The graphs are equivalent.

$f(x) = \log(1000x)$ ← Notice that $\log(1000x)$ is the logarithm of a product.

$= \log 1000 + \log x$ ← Rewrite the logarithm of the product as the sum of the logarithms of the factors.

$= 3 + \log x$ ← Evaluate $\log 1000$.

$= g(x)$ ← The result is equivalent to the function $g(x)$.

EXAMPLE **6**

Selecting strategies to simplify logarithmic expressions

Use the properties of logarithms to express $\log_a \sqrt{\dfrac{x^3 y^2}{w}}$ in terms of $\log_a x$, $\log_a y$, and $\log_a w$.

Solution

$$\log_a \sqrt{\frac{x^3 y^2}{w}} = \log_a \left(\frac{x^3 y^2}{w}\right)^{\frac{1}{2}}$$

Express the square root using the rational exponent of $\frac{1}{2}$.

$$= \frac{1}{2} \log_a \left(\frac{x^3 y^2}{w}\right)$$

Use the power law of logarithms to write an equivalent expression.

$$= \frac{1}{2} \left(\log_a x^3 y^2 - \log_a w\right)$$

Express the logarithm of the quotient of $x^3 y^2$ and w as a difference.

$$= \frac{1}{2} \left(\log_a x^3 + \log_a y^2 - \log_a w\right)$$

Express the logarithm of the product of $x^3 y^2$ as a sum.

$$= \frac{1}{2} \log_a x^3 + \frac{1}{2} \log_a y^2 - \frac{1}{2} \log_a w$$

Expand using the distributive property.

$$= \frac{1}{2} \times 3 \log_a x + \frac{1}{2} \times 2 \log_a y - \frac{1}{2} \log_a w$$

Use the power law of logarithms again to write an equivalent expression where appropriate.

$$= \frac{3}{2} \log_a x + \log_a y - \frac{1}{2} \log_a w$$

Simplify.

In Summary

Key Ideas

- The laws of logarithms are directly related to the laws of exponents, since logarithms are exponents.
- The laws of logarithms can be used to simplify logarithmic expressions if all the logarithms have the same base.

Need to Know

- The laws of logarithms are as follows, where $a > 0$, $x > 0$, $y > 0$, and $a \neq 1$:
  - **product law of logarithms:** $\log_a xy = \log_a x + \log_a y$
  - **quotient law of logarithms:** $\log_a \left(\dfrac{x}{y}\right) = \log_a x - \log_a y$
  - **power law of logarithms:** $\log_a x^r = r \log_a x$

CHECK Your Understanding

1. Write each expression as a sum or difference of logarithms.

   a) $\log(45 \times 68)$ c) $\log\left(\dfrac{123}{31}\right)$ e) $\log_2(14 \times 9)$

   b) $\log_m pq$ d) $\log_m\left(\dfrac{p}{q}\right)$ f) $\log_4\left(\dfrac{81}{30}\right)$

2. Express each of the following as a logarithm of a product or quotient.
   a) $\log 5 + \log 7$ d) $\log x - \log y$
   b) $\log_3 4 - \log_3 2$ e) $\log_6 7 + \log_6 8 + \log_6 9$
   c) $\log_m a + \log_m b$ f) $\log_4 10 + \log_4 12 - \log_4 20$

3. Express each of the following in the form $r \log_a x$.

   a) $\log 5^2$ c) $\log_m p^q$ e) $\log_7(36)^{0.5}$

   b) $\log_3 7^{-1}$ d) $\log \sqrt[3]{45}$ f) $\log_5 \sqrt[5]{125}$

PRACTISING

4. Use the laws of logarithms to simplify and then evaluate each
   K expression.

   a) $\log_3 135 - \log_3 5$ c) $\log 50 + \log 2$ e) $\log_2 224 - \log_2 7$

   b) $\log_5 10 + \log_5 2.5$ d) $\log_4 4^7$ f) $\log \sqrt{10}$

5. Describe how the graphs of $y = \log_2(4x)$, $y = \log_2(8x)$, and
   $y = \log_2\left(\dfrac{x}{2}\right)$ are related to the graph of $y = \log_2 x$.

6. Evaluate the following logarithms.

   a) $\log_{25} 5^3$ d) $\log_2 \sqrt{36} - \log_2 \sqrt{72}$

   b) $\log_6 54 + \log_6 2 - \log_6 3$ e) $\log_3 54 + \log_3\left(\dfrac{3}{2}\right)$

   c) $\log_6 6\sqrt{6}$ f) $\log_8 2 + 3\log_8 2 + \dfrac{1}{2}\log_8 16$

7. Use the laws of logarithms to express each of the following in terms
   of $\log_b x$, $\log_b y$, and $\log_b z$.
   a) $\log_b xyz$ c) $\log_b x^2 y^3$

   b) $\log_b\left(\dfrac{z}{xy}\right)$ d) $\log_b \sqrt{x^5 y z^3}$

8. Explain why $\log_5 3 + \log_5\dfrac{1}{3} = 0$.

9. Write each expression as a single logarithm.

a) $3 \log_5 2 + \log_5 7$

d) $\log_3 12 + \log_3 2 - \log_3 6$

b) $2 \log_3 8 - 5 \log_3 2$

e) $\log_4 3 + \dfrac{1}{2} \log_4 8 - \log_4 2$

c) $2 \log_2 3 + \log_2 5$

f) $2 \log 8 + \log 9 - \log 36$

10. Use the laws of logarithms to express each side of the equation as a single logarithm. Then compare both sides of the equation to solve.

A

a) $\log_2 x = 2 \log_2 7 + \log_2 5$

d) $\log_7 x = 2 \log_7 25 - 3 \log_7 5$

b) $\log x = 2 \log 4 + 3 \log 3$

e) $\log_3 x = 2 \log_3 10 - \log_3 25$

c) $\log_4 x + \log_4 12 = \log_4 48$

f) $\log_5 x - \log_5 8 = \log_5 6 + 3 \log_5 2$

11. Write each expression as a single logarithm. Assume that all the variables represent positive numbers.

a) $\log_2 x + \log_2 y + \log_2 z$

d) $\log_2 x^2 - \log_2 xy + \log_2 y^2$

b) $\log_5 u - \log_5 v + \log_5 w$

e) $1 + \log_3 x^2$

c) $\log_6 a - (\log_6 b + \log_6 c)$

f) $3 \log_4 x + 2 \log_4 x - \log_4 y$

12. Write $\dfrac{1}{2} \log_a x + \dfrac{1}{2} \log_a y - \dfrac{3}{4} \log_a z$ as a single logarithm. Assume that all the variables represent positive numbers.

13. Describe the transformations that take the graph of $f(x) = \log_2 x$ to the graph of $g(x) = \log_2(8x^3)$.

14. Use different expressions to create two logarithmic functions that have

T the same graph. Demonstrate algebraically why these functions have the same graph.

15. Explain how the laws of logarithms can help you evaluate $\log_3\left(\dfrac{\sqrt[5]{27}}{2187}\right)$.

C

Extending

16. Explain why $\log_x x^{m-1} + 1 = m$.

17. If $\log_b x = 0.3$, find the value of $\log_b x \sqrt{x}$.

18. Use graphing technology to draw the graphs of $y = \log x + \log 2x$ and $y = \log 2x^2$. Although the graphs are different, simplifying the first expression using the laws of logarithms produces the second expression. Explain why the graphs are different.

19. Create a pair of equivalent expressions that demonstrate each of the laws of logarithms. Prove that these expressions are equivalent.

FREQUENTLY ASKED Questions

Q: **In what ways can the equation of the inverse of an exponential function be written?**

Study | *Aid*
- See Lesson 8.1.
- Try Mid-Chapter Review Questions 1 and 2.

A: One way that the inverse of an exponential function can be written is in exponential form. For example, the inverse of the exponential function $y = a^x$ is $x = a^y$. Another way that the inverse can be written is in logarithmic form. For example, $x = a^y$ can be written as $y = \log_a x$. This means that a logarithm is an exponent. Specifically, $\log_a x$ means "the exponent that must be applied to a to get x." Since $x = a^y$ is equivalent to $y = \log_a x$, this exponent is y.

Q: **What does the graph of a logarithmic function of the form $y = \log_a x$ look like and what are its characteristics?**

A: The general shape of the graph of a logarithmic function depends on the value of its base.

When $a > 1$, the exponential function is an increasing function, and the logarithmic function is also an increasing function.

When $0 < a < 1$, the exponential function is a decreasing function, and the logarithmic function is also a decreasing function.

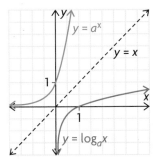

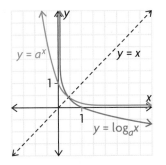

- The y-axis is the vertical asymptote for the logarithmic function. The x-axis is the horizontal asymptote for the exponential function.

- The x-intercept of the logarithmic function is 1, while the y-intercept of the exponential function is 1.

- The domain of the logarithmic function is $\{x \in \mathbf{R} \mid x > 0\}$, since the range of the exponential function is $\{y \in \mathbf{R} \mid y > 0\}$.

- The range of the logarithmic function is $\{y \in \mathbf{R}\}$, since the domain of the exponential function is $\{x \in \mathbf{R}\}$.

Study | Aid

- See Lesson 8.2, Examples 1 and 2.
- Try Mid-Chapter Review Questions 3 and 4.

Q: How does varying the parameters of the equation $y = a \log(k(x - d)) + c$ affect the graph of the parent function, $y = \log x$?

A: The value of the parameter a determines whether there is a vertical stretch or compression. The value of k determines whether there is a horizontal stretch or compression. The value of d indicates a horizontal translation, and the value of c indicates a vertical translation. If a is negative, there is a reflection of the parent function $y = \log x$ in the x-axis. If k is negative, there is a reflection of the parent function $y = \log x$ in the y-axis.

Study | Aid

- See Lesson 8.3, Examples 2 and 3.
- Try Mid-Chapter Review Questions 7, 8, and 9.

Q: How do you evaluate a logarithm?

A1: A logarithm of a number indicates the exponent to which the base must be raised to get the number.

For example, $\log_4 64$ means "the exponent to which you must raise 4 to get 64." The answer is 3.

A2: If the logarithm involves base 10, a calculator can be used to determine its value; $\log_{10} 25 = \log 25 \doteq 1.3979$.

A3: If the logarithm has a base other than 10, use the relationship $\log_a b = \dfrac{\log b}{\log a}$ and a calculator to determine its value;

$$\log_2 15 = \dfrac{\log 15}{\log 2} \doteq 3.9069.$$

Study | Aid

- See Lesson 8.4, Examples 4, 5, and 6.
- Try Mid-Chapter Review Questions 10 to 13.

Q: How do you simplify expressions that contain logarithms?

A: If the logarithms are written with the same base, you can simplify them using the laws of logarithms that correspond to the relevant exponent laws.

The log of a product can be expressed as a sum of the logs; for example, $\log_5 (6 \times 7) = \log_5 6 + \log_5 7$.

The log of a quotient can be expressed as the difference of the logs; for example, $\log_7 \left(\dfrac{25}{6} \right) = \log_7 25 - \log_7 6$.

The logarithm of a power can be expressed as the product of the exponent of the power and the logarithm of the base of the power; for example, $\log_3 4^6 = 6 \log_3 4$.

PRACTICE Questions

Lesson 8.1

1. Express in logarithmic form.
   a) $y = 5^x$
   c) $x = 10^y$
   b) $y = \left(\dfrac{1}{3}\right)^x$
   d) $m = p^q$

2. Express in exponential form.
   a) $y = \log_3 x$
   c) $k = \log m$
   b) $y = \log x$
   d) $t = \log_s r$

Lesson 8.2

3. Describe the transformations of the parent function $y = \log x$ that result in $f(x)$.
   a) $f(x) = 2 \log x - 4$
   b) $f(x) = -\log 3x$
   c) $f(x) = \dfrac{1}{4} \log \dfrac{1}{4} x$
   d) $f(x) = \log[2(x - 2)]$
   e) $f(x) = \log(x + 5) + 1$
   f) $f(x) = 5 \log(-x) - 3$

4. Given the parent function $y = \log_3 x$, write the equation of the function that results from each set of transformations.
   a) vertical stretch by a factor of 4, followed by a reflection in the x-axis
   b) horizontal translation 3 units to the left, followed by a vertical translation 1 unit up
   c) vertical compression by a factor of $\dfrac{2}{3}$, followed by a horizontal stretch by a factor of 2
   d) vertical stretch by a factor of 3, followed by a reflection in the y-axis and a horizontal translation 1 unit to the right

5. State the coordinates of the image point of $(9, 2)$ for each of the transformed functions in question 4.

6. How does the graph of $f(x) = 2 \log_2 x + 2$ compare with the graph of $g(x) = \log_2 x$?

Lesson 8.3

7. Evaluate.
   a) $\log_3 81$
   c) $\log_5 1$
   b) $\log_4 \dfrac{1}{16}$
   d) $\log_{\frac{2}{3}} \dfrac{27}{8}$

8. Evaluate to three decimal places.
   a) $\log 4$
   c) $\log 135$
   b) $\log 45$
   d) $\log 300$

9. Evaluate the value of each expression to three decimal places.
   a) $\log_2 21$
   c) $\log_7 141$
   b) $\log_5 117$
   d) $\log_{11} 356$

Lesson 8.4

10. Express as a single logarithm.
    a) $\log 7 + \log 4$
    c) $\log_3 11 + \log_3 4 - \log_3 6$
    b) $\log 5 - \log 2$
    d) $\log_p q + \log_p q$

11. Evaluate.
    a) $\log_{11} 33 - \log_{11} 3$
    b) $\log_7 14 + \log_7 3.5$
    c) $\log_5 100 + \log_5 \dfrac{1}{4}$
    d) $\log_{\frac{1}{2}} 72 - \log_{\frac{1}{2}} 9$
    e) $\log_4 \sqrt[3]{16}$
    f) $\log_3 9\sqrt{27}$

12. Describe how the graph of $f(x) = \log x^3$ is related to the graph of $g(x) = \log x$.

13. Use a calculator to evaluate each expression to two decimal places.
    a) $\log 4^8$
    d) $\log 200 \div \log 50$
    b) $\log \sqrt{40}$
    e) $(\log 20)^2$
    c) $\log 9^4$
    f) $5 \log 5$

Solving Exponential Equations

GOAL

Solve exponential equations in one variable using a variety of strategies.

LEARN ABOUT the Math

All radioactive substances decrease in mass over time.

Jamie works in a laboratory that uses radioactive substances. The laboratory received a shipment of 200 g of radioactive radon, and 16 days later, 12.5 g of the radon remained.

❓ What is the half-life of radon?

EXAMPLE 1	Selecting a strategy to solve an exponential equation

Calculate the half-life of radon.

Solution A: Solving the equation algebraically by writing both sides with the same base

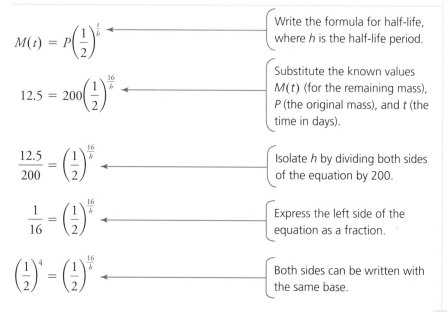

$$M(t) = P\left(\frac{1}{2}\right)^{\frac{t}{h}}$$

Write the formula for half-life, where h is the half-life period.

$$12.5 = 200\left(\frac{1}{2}\right)^{\frac{16}{h}}$$

Substitute the known values $M(t)$ (for the remaining mass), P (the original mass), and t (the time in days).

$$\frac{12.5}{200} = \left(\frac{1}{2}\right)^{\frac{16}{h}}$$

Isolate h by dividing both sides of the equation by 200.

$$\frac{1}{16} = \left(\frac{1}{2}\right)^{\frac{16}{h}}$$

Express the left side of the equation as a fraction.

$$\left(\frac{1}{2}\right)^{4} = \left(\frac{1}{2}\right)^{\frac{16}{h}}$$

Both sides can be written with the same base.

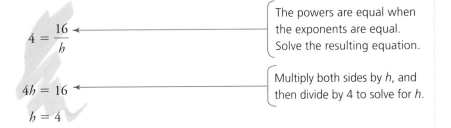

$$4 = \frac{16}{h}$$

The powers are equal when the exponents are equal. Solve the resulting equation.

$$4h = 16$$

Multiply both sides by h, and then divide by 4 to solve for h.

$$h = 4$$

The half-life of radon is 4 days.

Solution B: Solving the equation algebraically by taking the logarithm of both sides

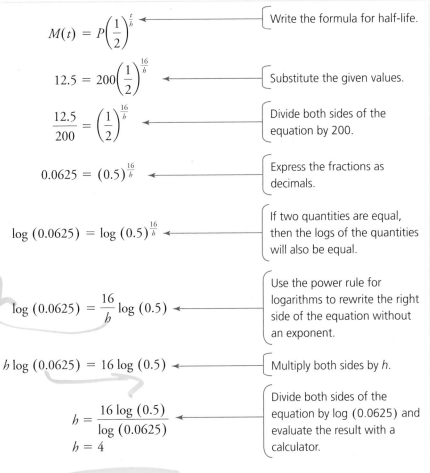

$$M(t) = P\left(\frac{1}{2}\right)^{\frac{t}{h}}$$

Write the formula for half-life.

$$12.5 = 200\left(\frac{1}{2}\right)^{\frac{16}{h}}$$

Substitute the given values.

$$\frac{12.5}{200} = \left(\frac{1}{2}\right)^{\frac{16}{h}}$$

Divide both sides of the equation by 200.

$$0.0625 = (0.5)^{\frac{16}{h}}$$

Express the fractions as decimals.

$$\log(0.0625) = \log(0.5)^{\frac{16}{h}}$$

If two quantities are equal, then the logs of the quantities will also be equal.

$$\log(0.0625) = \frac{16}{h}\log(0.5)$$

Use the power rule for logarithms to rewrite the right side of the equation without an exponent.

$$h\log(0.0625) = 16\log(0.5)$$

Multiply both sides by h.

$$h = \frac{16\log(0.5)}{\log(0.0625)}$$

$$h = 4$$

Divide both sides of the equation by $\log(0.0625)$ and evaluate the result with a calculator.

The half-life of radon is 4 days.

Solution C: Solving the equation graphically using graphing technology

$$M(t) = P\left(\frac{1}{2}\right)^{\frac{t}{h}}$$ — Write the formula for half-life.

$$12.5 = 200\left(\frac{1}{2}\right)^{\frac{16}{h}}$$ — Substitute the given values.

$$\frac{12.5}{200} = \left(\frac{1}{2}\right)^{\frac{16}{h}}$$ — To solve for h, divide both sides of the equation by 200.

$$0.0625 = (0.5)^{\frac{16}{h}}$$

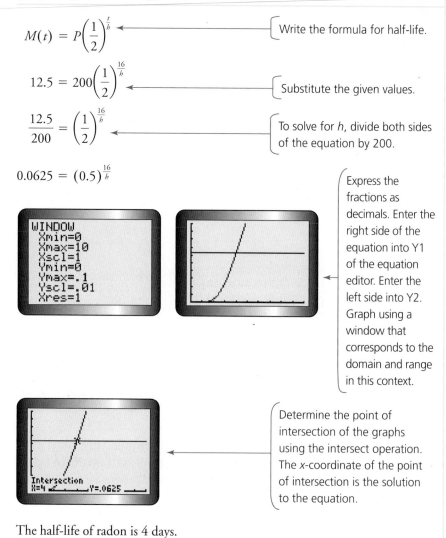

Express the fractions as decimals. Enter the right side of the equation into Y1 of the equation editor. Enter the left side into Y2. Graph using a window that corresponds to the domain and range in this context.

Determine the point of intersection of the graphs using the intersect operation. The x-coordinate of the point of intersection is the solution to the equation.

Tech | **Support**

For help using the graphing calculator to determine points of intersection, see Technical Appendix, T-12.

The half-life of radon is 4 days.

Reflecting

A. Why did the strategy that was used in Solution A result in an exact answer? Will this strategy always result in an exact answer? Explain.

B. Which of the strategies used in the three different solutions will always result in an exact answer? Explain.

C. Which of the three strategies do you prefer? Justify your preference.

APPLY the Math

EXAMPLE 2	Selecting a strategy to solve an exponential equation with more than one power

Solve $2^{x+2} - 2^x = 24$.

Solution

$2^{x+2} - 2^x = 24$ ← The terms on the left side of the equation cannot be combined.

$2^x(2^2 - 1) = 24$ ← Divide out the common factor of 2^x on the left side of the equation.
$2^x(4 - 1) = 24$

$2^x(3) = 24$ ← Simplify the expression in brackets. Divide both sides by 3. Express the right side of the equation as a power of 2.
$2^x = 8$
$2^x = 2^3$
$x = 3$

EXAMPLE 3	Using logarithms to solve a problem

An investment of $2500 grows at a rate of 4.8% per year, compounded annually. How long will it take for the investment to be worth $4000? Recall that the formula for compound interest is $A = P(1 + i)^n$.

Solution

$A = P(1 + i)^n$ ← Substitute the known values ($P = 2500$, $i = 0.048$, and $A = 4000$) into the formula. The variable n represents the number of years.
$4000 = 2500(1.048)^n$

$\dfrac{4000}{2500} = (1.048)^n$ ← Divide both sides of the equation by 2500.

$1.6 = (1.048)^n$ ← Express the result as a decimal.

$\log(1.6) = \log(1.048)^n$ ← Take the log of both sides to solve for n.

$\log(1.6) = n\log(1.048)$ ← Use the power rule for logarithms to rewrite the equation.

$n = \dfrac{\log 1.6}{\log(1.048)} \doteq 10.025$ ← Divide both sides of the equation by $\log(1.048)$ to solve for n.

It will take approximately 10.025 years for the investment to be worth $4000.

EXAMPLE 4 Selecting a strategy to solve an exponential equation with different bases

Solve $2^{x+1} = 3^{x-1}$ to three decimal places.

Solution

$$2^{x+1} = 3^{x-1}$$ ← Both sides of the equation cannot be written with the same base.

$$\log(2^{x+1}) = \log(3^{x-1})$$ ← Take the log of both sides of the equation.

$$(x+1)\log 2 = (x-1)\log 3$$ ← Use the power rule for logarithms to rewrite both sides of the equation with no exponents.

$$x\log 2 + \log 2 = x\log 3 - \log 3$$ ← Expand using the distributive property.

$$\log 2 + \log 3 = x\log 3 - x\log 2$$ ← Collect like terms to solve the equation.

$$\frac{\log 2 + \log 3}{\log 3 - \log 2} = \frac{x(\log 3 - \log 2)}{\log 3 - \log 2}$$ ← Divide out the common factor of x on the right side. Then divide both sides by $\log 3 - \log 2$.

$$\frac{\log 2 + \log 3}{\log 3 - \log 2} = x$$ ← Evaluate using a calculator.

$$4.419 \doteq x$$ ← Round the answer to the required number of decimal places.

In Summary

Key Ideas

- Two exponential expressions with the same base are equal when their exponents are equal. For example, if $a^m = a^n$, then $m = n$, where $a > 0$, $a \neq 1$, and $m, n \in \mathbf{R}$.
- If two expressions are equal, taking the log of both expressions maintains their equality. For example, if $M = N$, then $\log_a M = \log_a N$, where $M, N > 0$, $a > 0$, $a \neq 1$.

Need to Know

- To solve an exponential equation algebraically, take the logarithm of both sides of the equation using a base of 10, and then use the power rule for logarithms to simplify the equation and solve for the unknown.
- Sometimes an exponential equation can be solved algebraically by writing both sides of the equation with the same base (if possible), setting the exponents equal to each other, and solving for the unknown.
- Exponential equations can also be solved with graphing technology, using the same strategies that are used for other kinds of equations.

CHECK Your Understanding

1. Solve.
   a) $5^x = 625$
   c) $9^{x+1} = 27^{2x-3}$
   e) $2^{3x} = \dfrac{1}{2}$

   b) $4^{2x} = 2^{5-x}$
   d) $8^{x-1} = \sqrt[3]{16}$
   f) $4^{2x} = \dfrac{1}{16}$

2. Solve. Round your answers to three decimal places.
   a) $2^x = 17$
   c) $30(5^x) = 150$
   e) $5^{1-x} = 10$
   b) $6^x = 231$
   d) $210 = 40(1.5)^x$
   f) $6^{\frac{x}{3}} = 30$

3. Solve by rewriting in exponential form.
   a) $x = \log_3 243$
   c) $x = \log_5 5\sqrt{5}$
   e) $x = \log_2\left(\dfrac{1}{4}\right)$

   b) $x = \log_6 216$
   d) $x = \log_2 \sqrt[5]{8}$
   f) $x = \log_3\left(\dfrac{1}{\sqrt{3}}\right)$

PRACTISING

4. The formula to calculate the mass, $M(t)$, remaining from an original sample of radioactive material with mass P, is determined using the formula $M(t) = P\left(\dfrac{1}{2}\right)^{\frac{t}{h}}$, where t is time and h is the half-life of the substance. The half-life of a radioactive substance is 8 h. How long will it take for a 300 g sample to decay to each mass?
   a) 200 g
   b) 100 g
   c) 75 g
   d) 20 g

5. Solve.
   K a) $49^{x-1} = 7\sqrt{7}$
   d) $36^{2x+4} = \left(\sqrt{1296}\right)^x$

   b) $2^{3x-4} = 0.25$
   e) $2^{2x+2} + 7 = 71$

   c) $\left(\dfrac{1}{4}\right)^{x+4} = \sqrt{8}$
   f) $9^{2x+1} = 81(27^x)$

6. **A** a) If $500 is deposited into an account that pays 8%/a compounded annually, how long will it take for the deposit to double?
   b) A $1000 investment is made in a trust fund that pays 12%/a compounded monthly. How long will it take the investment to grow to $5000?
   c) A $5000 investment is made in a savings account that pays 10%/a compounded quarterly. How long will it take for the investment to grow to $7500?
   d) If you invested $500 in an account that pays 12%/a compounded weekly, how long would it take for your deposit to triple?

7. A bacteria culture doubles every 15 min. How long will it take for a culture of 20 bacteria to grow to a population of 163 840?

8. Solve for x.

a) $4^{x+1} + 4^x = 160$

b) $2^{x+2} + 2^x = 320$

c) $2^{x+2} - 2^x = 96$

d) $10^{x+1} - 10^x = 9000$

e) $3^{x+2} + 3^x = 30$

f) $4^{x+3} - 4^x = 63$

9. Choose a strategy to solve each equation, and explain your choice. (Do not solve.)

a) $225(1.05)^x = 450$

b) $3^{x+2} + 3^x = 270$

10. Solve. Round your answers to three decimal places.

a) $5^{t-1} = 3.92$

b) $x = \log_3 25$

c) $4^{2x} = 5^{2x-1}$

d) $x = \log_2 53.2$

11. A plastic sun visor allows light to pass through, but reduces the intensity of the light. The intensity is reduced by 5% if the plastic is 1 mm thick. Each additional millimetre of thickness reduces the intensity by another 5%.

a) Use an equation to model the relation between the thickness of the plastic and the intensity of the light.

b) How thick is a piece of plastic that reduces the intensity of the light to 60%?

12. Solve $3^{2x} - 5(3^x) = -6$.

T

13. If $\log_a x = y$, show that $y = \dfrac{\log x}{\log a}$. Explain how this relationship could

C be used to graph $y = \log_5 x$ on a graphing calculator.

Extending

14. Solve for x.

a) $2^{x^2} = 32(2^{4x})$

b) $3^{x^2+20} = \left(\dfrac{1}{27}\right)^{3x}$

c) $2 \times 3^x = 7 \times 5^x$.

15. If $\log_a 2 = \log_b 8$, show that $a^3 = b$.

16. Determine the point of intersection for the graphs of $y = 3(5^{2x})$ and $y = 6(4^{3x})$. Round your answer to three decimal places.

17. Solve for x, to two decimal places.

a) $6^{3x} = 4^{2x-3}$

b) $(1.2)^x = (2.8)^{x+4}$

c) $3(2)^x = 4^{x+1}$

18. Solve for x, to two decimal places.

$(2^x)^x = 10$

8.6 Solving Logarithmic Equations

GOAL

Solve logarithmic equations with one variable algebraically.

LEARN ABOUT the Math

The Richter scale is used to compare the intensities of earthquakes. The Richter scale magnitude, R, of an earthquake is determined using $R = \log\left(\frac{a}{T}\right) + B$, where a is the amplitude of the vertical ground motion in microns (μ), T is the period of the seismic wave in seconds, and B is a factor that accounts for the weakening of the seismic waves. (1 μ is equivalent to 10^{-6} m.)

? An earthquake measured 5.5 on the Richter scale, and the period of the seismic wave was 1.8 s. If B equals 3.2, what was the amplitude, a, of the vertical ground motion?

EXAMPLE 1   Selecting an algebraic strategy to solve a logarithmic equation

Determine the amplitude, a, of the vertical ground motion.

Solution

$$R = \log\left(\frac{a}{T}\right) + B$$

$$5.5 = \log\left(\frac{a}{1.8}\right) + 3.2$$ ← Substitute the given values into the equation.

$$2.3 = \log\left(\frac{a}{1.8}\right)$$ ← Isolate the term with the unknown, a, by subtracting 3.2 from both sides.

$$10^{2.3} = \frac{a}{1.8}$$ ← Rewrite the equation in exponential form.

$$10^{2.3} \times 1.8 = a$$ ← Multiply both sides by 1.8 to solve for a.

$$359.1\ \mu = a$$

The amplitude of the vertical ground motion was about 359.1 μ.

← To get a better idea of the size of this number, change microns to metres or centimetres. 359.1 μ = 0.000 359 1 m or 0.035 91 cm.

Reflecting

A. What strategies for solving a linear equation were used to solve this logarithmic equation?

B. Why was the equation rewritten in exponential form?

C. How would the strategies have changed if the value of a had been given and the value of T had to be determined?

APPLY the Math

EXAMPLE **2**	Selecting an algebraic strategy to solve a logarithmic equation

Solve.

a) $\log_x 0.04 = -2$ **b)** $\log_7(3x - 5) = \log_7 16$

Solution

a) $\log_x 0.04 = -2$

$$x^{-2} = 0.04 \quad\longleftarrow\quad \text{Express the equation in exponential form.}$$

$$x^{-2} = \frac{1}{25} \quad\longleftarrow\quad \text{Rewrite the decimal as a fraction.}$$
$$0.04 = \frac{4}{100} = \frac{1}{25}$$

$$x^{-2} = 5^{-2} \quad\longleftarrow\quad \text{Express } \frac{1}{25} \text{ as a power with exponent } -2. \text{ Since the exponents are equal, the bases must be equal.}$$
$$x = 5$$

b) $\log_7(3x - 5) = \log_7 16 \quad\longleftarrow\quad \text{If } \log_a M = \log_a N, \text{ then } M = N.$$

$$3x - 5 = 16 \quad\longleftarrow\quad \text{Since 7 is the base of both logs, the two expressions must be equal.}$$

$$3x = 21 \quad\longleftarrow\quad \text{Add 5 to both sides of the equation.}$$

$$x = 7$$

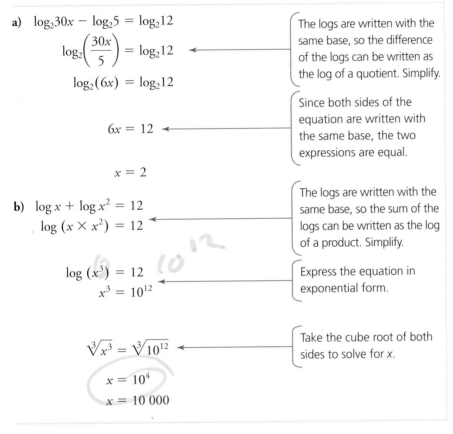

EXAMPLE 3 | Representing sums and differences of logs as single logarithms to solve a logarithmic equation

Solve.

a) $\log_2 30x - \log_2 5 = \log_2 12$ **b)** $\log x + \log x^2 = 12$

Solution

a) $\log_2 30x - \log_2 5 = \log_2 12$

$$\log_2\left(\frac{30x}{5}\right) = \log_2 12$$

$$\log_2(6x) = \log_2 12$$

> The logs are written with the same base, so the difference of the logs can be written as the log of a quotient. Simplify.

$$6x = 12$$

> Since both sides of the equation are written with the same base, the two expressions are equal.

$$x = 2$$

b) $\log x + \log x^2 = 12$

$$\log(x \times x^2) = 12$$

> The logs are written with the same base, so the sum of the logs can be written as the log of a product. Simplify.

$$\log(x^3) = 12$$

$$x^3 = 10^{12}$$

> Express the equation in exponential form.

$$\sqrt[3]{x^3} = \sqrt[3]{10^{12}}$$

> Take the cube root of both sides to solve for x.

$$x = 10^4$$

$$x = 10\,000$$

EXAMPLE 4 | Selecting a strategy to solve a logarithmic equation that involves quadratics

Solve $\log_2(x + 3) + \log_2(x - 3) = 4$.

Solution

$$\log_2(x + 3) + \log_2(x - 3) = 4$$

$$\log_2(x + 3)(x - 3) = 4$$

$$\log_2(x^2 - 3x + 3x - 9) = 4$$

$$\log_2(x^2 - 9) = 4$$

> Since both logarithms have base 2, rewrite the left side as a single logarithm using the product law. Multiply the binomials, and simplify.

$$x^2 - 9 = 2^4$$
$$x^2 - 9 = 16$$
$$x^2 = 25$$

Rewrite the equation in exponential form and solve for x^2.

$$x = \pm\sqrt{25}$$

Take the square root of both sides. There are two possible solutions for a quadratic equation.

$$x = \pm 5$$

Check to make sure that both solutions satisfy the equation.

Check: $x = -5$
LS: $\log_2(-5 + 3) + \log_2(-5 - 3)$
$$= \log_2(-2) + \log_2(-8)$$
$$\neq \text{RS}$$

When $x = -5$, the expression on the left side is undefined, since the logarithm of any negative number is undefined. Therefore, $x = -5$ is not a solution to the original equation. It is an inadmissible solution.

Check: $x = 5$
LS: $\log_2(5 + 3) + \log_2(5 - 3)$
$$= \log_2(8) + \log_2(2)$$
$$= 3 + 1$$
$$= 4$$
$$= \text{RS}$$

When $x = 5$, the expression on the left side gives the value on the right side. Therefore, $x = 5$ is the solution to the original equation.

The solution is $x = 5$.

In Summary

Key Ideas

- A logarithmic equation can be solved by expressing it in exponential form and solving the resulting exponential equation.
- If $\log_a M = \log_a N$, then $M = N$, where a, M, $N > 0$.

Need to Know

- A logarithmic equation can be solved by simplifying it using the laws of logarithms.
- When solving logarithmic equations, be sure to check for inadmissible solutions. A solution is inadmissible if its substitution in the original equation results in an undefined value. Remember that the **argument** and the base of a logarithm must both be positive.

CHECK *Your Understanding*

1. Solve.
   a) $\log_2 x = 2 \log_2 5$
   b) $\log_3 x = 4 \log_3 3$
   c) $\log x = 3 \log 2$
   d) $\log (x - 5) = \log 10$
   e) $\log_2 8 = x$
   f) $\log_2 x = \dfrac{1}{2} \log_2 3$

2. Solve.
   a) $\log_x 625 = 4$
   b) $\log_x 6 = -\dfrac{1}{2}$
   c) $\log_5 (2x - 1) = 2$
   d) $\log (5x - 2) = 3$
   e) $\log_x 0.04 = -2$
   f) $\log_5 (2x - 4) = \log_5 36$

3. Given the formula from Example 1 for the magnitude of an earthquake, $R = \log \left(\dfrac{a}{T} \right) + B$, determine the value of a if $R = 6.3$, $B = 4.2$, and $T = 1.6$.

PRACTISING

4. Solve.
   a) $\log_x 27 = \dfrac{3}{2}$
   b) $\log_x 5 = 2$
   c) $\log_3 (3x + 2) = 3$
   d) $\log x = 4$
   e) $\log_{\frac{1}{3}} 27 = x$
   f) $\log_{\frac{1}{2}} x = -2$

5. Solve.
   K a) $\log_2 x + \log_2 3 = 3$
   b) $\log 3 + \log x = 1$
   c) $\log_5 2x + \dfrac{1}{2} \log_5 9 = 2$
   d) $\log_4 x - \log_4 2 = 2$
   e) $3 \log x - \log 3 = 2 \log 3$
   f) $\log_3 4x + \log_3 5 - \log_3 2 = 4$

6. Solve $\log_6 x + \log_6 (x - 5) = 2$. Check for inadmissible roots.

7. Solve.
   a) $\log_7 (x + 1) + \log_7 (x - 5) = 1$
   b) $\log_3 (x - 2) + \log_3 x = 1$
   c) $\log_6 x - \log_6 (x - 1) = 1$
   d) $\log (2x + 1) + \log (x - 1) = \log 9$
   e) $\log (x + 2) + \log (x - 1) = 1$
   f) $3 \log_2 x - \log_2 x = 8$

8. Describe the strategy that you would use to solve each of the following equations. (Do not solve.)
   a) $\log_9 x = \log_9 4 + \log_9 5$
   b) $\log x - \log 2 = 3$
   c) $\log x = 2 \log 8$

9. The loudness, L, of a sound in decibels (dB) can be calculated using
A the formula $L = 10 \log\left(\frac{I}{I_0}\right)$, where I is the intensity of the sound
in watts per square metre (W/m^2) and $I_0 = 10^{-12}\,W/m^2$.

a) A teacher is speaking to a class. Determine the intensity of the teacher's voice if the sound level is 50 dB.

b) Determine the intensity of the music in the earpiece of an MP3 player if the sound level is 84 dB.

10. Solve $\log_a(x + 2) + \log_a(x - 1) = \log_a(8 - 2x)$.
T

11. Use graphing technology to solve each equation to two decimal places.

a) $\log(x + 3) = \log(7 - 4x)$ c) $2 \log x = 1$

b) $5^x = 3^{x+1}$ d) $\log(4x) = \log(x + 1)$

12. Solve $\log_5(x - 1) + \log_5(x - 2) - \log_5(x + 6) = 0$.

13. Explain why there are no solutions to the equations $\log_3(-8) = x$ and $\log_{-3} 9 = x$.

14. a) Without solving the equation, state the restrictions on the variable x in the following: $\log(2x - 5) - \log(x - 3) = 5$

b) Why do these restrictions exist?

15. If $\log\left(\frac{x + y}{5}\right) = \frac{1}{2}(\log x + \log y)$, where $x > 0, y > 0$, show that $x^2 + y^2 = 23xy$.

16. Solve $\dfrac{\log(35 - x^3)}{\log(5 - x)} = 3$.

17. Given $\log_2 a + \log_2 b = 4$, calculate all the possible integer values
C of a and b. Explain your reasoning.

Extending

18. Solve the following system of equations algebraically.
$$y = \log_2(5x + 4)$$
$$y = 3 + \log_2(x - 1)$$

19. Solve each equation.

a) $\log_5(\log_3 x) = 0$ b) $\log_2(\log_4 x) = 1$

20. If $\left(\frac{1}{2}\right)^{x+y} = 16$ and $\log_{x-y} 8 = -3$, calculate the values of x and y.

Solving Problems with Exponential and Logarithmic Functions

GOAL

Pose and solve problems based on applications of exponential and logarithmic functions.

INVESTIGATE the Math

The following data represent the prices of IBM personal computers and the demand for these computers at a computer store in 1997.

Price ($/computer)	2300	2000	1700	1500	1300	1200	1000
Demand (number of computers)	152	159	164	171	176	180	189

 Based on the data, what do you predict the demand would have been for computers priced at $1600?

A. What is the dependent variable in this situation? Enter the data into a graphing calculator, and create a scatter plot.

B. Is it clear what type of function you could use to model this situation? Explain.

C. Try fitting a function to the scatter plot you created. Try linear, quadratic, cubic, and exponential functions.

D. Use the regression feature of the calculator to determine the equation of the curve of best fit. Try linear, quadratic, cubic, and exponential regression.

E. Which type of function gives you the best fit?

F. Use the algebraic model you found to determine the price that would have a demand of 195 computers.

G. Use your model to predict the demand for computers priced at $1600.

> **Tech | Support**
>
> For help using the graphing calculator to create scatter plots or using regression to determine the equation of best fit, see Technical Appendix, T-11.

Reflecting

H. How could you use the table of values to determine what type of function the data approximates?

I. How could you have used your graph to answer parts F and G?

APPLY the Math

EXAMPLE 1   Solving a problem using a logarithmic equation

In chemistry, the pH (the measure of acidity or alkalinity of a substance) is based on a logarithmic scale. A logarithmic scale uses powers of 10 to compare numbers that vary greatly in size. For example, very small and very large concentrations of the hydrogen ion in a solution influence its classification as either a base or an acid.

Concentration of hydrogen ions compared to distilled water		Examples of solutions at this pH
10 000 000	pH = 0	battery acid, strong hydrofluoric acid
1 000 000	pH = 1	hydrochloric acid secreted by stomach lining
100 000	pH = 2	lemon juice, gastric acid, vinegar
10 000	pH = 3	grapefruit, orange juice, soda
1000	pH = 4	tomato juice, acid rain
100	pH = 5	soft drinking water, black coffee
10	pH = 6	urine, saliva
1	pH = 7	"pure" water
$\frac{1}{10}$	pH = 8	seawater
$\frac{1}{100}$	pH = 9	baking soda
$\frac{1}{1000}$	pH = 10	Great Salt Lake, milk of magnesia
$\frac{1}{10\,000}$	pH = 11	ammonia solution
$\frac{1}{100\,000}$	pH = 12	soapy water
$\frac{1}{1\,000\,000}$	pH = 13	bleaches, oven cleaner
$\frac{1}{10\,000\,000}$	pH = 14	liquid drain cleaner

A difference of one pH unit represents a tenfold (10 times) change in the concentration of hydrogen ions in the solution. For example, the acidity of a sample with a pH of 5 is 10 times greater than the acidity of a sample with a pH of 6. A difference of 2 units, from 6 to 4, would mean that the acidity is 100 times greater, and so on.

- A liquid with a pH less than 7 is considered *acidic*.
- A liquid with a pH greater than 7 is considered *alkaline*.
- A liquid with a pH of 7 is considered *neutral*. Pure distilled water has a pH value of 7.

The relationship between pH and hydrogen ion concentration is given by the formula $pH = -\log[H^+]$, where $[H^+]$ is the concentration of hydrogen ions in moles per litre (mol/L).
a) Calculate the pH if the concentration of hydrogen ions is 0.0001 mol/L.
b) The pH of lemon juice is 2. Calculate the hydrogen ion concentration.
c) If the hydrogen ion concentration is a measure of the strength of an acid, how much stronger is an acid with pH 1.6 than an acid with pH 2.5?

Solution

a)
$$pH = -\log[H^+]$$
$$pH = -\log(0.0001)$$
$$pH = -(-4)$$
$$pH = 4$$
The pH of the liquid is 4.

> Substitute the value for $[H^+]$ into the equation. Evaluate $\log(0.0001)$.

b)
$$pH = -\log[H^+]$$
$$2 = -\log[H^+]$$

> Substitute the value 2 for the pH.

$$-2 = \log[H^+]$$

> Divide both sides of the equation by -1.

$$10^{-2} = [H^+]$$

> Rewrite the equation in exponential form.

$$0.01 = [H^+]$$

> Evaluate the negative exponent to determine $[H^+]$.

The concentration of hydrogen ions is 0.01 mol/L.

c)
$$pH = -\log[H^+]$$

> To calculate the hydrogen ion concentration of both solutions, substitute the given pH values into the equation.

$$1.6 = -\log[H^+] \quad 2.5 = -\log[H^+]$$

> Express both equations in exponential form, and evaluate.

$$10^{-1.6} = [H^+] \quad 10^{-2.5} = [H^+]$$
$$0.0251 \doteq [H^+] \quad 0.0032 \doteq [H^+]$$

> Divide the concentration of the first acid by the concentration of the second acid to find the relative strength of the acids.

$$\frac{0.0251}{0.0032} = 7.84$$

An acid with pH 1.6 is about 7.8 times stronger than an acid with pH 2.5.

EXAMPLE **2**

Representing exponential values using the Richter scale

The Richter magnitude scale uses logarithms to compare intensity of earthquakes.

True Intensity	Richter Scale Magnitude
10^1	$\log_{10}10^1 = 1$
10^4	$\log_{10}10^4 = 4$
$10^{5.8}$	$\log_{10}10^{5.8} = 5.8$

An earthquake of magnitude 2 is actually 10 times more intense than an earthquake of magnitude 1. The difference between the magnitudes of two earthquakes can be used to determine the difference in intensity. If the average earthquake measures 4.5 on the Richter scale, how much more intense is an earthquake that measures 8?

Solution

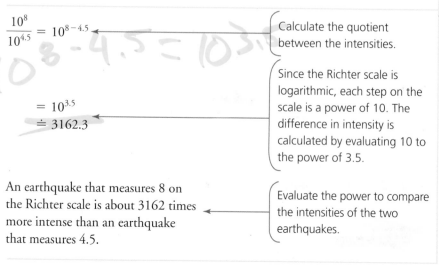

$$\frac{10^8}{10^{4.5}} = 10^{8-4.5}$$

Calculate the quotient between the intensities.

$$= 10^{3.5}$$
$$\doteq 3162.3$$

Since the Richter scale is logarithmic, each step on the scale is a power of 10. The difference in intensity is calculated by evaluating 10 to the power of 3.5.

An earthquake that measures 8 on the Richter scale is about 3162 times more intense than an earthquake that measures 4.5.

Evaluate the power to compare the intensities of the two earthquakes.

EXAMPLE **3**

Solving a problem using an exponential equation and logarithms

Blue jeans fade when washed due to the loss of blue dye from the fabric. If each washing removes about 2.2% of the original dye from the fabric, how many washings are required to give a pair of jeans a well-worn look? (For a well-worn look, jeans should contain, at most, 30% of the original dye.)

Solution

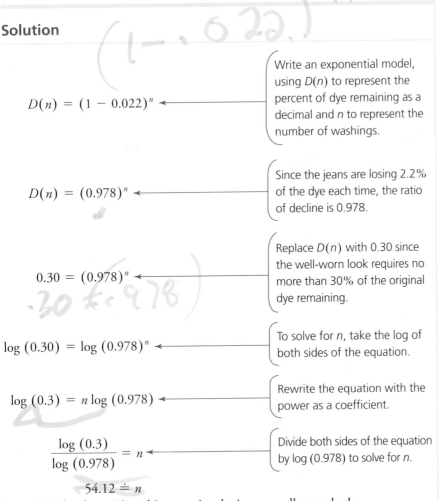

$$D(n) = (1 - 0.022)^n$$

Write an exponential model, using $D(n)$ to represent the percent of dye remaining as a decimal and n to represent the number of washings.

$$D(n) = (0.978)^n$$

Since the jeans are losing 2.2% of the dye each time, the ratio of decline is 0.978.

$$0.30 = (0.978)^n$$

Replace $D(n)$ with 0.30 since the well-worn look requires no more than 30% of the original dye remaining.

$$\log (0.30) = \log (0.978)^n$$

To solve for n, take the log of both sides of the equation.

$$\log (0.3) = n \log (0.978)$$

Rewrite the equation with the power as a coefficient.

$$\frac{\log (0.3)}{\log (0.978)} = n$$

Divide both sides of the equation by $\log (0.978)$ to solve for n.

$$54.12 \doteq n$$

It would take about 54 washings to give the jeans a well-worn look.

EXAMPLE 4 Solving a problem about sound intensity using logarithms

The dynamic range of human hearing and sound intensity spans from 10^{-12} W/m² to about 10 W/m². The highest sound intensity that can be heard is 10 000 000 000 000 times as loud as the quietest! This span of sound intensity is impractical for normal use. A more convenient way to express loudness is a relative logarithmic scale, with the lowest sound that can be heard by the human ear, $I_0 = 10^{-12}$ W/m², given the measure of loudness of 0 dB.

Recall that the formula that is used to measure sound is $L = 10 \log \left(\frac{I}{I_0}\right)$, where L is the loudness measured in decibels, I is the intensity of the sound being measured, and I_0 is the intensity of sound at the threshold of hearing. The following table shows the loudness of a selection of sounds measured in decibels.

Sound	Loudness (dB)
soft whisper	30
normal conversation	60
shouting	80
subway	90
screaming	100
rock concert	120
jet engine	140
space-shuttle launch	180

How many times more intense is the sound of a rock concert than the sound of a subway?

Solution

$$L = 10 \log \left(\frac{I}{I_0} \right)$$

$$120 = 10 \log \left(\frac{I_{RC}}{I_0} \right) \qquad 90 = 10 \log \left(\frac{I_S}{I_0} \right)$$

Let the intensity of sound for a rock concert be I_{RC} and for a subway be I_S. Find the values for the loudness of these sounds in the table, and substitute into the formula.

$$12 = \log \left(\frac{I_{RC}}{I_0} \right) \qquad 9 = \log \left(\frac{I_S}{I_0} \right)$$

Divide both sides of the equations by 10.

$$10^{12} = \frac{I_{RC}}{I_0} \qquad 10^9 = \frac{I_S}{I_0}$$

Express both equations in exponential form.

$$10^{12} I_0 = I_{RC} \qquad 10^9 I_0 = I_S$$

Isolate the variables for comparison.

$$\frac{I_{RC}}{I_S} = \frac{10^{12} I_0}{10^9 I_0} = 10^3 = 1000$$

Divide the results to compare the sound of a rock concert with the sound of a subway.

The sound of a rock concert is 1000 times more intense than the sound of a subway.

In Summary

Key Ideas

- When a range of values can vary greatly, using a logarithmic scale with powers of 10 makes comparisons between the large and small values more manageable.
- Growth and decay situations can be modelled by exponential functions of the form $f(x) = ab^x$. Note that
  - $f(x)$ is the final amount or number
  - a is the initial amount or number
  - for exponential growth, $b = 1 + $ growth rate
  - for exponential decay, $b = 1 - $ decay rate
  - x is the number of growth or decay periods

Need to Know

- Scales that measure a wide range of values, such as the pH scale, Richter scale, and decibel scale, are logarithmic scales.
- To compare concentrations on the pH scale, intensity on the Richter scale, or sound intensities, determine the quotient between the values being compared.
- Data from a table of values can be graphed and a curve of best fit determined. If the curve of best fit appears to be exponential, use the regression feature of the graphing calculator to determine an equation that models the data.

CHECK *Your Understanding*

1. If one earthquake has a magnitude of 5.2 on the Richter scale and a second earthquake has a magnitude of 6, compare the intensities of the two earthquakes.

2. Calculate the pH of a swimming pool with a hydrogen ion concentration of 6.21×10^{-8} mol/L.

3. A particular sound is 1 000 000 times more intense than a sound you can just barely hear. What is the loudness of the sound in decibels?

PRACTISING

4. The loudness of a heavy snore is 69 dB. How many times as loud as a
   K normal conversation of 60 dB is a heavy snore?

5. Calculate the hydrogen ion concentration of each substance.
   a) baking soda, with a pH of 9
   b) milk, with a pH of 6.6
   c) an egg, with a pH of 7.8
   d) oven cleaner, with a pH of 13

6. Calculate to two decimal places the pH of a solution with each concentration of H^+.
   a) concentration of $H^+ = 0.000\,32$
   b) concentration of $H^+ = 0.000\,3$
   c) concentration of $H^+ = 0.000\,045$
   d) concentration of $H^+ = 0.005$

7. a) Distilled water has an H^+ concentration of 10^{-7} mol/L. Calculate the pH of distilled water.
   b) Drinking water from a particular tap has a pH between 6.3 and 6.6. Is this tap water more or less acidic than distilled water? Explain your answer.

8. **A** The sound level of a moving power lawn mower is 109 dB. The noise level in front of the amplifiers at a concert is about 118 dB. How many times louder is the noise at the front of the amplifiers than the noise of a moving power lawn mower?

9. The following data represent the amount of an investment over 10 years.

Year	0	1	2	5	7	9	10
Amount ($)	5000	5321	5662.61	6824.74	7729.17	8753.45	9315.42

   a) Create a scatter plot, and determine the equation that models this situation.
   b) Determine the average annual interest rate.
   c) Use your equation to determine how long it took for the investment to double.

10. The intensity, I, of light passing through water can be modelled by the equation $I = 10^{1 - 0.13x}$, where x is the depth of the water in metres. Most aquatic plants require a light intensity of 4.2 units for strong growth. Determine the depth of water at which most aquatic plants receive the required light.

11. The following data represent the growth of a bacteria population over time.

Number of Hours	0	7	12	20	42
Number of Bacteria	850	2250	4500	13 500	287 200

   a) Create both a graphical model and an algebraic model for the data.
   b) Determine the length of time it took for the population to double.

12. The amount of water vapour in the air is a function of temperature,
T as shown in the following table.

Temperature (°C)	0	5	10	15	20	25	30	35
Saturation (mL/m³ of air)	4.847	6.797	9.399	12.830	17.300	23.050	30.380	39.630

a) Calculate the growth factors for the saturation row of the table, to the nearest tenth.
b) Determine the average growth factor.
c) Write an exponential model for the amount of water vapour as a function of the temperature.
d) Determine the exponential function with a graphing calculator, using exponential regression.
e) What temperature change will double the amount of water in 1 m³ of air?

13. Dry cleaners use a cleaning fluid that is purified by evaporation and condensation after each cleaning cycle. Every time the fluid is purified, 2.1% of it is lost. The fluid has to be topped up when half of the original fluid remains. After how many cycles will the fluid need to be topped up?

14. How long will it take for $2500 to accumulate to $4000 if it is invested at an interest rate of 6.5%/a, compounded annually?

15. A wound, initially with an area of 80 cm², heals according to the formula $A(t) = 80(10^{-0.023t})$, where $A(t)$ is the area of the wound in square centimetres after t days of healing. In how many days will 75% of the wound be healed?

16. Create a problem that could be solved using logarithms and another
C problem that could be solved without using logarithms. Explain how the two problems are different.

Extending

17. A new car has an interior sound level of 70 dB at 50 km/h. A second car, at the same speed, has an interior sound level that is two times more intense than that of the new car. Calculate the sound level inside the second car.

18. Assume that the annual rate of inflation will average 3.8% over the next 10 years.
a) Write an equation to model the approximate cost, C, of goods and services during any year in the next decade.
b) If the price of a brake job for a car is presently $400, estimate the price 10 years from now.
c) If the price of an oil change 10 years from now will be $47.95, estimate the price of an oil change today.

8.8 Rates of Change in Exponential and Logarithmic Functions

YOU WILL NEED

- graphing calculator

GOAL

Solve problems that involve average and instantaneous rates of change of exponential and logarithmic functions.

INVESTIGATE the Math

The following data from the U.S. Census Bureau represent the population of the United States, to the nearest million, every 10 years from 1900 to 2000.

Year	1900	1910	1920	1930	1940	1950	1960	1970	1980	1990	2000
Population (millions)	76	92	106	123	132	151	179	203	227	249	281

? At what rate was the population changing in the United States at the start of 1950?

A. Calculate the average rate of change in population over the entire 100 years.

B. Calculate the average rate of change in population over the first 50 years and over the last 50 years. Is the average rate of change in each 50-year period the same, less than, or greater than the average rate of change for the entire time period? Suggest reasons.

C. Estimate the instantaneous rate of change in population at the start of 1950 using an average rate of change calculation and a centred interval.

D. Use a graphing calculator to create a scatter plot using years since 1900 as the independent variable.

E. Determine an exponential equation that models the data.

F. Estimate the instantaneous rate of change in population at the start of 1950 using the model you found and a very small interval after 1950.

G. Estimate the instantaneous rate of change in population at the start of 1950 by drawing the appropriate tangent on your graph.

H. Compare your estimates from parts C, F, and G. Which estimate better represents the rate at which the U.S. population was changing in 1950? Explain.

Tech | Support

For help using a graphing calculator to create scatter plots, and using regression to determine the equation of best fit, see Technical Appendix, T-11.

Reflecting

I. How could you use your graph to determine the year that had the least or greatest instantaneous change in population?

J. Describe how the rate at which the U.S. population grew changed during the period from 1900 to 2000.

APPLY the Math

EXAMPLE **1**	Selecting a numerical strategy to calculate the average rate of change

The average number of students per computer in public schools is given in the table. Year 1 is 1983.

a) Calculate the average rate of change in students per computer during the entire time period and during the middle five years of the data.

b) What conclusions can you draw?

Year	Students per Computer
1	125
2	75
3	50
4	37
5	32
6	25
7	22
8	20
9	18
10	16
11	14
12	10.5
13	10

Solution

a) Average rate of change $= \dfrac{10 - 125}{13 - 1}$ ◀ To calculate the average rate of change during the entire time period, use the values for the number of students per computer for year 13 and year 1.

$= \dfrac{-115}{12}$ ◀ Average the difference over 12 years.

$\doteq -9.58$

The average rate of change in students per computer decreased by about 10 students per computer.

The middle five years are years 5 to 9.

Average rate of change $= \dfrac{18 - 32}{9 - 5}$ ◀ Calculate the difference in the number of students per computer for years 9 and 5.

$= \dfrac{-14}{4}$ ◀ Divide the difference by 4, since years 5 to 9 are a 4-year span.

$= -3.5$

The average rate of change in students per computer decreased by 3.5 students per computer.

b) Since the rate of decline was faster over the entire period than during the middle period, the greatest change was either in the first four years or the last four years. The data show that there was a greater change in the number of students per computer during the first four years, so the decline was faster during this period.

| EXAMPLE **2** | Selecting a strategy for calculating the instantaneous rate of change |

Using the data from Example 1, determine the instantaneous rate of change in students per computer for year 8.

Solution A: Calculating numerically

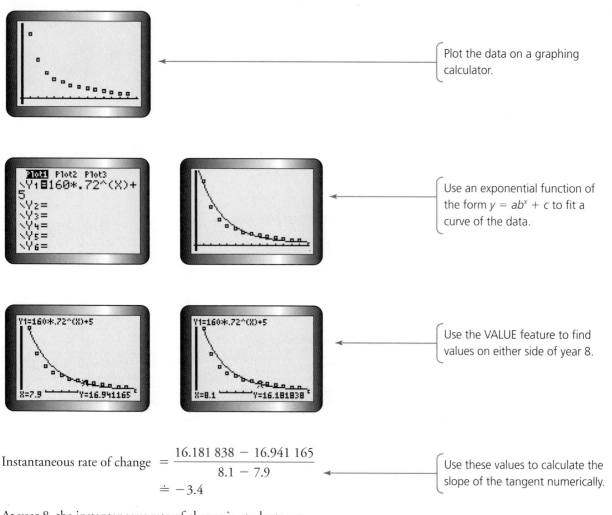

Plot the data on a graphing calculator.

Use an exponential function of the form $y = ab^x + c$ to fit a curve of the data.

Use the VALUE feature to find values on either side of year 8.

Instantaneous rate of change $= \dfrac{16.181\ 838 - 16.941\ 165}{8.1 - 7.9}$

$\doteq -3.4$

Use these values to calculate the slope of the tangent numerically.

At year 8, the instantaneous rate of change in students per computer was decreasing by about 3 students per computer.

Solution B: Calculating graphically

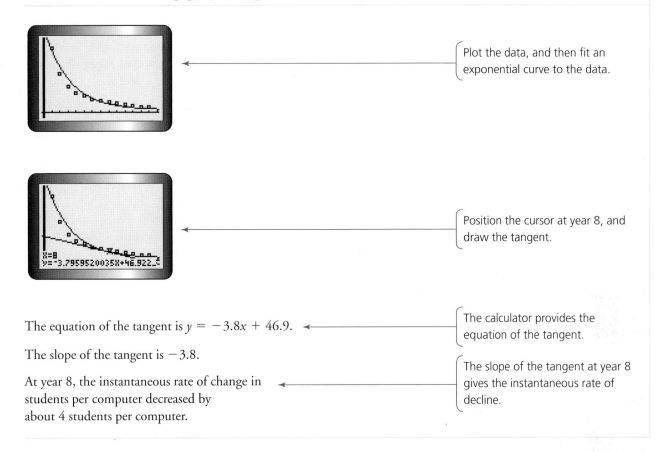

Plot the data, and then fit an exponential curve to the data.

Position the cursor at year 8, and draw the tangent.

The equation of the tangent is $y = -3.8x + 46.9$.

The calculator provides the equation of the tangent.

The slope of the tangent is -3.8.

At year 8, the instantaneous rate of change in students per computer decreased by about 4 students per computer.

The slope of the tangent at year 8 gives the instantaneous rate of decline.

EXAMPLE 3	Comparing instantaneous rates of change in exponential and logarithmic functions

The graphs of $y = 10^x$ and $y = \log x$ are shown below. Discuss how the instantaneous rate of change in the y-values for each function changes as x grows larger.

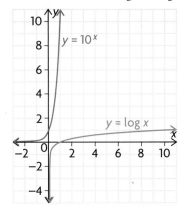

Solution

Tangents to $y = 10^x$

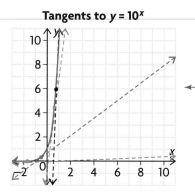

The instantaneous rate of change in the y-values is close to 0 for small values of x. As x increases, the instantaneous rate of change gets large very quickly. As $x \to \infty$, the instantaneous rate of change $\to \infty$.

Tangents to $y = \log x$

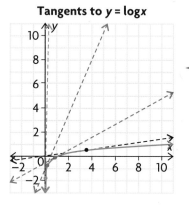

The graph of $y = 10^x$ has a horizontal asymptote. This means that the tangent lines at points with large negative values of x have a small slope, because the tangent lines are almost horizontal. As x increases, the slopes of the tangent lines also increase.

The graph of $y = \log x$ has a vertical asymptote. This means that the tangent lines at points with very small values of x have very large slopes, because the tangent lines are almost vertical. As x gets larger, the tangent lines become less steep. When x is relatively small, small increases in x result in large changes in the slope of the tangent line. As x grows larger, however, the changes in the slope of the tangent line become smaller and the tangent slopes approach zero.

The instantaneous rate of change in the y-values is very large for small values of x. As x gets larger, the instantaneous rate of change gets smaller very quickly. As $x \to \infty$, the instantaneous rate of change $\to 0$.

In Summary

Key Ideas

- The average rate of change is not constant for exponential and logarithmic functions.
- The instantaneous rate of change at a particular point can be estimated by using the same strategies used with polynomial, rational, and trigonometric functions.

Need to Know

- The instantaneous rate of change for an exponential or logarithmic function can be determined numerically or graphically.
- The graph of an exponential or logarithmic function can be used to determine the period during which the average rate of change is least or greatest.
- The graph of an exponential or logarithmic function can be used to predict the greatest and least instantaneous rates of change and when they occur.

CHECK *Your Understanding*

Use the data from Example 1 for questions 1 to 3.

1. Calculate the average rate of change in number of students per computer during the following time periods.
   a) years 2 to 10   **b)** years 1 to 5   **c)** years 10 to 13

2. Predict when the instantaneous rate of change in number of students per computer was the greatest. Give a reason for your answer.

3. Estimate the instantaneous rate of change in number of students per computer for the following years.
   a) year 2   **b)** year 7   **c)** year 12

PRACTISING

4. Jerry invests $6000 at 7.5%/a, compounded annually.
   a) Determine the equation of the amount, A, after t years.
   b) Estimate the instantaneous rate of change in the value at 10 years.
   c) Suppose that the interest rate was compounded semi-annually instead of annually. What would the instantaneous rate of change be at 10 years?

5. **K** You invest $1000 in a savings account that pays 6%/a, compounded annually.
   a) Calculate the rate at which the amount is growing over the first
      i) 2 years   **ii)** 5 years   **iii)** 10 years
   b) Why is the rate of change not constant?

6. For 500 g of a radioactive substance with a half-life of 5.2 h, the amount remaining is given by the formula $M(t) = 500(0.5)^{\frac{t}{5.2}}$, where M is the mass remaining and t is the time in hours.
   a) Calculate the amount remaining after 1 day.
   b) Estimate the instantaneous rate of change in mass at 1 day.

7. The table shows how the mass of a chicken embryo inside an egg changes over the first 20 days after the egg is laid.
   a) Calculate the average rate of change in the mass of the embryo from day 1 to day 20.
   b) Determine an exponential equation that models the data.
   c) Estimate the instantaneous rate of change in mass for the following days.
      i) day 4   **ii)** day 12   **iii)** day 20
   d) According to your model, when will the mass be 6.0000 g?

Days after Egg is Laid	Mass of Embryo (g)
1	0.0002
4	0.0500
8	1.1500
12	5.0700
16	15.9800
20	30.2100

8. A certain radioactive substance decays exponentially. The percent, P, of the substance left after t years is given by the formula $P(t) = 100(1.2)^{-t}$.
   a) Determine the half-life of the substance.
   b) Estimate the instantaneous rate of decay at the end of the first half-life period.

9. The population of a town is decreasing at a rate of $1.8\%/a$. The **A** current population of the town is 12 000.
   a) Write an equation that models the population of the town.
   b) Estimate the instantaneous rate of change in the population 10 years from now.
   c) Determine the instantaneous rate of change when the population is half its current population.

10. The graphs of $y = \left(\frac{1}{2}\right)^x$ and $y = \log_{\frac{1}{2}} x$ are given. Discuss how the **T** instantaneous rate of change for each function changes as x grows larger.

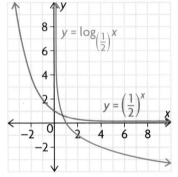

$y = \log_{\left(\frac{1}{2}\right)} x$

$y = \left(\frac{1}{2}\right)^x$

11. As a tornado moves, its speed increases. The function $S(d) = 93 \log d + 65$ relates the speed of the wind, S, in miles per hour, near the centre of a tornado to the distance that the tornado has travelled, d, in miles.
   a) Graph this function.
   b) Calculate the average rate of change for the speed of the wind at the centre of a tornado from mile 10 to mile 100.
   c) Estimate the rate at which the speed of the wind at the centre of a tornado is changing at the moment it has travelled its 10th mile and its 100th mile.
   d) Use your graph to discuss how the rate at which the speed of the wind at the centre of a tornado changes as the distance that the tornado travels increases.

12. Explain how you could estimate the instantaneous rate of change **C** for an exponential function if you did not have access to a graphing calculator.

Extending

13. How is the instantaneous rate of change affected by changes in the parameters of the function?
   a) $y = a \log[k(x - d)] + c$
   b) $y = ab^{[k(x-d)]} + c$

FREQUENTLY ASKED Questions

Q: **How do you solve an exponential equation?**

A1: All exponential equations can be solved using the following property:

If $\log_a M = \log_a N$, then $M = N$.

Take the logarithm of both sides of an exponential equation using a base of 10. Then use the power rule for logs to simplify the equation.

A2: Some exponential equations can be solved by using this property:

If $a^x = a^y$, then $x = y$, where $a > 0$, and $a \neq 1$.

Write both sides of an exponential equation with the same base, and set the exponents equal to each other.

A3: If graphing technology is available, treat both sides of an exponential equation as functions, and graph them simultaneously. The x-coordinate of the point of intersection of the two functions is the solution to the equation. There can be more than one solution.

> **Study | Aid**
> - See Lesson 8.5, Examples 1 to 4.
> - Try Chapter Review Questions 10 to 13.

Q: **How do you solve an equation that contains logarithms?**

A1: If there is a single logarithm in the equation, isolate the log term and then rewrite the equation in exponential form to solve it.

A2: If there is more than one term with a logarithm in the equation, simplify the equation using the laws of logarithms. The equation can then be expressed in exponential form to solve it. If there are terms with logs on both sides of the equation, use the following property:

If $\log_a M = \log_a N$, then $M = N$, where $a, M, N > 0$.

> **Study | Aid**
> - See Lesson 8.6, Examples 1 to 3.
> - Try Chapter Review Questions 14, 15, and 16.

Q: **How do you compare two values on a logarithmic scale?**

A: A logarithmic scale increases exponentially, usually by powers of 10. This means that each value on a logarithmic scale is an increase of 10 times the previous value. To compare the values, use the ratio rather than the difference.

> **Study | Aid**
> - See Lesson 8.7, Example 1.
> - Try Chapter Review Questions 17 to 20.

PRACTICE Questions

Lesson 8.1

1. Determine the inverse of each function. Express your answers in logarithmic form.
   - a) $y = 4^x$
   - c) $y = \left(\dfrac{3}{4}\right)^x$
   - b) $y = a^x$
   - d) $m = p^q$

Lesson 8.2

2. Describe the transformations that must be applied to the parent function $y = \log x$ to obtain each of the following functions.
   - a) $f(x) = -3 \log (2x)$
   - b) $f(x) = \log (x - 5) + 2$
   - c) $f(x) = \dfrac{1}{2} \log 5x$
   - d) $f(x) = \log\left(-\dfrac{1}{3}x\right) - 3$

3. For each sequence of transformations of the parent function $y = \log x$, write the equation of the resulting function.
   - a) vertical compression by a factor of $\dfrac{2}{5}$, followed by a vertical translation 3 units down
   - b) reflection in the x-axis, followed by a horizontal stretch by a factor of 2, and a horizontal translation 3 units to the right
   - c) vertical stretch by a factor of 5, followed by a horizontal compression by a factor of $\dfrac{1}{2}$, and a reflection in the y-axis
   - d) a reflection of the y-axis, a horizontal translation 4 units to the left, followed by a vertical translation 2 units down

4. Describe how the graphs of $f(x) = \log x$ and $g(x) = 3 \log (x - 1) + 2$ are similar yet different.

Lesson 8.3

5. Evaluate.
   - a) $\log_7 343$
   - c) $\log_{19} 1$
   - b) $\log_{\frac{1}{5}} 25$
   - d) $\log_4\left(\dfrac{1}{256}\right)$

6. Estimate the value to three decimal places.
   - a) $\log_3 53$
   - c) $\log_6 159$
   - b) $\log_4 \dfrac{1}{10}$
   - d) $\log_{15} 1456$

Lesson 8.4

7. Express as a single logarithm.
   - a) $\log 5 + \log 11$
   - b) $\log 20 - \log 4$
   - c) $\log_5 6 + \log_5 8 - \log_5 12$
   - d) $2 \log 3 + 4 \log 2$

8. Use the laws of logarithms to evaluate.
   - a) $\log_6 42 - \log_6 7$
   - b) $\log_3 5 + \log_3 18 - \log_3 10$
   - c) $\log_7 \sqrt[3]{49}$
   - d) $2 \log_4 8$

9. Describe how the graph of $y = \log (10\,000x)$ is related to the graph of $y = \log x$.

Lesson 8.5

10. Solve.
    - a) $5^x = 3125$
    - c) $4^{5x} = 16^{2x-1}$
    - b) $4^x = 16\sqrt{128}$
    - d) $3^{5x}9^{x^2} = 27$

11. Solve. Express each answer to three decimal places.
    - a) $6^x = 78$
    - c) $8(3^x) = 132$
    - b) $(5.4)^x = 234$
    - d) $200(1.23)^x = 540$

12. Solve.
    - a) $4^x + 6(4^{-x}) = 5$
    - b) $8(5^{2x}) + 8(5^x) = 6$

13. The half-life of a certain substance is 3.6 days. How long will it take for 20 g of the substance to decay to 7 g?

Lesson 8.6

14. Solve.
  a) $\log_5(2x - 1) = 3$
  b) $\log 3x = 4$
  c) $\log_4(3x - 5) = \log_4 11 + \log_4 2$
  d) $\log(4x - 1) = \log(x + 1) + \log 2$

15. Solve.
  a) $\log(x + 9) - \log x = 1$
  b) $\log x + \log(x - 3) = 1$
  c) $\log(x - 1) + \log(x + 2) = 1$
  d) $\log \sqrt{x^2 - 1} = 2$

16. Recall that $L = 10 \log\left(\dfrac{I}{I_0}\right)$, where I is the intensity of sound in watts per square metre (W/m^2) and $I_0 = 10^{-12}\ W/m^2$. Determine the intensity of a baby screaming if the noise level is 100 dB.

Lesson 8.7

17. What is the sound intensity in watts per square metre (W/m^2) of an engine that is rated at 82 dB?

18. How many times more intense is an earthquake of magnitude 6.2 than an earthquake of magnitude 5.5?

19. Pure water has a pH value of 7.0. How many times more acidic is milk, with a pH value of 6.4, than pure water?

20. Does an increase in acidity from pH 4.7 to pH 2.3 result in the same change in hydrogen ion concentration as a decrease in alkalinity from 12.5 to 10.1? Explain.

21. Is an exponential model appropriate for the data in the following table? If it is, determine the equation that models the data.

x	0	2	4	6	8	10
y	3.0	15.2	76.9	389.2	1975.5	9975.8

22. The population of a town is decreasing at the rate of 1.6%/a. If the population today is 20 000, how long will it take for the population to decline to 15 000?

Lesson 8.8

23. The following table gives the population of a city over time.

Year	1950	1970	1980	1990	1994
Population	132 459	253 539	345 890	465 648	514 013

  a) Calculate the average rate of growth over the entire time period.
  b) Calculate the average rate of growth for the first 30 years. How does it compare with the rate of growth for the entire time period?
  c) Determine an exponential model for the data.
  d) Estimate the instantaneous rate of growth in
    i) 1970   ii) 1990

24. The following data show the number of people (in thousands) who own a DVD player in a large city or linear is best for over a period of years.

Year	1998	1999	2000	2001	2002
Number of DVD Owners (thousands)	23	27	31	37	43

  a) Determine if an exponential or linear model is best for this data.
  b) Use your model to predict how many people will own a DVD player in the year 2015.
  c) What assumptions did you make to make your prediction in part b)? Do you think this is reasonable? Explain.
  d) Determine the average rate of change in the number of DVD players in this city between 1999 and 2002.
  e) Estimate the instantaneous rate of change in the number of DVD players in this city in 2000.
  f) Explain why using an exponential model to answer part b) does not make sense.

1. Write the equation of the inverse of each function in both exponential and logarithmic form.
   a) $y = 4^x$
   b) $y = \log_6 x$

2. State the transformations that must be applied to $f(x) = \log x$ to graph $g(x)$.
   a) $g(x) = \log[2(x - 4)] + 3$
   b) $g(x) = -\frac{1}{2}\log(x + 5) - 1$

3. Evaluate.
   a) $\log_3 \frac{1}{9}$
   b) $\log_5 100 - \log_5 4$

4. Evaluate.
   a) $\log 15 + \log 40 - \log 6$
   b) $\log_7 343 + 2\log_7 49$

5. Express $\log_4 x^2 + 3\log_4 y^{\frac{1}{3}} - \log_4 x$ as a single logarithm. Assume that x and y represent positive numbers.

6. Solve $5^{x+2} = 6^{x+1}$. Round your answer to three decimal places.

7. Solve.
   a) $\log_4(x + 2) + \log_4(x - 1) = 1$
   b) $\log_3(8x - 2) + \log_3(x - 1) = 2$

8. Carbon-14 is used by scientists to estimate how long ago a plant or animal lived. The half-life of carbon-14 is 5730 years. A particular plant contained 100 g of carbon-14 at the time that it died.
   a) How much carbon-14 would remain after 5730 years?
   b) Write an equation to represent the amount of carbon-14 that remains after t years.
   c) After how many years would 80 g of carbon-14 remain?
   d) Estimate the instantaneous rate of change at 100 years.

9. The equation that models the amount of time, t, in minutes that a cup of hot chocolate has been cooling as a function of its temperature, T, in degrees Celsius is $t = \log\left(\frac{T - 22}{75}\right) \div \log(0.75)$. Calculate the following.
   a) the cooling time if the temperature is $35\,^\circ C$
   b) the initial temperature of the drink

Comparing Growth Rates in Bacteria Cultures

In an experiment, bacteria were placed in a hostile environment and a bacterial count was made every hour. The results are given in the following table.

Time Interval (*t* hours)	1	2	3	4	5	6
Bacterial Count (*c*) for Culture A	560	320	180	100	60	30

In a second experiment conducted simultaneously, more of the same bacteria were placed in an environment that encouraged their growth. A bacterial count was made every hour. The results are given in the table below.

Time Interval (*t* hours)	1	2	3	4	5	6
Bacterial Count (*c*) for Culture B	42	68	110	156	212	380

? When did the cultures have the same bacterial count, and at what rate was the population of each culture changing at this time?

A. Graph the data for experiment 1.

B. Determine the equation that best models the data. Explain the process you used to determine the equation.

C. Graph the data for experiment 2.

D. Determine the equation that best models these data.

E. Use your models to estimate the bacterial count in both cultures after 10 h.

F. Determine the average rate of change in population for each culture over the first 4 h.

G. When will the cultures have the same bacterial count? Justify your answer in two ways.

H. Estimate the rate at which populations of both cultures are changing when their bacterial counts are the same.

Task | *Checklist*

✔ Did you draw well-labelled graphs, including some values?

✔ Did you explain the process that you used to obtain an equation that best models the data?

✔ Did you justify your answer for part G in two different ways?

✔ Did you calculate the appropriate rate of change for part H?

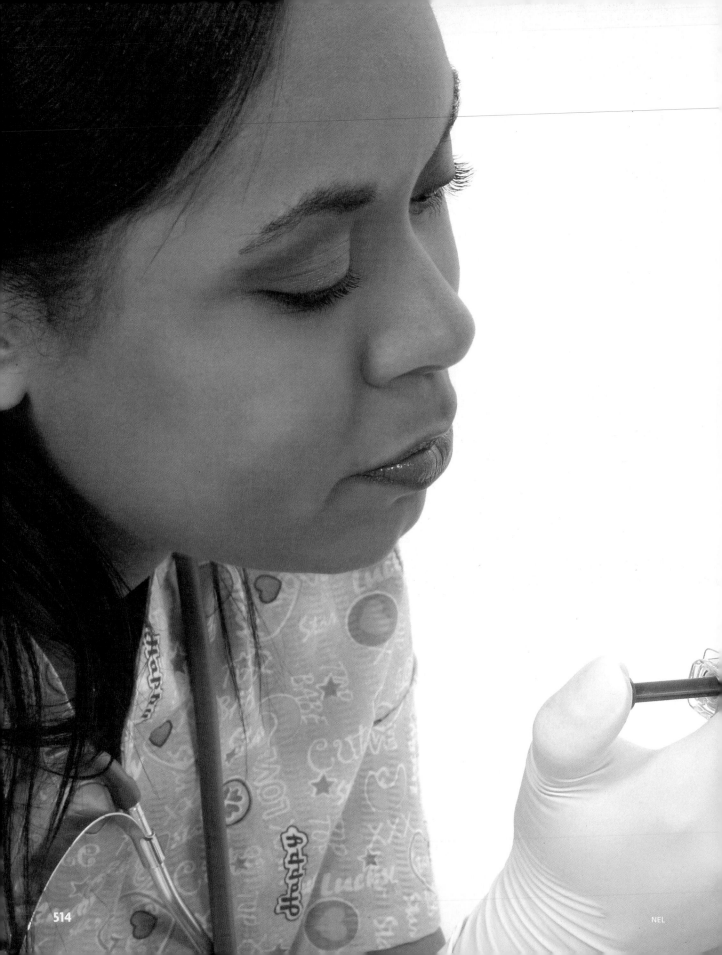

Combinations of Functions

▶ **GOALS**

You will be able to

- Consolidate your understanding of the characteristics of functions

- Create new functions by adding, subtracting, multiplying, and dividing functions

- Investigate the creation of composite functions numerically, graphically, and algebraically

- Determine key characteristics of these new functions

- Solve problems using a variety of function models

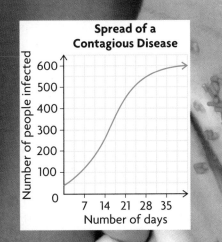

Spread of a Contagious Disease

Number of people infected

600
500
400
300
200
100
0

7 14 21 28 35
Number of days

? *Epidemiology* is the scientific study of contagious diseases. A combination of functions is often used to model the way that a contagious disease spreads through a population. What types of functions could be combined to create an algebraic model that represents the graph shown?

SKILLS AND CONCEPTS *You Need*

Study | *Aid*

- For help, see the Review of Essential Skills found at the Nelson Advanced Functions website.

Question	Appendix
3	R-8

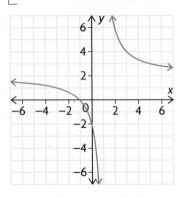

1. Evaluate each of the following functions for $f(-1)$ and $f(4)$. Round your answers to two decimal places, if necessary.

   a) $f(x) = x^3 - 3x^2 - 10x + 24$

   b) $f(x) = \dfrac{4x}{1 - x}$

   c) $f(x) = 3 \log_{10}(x)$

   d) $f(x) = -5(0.5^{(x-1)})$

2. Identify the following characteristics of functions for the graph displayed.

   - domain and range
   - maximum or minimum values
   - interval(s) where the function is increasing
   - interval(s) where the function is decreasing
   - end behaviour
   - equations of asymptotes

3. For each parent function, apply the given transformation(s) and write the equation of the new function.

   a) $y = |x|$; vertical stretch by a factor of 2, shift 3 units to the right

   b) $y = \cos(x)$; reflection in the x-axis, horizontal compression by a factor of $\dfrac{1}{2}$

   c) $y = \log_3 x$; reflection in the y-axis, shift 4 units left and 1 unit down

   d) $y = \dfrac{1}{x}$; vertical stretch by a factor of 4, reflection in the x-axis, shift 5 units down

4. Solve each equation for x, $x \in \mathbf{R}$. State any restrictions on x, as required.

   a) $2x^3 - 7x^2 - 5x + 4 = 0$

   b) $\dfrac{2x + 3}{x + 3} + \dfrac{1}{2} = \dfrac{x + 1}{x - 1}$

   c) $\log x + \log(x - 3) = 1$

   d) $10^{-4x} - 22 = 978$

   e) $5^{x+3} - 5^x = 0.992$

   f) $2 \cos^2 x = \sin x + 1, 0 \le x \le 2\pi$

5. Solve each inequality for x, $x \in \mathbf{R}$.

   a) $x^3 - x^2 - 14x + 24 < 0$

   b) $\dfrac{(2x - 3)(x - 4)}{(x + 2)} \ge 0$

6. Identify each function as even, odd, or neither.

   a) $f(x) = 2\sin(x - \pi)$

   b) $f(x) = \dfrac{3}{4 - x}$

   c) $f(x) = 4x^4 - 3x^2$

   d) $f(x) = 2^{3x-1}$

7. Classify the types of functions you have studied (polynomial, rational, exponential, logarithmic, and trigonometric) as continuous or not.

APPLYING *What You Know*

Building a Sandbox

Duncan is planning to build a rectangular sandbox in his backyard for his son to play in during the summer. He has designed the sandbox so that it will have an open top and a volume of 2 m³. The length of the base will measure four times the height of the sandbox. The wood for the base will cost $5/m², and the wood for the sides will cost $4/m².

❓ What dimensions should Duncan use to minimize the cost of the sandbox he has designed?

A. Let h represent the height (in metres) and let w represent the width of the sandbox. Determine an expression for the width of the sandbox in terms of its height.

B. Write an expression for the cost of the wood for the base of the sandbox in terms of its height.

C. Express the cost of the wood for the two longer sides in terms of the height. Is the cost for the two shorter sides the same?

D. Let $C(h)$ represent the total cost of the wood for the sandbox as a function of its height. Determine the equation for $C(h)$.

E. What types of functions are added in your equation for $C(h)$?

F. What would be a reasonable domain and range for this cost function? Explain.

G. Using graphing technology, graph the cost function using window settings that correspond to its domain and range.

H. Determine the height of the sandbox that will minimize the total cost.

I. What dimensions would you recommend that Duncan use to build the sandbox? Justify your answer.

Exploring Combinations of Functions

YOU WILL NEED

• graphing calculator or graphing software

GOAL

Explore the characteristics of new functions created by combining functions.

Explore the Math

Ahmad was given the graphs pictured below. They were created by combining two familiar functions.

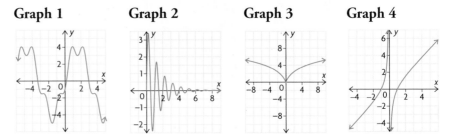

Graph 1   **Graph 2**   **Graph 3**   **Graph 4**

Ahmad does not recognize these new functions and wonders which type of functions have been combined to create them. He also wonders whether any of these graphs could model a real-life situation.

? How can two functions be combined to create a new function?

A. Compare each of the graphs above with the function equations in the table below.

$y = x\sqrt{x-1}$	$y = 4\sin x - \cos 4x$	$y = x - \dfrac{1}{x}$	$y = 5\log(\lvert x \rvert + 1)$
$y = (x^2)(\sin(x))$	$y = \begin{cases} -0.5(x-2)^2 + 2, & x < 0 \\ 0.5(x-2)^2 - 2, & x \geq 0 \end{cases}$	$y = (0.5^x)(4\sin(2\pi x))$	$y = x^3 \div (x+1)$

Predict which equations will match each graph. Copy the table on the next page, and record your predictions and your rationale for each.

Graph	Equation of Function	Rationale
1		
2		
3		
4		

B. Compare your predictions with a partner's predictions. Explain to each other why you made each prediction.

C. Using graphing technology in radian mode, graph the equation that you predicted would match graph 1. Use a domain and range in the window settings that match the scale given on each of the given graphs.

D. Does the graph of your equation match graph 1? If it does not, choose another equation from the table and try again.

E. Once you have correctly matched the equation with graph 1, repeat parts C and D until all the graphs have been correctly matched.

F. Examine the equation that matches each graph.
- List the parent functions in each equation.
- State the transformations that were applied to each parent function.
- Explain how the parent functions were combined.

Reflecting

G. Which of the four given graphs is periodic? How does it differ from other periodic functions you have seen before? What type of combination produced this effect?

H. Do any of the graphs represent an even function? Do any represent an odd function? Explain how you know.

I. Which graph contains an asymptote? Describe the functions that were combined to produce this graph. Explain how you can tell from the equation where the vertical asymptote occurs.

J. Which graph could be used to model the motion of a swaying building moments after an earthquake? Explain why.

In Summary

Key Idea

- Many interesting functions can be created by combining two or more simpler functions. This can be done by adding, subtracting, multiplying, or dividing functions to create more complex functions.

Need to Know

- The characteristics of the functions that are combined affect the properties and characteristics of the resulting function.

FURTHER Your Understanding

1. Using graphing technology (in radian mode) and the functions given in the chart below, experiment to create new functions by combining different types of functions. Each time, use different operations and different types of functions. You may need to experiment with the window settings to get a clear picture of what the graph looks like. Include a sketch of your new graphs and the equations that were used for the models.

$y = 2 - 0.5x$	$y = 2^x$	$y = \sin 2\pi x$	$y = \cos 2\pi x$
$y = \log x$	$y = \left(\dfrac{1}{2}\right)^x$	$y = x^4 - x^2$	$y = 2x$

2. Using the functions in the chart above, create a new function that has each of the characteristics given below. Include a sketch of your new graphs and the equations that were used for the models.
   a) a function that has a vertical asymptote and a horizontal asymptote
   b) a function that is even
   c) a function that is odd
   d) a function that is periodic
   e) a function that resembles a periodic function with decreasing maximum values and increasing minimum values
   f) a function that resembles a periodic function with increasing maximum values and decreasing minimum values

3. Select any two functions that you have studied in this course. Experiment by combining these functions in various ways and graphing them on a graphing calculator. Include a sketch of your new graphs and the equations of the functions you selected. Challenge your classmates to see who can produce the most interesting graph.

Combining Two Functions: Sums and Differences

Represent the sums and differences of two functions graphically and algebraically, and determine their properties.

YOU WILL NEED

• graphing calculator or graphing software

INVESTIGATE the Math

The sound produced when a person strums a guitar chord represents the combination of sounds made by several different strings. The sound made by each string can be represented by a sine function. The period of each function is based on the frequency of the sound, whereas the loudness of the individual sounds varies and is related to the amplitude of each function. These sine functions are literally added together to produce the desired sound. The sound of a G chord played on a six-string acoustic guitar can be approximated by the following combination of sine functions:

$$y = 16 \sin 196x + 9 \sin 392x + 4 \sin 784x$$

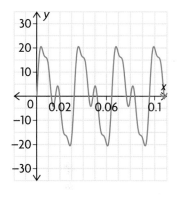

? When functions are added or subtracted, how do the resulting characteristics of the new function compare with those of the original functions?

A. Explore a similar but simpler combination of sine functions by examining the properties of the sum defined by $y = \sin x + \sin 2x$. Copy and complete the table of values, and use your results and the graphs shown to sketch the graph of $y = \sin x + \sin 2x$, where $0 \le x \le 2\pi$.

x	sin x	sin 2x	sin x + sin 2x
0	0	0	
$\frac{\pi}{4}$	0.7071	1	
$\frac{\pi}{2}$	1	0	
$\frac{3\pi}{4}$	0.7071	−1	
π	0	0	
$\frac{5\pi}{4}$	−0.7071	1	
$\frac{3\pi}{2}$	−1	0	
$\frac{7\pi}{4}$	−0.7071	−1	
2π	0	0	

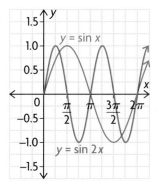

B. Set the calculator to radian mode. Adjust the window settings so that $0 \le x \le 4\pi$ using an Xscl $= \frac{\pi}{4}$, and $-2 \le y \le 2$ using a Yscl $= 1$. Verify your graph in part A by graphing $y = \sin x + \sin 2x$.

C. What is the period of $y = \sin x + \sin 2x$? How does it compare with the periods of $y = \sin x$ and $y = \sin 2x$?

D. What is the amplitude of $y = \sin x + \sin 2x$? How does it compare with the amplitudes of $y = \sin x$ and $y = \sin 2x$?

E. Create a new table of values, and use your results and the graphs of $y = \sin x$ and $y = \sin 2x$ to sketch the graph of $y = \sin x - \sin 2x$, where $0 \le x \le 2\pi$. Repeat parts B to D using this difference function.

F. Do you think that the graph of $y = \sin 2x - \sin x$ will be the same as the graph you created in part E? Explain. Check your conjecture by using graphing technology to graph this function.

G. Investigate the sum of other types of functions. Use graphing technology to graph each set of functions, and describe how the characteristics of the functions are related.
  i) $y_1 = -x, y_2 = x^2, y_3 = -x + x^2$
  ii) $y_1 = \sqrt{x}, y_2 = \sqrt{x + 2}, y_3 = \sqrt{x} + \sqrt{x + 2}$
  iii) $y_1 = 2^x, y_2 = 2^{-x}, y_3 = 2^x + 2^{-x}$
  iv) $y_1 = \cos x, y_2 = \cos 2x, y_3 = \cos x + \cos 2x$

H. Investigate the difference of each set of functions in part G by graphing y_1 and y_2, and changing y_3 to $y_3 = y_1 - y_2$. Describe how the characteristics of the functions are related.

Reflecting

I. How does the degree of the sum or difference of two polynomial functions compare with the degree of the individual functions?

J. How does the period of the sum or difference of two trigonometric functions compare with the periods of the individual functions?

K. When looking at the sum of two functions, does the phrase "for each x, add the corresponding y-values together" describe the result you observed for every pair of functions? What phrase would you use to describe finding the difference of two functions?

L. Looking at the graphs of the two square root functions, explain why the domain of the graph of their sum is $x \ge 0$.

M. Determine the y-intercept of y_3, where y_3 represents the difference of the two exponential functions. What does this point represent with respect to y_1 and y_2?

APPLY *the Math*

EXAMPLE **1**	Selecting a strategy to combine functions by addition and subtraction

Given $f(x) = -x^2 + 3$ and $g(x) = -2x$, determine the graphs of $f(x) + g(x)$ and $f(x) - g(x)$. Discuss the key characteristics of the resulting graphs.

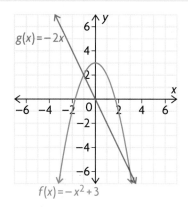

Solution A: Using a graphical strategy

x	f(x)	g(x)	f(x) + g(x)	f(x) − g(x)
−3	−6	6	−6 + 6 = 0	−6 − 6 = −12
−2	−1	4	3	−5
−1	2	2	4	0
−0.5	2.75	1	3.75	1.75
0	3	0	3	3
1	2	−2	0	4
2	−1	−4	−5	3
3	−6	−6	−12	0

Make a table of values for $f(x)$ and $g(x)$, for selected values of x. Create $f + g$ by adding the y-coordinates of f and g together. Create $f - g$ by subtracting the y-coordinates of g from f.

These functions can be added or subtracted over their entire domains since they both have the same domain $\{x \in \mathbf{R}\}$.

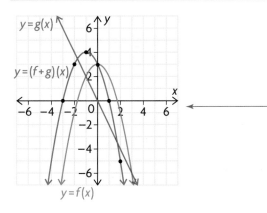

Plot the ordered pairs $(x, f(x) + g(x))$. Join the plotted points with a smooth curve.

Observe that the zeros of the new function occur when the y-values of f and g are the same distance from the x-axis, but on opposite sides. When a zero occurs for either f or g, the value of $f + g$ is the value of the other function.

At any point where f and g intersect, the value of $f + g$ is double the value of f (or g) for the corresponding x.

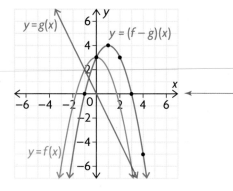

Plot the ordered pairs $(x, f(x) - g(x))$ from the table, and join them with a smooth curve to produce the graph of $f - g$.

Observe that the zeros of this $f - g$ graph occur when the graphs of f and g intersect.

Where g has a zero, the value of $f - g$ is the same as the value of f. Where f has a zero, the value of $f - g$ is the opposite of the value of g.

Solution B: Using an algebraic strategy

$f(x) = -x^2 + 3$ and $g(x) = -2x$

$$(f + g)(x) = f(x) + g(x)$$
$$= (-x^2 + 3) + (-2x)$$
$$= -x^2 - 2x + 3$$

Remember that adding two functions means adding their y-values for a given value of x.

Since the expressions for $f(x)$ and $g(x)$ represent the y-values for each function, we determine an expression for $f + g$ by adding the two expressions.

$$(f + g)(x) = -[x^2 + 2x] + 3$$
$$= -[x^2 + 2x + 1 - 1] + 3$$
$$= -[(x + 1)^2 - 1] + 3$$
$$= -(x + 1)^2 + 4$$

Recognizing that $f + g$ is a quadratic function, we can complete the square to change the expression into vertex form.

The graph of $f + g$ can be sketched by starting with the graph of $y = x^2$ and applying the following transformations: reflection in the x-axis, followed by a shift of 1 unit to the left and 4 units up.

The graph of $y = (f + g)(x)$ has the following characteristics: it is neither odd nor even; it is increasing on the interval $(-\infty, -1)$ and decreasing on the interval $(-1, \infty)$; it has zeros at $(-3, 0)$ and $(1, 0)$; it has a maximum value of $y = 4$ when $x = -1$; its domain is $\{x \in \mathbf{R}\}$; its range is $\{y \in \mathbf{R} \mid y \leq 4\}$.

$$(f - g)(x) = f(x) - g(x)$$
$$= (-x^2 + 3) - (-2x)$$
$$= -x^2 + 2x + 3$$

Similarly, we obtain the expression for $f - g$ by subtracting $g(x)$ from $f(x)$.

In vertex form,

$$(f - g)(x) = -[x^2 - 2x] + 3$$
$$= -[x^2 - 2x + 1 - 1] + 3$$
$$= -(x - 1)^2 + 4$$

Again, we can rewrite the quadratic expression in vertex form to graph it.

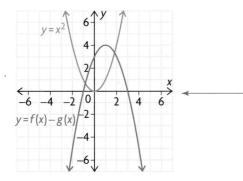

The graph of $f - g$ resembles the graph of $f + g$, except it has been shifted 1 unit to the right instead of 1 unit left.

The graph of $y = (f - g)(x)$ has the following characteristics: it is neither odd nor even; it is increasing on the interval $(-\infty, 1)$ and decreasing on the interval $(1, \infty)$; it has zeros at $(-1, 0)$ and $(3, 0)$; it has a maximum value of $y = 4$ when $x = 1$; its domain is $\{x \in \mathbf{R}\}$; its range is $\{y \in \mathbf{R} | y \leq 4\}$.

EXAMPLE 2   Connecting the domains of the sum and difference of two functions

Determine the domain and range of $(f - g)(x)$ and $(f + g)(x)$ if $f(x) = 10^x$ and $g(x) = \log(x + 5)$.

Solution

Sketch the graphs of f and g.

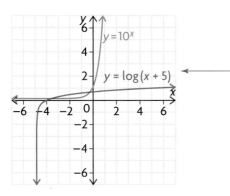

$f(x) = 10^x$ is an exponential function that has the x-axis as its horizontal asymptote. Exponential functions are defined for all real numbers, so its domain is $\{x \in \mathbf{R}\}$.

$g(x) = \log(x + 5)$ is a logarithmic function in base 10. Logarithmic functions are only defined for positive values: $x + 5 > 0$, so $x > -5$. This function has a vertical asymptote defined by $x = -5$. Its domain is $\{x \in \mathbf{R} | x > -5\}$.

$$(f - g)(x) = f(x) - g(x)$$
$$= 10^x - \log(x + 5)$$
$$(f + g)(x) = f(x) + g(x)$$
$$= 10^x + \log(x + 5)$$

The domain of the functions $(f - g)(x)$ and $(f + g)(x)$ is $\{x \in \mathbf{R} | x > -5\}$.

Values for the functions $f - g$ and $f + g$ can only be determined when functions f and g are both defined. This occurs for all values of x that are common to the domains of both f and g.

This is the **intersection** of the domains of f and g.
$$\{x \in \mathbf{R}\} \cap \{x \in \mathbf{R} | x > -5\}$$
$$= \{x \in \mathbf{R} | x > -5\}$$

intersection

a set that contains the elements that are common to both sets; the symbol for intersection is ∩

EXAMPLE **3**   Modelling a situation using a sum of two functions

In the past, biologists have found that the function $P(t) = 5000 - 1000 \cos\left(\frac{\pi}{6}t\right)$ models the deer population in a provincial park, which undergoes a seasonal fluctuation. In this case, $P(t)$ is the size of the deer population t months after January. A disease in the wolf population has caused its population to decline, and the biologists have discovered that the deer population is increasing by 50 deer each month. Assuming that this pattern continues, determine the new function that will model the deer population over time and discuss its characteristics.

Solution

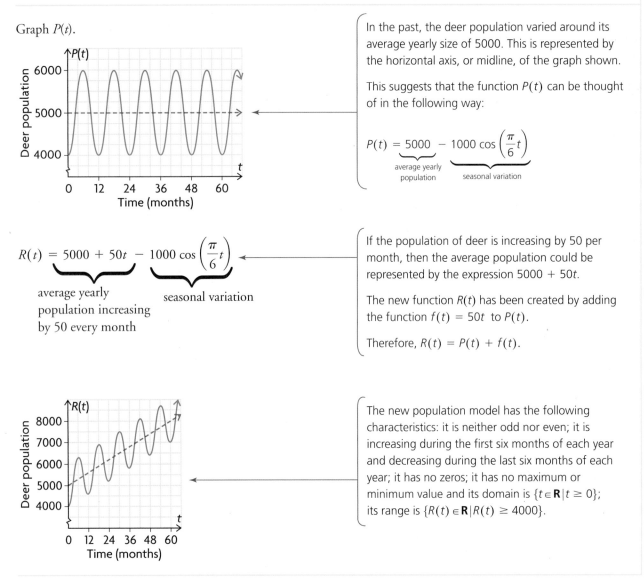

Graph $P(t)$.

In the past, the deer population varied around its average yearly size of 5000. This is represented by the horizontal axis, or midline, of the graph shown.

This suggests that the function $P(t)$ can be thought of in the following way:

$$P(t) = \underbrace{5000}_{\substack{\text{average yearly} \\ \text{population}}} - \underbrace{1000 \cos\left(\frac{\pi}{6}t\right)}_{\text{seasonal variation}}$$

$$R(t) = \underbrace{5000 + 50t}_{\substack{\text{average yearly} \\ \text{population increasing} \\ \text{by 50 every month}}} - \underbrace{1000 \cos\left(\frac{\pi}{6}t\right)}_{\text{seasonal variation}}$$

If the population of deer is increasing by 50 per month, then the average population could be represented by the expression $5000 + 50t$.

The new function $R(t)$ has been created by adding the function $f(t) = 50t$ to $P(t)$.

Therefore, $R(t) = P(t) + f(t)$.

The new population model has the following characteristics: it is neither odd nor even; it is increasing during the first six months of each year and decreasing during the last six months of each year; it has no zeros; it has no maximum or minimum value and its domain is $\{t \in \mathbf{R} \mid t \geq 0\}$; its range is $\{R(t) \in \mathbf{R} \mid R(t) \geq 4000\}$.

EXAMPLE 4   Reasoning about families of functions

Use graphing technology to explore the graph of $f - g$, where $f(x) = x^2$ and $g(x) = nx$, and $n \in \mathbf{W}$. Discuss your results with respect to the type of function, its shape and symmetry, zeros, maximum and minimum values, intervals of increase/decrease, and domain and range.

Solution

$(f - g)(x) = f(x) - g(x),$
then for $f(x) = x^2$ and $g(x) = nx,$
$(f - g)(x) = x^2 - nx$, where $n \in \mathbf{W}$

> $f - g$ will always be a quadratic function, regardless of the value of n.

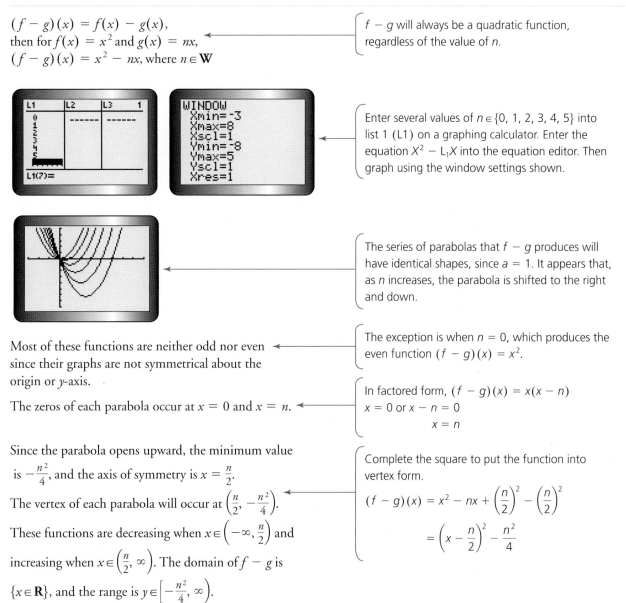

> Enter several values of $n \in \{0, 1, 2, 3, 4, 5\}$ into list 1 (L1) on a graphing calculator. Enter the equation $X^2 - L_1 X$ into the equation editor. Then graph using the window settings shown.

> The series of parabolas that $f - g$ produces will have identical shapes, since $a = 1$. It appears that, as n increases, the parabola is shifted to the right and down.

Most of these functions are neither odd nor even since their graphs are not symmetrical about the origin or y-axis.

> The exception is when $n = 0$, which produces the even function $(f - g)(x) = x^2$.

The zeros of each parabola occur at $x = 0$ and $x = n$.

> In factored form, $(f - g)(x) = x(x - n)$
> $x = 0$ or $x - n = 0$
> $\qquad x = n$

Since the parabola opens upward, the minimum value is $-\frac{n^2}{4}$, and the axis of symmetry is $x = \frac{n}{2}$.

The vertex of each parabola will occur at $\left(\frac{n}{2}, -\frac{n^2}{4}\right)$.

These functions are decreasing when $x \in \left(-\infty, \frac{n}{2}\right)$ and

increasing when $x \in \left(\frac{n}{2}, \infty\right)$. The domain of $f - g$ is

$\{x \in \mathbf{R}\}$, and the range is $y \in \left[-\frac{n^2}{4}, \infty\right)$.

> Complete the square to put the function into vertex form.
> $(f - g)(x) = x^2 - nx + \left(\frac{n}{2}\right)^2 - \left(\frac{n}{2}\right)^2$
> $\qquad = \left(x - \frac{n}{2}\right)^2 - \frac{n^2}{4}$

In Summary

Key Ideas

- When two functions $f(x)$ and $g(x)$ are combined to form the function $(f + g)(x)$, the new function is called the sum of f and g. For any given value of x, the value of the function is represented by $f(x) + g(x)$. The graph of $f + g$ can be obtained from the graphs of functions f and g by adding corresponding y-coordinates.

- Similarly, the difference of two functions, $f - g$, is $(f - g)(x) = f(x) - g(x)$. The graph of $f - g$ can be obtained by subtracting the y-coordinate of g from the y-coordinate of f for every pair of corresponding x-values.

Need to Know

- Algebraically, $(f + g)(x) = f(x) + g(x)$ and $(f - g)(x) = f(x) - g(x)$.

- The domain of $f + g$ or $f - g$ is the intersection of the domains of f and g. This means that the functions $f + g$ and $f - g$ are only defined where the domains of both f and g overlap.

CHECK Your Understanding

1. Let $f = \{(-4, 4), (-2, 4), (1, 3), (3, 5), (4, 6)\}$ and $g = \{(-4, 2), (-2, 1), (0, 2), (1, 2), (2, 2), (4, 4)\}$.
   Determine:

   a) $f + g$ c) $f - g$ e) $f + f$

   b) $g + f$ d) $g - f$ f) $g - g$

2. a) Determine $(f + g)(4)$ when $f(x) = x^2 - 3$ and $g(x) = -\dfrac{6}{x - 2}$.

   b) For which value of x is $(f + g)(x)$ undefined? Explain why.

   c) What is the domain of $(f + g)(x)$ and $(f - g)(x)$?

3. What is the domain of $f - g$, where $f(x) = \sqrt{x + 1}$ and $g(x) = 2 \log[-(x + 1)]$?

4. Make a reasonable sketch of the graph of $f + g$ and $f - g$, where $0 \le x \le 6$, for the functions shown.

5. a) Given the function $f(x) = |x|$ (which is even) and $g(x) = x$ (which is odd), determine $f + g$.

b) Is $f + g$ even, odd, or neither?

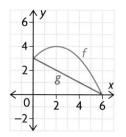

PRACTISING

6. $f = \{(-9, -2), (-8, 5), (-6, 1), (-3, 7), (-1, -2), (0, -10)\}$
K and $g = \{(-7, 7), (-6, 6), (-5, 5), (-4, 4), (-3, 3)\}$.
Calculate:

a) $f + g$ **c)** $f - g$ **e)** $f - f$
b) $g + f$ **d)** $g - f$ **f)** $g + g$

7. a) If $f(x) = \dfrac{1}{3x + 4}$ and $g(x) = \dfrac{1}{x - 2}$, what is $f + g$?

b) What is the domain of $f + g$?

c) What is $(f + g)(8)$?

d) What is $(f - g)(8)$?

8. The graphs of $f(x)$ and $g(x)$, where $0 \le x \le 5$, are shown. Sketch the graphs of $(f + g)(x)$ and $(f - g)(x)$.

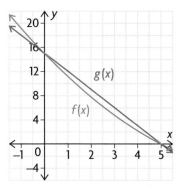

9. For each pair of functions, determine the equations of $f(x) + g(x)$ and $f(x) - g(x)$. Using graphing technology, graph these new functions and discuss each of the following characteristics of the resulting graphs: symmetry, intervals of increase/decrease, zeros, maximum and minimum values, period (where applicable), and domain and range.

a) $f(x) = 2^x, g(x) = x^3$

b) $f(x) = \cos(2\pi x), g(x) = x^4$

c) $f(x) = \log(x), g(x) = 2x$

d) $f(x) = \sin(2\pi x), g(x) = 2\sin(\pi x)$

e) $f(x) = \sin(2\pi x) + 2, g(x) = \dfrac{1}{x}$

f) $f(x) = \sqrt{x - 2}, g(x) = \dfrac{1}{x - 2}$

10. a) Is the sum of two even functions even, odd, or neither? Explain.
b) Is the sum of two odd functions even, odd, or neither? Explain.
c) Is the sum of an even function and an odd function even, odd, or neither? Explain.

11. Recall, from Example 3, the function $P(t) = 5000 - 1000 \cos\left(\frac{\pi}{6}t\right)$, which models the deer population in a provincial park. A disease in the deer population has caused it to decline. Biologists have discovered that the deer population is decreasing by 25 deer each month.
a) Assuming that this pattern continues, determine the new function that will model the deer population over time and discuss its characteristics.
b) Estimate when the deer population in this park will be extinct.

12. When the driver of a vehicle observes an obstacle in the vehicle's path, the driver reacts to apply the brakes and bring the vehicle to a complete stop. The distance that the vehicle travels while coming to a stop is a combination of the reaction distance, r, in metres, given by $r(x) = 0.21x$, and the braking distance, b, also in metres, given by $b(x) = 0.006x^2$. The speed of the vehicle is x km/h. Determine the stopping distance of the vehicle as a function of its speed, and calculate the stopping distance if the vehicle is travelling at 90 km/h.

13. Determine a sine function, f, and a cosine function, g, such that $y = \sqrt{2} \sin(\pi(x - 2.25))$ can be written in the form of $f - g$.

14. Use graphing technology to explore the graph of $f + g$, where $f(x) = x^3$, $g(x) = nx^2$, and $n \in \mathbf{W}$. Discuss your results with respect to the type of function, its shape and symmetry, zeros, maximum and minimum values, intervals of increase/decrease, and domain and range.

15. Describe or give an example of
a) two odd functions whose sum is an even function
b) two functions whose sum represents a vertical stretch applied to one of the functions
c) two rational functions whose difference is a constant function

Extending

16. Let $f(x) = x^2 - nx + 5$ and $g(x) = mx^2 + x - 3$. The functions are combined to form the new function $h(x) = f(x) + g(x)$. Points $(1, 3)$ and $(-2, 18)$ satisfy the new function. Determine the values of m and n.

9.3 Combining Two Functions: Products

GOAL

Represent the product of two functions graphically and algebraically, and determine the characteristics of the product.

YOU WILL NEED

- graphing calculator or graphing software

LEARN ABOUT the Math

In the previous section, you learned that music is made up of combinations of sine waves. Have you ever wondered how sound engineers cause the music to fade out, gradually, at the end of a song? The music fades out because the sine waves that represent the music are being squashed or **damped**. Mathematically, this can be done by multiplying a sine function by another function.

The functions defined by $g(x) = \sin(2\pi x)$ and $f(x) = 2^{-x}$, where $\{x \in \mathbf{R} \mid x \geq 0\}$, are shown below. Observe what happens when these functions are multiplied to produce the graph of $(f \times g)(x) = 2^{-x}\sin(2\pi x)$.

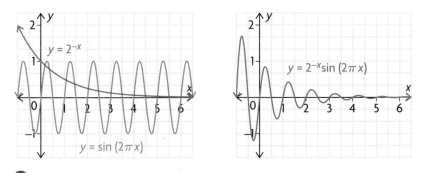

? Can the product of two functions be constructed using the same strategies that are used to create the sum or difference of two functions?

EXAMPLE 1   **Connecting the values of a product function to the values of each function**

Investigate the product of the functions $f(x) = 2^{-x}$ and $g(x) = \sin(2\pi x)$.

Solution

	A	B	C	D
1	x	f(x)=2^−x	g(x)=sin(2πx)	(fxg)(x)=(2^−x)sin(2πx)
2	0.00	1.00	0.00	0.00
3	0.25	0.84	1.00	0.84
4	0.50	0.71	0.00	0.00
5	0.75	0.59	−1.00	−0.59
6	1.00	0.50	0.00	0.00
7	1.25	0.42	1.00	0.42
8	1.50	0.35	0.00	0.00
9	1.75	0.30	−1.00	−0.30
10	2.00	0.25	0.00	0.00
11	2.25	0.21	1.00	0.21
12	2.50	0.18	0.00	0.00
13	2.75	0.15	−1.00	−0.15
14	3.00	0.13	0.00	0.00
15	3.25	0.11	1.00	0.11
16	3.50	0.09	0.00	0.00
17	3.75	0.07	−1.00	−0.07
18	4.00	0.06	0.00	0.00

In a spreadsheet, enter some values of x in column A, and enter the formulas for f, g, and f × g in columns B, C, and D, respectively.

The values in the table have been rounded to two decimal places.

Looking at each row of the table, for any given value of x, the function value of $(f \times g)(x)$ is represented by $f(x) \times g(x)$.

This makes sense since the new function is created by multiplying the original functions together.

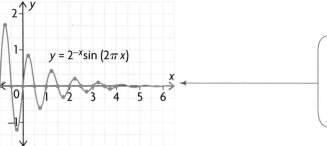

$y = 2^{-x}\sin(2\pi x)$

Plotting the ordered pairs $(x, (f \times g)(x))$ results in the graph of the dampened sine wave. This means that the graph of f × g can be obtained from the graphs of functions f and g by multiplying corresponding y-coordinates.

```
Plot1 Plot2 Plot3
\Y1=2^-X
\Y2=sin(2πX)
\Y3=Y1*Y2
\Y4=(2^-X)(sin(2
πX))
\Y5=
\Y6=
```

Use a graphing calculator to verify the results. Enter the functions into the equation editor as shown. Turn off the first two functions, and choose a bold line to graph the third function.

```
WINDOW
 Xmin=0
 Xmax=6
 Xscl=1
 Ymin=-2
 Ymax=2
 Yscl=1
 Xres=1
```

Use window settings that match the given graph of $(f \times g)(x)$.

The graph of Y4 traces over the graph of the product function Y3. This confirms that the product function is identical to, and obtained by, multiplying the expressions of the two functions together.

The graph of Y3 shows the graph produced by multiplying the corresponding y-values of the functions stored in Y1 and Y2.

Reflecting

A. If $(0.4, 0.76) \in f(x)$ and $(0.4, 0.59) \in g(x)$, what ordered pair belongs to $(f \times g)(x)$?

B. If $f(1) = 0.5$ and $(f \times g)(1) = 0$, what do you know about the value of $g(1)$? Explain.

C. Look at the original graphs of $f(x)$ and $g(x)$. How can you predict the locations of the zeros of $(f \times g)(x)$ before you construct a table of values or a graph? Explain.

D. What is the domain of $f \times g$? How does it compare with the domains of f and g?

E. If function $f(x)$ was replaced by $f(x) = \sqrt{x}$, explain how this would change the domain of $(f \times g)(x)$.

APPLY the Math

EXAMPLE **2**	Constructing the product of two functions graphically

Determine the graph of $y = (f \times g)(x)$, given the graphs of $f(x) = x^2 + x - 6$ and $g(x) = x$.

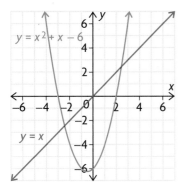

Solution

x	f(x)	g(x)	(f × g)(x)
−4	6	−4	−24
−3	0	−3	0
−2	−4	−2	8
−1	−6	−1	6
0	−6	0	0
1	−4	1	−4
2	0	2	0
3	6	3	18
4	14	4	56

Use the graph to determine some of the points on the graphs of f and g, and create a table of values.

The graphs indicate that both functions have the same domain, $\{x \in \mathbf{R}\}$.

Determine the values of $(f \times g)(x)$ by multiplying the y-coordinates of f and g together for the same value of x.

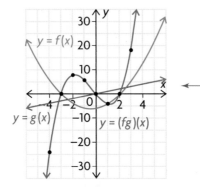

The domain of the product function is the intersection of the domains of f and g, $\{x \in \mathbf{R}\}$.

Plot some of the ordered pairs $(x, (f \times g)(x))$, and use these to sketch the graph of the product function.

Notice that the zeros of the two functions, f and g, result in points that are also zeros of f × g. This makes sense since the product of zero and any number is still zero.

Also notice that $(f \times g)(1) = f(1)$ because $g(1) = 1$. As a result, $(f \times g)(1) = f(1) \times 1 = -4 \times 1 = -4$. Similarly, $(f \times g)(-1) = -f(-1)$ because $g(-1) = -1$, so $(f \times g)(-1) = f(-1) \times (-1)$ $= -6 \times -1 = 6$.

Functions f and g are second and first degree polynomial functions, so the product function fg is a third degree polynomial function (also called a cubic function).

EXAMPLE 3	Constructing the product of two functions algebraically

Let $f(x) = \sqrt{x}$ and $g(x) = \frac{1}{2}x - 2$.

a) Find the equation of the function $(f \times g)(x)$.
b) Determine $(f \times g)(4)$.
c) Find the domain of $y = (f \times g)(x)$.
d) Use graphing technology to graph $y = (f \times g)(x)$, and discuss the key characteristics of the graph.

Solution

a) $(f \times g)(x) = f(x) \times g(x)$

$= \sqrt{x}\left(\frac{1}{2}x - 2\right)$

To find the formula for the product of the functions, take the expression for $f(x)$ and multiply it by the expression for $g(x)$.

b) $(f \times g)(4) = \sqrt{4}\left(\frac{1}{2}(4) - 2\right)$

$= 2(0)$

$= 0$

Calculate the value of $(f \times g)(4)$ by substituting $x = 4$ into the expression $(f \times g)(x)$.

c) The domain of g is $\{x \in \mathbf{R}\}$, but the domain of f is $\{x \in \mathbf{R} \mid x \geq 0\}$. So, the domain of $f \times g$ is $\{x \in \mathbf{R} \mid x \geq 0\}$.

The domain of $f \times g$ can only consist of x-values that exist in the domains of both f and g.

-10 -8 -6 -4 -2 0 2 4 6 8 10

d)

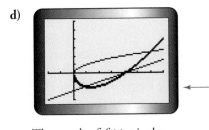

The graph of $f \times g$ is the bold line.

The graph of $f \times g$
- lies below the x-axis when $x \in (0, 4)$, since $f(x) > 0$ and $g(x) < 0$ in that interval
- has zeros occurring at $x = 0$ when $f(x) = 0$ and at $x = 4$ when $g(x) = 0$; no other zeros will occur, since both functions are positive
- is neither odd nor even since it has no symmetry about the origin or the y-axis

EXAMPLE 4

Modelling a situation using a product function

The rate at which a contaminant leaves a storm sewer and enters a lake depends on two factors: the concentration of the contaminant in the water from the sewer and the rate at which the water leaves the sewer. Both of these factors vary with time. The concentration of the contaminant, in kilograms per cubic metre of water, is given by $c(t) = t^2$, where t is in seconds. The rate at which water leaves the sewer, in cubic metres per second, is given by $w(t) = \dfrac{1}{t^4 + 20}$. Determine the time at which the contaminant leaves the sewer and enters the lake at the maximum rate.

Solution

$c(t)$ is in $\dfrac{\text{kg}}{\text{m}^3}$ and $w(t)$ is in $\dfrac{\text{m}^3}{\text{s}}$

$c(t) \times w(t) \rightarrow \left(\dfrac{\text{kg}}{\text{m}^3}\right)\left(\dfrac{\text{m}^3}{\text{s}}\right) = \dfrac{\text{kg}}{\text{s}}$

The product of the concentration function and the water rate function results in a function that describes the rate of contaminant flow into the lake.

> Analyze the units of both functions to help you determine the relationship between the functions that can be used to determine a function for the rate at which the contaminant flows into the lake.

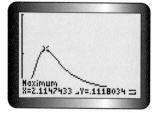

$c(t) \times w(t) = (t^2)\left(\dfrac{1}{t^4 + 20}\right)$

$= \dfrac{t^2}{t^4 + 20}$

> In this context, the domain of both functions is $\{t \in \mathbf{R} \mid t \geq 0\}$ since both functions have time as the independent variable. Thus, $\{t \in \mathbf{R} \mid t \geq 0\}$ is also the domain of $c(t) \times w(t)$.

Tech Support

For help determining the maximum value of a function using a graphing calculator, see Technical Appendix, T-9.

Maximum
X=2.1147433 Y=.1118034

> Use the maximum operation on a graphing calculator to graph $c(t) \times w(t)$ on its domain and estimate when its maximum value occurs.

WINDOW
Xmin=0
Xmax=10
Xscl=1
Ymin=0
Ymax=.2
Yscl=.1
Xres=1

The contaminant is flowing into the lake at a maximum rate of about 0.11 kg/s. This occurs at about 2 s after the water begins to flow into the lake.

In Summary

Key Idea

- When two functions, $f(x)$ and $g(x)$, are combined to form the function $(f \times g)(x)$, the new function is called the product of f and g. For any given value of x, the function value is represented by $f(x) \times g(x)$. The graph of $f \times g$ can be obtained from the graphs of functions f and g by multiplying each y-coordinate of f by the corresponding y-coordinate of g.

Need to Know

- Algebraically, $f \times g$ is defined as $(f \times g)(x) = f(x) \cdot g(x)$.
- The domain of $f \times g$ is the intersection of the domains of f and g.
- If $f(x) = 0$ or $g(x) = 0$, then $(f \times g)(x) = 0$.
- If $f(x) = \pm 1$, then $(f \times g)(x) = \pm g(x)$. Similarly, if $g(x) = \pm 1$, then $(f \times g)(x) = \pm f(x)$.

CHECK Your Understanding

1. For each of the following pairs of functions, determine $(f \times g)(x)$.
   a) $f(x) = \{(0, 2), (1, 5), (2, 7), (3, 12)\}$,
      $g(x) = \{(0, -1), (1, -2), (2, 3), (3, 5)\}$
   b) $f(x) = \{(0, 3), (1, 6), (2, 10), (3, -5)\}$,
      $g(x) = \{(0, 4), (2, -2), (4, 1), (6, 3)\}$
   c) $f(x) = x, g(x) = 4$
   d) $f(x) = x, g(x) = 2x$
   e) $f(x) = x + 2, g(x) = x^2 - 2x + 1$
   f) $f(x) = 2^x, g(x) = \sqrt{x - 2}$

2. a) Graph each pair of functions in question 1, parts c) to f), on the same grid.
   b) State the domains of f and g.
   c) Use your graph to make an accurate sketch of $y = (f \times g)(x)$.
   d) State the domain of $f \times g$.

3. If $f(x) = \sqrt{1 + x}$ and $g(x) = \sqrt{1 - x}$, determine the domain of $y = (f \times g)(x)$.

PRACTISING

4. Determine $(f \times g)(x)$ for each of the following pairs of functions.
   K a) $f(x) = x - 7, g(x) = x + 7$
   b) $f(x) = \sqrt{x + 10}, g(x) = \sqrt{x + 10}$
   c) $f(x) = 7x^2, g(x) = x - 9$
   d) $f(x) = -4x - 7, g(x) = 4x + 7$
   e) $f(x) = 2 \sin x, g(x) = \dfrac{1}{x - 1}$
   f) $f(x) = \log(x + 4), g(x) = 2^x$

5. For each of the problems in question 4, state the domain and range of $(f \times g)(x)$.

6. For each of the problems in question 4, use graphing technology to graph $(f \times g)(x)$ and then discuss each of the following characteristics of the graphs: symmetry, intervals of increase/decrease, zeros, maximum and minimum values, and period (where applicable).

7. The graph of the function $f(x)$ is a line passing through the origin with a slope of -4, whereas the graph of the function $g(x)$ is a line with a y-intercept of 1 and a slope of 6. Sketch the graph of $(f \times g)(x)$.

8. For each of the following pairs of functions, state the domain of $(f \times g)(x)$.

   a) $f(x) = \dfrac{1}{x^2 - 5x - 14}, g(x) = \sec x$

   b) $f(x) = 99^x, g(x) = \log(x - 8)$

   c) $f(x) = \sqrt{x + 81}, g(x) = \csc x$

   d) $f(x) = \log(x^2 + 6x + 9), g(x) = \sqrt{x^2 - 1}$

9. If the function $f(t)$ describes the per capita energy consumption in a particular country at time t, and the function $p(t)$ describes the population of the country at time t, then explain what the product function $(f \times p)(t)$ represents.

10. An average of 20 000 people visit the Lakeside Amusement Park each
    A day in the summer. The admission fee is $25.00. Consultants predict that, for each $1.00 increase in the admission fee, the park will lose an average of 750 customers each day.
    a) Determine the function that represents the projected daily revenue if the admission fee is increased.
    b) Is the revenue function a product function? Explain.
    c) Estimate the ticket price that will maximize revenue.

11. A water purification company has patented a unique process to remove contaminants from a container of water at the same time that more contaminated water is added for purification. The percent of contaminated material in the container of water being purified can be modelled by the function $c(t) = (0.9)^t$, where t is the time in seconds. The number of litres of water in the container can be modelled by the function $l(t) = 650 + 300t$. Write a function that represents the number of litres of contaminated material in the container at any time t, and estimate when the amount of contaminated material is at its greatest.

12. Is the following statement true or false? "If $f(x) \times g(x)$ is an odd
T function, then both $f(x)$ and $g(x)$ are odd functions." Justify your answer.

13. Let $f(x) = mx^2 + 2x + 5$ and $g(x) = 2x^2 - nx - 2$. The functions
are combined to form the new function $h(x) = f(x) \times g(x)$. Points
$(1, -40)$ and $(-1, 24)$ satisfy the new function. Determine $f(x)$
and $g(x)$.

14. Let $f(x) = \sqrt{-x}$ and $g(x) = \log(x + 10)$.
C **a)** Determine the equation of the function $y = (f \times g)(x)$, and
state its domain.
b) Provide two different strategies for sketching $y = (f \times g)(x)$.
Discuss the merits of each strategy.
c) Choose one of the strategies you discussed in part b), and make an
accurate sketch.

15. **a)** If $f(x) = x^2 - 25$, determine the equation of the product
function $f(x) \times \dfrac{1}{f(x)}$.
b) Determine the domain, and sketch the graph of the product
function you found in part a).
c) If $f(x)$ is a polynomial function, explain how the domain and
range of $f(x) \times \dfrac{1}{f(x)}$ changes as the degree of $f(x)$ changes.

Extending

16. Given the following graphs, determine the equations of $y = f(x)$,
$y = g(x)$, and $y = (f \times g)(x)$.

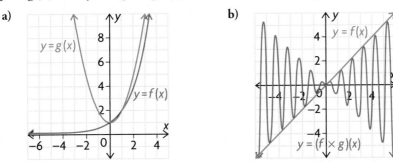

17. Determine two functions, f and g, whose product would result in
each of the following functions.
a) $(f \times g)(x) = 4x^2 - 81$ **c)** $(f \times g)(x) = 4x^{\frac{5}{2}} - 3x^{\frac{3}{2}} + x^{\frac{1}{2}}$

b) $(f \times g)(x) = 8\sin^3 x + 27$ **d)** $(f \times g)(x) = \dfrac{6x - 5}{2x + 1}$

Exploring Quotients of Functions

GOAL

Represent the quotient of two functions graphically and algebraically, and determine the characteristics of the quotient.

EXPLORE the Math

The logistic function is often used to model growth. This function has the general equation $P(t) = \dfrac{c}{1 + ab^t}$, where $a > 0$, $0 < b < 1$, and $c > 0$. In this function, t is time. For example, the height of a sunflower plant can be modelled using the function $h(t) = \dfrac{260}{1 + 24(0.9)^t}$, where $h(t)$ is the height in centimetres and t is the time in days. The function $h(t) = \dfrac{f(t)}{g(t)}$ is the quotient of two functions, where $f(t) = 260$ (a constant function) and $g(t) = 1 + 24(0.9)^t$ (an exponential function). The table and graphs show that the values of a quotient function can be determined by dividing the values of the two functions.

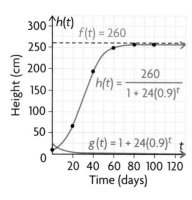

t (days)	$f(t) = 260$	$g(t) = 1 + 24(0.9)^t$	$h(t) = \dfrac{260}{1 + 24(0.9)^t}$
0	260	25	$\dfrac{260}{25} = 10.4$
20	260	3.92	66.3
40	260	1.35	192.6
60	260	1.04	250.0
80	260	1.01	257.4
100	260	1.00	260.0

This function shows slow growth for small values of t, then rapid growth, and then slow growth again when the height of the sunflower approaches its maximum height of 260 cm.

The logistic function is an example of a quotient function. In function notation, we can express this as $(f \div g)(x) = f(x) \div g(x)$.

> **?** What are the characteristics of functions that are produced by quotients of other types of functions?

A. Consider the function defined by $y = \dfrac{4}{x + 2}$ in the form $y = \dfrac{f(x)}{g(x)}$. Write the expressions for functions f and g.

B. On graph paper, draw and label the graphs of $y = f(x)$ and $y = g(x)$, and state their domains.

C. Locate any points on your graph of g where $g(x) = 0$. What will happen when you calculate the value of $f \div g$ for these x-coordinates? How would this appear on a graph?

D. Locate any points on your graph where $g(x) = \pm 1$. What values of x produced these results? Explain how you could determine these x-values algebraically.

E. Determine the value of $f \div g$ for each of the x's in part D. How do your answers compare with the corresponding values of f? Explain.

F. Over what interval(s) is $g(x) > 0$? Over what interval(s) is $f(x) > 0$?

G. Determine all the intervals where both f and g are positive or where both are negative. Will the function $f \div g$ be positive in the same intervals? Justify your answer.

H. Determine any intervals where either f or g is positive and the other is negative. Discuss the behaviour of $f \div g$ over these intervals. If no such intervals exist, what implication would this have for $f \div g$? Explain.

I. For what values of x is $(f \div g)(x) = f(x)$? For what values of x is $(f \div g)(x) = -f(x)$?

J. Using all the information about $f \div g$ that you have determined, make an accurate sketch of $y = (f \div g)(x)$ and state its domain.

K. Verify your results by graphing f, g, and $f \div g$ using graphing technology.

L. Repeat parts A to K using the following functions.

i) $y = \dfrac{x + 1}{(x + 3)(x - 1)}$ iii) $y = \dfrac{\sin x}{x}$

ii) $y = \dfrac{4}{x^2 + 1}$ iv) $y = \dfrac{2^x}{\sqrt{x}}$

Reflecting

M. The graphs of $y = \dfrac{4}{x + 2}$, $y = \dfrac{x + 1}{(x + 3)(x - 1)}$, and $y = \dfrac{2x}{\sqrt{x}}$ have vertical asymptotes, but the graphs of $h(t) = \dfrac{260}{1 + 24(0.9)^t}$, $y = \dfrac{4}{x^2 + 1}$, and $y = \dfrac{\sin x}{x}$ do not. Explain.

N. The graph of $y = \dfrac{x + 1}{(x + 3)(x - 1)}$ lies above the x-axis in the interval $x \in (-3, -1)$. By examining the behaviour of functions f and g, explain how you can reach this conclusion.

In Summary

Key Idea

- When two functions, $f(x)$ and $g(x)$, are combined to form the function $(f \div g)(x)$, the new function is called the quotient of f and g. For any given value of x, the value of the function is represented by $f(x) \div g(x)$. The graph of $f \div g$ can be obtained from the graphs of functions f and g by dividing each y-coordinate of f by the corresponding y-coordinate of g.

Need to Know

- Algebraically, $(f \div g)(x) = f(x) \div g(x)$.
- $f \div g$ will be defined for all x-values that are in the intersection of the domains of f and g, except in the case where $g(x) = 0$. If the domain of f is A, and the domain of g is B, then the domain of $f \div g$ is $\{x \in \mathbf{R} \,|\, x \in A \cap B, g(x) \neq 0\}$.
- If $f(x) = 0$ when $g(x) \neq 0$, then $(f \div g)(x) = 0$.
- If $f(x) = \pm 1$, then $(f \div g)(x) = \pm \dfrac{1}{g(x)}$. Similarly, if $g(x) = \pm 1$, then $(f \div g)(x) = \pm f(x)$. Also, if $f(x) = \pm g(x)$, then $(f \div g)(x) = \pm 1$

Further Your Understanding

1. For each of the following pairs of functions, write the equation of $y = (f \div g)(x)$.

   a) $f(x) = 5, g(x) = x$ d) $f(x) = x + 2, g(x) = \sqrt{x - 2}$

   b) $f(x) = 4x, g(x) = 2x - 1$ e) $f(x) = 8, g(x) = 1 + \left(\dfrac{1}{2}\right)^x$

   c) $f(x) = 4x, g(x) = x^2 + 4$ f) $f(x) = x^2, g(x) = \log(x)$

2. a) Graph each pair of functions in question 1 on the same grid.
   b) State the domains of f and g.
   c) Use your graphs to make an accurate sketch of $y = (f \div g)(x)$.
   d) State the domain of $f \div g$.

3. Recall that the function $h(t) = \dfrac{260}{1 + 24(0.9)^t}$ models the growth of a sunflower, where $h(t)$ is the height in centimetres and t is the time in days.
   a) Calculate the average rate of growth of the sunflower over the first 20 days.
   b) Determine when the sunflower has grown to half of its maximum height.
   c) Estimate the instantaneous rate of change in height at the time you found in part b).
   d) What happens to the instantaneous rate of change in height as the sunflower approaches its maximum height? How does this relate to the shape of the graph?

FREQUENTLY ASKED Questions

Q: **If you are given the graphs of two functions, f and g, how can you determine the location of a point that would appear on the graphs of $f + g$, $f - g$, $f \times g$, and $f \div g$?**

Study | **Aid**
• See Lessons 9.1 to 9.4.
• Try Mid-Chapter Review Question 2.

A: For any particular x-value, determine the y-value on each graph, separately. For $f + g$, add these two y-values together. For $f - g$, subtract the y-value of g from the y-value of f. For $f \times g$, multiply these two y-values together. For $f \div g$, divide the y-value of f by the y-value of g. Each of these points has, as its coordinates, the same x-value and the new y-value.

Q: **If you are given the equations of two functions, f and g, how can you determine the equations of the functions $f + g$, $f - g$, $f \times g$, and $f \div g$?**

Study | **Aid**
• See Lessons 9.1 to 9.4.
• Try Mid-Chapter Review Questions 5 and 7.

A: Every time you combine two functions in one of these ways, you are simply performing a different arithmetic operation on every pair of y-values, one from each of the functions being combined, provided that the x-values are the same. Since the equation of each function defines the y-values of each function, the new equation can be determined by adding, subtracting, multiplying, or dividing the y-value expressions as required.

For example, if $f(x) = x^2 + 8$ and $g(x) = 5^x$, then

$$
\begin{aligned}
(f + g)(x) &= f(x) + g(x) \\
&= x^2 + 8 + 5^x
\end{aligned}
\qquad
\begin{aligned}
(f \times g)(x) &= f(x) \times g(x) \\
&= (x^2 + 8)(5^x)
\end{aligned}
$$

$$
\begin{aligned}
(f - g)(x) &= f(x) - g(x) \\
&= x^2 + 8 - 5^x
\end{aligned}
\qquad
\begin{aligned}
(f \div g)(x) &= f(x) \div g(x) \\
&= \frac{x^2 + 8}{5^x}
\end{aligned}
$$

Q: **How can you determine the domain of the combined functions $f + g$, $f - g$, $f \times g$, and $f \div g$?**

Study | **Aid**
• See Lessons 9.1 to 9.4.
• Try Mid-Chapter Review Questions 5 and 7.

A: Since you can only combine points from two functions when they share the same x-value, the domain of the combined function must consist of the set of x-values where the domains of the two given functions intersect. The only exception occurs when you are dividing two functions. The function $f \div g$ is not defined when its denominator is equal to zero, since division by zero is undefined. As a result, x-values that cause $g(x)$ to equal zero must be excluded from the domain.

PRACTICE Questions

Lesson 9.1

1. Given the functions $f(x) = \cos x$ and $g(x) = \sin x$, which operations can be used to combine the two functions to create a new function with an amplitude that is less than 1?

Lesson 9.2

2. Let $f(x) = \{(-9, -2), (-6, -3), (-3, 0), (0, 2), (3, 7)\}$ and $g(x) = \{(-12, 9), (-9, 4), (-8, 1), (-7, 10), (-6, -6), (0, 12)\}$. Determine
   a) $(f + g)(x)$ c) $(f - g)(x)$
   b) $(g + f)(x)$ d) $(g - f)(x)$

3. The cost, in thousands of dollars, for a company to produce x thousand of its product is given by the function $C(x) = 10x + 30$. The revenue from the sales of the product is given by the function $R(x) = -5x^2 + 150x$.
   a) Write the function that represents the company's profit on sales of x thousand of its product.
   b) Graph the cost, revenue, and profit functions on the same coordinate grid, where $0 \le x \le 40$.
   c) What is the company's profit on the sale of 7500 of its product?

4. Steve earns $24.39/h operating an industrial plasma torch at a rail-car manufacturing plant. He receives $0.58/h more for working the night shift, as well as $0.39/h more for working weekends.
   a) Write a function that describes Steve's daily earnings under regular pay.
   b) What function shows his daily earnings under the night-shift premium?
   c) What function shows his daily earnings under the weekend premium?
   d) What function represents his earnings for the night shift on Saturday?
   e) How much does Steve earn for working 11 h on Saturday night, if he earns time and a half on that day's rate for more than 8 h of work?

Lesson 9.3

5. Determine $(f \times g)(x)$ for each of the following pairs of functions, and state its domain.
   a) $f(x) = x + \dfrac{1}{2}, g(x) = x + \dfrac{1}{2}$
   b) $f(x) = \sqrt{x} - 10, g(x) = \sin(3x)$
   c) $f(x) = 11x^3, g(x) = \dfrac{2}{x + 5}$
   d) $f(x) = 90x - 1, g(x) = 90x + 1$

6. A diner is open from 6 a.m. to 6 p.m., and the average number of customers in the diner at any time can be modelled by the function $C(h) = -30 \cos\left(\dfrac{\pi}{6}h\right) + 34$, where h is the number of hours after the 6 a.m. opening time. The average amount of money, in dollars, that each customer in the diner will spend can be modelled by the function $D(h) = -3 \sin\left(\dfrac{\pi}{6}h\right) + 7$.
   a) Write the function that represents the diner's average revenue from the customers.
   b) Graph the function you wrote in part a).
   c) What is the average revenue from the customers in the diner at 2 p.m.?

Lesson 9.4

7. Calculate $(f \div g)(x)$ for each of the following pairs of functions, and state its domain.
   a) $f(x) = 240, g(x) = 3x$
   b) $f(x) = 10x^2, g(x) = x^3 - 3x$
   c) $f(x) = x + 8, g(x) = \sqrt{x} - 8$
   d) $f(x) = 14x^2, g(x) = 2 \log x$

8. Recall that $y = \tan x$ can be written as the quotient of two functions: $f(x) = \sin x$ and $g(x) = \cos x$. List as many other trigonometric functions as possible that could be written as the quotient of two functions.

Composition of Functions

Determine the composition of two functions numerically, graphically, and algebraically.

LEARN ABOUT the Math

Sometimes you will find a situation in which two related functions are present. Often both functions are needed to analyze the situation or solve a problem.

Forest fires often spread in a roughly circular pattern. The area burned depends on the radius of the fire. The radius, in turn, may increase at a constant rate each day.

Suppose that $A(r) = \pi r^2$ represents the area, A, of a fire as a function of its radius, r. If the radius of the fire increases by 0.5 km/day, then $r(t) = 0.5t$ represents the radius of the fire as a function of time, t. The area is measured in square kilometres, the radius is measured in kilometres, and the time is measured in days.

? How can the area burned be determined on the sixth day of the fire?

EXAMPLE 1	Reasoning numerically, graphically, and algebraically about a composition of functions

Determine the area burned by the fire on the sixth day.

Solution A: Using graphical and numerical analysis

Use the given functions to make tables of values.

t	$r(t) = 0.5t$
0	0
2	1
4	2
6	3
8	4

r	$A(r) = \pi r^2$
0	0
1	3.14
2	12.57
3	28.27
4	50.27

Both time and radius must be positive, so $t \geq 0$ and $r \geq 0$.

$r(t)$ is a linear function, and $A(r)$ is a quadratic function.

Use the tables of values to sketch the graphs.

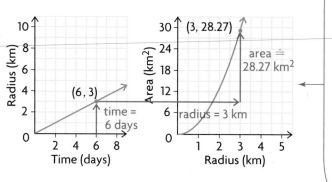

To find the radius of the area burned by the forest fire, the length of time that the fire has been burning must be known. Once the radius is known, the total area burned can be determined.

Reading from the first graph, the radius is 3 km when $t = 6$ days. Then reading from the second graph, a radius of 3 km indicates an area of about 28.3 km².

In the tables of values, time corresponds with radius, and radius corresponds with area.

r: time → radius
A: radius → area

The output in the first table becomes the input in the second table.

$$6 \xrightarrow{} 3 \xrightarrow{} 28.3$$
$$r(6) \qquad A(r(6))$$
$$= A(3)$$
$$\doteq 28.3$$

Determine the radius after six days, $r(6)$, and use it as the input for the area function, $A(r(6))$, to determine the area burned after six days.

$r(6) = 0.5(6) = 3$ and $A(3) = \pi(3)^2 \doteq 28.3$

The fire has burned about 28.3 km² on the sixth day.

Solution B: Using algebraic analysis

$r = g(t) = 0.5t$
$A = f(r) = \pi r^2$

The radius of the fire, r, grows at 0.5 km per day, so it is a function of time.

The area, A, of the fire increases in a circular pattern as its radius, r, increases, so it is a function of the circle's radius.

Since $r = g(t)$
$A = f(r) = f(g(t))$

To solve the problem, combine the area function with the radius function by using the output for the radius function as the input for the area function.

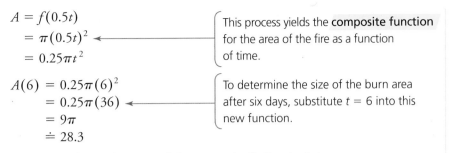

$$A = f(0.5t)$$
$$= \pi(0.5t)^2$$
$$= 0.25\pi t^2$$

This process yields the **composite function** for the area of the fire as a function of time.

$$A(6) = 0.25\pi(6)^2$$
$$= 0.25\pi(36)$$
$$= 9\pi$$
$$\doteq 28.3$$

To determine the size of the burn area after six days, substitute $t = 6$ into this new function.

The fire has burned an area of about 28.3 km² after six days.

composite function

a function that is the composite of two other functions; the function $f(g(t))$ is called the composition of f with g; the function $f(g(t))$ is denoted by $(f \circ g)(t)$ and is defined by using the output of the function g as the input for the function f

Reflecting

A. A point on the second graph was used to solve the problem. Explain how the x-coordinate of this point was determined.

B. What connection was observed between the tables of values for the two functions? Why does it make sense that there is a function that combines the two functions to solve the forest fire problem?

C. Explain how the two functions were combined algebraically to determine a single function that predicts the area burned for a given time. How is the range of r related to the domain of A in this combination?

Communication | Tip

$f \circ g$ is read as "f operates on g" while $f(g(x))$ is read as "f of g of x."

APPLY the Math

EXAMPLE 2 | Reasoning about the order in which two functions are composed

Given the functions $f(x) = 2x + 3$ and $g(x) = \sqrt{x}$, determine whether $(f \circ g)(x) = (g \circ f)(x)$.

Solution

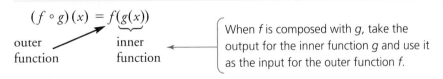

$$(f \circ g)(x) = f(g(x))$$

outer function   inner function

When f is composed with g, take the output for the inner function g and use it as the input for the outer function f.

$$x \xrightarrow{\ g\ } g(x) \xrightarrow{\ f\ } f(g(x))$$
$$\qquad\qquad = \sqrt{x} \qquad = f(\sqrt{x})$$
$$\qquad\qquad\qquad\qquad\qquad = 2(\sqrt{x}) + 3$$
$$\qquad\qquad\qquad\qquad\qquad = 2\sqrt{x} + 3$$

> The output for g is the expression $\sqrt{x}$. Use this as the input for f, replacing x everywhere it occurs with $\sqrt{x}$.

$f(g(x)) = 2\sqrt{x} + 3$

Algebraically, the composition of f with g is the function $y = 2\sqrt{x} + 3$.

> In terms of transformations, $f \circ g$ represents the function $y = g(x)$ stretched vertically by a factor of 2 and translated 3 units up. Its domain is $\{x \in \mathbf{R} \mid x \geq 0\}$.

$$(g \circ f)(x) = g(\underbrace{f(x)}_{})$$

outer   inner
function   function

> When g is composed with f, take the output from the inner function f and use it as the input for the outer function g.

$$x \xrightarrow{\ f\ } f(x) \xrightarrow{\ g\ } g(f(x))$$
$$\qquad\qquad = 2x + 3 \qquad = g(2x + 3)$$
$$\qquad\qquad\qquad\qquad\qquad = \sqrt{(2x + 3)}$$

> The output from f is the expression $2x + 3$. Use this as the input for g, and replace x everywhere it occurs with $2x + 3$.

$g(f(x)) = \sqrt{2x + 3}$

Algebraically, the composition of g with f is the function

$g(f(x)) = \sqrt{2x + 3} = \sqrt{2(x + 1.5)}$

> In terms of transformations, $y = g(x)$ is compressed horizontally by a factor of $\frac{1}{2}$ and translated 1.5 units to the left. Its domain is $\left\{x \in \mathbf{R} \mid x \geq -\frac{3}{2}\right\}$.

> Clearly, the expressions for $y = (f \circ g)(x)$ and $y = (g \circ f)(x)$ are different. Comparing their graphs illustrates the result of applying different sequences of transformations to $y = g(x)$.

$(f \circ g)(x) \neq (g \circ f)(x)$. The compositions of these two functions generate different answers depending on the order of the composition.

| EXAMPLE **3** | Reasoning about the domain of a composite function |

Let $f(x) = \log_2 x$ and $g(x) = x + 4$.
a) Determine $f \circ g$, and find its domain.
b) What is the relationship between the domain of $f \circ g$ and the domain and range of f and g?

Solution

a) $(f \circ g)(x) = f(g(x))$

$\quad\quad\quad\quad = f(x + 4)$

$\quad\quad\quad\quad = \log_2(x + 4)$

Since $x + 4 > 0 \Rightarrow x > -4$.
The domain of $f \circ g$ is $x \in (-4, \infty)$.

> Use the output for g as the input for f.

> The domain of a logarithmic function with base a contains only positive real numbers, so the expression $x + 4$ must be greater than zero.

b) Domain of f: $x \in (0, \infty)$ Range of f: $y \in \mathbf{R}$
   Domain of g: $x \in \mathbf{R}$ Range of g: $y \in \mathbf{R}$

> Looking at the domain of $f \circ g$, we can see that it is not equal to either the domain of f or the domain of g.

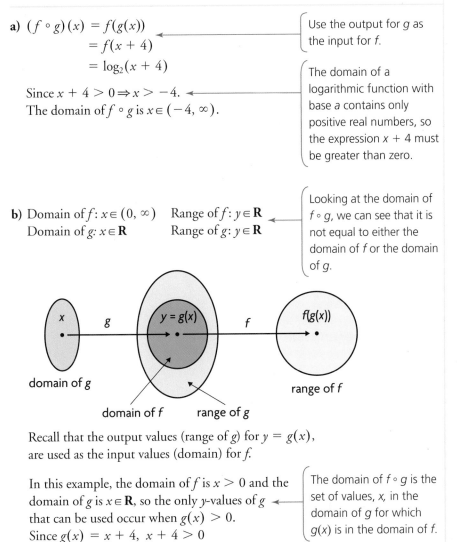

Recall that the output values (range of g) for $y = g(x)$, are used as the input values (domain) for f.

In this example, the domain of f is $x > 0$ and the domain of g is $x \in \mathbf{R}$, so the only y-values of g that can be used occur when $g(x) > 0$.
Since $g(x) = x + 4$, $x + 4 > 0$

$$x > -4$$

> The domain of $f \circ g$ is the set of values, x, in the domain of g for which $g(x)$ is in the domain of f.

EXAMPLE **4**

Reasoning about a function composed with its inverse

Show that, if $f(x) = \dfrac{1}{x-2}$ then $(f \circ f^{-1})(x) = (f^{-1} \circ f)(x)$.

Solution

$$x = \frac{1}{y-2}$$

$$x(y-2) = 1$$

$$y - 2 = \frac{1}{x}$$

$$y = \frac{1}{x} + 2 \text{ or } f^{-1}(x) = \frac{1}{x} + 2$$

To find the inverse of f, switch x and y and then solve for y.

$$(f \circ f^{-1})(x) = f(f^{-1}(x))$$

$$= f\left(\frac{1}{x} + 2\right)$$

$$= \frac{1}{\left(\frac{1}{x} + 2\right) - 2}$$

$$= \frac{1}{\left(\frac{1}{x}\right)}$$

$$= x$$

So, $(f \circ f^{-1})(x) = x$

The composition of f with its inverse maps a number in the domain of f onto itself. In other words, the result of this composition is the line $y = x$.

$$(f^{-1} \circ f)(x) = f^{-1}(f(x))$$

$$= f^{-1}\left(\frac{1}{x-2}\right)$$

$$= \frac{1}{\left(\frac{1}{x-2}\right)} + 2$$

$$= x - 2 + 2$$

$$= x$$

So, $(f^{-1} \circ f)(x) = x$

The composition of f^{-1} with f maps a number in the domain of f^{-1} onto itself. In other words, the result of this composition is also the line $y = x$.

Therefore, $(f \circ f^{-1})(x) = (f^{-1} \circ f)(x)$

Even though the order of the functions in the composition is reversed, the results are the same.

| EXAMPLE 5 | Working backward to decompose a composite function |

Given $h(x) = |x^3 - 1|$, find two functions, f and g, such that $h = f \circ g$.

Solution

To evaluate h for any value of x, take that value, cube it, and subtract 1. This defines a sequence of operations for the inner function. Then, take the absolute value. This defines the outer function.

Let $g(x) = x^3 - 1$ and $f(x) = |x|.$ ◀——

$$\text{Then } (f \circ g)(x) = f(g(x))$$
$$= f(x^3 - 1)$$
$$= |x^3 - 1|$$
$$= h(x)$$
$$h(x) = (f \circ g)(x) ◀$$

> When evaluating the composition of f with g, you start by evaluating g for some value of x. So, it makes sense to define the inner function g that h performs on any input value. Then define the outer function f to represent the remaining operation(s) required by h.

> Another solution would be to let $g(x) = x^3$ and $f(x) = |x - 1|$.

In Summary

Key Idea

- Two functions, f and g, can be combined using a process called composition, which can be represented by $f(g(x))$. The output for the inner function g is used as the input for the outer function f. The function $f(g(x))$ can be denoted by $(f \circ g)(x)$.

Need to Know

- Algebraically, the composition of f with g is denoted by $(f \circ g)(x)$, whereas the composition of g with f is denoted by $(g \circ f)(x)$. In most cases, $(f \circ g)(x) \neq (g \circ f)(x)$ because the order in which the functions are composed matters.
- Let $(a, b) \in g$ and $(b, c) \in f$. Then $(a, c) \in f \circ g$. A point in $f \circ g$ exists where an element in the range of g is also in the domain of f. The function $f \circ g$ exists only when the range of g overlaps the domain of f.

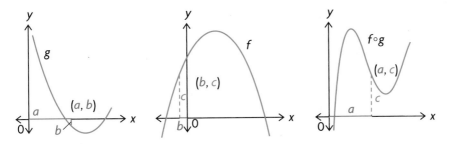

- The domain of $(f \circ g)(x)$ is a subset of the domain of g. It is the set of values, x, in the domain of g for which $g(x)$ is in the domain of f.
- If both f and f^{-1} are functions, then $(f^{-1} \circ f)(x) = x$ for all x in the domain of f, and $(f \circ f^{-1})(x) = x$ for all x in the domain of f^{-1}.

CHECK Your Understanding

1. Use $f(x) = 2x - 3$ and $g(x) = 1 - x^2$ to evaluate the following expressions.

   a) $f(g(0))$

   b) $g(f(4))$

   c) $(f \circ g)(-8)$

   d) $(g \circ g)\left(\dfrac{1}{2}\right)$

   e) $(f \circ f^{-1})(1)$

   f) $(g \circ g)(2)$

2. Given $f = \{(0, 1), (1, 2), (2, 5), (3, 10)\}$ and $g = \{(2, 0), (3, 1), (4, 2), (5, 3), (6, 4)\}$, determine the following values.

   a) $(g \circ f)(2)$

   b) $(f \circ f)(1)$

   c) $(f \circ g)(5)$

   d) $(f \circ g)(0)$

   e) $(f \circ f^{-1})(2)$

   f) $(g^{-1} \circ f)(1)$

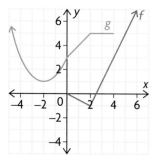

3. Use the graphs of f and g to evaluate each expression.

   a) $f(g(2))$

   b) $g(f(4))$

   c) $(g \circ g)(-2)$

   d) $(f \circ f)(2)$

4. For a car travelling at a constant speed of 80 km/h, the distance driven, d kilometres, is represented by $d(t) = 80t$, where t is the time in hours. The cost of gasoline, in dollars, for the drive is represented by $C(d) = 0.09d$.

   a) Determine $C(d(5))$ numerically, and interpret your result.

   b) Describe the relationship represented by $C(d(t))$.

PRACTISING

5. In each case, functions f and g are defined for $x \in \mathbf{R}$. For each pair of functions, determine the expression and the domain of $f(g(x))$ and $g(f(x))$. Graph each result.

   a) $f(x) = 3x^2, g(x) = x - 1$

   b) $f(x) = 2x^2 + x, g(x) = x^2 + 1$

   c) $f(x) = 2x^3 - 3x^2 + x - 1, g(x) = 2x - 1$

   d) $f(x) = x^4 - x^2, g(x) = x + 1$

   e) $f(x) = \sin x, g(x) = 4x$

   f) $f(x) = |x| - 2, g(x) = x + 5$

6. For each of the following,
   • determine the defining equation for $f \circ g$ and $g \circ f$
   • determine the domain and range of $f \circ g$ and $g \circ f$

   a) $f(x) = 3x, g(x) = \sqrt{x - 4}$

   b) $f(x) = \sqrt{x}, g(x) = 3x + 1$

   c) $f(x) = \sqrt{4 - x^2}, g(x) = x^2$

   d) $f(x) = 2^x, g(x) = \sqrt{x - 1}$

   e) $f(x) = 10^x, g(x) = \log x$

   f) $f(x) = \sin x, g(x) = 5^{2x} + 1$

7. For each function h, find two functions, f and g, such that
$h(x) = f(g(x))$.

a) $h(x) = \sqrt{x^2 + 6}$ **d)** $h(x) = \dfrac{1}{x^3 - 7x + 2}$

b) $h(x) = (5x - 8)^6$ **e)** $h(x) = \sin^2(10x + 5)$

c) $h(x) = 2^{(6x+7)}$ **f)** $h(x) = \sqrt[3]{(x + 4)^2}$

8. a) Let $f(x) = 2x - 1$ and $g(x) = x^2$. Determine $(f \circ g)(x)$.
b) Graph f, g, and $f \circ g$ on the same set of axes.
c) Describe the graph of $f \circ g$ as a transformation of the graph of $y = g(x)$.

9. Let $f(x) = 2x - 1$ and $g(x) = 3x + 2$.
a) Determine $f(g(x))$, and describe its graph as a transformation of $g(x)$.
b) Determine $g(f(x))$, and describe its graph as a transformation of $f(x)$.

10. A banquet hall charges \$975 to rent a reception room, plus \$39.95
A per person. Next month, however, the banquet hall will be offering a 20% discount off the total bill. Express this discounted cost as a function of the number of people attending.

11. The function $f(x) = 0.08x$ represents the sales tax owed on a purchase with a selling price of x dollars, and the function $g(x) = 0.75x$ represents the sale price of an item with a price tag of x dollars during a 25% off sale. Write a function that represents the sales tax owed on an item with a price tag of x dollars during a 25% off sale.

12. An airplane passes directly over a radar station at time $t = 0$. The plane maintains an altitude of 4 km and is flying at a speed of 560 km/h. Let d represent the distance from the radar station to the plane, and let s represent the horizontal distance travelled by the plane since it passed over the radar station.
a) Express d as a function of s, and s as a function of t.
b) Use composition to express the distance between the plane and the radar station as a function of time.

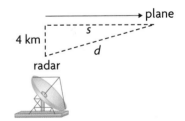

13. In a vehicle test lab, the speed of a car, v kilometres per hour, at a time of t hours is represented by $v(t) = 40 + 3t + t^2$. The rate of gasoline consumption of the car, c litres per kilometre, at a speed of v kilometres per hour is represented by $c(v) = \left(\dfrac{v}{500} - 0.1\right)^2 + 0.15$.
Determine algebraically $c(v(t))$, the rate of gasoline consumption as a function of time. Determine, using technology, the time when the car is running most economically during a 4 h simulation.

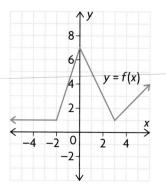

14. Given the graph of $y = f(x)$ shown and the functions below, match
the correct composition with each graph. Justify your choices.

  i) $g(x) = x + 3$ iii) $h(x) = x - 3$ v) $k(x) = -x$
  ii) $m(x) = 2x$ iv) $n(x) = -0.5x$ vi) $p(x) = x - 4$

  a) $y = (f \circ g)(x)$ **g)** $y = (g \circ f)(x)$
  b) $y = (f \circ h)(x)$ **h)** $y = (h \circ f)(x)$
  c) $y = (f \circ k)(x)$ **i)** $y = (k \circ f)(x)$
  d) $y = (f \circ m)(x)$ **j)** $y = (m \circ f)(x)$
  e) $y = (f \circ n)(x)$ **k)** $y = (n \circ f)(x)$
  f) $y = (f \circ p)(x)$ **l)** $y = (p \circ f)(x)$

A

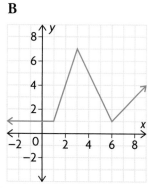

C

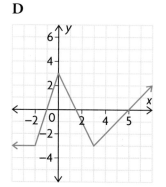

E

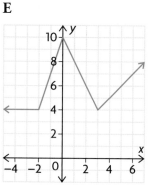

B

D

F

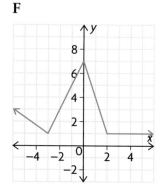

15. Find two functions, f and g, to express the given function in the centre
box of the chart in each way shown.

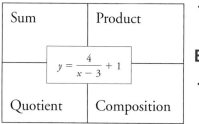

Extending

16. a) If $y = 3x - 2$, $x = 3t + 2$, and $t = 3k - 2$, find an expression
for $y = f(k)$.

  b) Express y as a function of k if $y = 2x + 5$, $x = \sqrt{3t - 1}$, and
$t = 3k - 5$.

Techniques for Solving Equations and Inequalities

Solve equations and inequalities that involve combinations of functions using a variety of techniques.

YOU WILL NEED

• graphing calculator

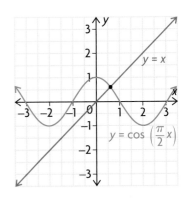

LEARN ABOUT the Math

On the graph are the functions $y = \cos\left(\frac{\pi}{2}x\right)$ and $y = x$. The point of intersection of the two functions is the point where $\cos\left(\frac{\pi}{2}x\right) = x$.

❓ How can the equation $\cos\left(\frac{\pi}{2}x\right) = x$ be solved to determine the point of intersection of these two functions?

EXAMPLE 1	**Selecting tools and strategies to solve an equation**

Solve the equation $\cos\left(\frac{\pi}{2}x\right) = x$ to the nearest hundredth.

Solution A: Selecting a guess and improvement strategy that involves a numerical approach

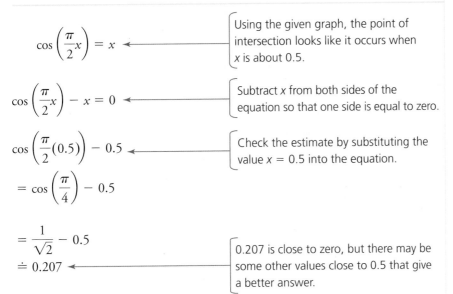

$$\cos\left(\frac{\pi}{2}x\right) = x$$

Using the given graph, the point of intersection looks like it occurs when x is about 0.5.

$$\cos\left(\frac{\pi}{2}x\right) - x = 0$$

Subtract x from both sides of the equation so that one side is equal to zero.

$$\cos\left(\frac{\pi}{2}(0.5)\right) - 0.5$$

Check the estimate by substituting the value $x = 0.5$ into the equation.

$$= \cos\left(\frac{\pi}{4}\right) - 0.5$$

$$= \frac{1}{\sqrt{2}} - 0.5$$

$$\doteq 0.207$$

0.207 is close to zero, but there may be some other values close to 0.5 that give a better answer.

When $x = 0.4$,

$$\cos\left(\frac{\pi}{2}(0.4)\right) - 0.4 \doteq 0.409 \longleftarrow$$

Repeat the process for $x = 0.4$.

The result is farther away from zero than the previous estimate, so try a number larger than 0.5.

When $x = 0.6$,

$$\cos\left(\frac{\pi}{2}(0.6)\right) - 0.6 \doteq -0.0122 \longleftarrow$$

Repeat the process for $x = 0.6$.

The result is closer to zero than the previous two estimates, but is a little below zero. Try a number a bit smaller than 0.6.

When $x = 0.59$,

$$\cos\left(\frac{\pi}{2}(0.59)\right) - 0.59 \doteq 0.0104$$

$$\cos\left(\frac{\pi}{2}x\right) = x \text{ when } x \doteq 0.59$$

Repeat the process for $x = 0.59$.

$x = 0.59$ is a much better answer because it gives a y-value that is almost equal to zero.

Solution B: Selecting a graphical strategy that involves the points of intersection

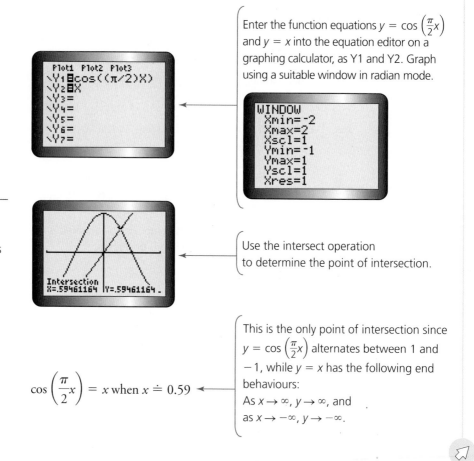

Enter the function equations $y = \cos\left(\frac{\pi}{2}x\right)$ and $y = x$ into the equation editor on a graphing calculator, as Y1 and Y2. Graph using a suitable window in radian mode.

Use the intersect operation to determine the point of intersection.

Tech | **Support**

For help using a graphing calculator to determine points of intersection, see Technical Appendix, T-12.

$$\cos\left(\frac{\pi}{2}x\right) = x \text{ when } x \doteq 0.59 \longleftarrow$$

This is the only point of intersection since $y = \cos\left(\frac{\pi}{2}x\right)$ alternates between 1 and -1, while $y = x$ has the following end behaviours:

As $x \to \infty$, $y \to \infty$, and as $x \to -\infty$, $y \to -\infty$.

Solution C: Selecting a graphical strategy that involves the zeros

Recall that solving for the roots of an equation is related to finding the zeros of a corresponding function.

$$\cos\left(\frac{\pi}{2}x\right) = x \text{ is equivalent to}$$

$$\cos\left(\frac{\pi}{2}x\right) - x = 0$$

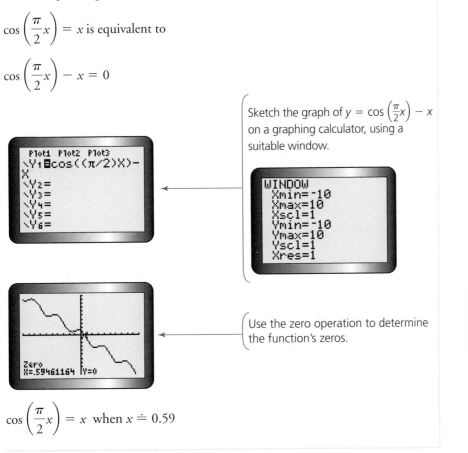

Sketch the graph of $y = \cos\left(\frac{\pi}{2}x\right) - x$ on a graphing calculator, using a suitable window.

Use the zero operation to determine the function's zeros.

$$\cos\left(\frac{\pi}{2}x\right) = x \text{ when } x \doteq 0.59$$

Tech | **Support**

For help using a graphing calculator to determine the zeros of a function, see Technical Appendix, T-8.

Reflecting

A.   What are the advantages of using a guess and improvement strategy versus a graphing strategy? What are the disadvantages?

B.   When using a guess and improvement strategy, how will you know when a given value of x gives you an accurate answer?

C.   Which graphical strategy do you prefer? Explain.

APPLY the Math

EXAMPLE **2**	Using an equation to solve a problem

According to data collected from 1996 to 2001, the average price of a new condominium in Toronto was $144 144 in 2001 and increased by 6.6% each year. A new condominium in Regina cost $72 500 on average, but prices were growing by 10% per year there. If these trends continue, when will a new condominium in Regina be the same price as one in Toronto?

Solution

Let x be the number of years since 2001.
Let y be the price of a new condominium.

Toronto: $y = 144\,144(1.066)^x$

Regina: $y = 72\,500(1.10)^x$

> These are the exponential functions that model the average price of a new condominium in Toronto and Regina since 2001.

Solve $144\,144(1.066)^x = 72\,500(1.10)^x$.

> To determine when the prices are the same, set the two functions equal to each other.

$$\frac{144\,144(1.066)^x}{72\,500} = \frac{72\,500(1.10)^x}{72\,500}$$

$$1.9882(1.066)^x \doteq (1.10)^x$$

> This exponential equation can be solved algebraically.

$$\frac{1.9882\ \overset{1}{\cancel{(1.066)^x}}}{\underset{1}{\cancel{(1.066)^x}}} = \frac{(1.10)^x}{(1.066)^x}$$

> Divide both sides by 72 500.

$$1.9882 = \left(\frac{1.10}{1.066}\right)^x$$

> Divide both sides by 1.066^x.

$$\log(1.9882) = \log\left(\frac{1.10}{1.066}\right)^x$$

> Take the log of both sides.

$$\log(1.9882) = x\log\left(\frac{1.10}{1.066}\right)$$

> Rewrite the right side using the logarithm laws.

$$\log(1.9882) = x(\log(1.10) - \log(1.066))$$

> Divide both sides by $\log(1.10) - \log(1.066)$.

$$\frac{\log(1.9882)}{\log(1.10) - \log(1.066)} = \frac{x\ \overset{1}{\cancel{\log(1.10) - \log(1.066))}}}{\underset{1}{\cancel{(\log(1.10) - \log(1.066))}}}$$

$$21.89 \doteq x$$

> Evaluate the left side.

If these trends continue, the price of a new condominium in Regina will be the same as the price of a new condominium in Toronto by the end of the year 2023.

> $2001 + 21.89 \doteq 2023$

EXAMPLE 3 | Selecting a graphing strategy to solve an inequality

Given $f(x) = 4\log(x + 1)$ and $g(x) = x - 1$, determine all values of x such that $f(x) > g(x)$.

Solution A: Using a single function and comparing its position to the x-axis

If $f(x) > g(x)$, then $f(x) - g(x) > 0$.

Let $y_1 = (f - g)(x) = 4\log(x + 1) - (x - 1)$.

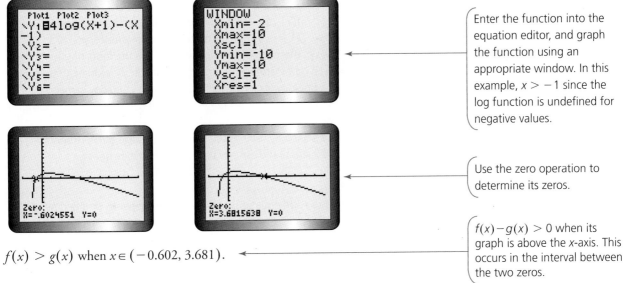

Enter the function into the equation editor, and graph the function using an appropriate window. In this example, $x > -1$ since the log function is undefined for negative values.

Use the zero operation to determine its zeros.

$f(x) > g(x)$ when $x \in (-0.602, 3.681)$.

$f(x) - g(x) > 0$ when its graph is above the x-axis. This occurs in the interval between the two zeros.

Solution B: Using both functions and comparing the position of one to the other

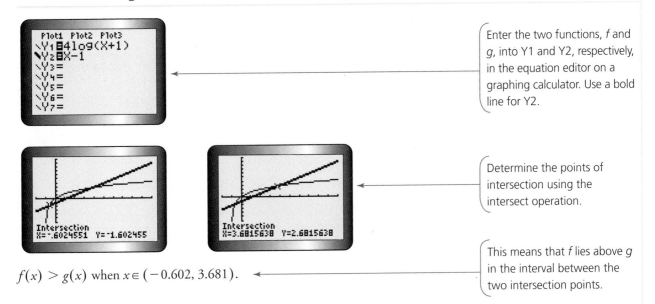

Enter the two functions, f and g, into Y1 and Y2, respectively, in the equation editor on a graphing calculator. Use a bold line for Y2.

Determine the points of intersection using the intersect operation.

$f(x) > g(x)$ when $x \in (-0.602, 3.681)$.

This means that f lies above g in the interval between the two intersection points.

In Summary

Key Ideas

- The equation $f(x) = g(x)$ can be solved using a guess and improvement strategy. Estimate where the intersection of $f(x)$ and $g(x)$ will occur, and substitute this value into both sides of the equation. Based on the outcome, adjust your estimate. Repeat this process until the desired degree of accuracy is found.
- If graphing technology is available, the equation $f(x) = g(x)$ can be solved by graphing the two functions and using the intersect operation to determine the point of intersection.
- The equation $f(x) = g(x)$ can also be solved by rewriting the equation in the form $f(x) - g(x) = 0$ to obtain the corresponding function, $h(x) = f(x) - g(x)$. The zeros of this function are also the roots of the equation. These can be determined using a guess and improvement strategy when graphing technology is not available. Graphing technology can also be used to graph the function $h(x) = f(x) - g(x)$ and determine its zeros using the zero operation.
- Inequalities can be solved by using these strategies to solve the corresponding equation, and then selecting the intervals that satisfy the inequality.

Need to Know

- The method used to solve equations and inequalities depends on the degree of accuracy required and the access to graphing technology. A solution using graphing technology will usually result in a closer approximation to the root (zero) of the equation than a solution generated by a numerical strategy with the aid of a scientific calculator.
- The difference between the solution to a strict inequality, $f(x) > g(x)$, and an inclusive inequality, $f(x) \geq g(x)$, is that the value of each root (zero) is included in the solution to the inclusive inequality.

CHECK Your Understanding

1. For each graph shown below, state the solution to each of the following:

   a) $f(x) = g(x)$

   b) $f(x) > g(x)$

   c) $f(x) \leq g(x)$

   d) $f(x) \geq g(x)$

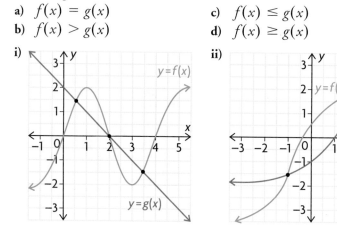

2. Use a guess and improvement strategy to determine the best one-decimal-place approximation to the solution of each equation in the interval provided.
   a) $3 = 2^{2x}$, when $x \in [0, 2]$
   b) $0 = \sin(0.25x^2)$, when $x \in [0, 5]$
   c) $3x = 0.5x^3$, when $x \in [-8, -1]$
   d) $\cos x = x$, when $x \in \left[0, \dfrac{\pi}{2}\right]$

3. Use graphing technology to determine the solution to $f(x) = g(x)$, where $f(x) = 2\sqrt{x + 3}$ and $g(x) = x^2 + 1$, in two different ways.

PRACTISING

4. In the graph shown, $f(x) = 3\sqrt[3]{x}$ and $g(x) = \tan x$. State the values of x in the interval $[0, 3]$ for which $f(x) < g(x), f(x) = g(x)$, and $f(x) > g(x)$. Express the values to the nearest tenth.

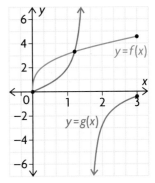

5. Solve each of the following equations for x in the given interval, using a guess and improvement strategy. Express your answers to the nearest tenth.
   a) $5 \sec x = -x^2, 0 \le x \le \pi$
   b) $\sin^3 x = \sqrt{x} - 1, 0 \le x \le \pi$
   c) $5^x = x^5, -2 \le x \le 2$
   d) $\cos x = \dfrac{1}{x}, -4 \le x \le 0$
   e) $\log(x) = (x - 10)^2 + 1, 0 \le x \le 10$
   f) $\sin(2\pi x) = -4x^2 + 16x - 12, 0 \le x \le 5$

6. Use graphing technology to solve each of the following equations. Round to two decimal places, if necessary.
   a) $2^x - 1 = \log(x + 2)$
   b) $\sqrt{x + 5} = x^2$
   c) $\sqrt{x + 3} - 5 = -x^4$
   d) $\sqrt[3]{\sin x} = 2x^3$ for x in the interval $-3 \le x \le 3$
   e) $\cos(2\pi x) = -x + 0.5$ in the interval $0 \le x \le 1$
   f) $\tan(2\pi x) = 2 \sin(3\pi x)$ in the interval $0 \le x \le 1$

7. To solve the equation $-\csc x = -3x^2$ for x in the interval $0 \le x \le 2$, the graph shown can be used. Determine the coordinates of the point where the graphs of the functions $f(x) = -\csc x$ and $g(x) = -3x^2$ intersect in the interval $0 \le x \le 2$.

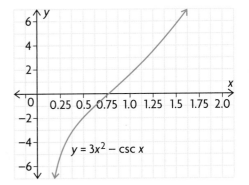

8. Two jurisdictions in Canada and the United States are attempting
A to decrease the numbers of mountain pine beetles that have been
damaging their national forests. A section of forest under study
in British Columbia at the beginning of 1997 had an estimated
2.3 million of the pests, while there were about 1.95 million of the
pests in a similar-sized section of forest in the state of Washington.
British Columbia has been decreasing the number of mountain pine
beetles by 4% per year, while Washington has been decreasing the
number by 3% per year. When will there be about the same number
of pests in the sections of forest under study in each jurisdiction?

9. Solve each of the following inequalities using graphing technology.
State your solutions using interval notation, rounding to the nearest
hundredth as required.

a) $2x^2 < 2^x$

b) $\log (x + 1) \geq x^3$

c) $\left(\dfrac{1}{2}\right)^x > \dfrac{1}{x}$

d) $\sin (\pi x) > \cos (2\pi x)$, where $x \in [0, 1]$

e) $\cos (\pi x) \leq \left(\dfrac{1}{10}\right)^x$, where $x \in [0, 2]$

f) $\tan (\pi x) > \sqrt{x}$, where $x \in [0, 1]$

10. Give an example of two functions, f and g, such that $f(x) > g(x)$
T when $x \in [-4, -2]$ or $x \in [1, \infty)$.

11. Give an example of two functions, f and g, such that $f(x) > 0$ when
$x \in [-5, 5]$ and $f(x) > g(x)$ when $x \in [-4, 5]$.

12. Two of the solutions to the equation $a \cos x = bx^3 + 6$, where a and b
are integers, are $x = -1.2$ and $x = -0.7$. These solutions are
rounded to the nearest tenth. What are the values of a and b?

13. Construct a flow chart to describe the process of finding the solutions
C to an equation using your preferred strategy.

Extending

14. Determine the general solution to the equation
$\tan (0.5\pi x) = 2 \sin (\pi x)$.

15. Determine the general solution to the inequality $\sin (\pi x) > 0$.

Modelling with Functions

GOAL

Use a variety of functions to model real-life situations.

LEARN ABOUT *the Math*

About 5000 people live in Sanjay's town. One person in his school came back from their March Break trip to Florida with a virus. A week later, 70 additional people have the virus, and doctors in the town estimate that about 8% of the town's residents will eventually get this virus.

? What types of functions could be used to model the spread of the virus in this town?

EXAMPLE 1 Selecting a function to model the situation

Select an appropriate function to model the spread of the virus in Sanjay's town.

Solution A: Selecting a linear model

Use the given data to sketch a graph.

Time, t (days)	People Infected, P
0	1
7	71

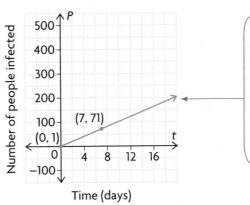

The general equation of the linear model is $y = mx + b$, where m is the slope of the line and b is the y-intercept.

Time, t, is the independent variable. The number of people infected, P, is the dependent variable.

In this case, the vertical or y-intercept is 1 and the slope is

$$\frac{\Delta P}{\Delta t} = \frac{71 - 1}{7 - 0}$$
$$= 10$$

Two points are sufficient to determine the equation of a line.

The linear model is $P(t) = 10t + 1$ and predicts that the number of people infected by the virus will grow at a constant rate of 10 people per day.

$P(t) = 400$

$400 = 10t + 1$

$399 = 10t$

$39.9 = t$

8% of 5000 is 400.
At a rate of 10 people per day, it will take about 40 days for the virus to spread to the expected number of 400 people.

Solution B: Selecting an exponential model

Use the given data to sketch a graph.

Time, t (days)	People Infected, P
0	1
7	71

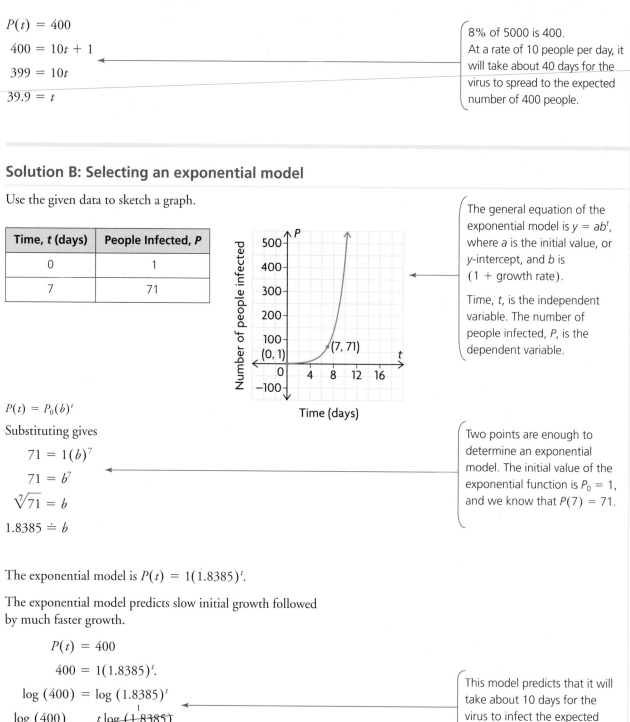

The general equation of the exponential model is $y = ab^t$, where a is the initial value, or y-intercept, and b is $(1 + \text{growth rate})$.

Time, t, is the independent variable. The number of people infected, P, is the dependent variable.

$P(t) = P_0(b)^t$

Substituting gives

$71 = 1(b)^7$

$71 = b^7$

$\sqrt[7]{71} = b$

$1.8385 \doteq b$

Two points are enough to determine an exponential model. The initial value of the exponential function is $P_0 = 1$, and we know that $P(7) = 71$.

The exponential model is $P(t) = 1(1.8385)^t$.

The exponential model predicts slow initial growth followed by much faster growth.

$P(t) = 400$

$400 = 1(1.8385)^t$

$\log(400) = \log(1.8385)^t$

$\dfrac{\log(400)}{\log(1.8385)} = \dfrac{t\log(1.8385)}{\log(1.8385)}$

$9.84 \doteq t$

This model predicts that it will take about 10 days for the virus to infect the expected number of 400 people.

Solution C: Selecting a logistic model

Use the given data to sketch a graph.

Time, *t* (days)	People Infected, *P*
0	1
7	71

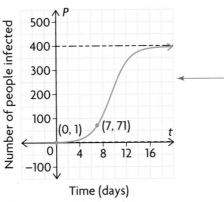

The general equation of the logistic model is $P(t) = \dfrac{c}{1 + ab^t}$ where c is the carrying capacity, or maximum value, that the function attains.

Time, *t*, is the independent variable. The number of people infected, *P*, is the dependent variable.

The carrying capacity, *c*, or maximum number of people infected, is 8% of 5000 = 400.

Substituting $P(0) = 1$ gives

$$1 = \frac{400}{1 + ab^0}$$

$$1 = \frac{400}{1 + a}$$

$$a = 399$$

Substituting $P(7) = 71$ gives

$$71 = \frac{400}{1 + 399b^7}$$

$$1 + 399b^7 = \frac{400}{71}$$

$$399b^7 \doteq 5.6338 - 1$$

$$b^7 \doteq 0.011\ 614$$

$$b \doteq 0.5291$$

The parameters *a* and *b* can be determined if two points on the function are known.

The logistic model is $P(t) = \dfrac{400}{1 + 399(0.5291)^t}$.

The logistic model predicts slow growth followed by rapid growth, and then a slowing of the growth rate again as the maximum number of infected people nears 400.

The graph approaches a horizontal asymptote at $P = 400$ when *t* is close to 12.

This model predicts that it will take about 12 days for the virus to infect the expected number of 400 people.

Reflecting

A. Compare the growth curves for the three mathematical models. How do the graphs differ? How are they similar?

B. How do the growth rates for the three mathematical models compare?

C. No mathematical model is perfect; what we hope for is a useful description of the situation. Which of these models do you think is the least realistic, and which one the most realistic? Why?

D. What could you do in a situation like this to improve the accuracy of your mathematical model?

E. Are there any other types of functions that you think could be used to model this situation? Explain.

APPLY the Math

EXAMPLE 2	Selecting a function model to fit to a data set

The table shows the median annual price for unleaded gasoline in Toronto for a 26-year period. Determine a mathematical model for the data, compare the values with the given values, and use the values to predict the median price of unleaded gasoline in 2010.

Year	Years since 1981	Price (cents/L)	Year	Years since 1981	Price (cents/L)
1981	0	40.5	1994	13	50.65
1982	1	45.4	1995	14	53.5
1983	2	47.95	1996	15	58.0
1984	3	48.4	1997	16	58.05
1985	4	51.65	1998	17	53.45
1986	5	44.1	1999	18	58.1
1987	6	48.8	2000	19	72.75
1988	7	47.6	2001	20	69.85
1989	8	51.5	2002	21	70.85
1990	9	56.55	2003	22	72.45
1991	10	54.4	2004	23	79.55
1992	11	54.35	2005	24	88.25
1993	12	52.3	2006	25	93.65

Solution A: Selecting a cubic model using regression on a graphing calculator

Enter the data into lists, and create a scatter plot.

The scatter plot clearly shows a non-linear trend. The graph increases, so possible functions include an exponential model, a quadratic model, and a cubic model.

Other functions are possible too, but a relatively simple model is preferred for ease of computation and use.

Since the data indicate that gas prices rose, then dropped a little, and then rose again, try a cubic model.

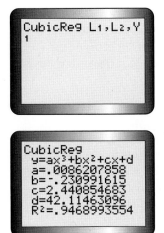

Perform a cubic regression on L1 and L2.

Note that the value of R^2 in the calculator output is 0.947. This means that 94.7% of the variation in gasoline prices is explained by our mathematical model.

The output is displayed, and the coefficients in the cubic polynomial are rounded.

$$f(x) = 0.0086x^3 - 0.2310x^2 + 2.4409x + 42.1146$$

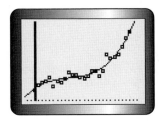

The regression curve fits the scatter plot well.

The year 2010 is 29 years after 1981, so substitute $t = 29$ to obtain a prediction of the price of gasoline.

$$f(29) = 0.0086(29)^3 - 0.2310(29)^2$$
$$+ \ 2.4409(29) + 42.1146$$
$$\doteq 128.38$$

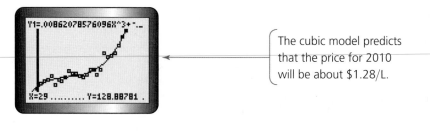

The cubic model predicts that the price for 2010 will be about $1.28/L.

Solution B: Selecting an exponential model using Fathom

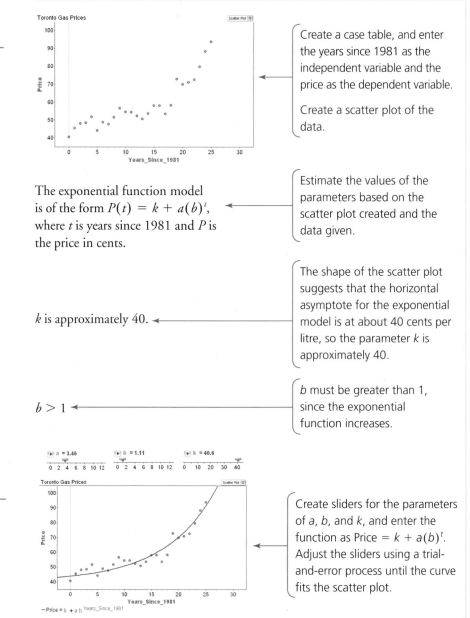

Create a case table, and enter the years since 1981 as the independent variable and the price as the dependent variable.

Create a scatter plot of the data.

The exponential function model is of the form $P(t) = k + a(b)^t$, where t is years since 1981 and P is the price in cents.

Estimate the values of the parameters based on the scatter plot created and the data given.

The shape of the scatter plot suggests that the horizontal asymptote for the exponential model is at about 40 cents per litre, so the parameter k is approximately 40.

k is approximately 40.

$b > 1$

b must be greater than 1, since the exponential function increases.

Create sliders for the parameters of a, b, and k, and enter the function as Price $= k + a(b)^t$. Adjust the sliders using a trial-and-error process until the curve fits the scatter plot.

An exponential model is
$$P(t) = 40.59 + 3.46(1.1134)^t.$$
$$P(29) = 40.59 + 3.46(1.1134)^{29}$$
$$= 118.57 \text{ cents per litre}$$
$$= \$1.19/L$$

> The year 2010 is 29 years after 1981, so substitute $t = 29$ to obtain a prediction of the price of gasoline in 2010.

In Summary

Key Ideas

- A mathematical model is just that—a model. It will not be a perfect description of a real-life situation; but if it is a good model, then you will be able to use it to describe the real-life situation and make predictions.
- Increasing the amount of data you have for creating a mathematical model improves the accuracy of the model.
- A scatter plot gives you a visual representation of the data. Examining the scatter plot may give you an idea of what kind of function could be used to model the data. Graphing your mathematical model on the scatter plot is a visual way to confirm that it is a good fit.

Need to Know

- If you have to choose between a simple function and a complicated function, and if both fit the data equally well, the simple function is generally preferred.
- The function you choose should make sense in the context of the problem; for the growth of a population, you may want to consider an exponential model or a logistic model.
- One way to compare mathematical models created using regression analysis is to examine the value of R^2. This is the fraction of the variation in the response variable (y), which is explained by the mathematical model based on the predictor variable (x).
- Mathematical models are useful for **interpolating**. They are not necessarily useful for **extrapolating** because they assume that the trend in the data will continue. Many factors can affect the relationship between the independent variable and the dependent variable and change the trend.
- It is often necessary to restrict the domain of a mathematical model to represent a realistic situation.

CHECK Your Understanding

1. An above-ground swimming pool in the shape of a cylinder, with diameter 5 m, is filled at a constant rate to a depth of 1 m. It takes 4 h to fill the pool with a hose.
   a) Make a graph showing volume of water in the pool as a function of time.
   b) Determine the equation of a mathematical model for volume as a function of time.
   c) When will the volume of the water be 8 m³?

5 m

2. After being filled, the swimming pool in question 1 is accidentally punctured at the bottom and water leaks out. The volume of the pool reaches zero in 8 h. The volume of water remaining at time t follows a quadratic model, with the minimum point (vertex) at the time when the last of the water drains out.
   a) Make a graph showing the volume of water in the pool versus time.
   b) Find the equation for the quadratic model.
   c) Use the model to predict the volume of water at the 2 h mark.
   d) What is the average rate of change in the volume of the water during the first 2 h?
   e) How does the rate of change in volume vary as time elapses?

3. An abandoned space station in orbit contains 200 m³ of oxygen. It is punctured by a piece of space debris, and oxygen begins to leak out. After 4 h, there is 80 m³ of oxygen remaining in the space station.
   a) Make a graph showing the two data points provided. Sketch two or three possible graphs that might show how volume decreases with time.
   b) The simplest model would be linear. Determine the equation of the linear model, and use this model to find the amount of time it will take for the last of the oxygen to escape.
   c) A more realistic model would be an exponential model, since the rate of change in volume is likely to be proportional to the volume of oxygen remaining. Determine the equation of an exponential model of the form $V(t) = a(b)^t$. Use this model to estimate the time it will take for 90% of the original volume of oxygen to escape.

PRACTISING

4. A lake in Northern Ontario has recovered from an acid spill that killed all of its trout. A restocking program puts 800 trout in the lake. Ten years later, the population is estimated to be 6000. The carrying capacity of the lake is believed to be 8000.
   a) Make a graph to show the given information. Extend the time scale to 20 years.
   b) Determine the parameters for a logistic model of the form $P(t) = \dfrac{c}{1 + a(b)^t}$ to model the growth of the trout population, and graph the function for $t \in [0, 20]$.
   c) Use the model to estimate the number of trout that were in the lake four years after restocking.
   d) Use the model to estimate the average rate of change in the number of trout over the first four years of the restocking program.

5. Consider again the population of trout in question 4. Another possible model for the trout situation is a transformed exponential function of the form $P(t) = c - a(b)^t$. A graph of this type of model, $y = P(t)$, is shown below.

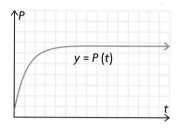

a) What feature of the graph does the parameter c represent? What is the value of c for the trout population?

b) Determine the values of a and b by substituting the two known ordered pairs.

c) Graph this exponential model of the trout population for $t \in [0, 20]$.

d) Use the model to estimate the number of trout that were in the lake four years after restocking.

e) Use the model to estimate the average rate of change in the number of trout over the first four years of the restocking program.

f) Explain how this model differs from the logistic model in question 4.

6. Recall the cubic and exponential model equations for gasoline prices in Example 2. Which model more accurately calculates the current price of gasoline?

7. The following table shows the velocity of air, in litres per second, of a typical person's breathing while at rest.

Time (s)	0	0.25	0.50	0.75	1.00	1.25	1.50	1.75	2.00	2.25	2.50	2.75	3.00
Velocity (L/s)	0	0.22	0.45	0.61	0.75	0.82	0.85	0.83	0.74	0.61	0.43	0.23	0

a) Graph the data, and determine an equation that models the situation.

b) Use a graphing calculator to draw a scatter plot of the data. Enter your equation into the equation editor, and graph. Comment on the closeness of fit between the scatter plot and the graph.

c) At $t = 6$, what is the velocity of a typical person's breathing?

d) Estimate when the rate of change in the velocity of a person's breathing is the smallest during the first 3 s.

e) What is the significance of the value you found in part d)?

f) Estimate when the rate of change in the velocity of a person's breathing is the greatest during the first 3 s.

8. The following table shows the average number of monthly hours of sunshine for Toronto.

Month	J	F	M	A	M	J	J	A	S	O	N	D
Average Monthly Sunshine (h)	95.5	112.6	150.5	187.7	229.7	254.9	278.0	244.0	184.7	145.7	82.3	72.6

Source: Environment Canada

a) Create a scatter plot of the number of hours of sunshine versus time, where $t = 1$ represents January, $t = 2$ represents February, and so on.

b) Draw the curve of best fit.

c) Determine a function that models this situation.

d) When will the number of monthly hours of sunshine be at a maximum according to the function? When will it be a minimum according to the function?

e) Discuss how well the model fits the data.

9. The wind chill index measures the sensation of cold on the human skin.
T In October 2001, Environment Canada introduced the wind chill index shown. Each curve represents the combination of air temperature and wind speed that would produce the given wind chill value.

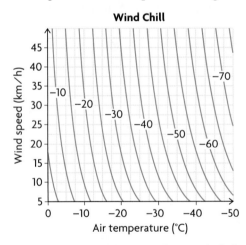

Wind Chill

The following table gives the wind chill values when the temperature is $-20\,°C$.

Wind Speed (km/h)	5	10	15	20	25	30	35	40	45	50	55	60	65	70	75	80
Wind Chill (°C)	−24	−27	−29	−31	−32	−33	−33	−34	−35	−35	−36	−37	−37	−37	−38	−38

Source: Environment Canada

a) Create a graphical model for the data.

b) Determine an algebraic model for the data.

c) Use your model from part b) to predict the wind chill for a wind speed of 0 km/h, 100 km/h, and 200 km/h (hurricane force winds). Comment on the reasonableness of each answer.

9.7

10. The population of Canada is measured on a regular basis by taking a
[A] census. The table shows the population of Canada at the end of each
period. From 1851 to 1951, each period is a 10-year interval. From
1951 to 2006, each period is a five-year interval.

Period	Census Population at the End of a Period (in thousands)	Period	Census Population at the End of a Period (in thousands)
1851–1861	3 230	1951–1956	16 081
1861–1871	3 689	1956–1961	18 238
1871–1881	4 325	1961–1966	20 015
1881–1891	4 833	1966–1971	21 568
1891–1901	5 371	1971–1976	23 450
1901–1911	7 207	1976–1981	24 820
1911–1921	8 788	1981–1986	26 101
1921–1931	10 377	1986–1991	28 031
1931–1941	11 507	1991–1996	29 672
1941–1951	13 648	1996–2001	30 755
		2001–2006	31 613

Source: Statistics Canada, Demography Division

a) Use technology to investigate polynomial and exponential models
for the relationship of the population and years since 1861.
Describe how well each model fits the data.
b) Use each model to estimate Canada's population in 2016.
c) Which model gives the most realistic answer? Explain.
d) Use the model you chose in part c) to estimate the rate at which
Canada's population was increasing in 2000.

11. The data shown model the growth of a rabbit population in an
environment where the rabbits have no natural predators.
a) Determine an algebraic model for the data.
b) The original population of rabbits was 75; when does the model
predict this was?
c) Discuss the growth rate of the rabbit population between 1955
and 1990.
d) Predict the rabbit population in 2020.

Year	Rabbit Population
1955	650
1958	2 180
1960	5 300
1961	8 200
1962	12 400
1965	35 500
1968	66 300
1975	91 600
1980	92 900
1986	92 800
1990	93 100

12. Household electrical power in North America is provided in the form
of alternating current. Typically, the voltage cycles smoothly between
$+155.6$ volts and -155.6 volts 60 times per second. Assume that at
time zero the voltage is $+155.6$ volts.
a) Determine a sine function to model the alternating voltage.
b) Determine a cosine function to model the alternating voltage.
c) Which sinusoidal function was easier to determine? Explain.

NEL

Chapter 9 **573**

Time, t (min)	Pressure, P (kPa)
0	400
5	335
10	295
15	255
20	225
25	195
30	170

13. The pressure of a car tire with a slow leak is given in the table of values.
   a) Use technology to investigate linear, quadratic, and exponential models for the relationship of the tire pressure and time. Describe how well each model fits the data.
   b) Use each model to predict the pressure after 60 min.
   c) Which model gives the most realistic answer? Explain.

14. Explain why population growth is often exponential.

15. Consider the various functions that could be used for mathematical
   C models.
   a) Which functions could be used to model a situation in which the values of the dependent variable increase toward infinity? Explain.
   b) Which functions could be used to model a situation in which the values of the dependent variable decrease to zero? Explain.
   c) Which functions could be used to model a situation in which the values of the dependent variable approach a non-zero value? Explain.

Extending

16. The numbers 1, 4, 10, 20, and 35 are called tetrahedral numbers because they are related to a four-sided shape called a tetrahedron.

tetrahedron

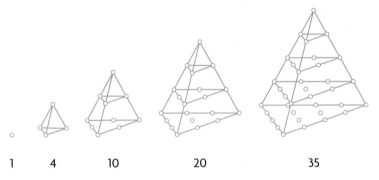

1   4   10   20   35

   a) Determine a mathematical model that you can use to generate the nth tetrahedral number.
   b) Is 47 850 a tetrahedral number? Justify your answer.

17. According to Statistics Canada, Canada's population reached 30.75 million on July 1, 2000—an increase of 256 700 from the previous year. The rate of growth for that year was the same as the rate of growth for the year before. Both Ontario and Alberta, however, recorded 1.3% growth rates in 2000.
   a) Create algebraic and graphical models for the population growth of Canada. Assume that the percent rate of growth was the same for every year.
   b) How does the growth rate for Canada's population compare with the growth rate reported by Ontario and Alberta?

FREQUENTLY ASKED Questions

Q: How can you determine the composition of two functions, *f* and *g*?

A1: The composition of *f* with *g* can be determined numerically by evaluating *g* for some input value, *x*, and then evaluating *f* using $g(x)$ as the input value.

A2: The composition of *f* with *g* can be determined graphically by interpolating on the graph of *g* to determine its output for some input value, *x*, and then interpolating on the graph of *f* using the input value $g(x)$.

A3: The composition of *f* with *g* can be determined algebraically by taking the expression for *g* and then substituting this into the function *f*.

> **Study | *Aid***
> • See Lesson 9.5, Examples 1 and 2.
> • Try Chapter Review Questions 8, 9, and 10.

Q: How do you solve an equation or inequality when an algebraic strategy is difficult or not possible?

A1: If you have access to graphing technology, there are two different strategies you can use to solve an equation:
  • Represent the two sides of the equation/inequality as separate functions. Then graph the functions together using a graphing calculator or graphing software, and apply the intersection operation to determine the solution(s).
  • Rewrite the equation/inequality so that one side is zero. Graph the nonzero side as a function. Use the zero operation to determine each of the zeros of the function.

A2: If you do not have access to graphing technology, you can use a guess and improvement strategy to solve an equation. Estimate where the intersection of $f(x)$ and $g(x)$ will occur, and substitute this value into both sides of the equation. Based on the outcome, adjust your estimate. Repeat this process until the desired degree of accuracy is found.

A3: Solving an inequality requires using either of the three previous strategies to find solutions to either $f(x) - g(x) = 0$ or $f(x) = g(x)$. Use these values to construct intervals. Test each interval to see whether it satisfies the inequality.

> **Study | *Aid***
> • See Lesson 9.6, Example 3.
> • Try Chapter Review Question 12.

PRACTICE Questions

Lesson 9.1

1. Given the functions $f(x) = x + 5$ and $g(x) = x^2 - 6x - 55$, determine which of the following operations can be used to combine the two functions into one function that has both a vertical asymptote and a horizontal asymptote: addition, subtraction, multiplication, division.

Lesson 9.2

2. A franchise owner operates two coffee shops. The sales, S_1, in thousands of dollars, for shop 1 are represented by $S_1(t) = 700 - 1.4t^2$, where $t = 0$ corresponds to the year 2000. Similarly, the sales for shop 2 are represented by $S_2(t) = t^3 + 3t^2 + 500$.
   a) Which shop is showing an increase in sales after the year 2000?
   b) Determine a function that represents the total sales for the two coffee shops.
   c) What are the expected total sales for the year 2006?
   d) If sales continue according to the individual functions, what would you recommend that the owner do? Explain.

3. A company produces a product for $9.45 per unit, plus a fixed operating cost of $52 000. The company sells the product for $15.80 per unit.
   a) Determine a function, $C(x)$, to represent the cost of producing x units.
   b) Determine a function, $I(x)$, to represent income from sales of x units.
   c) Determine a function that represents profit.

Lesson 9.3

4. Calculate $(f \times g)(x)$ for each of the following pairs of functions.
   a) $f(x) = 3 \tan(7x), g(x) = 4 \cos(7x)$
   b) $f(x) = \sqrt{3x^2}, g(x) = 3\sqrt{3x^2}$
   c) $f(x) = 11x - 7, g(x) = 11x + 7$
   d) $f(x) = ab^x, g(x) = 2ab^{2x}$

5. A country projects that the average amount of money, in dollars, that it will collect in taxes from each taxpayer over the next 50 years can be modelled by the function $A(t) = 2850 + 200t$, where t is the number of years from now. It also projects that the number of taxpayers over the next 50 years can be modelled by the function $C(t) = 15\,000\,000(1.01)^t$.
   a) Write the function that represents the amount of money, in dollars, that the country expects to collect in taxes over the next 50 years.
   b) Graph the function you wrote in part a).
   c) How much does the country expect to collect in taxes 26 years from now?

Lesson 9.4

6. Calculate $(f \div g)(x)$ for each of the following pairs of functions.
   a) $f(x) = 105x^3, g(x) = 5x^4$
   b) $f(x) = x - 4, g(x) = 2x^2 + x - 36$
   c) $f(x) = \sqrt{x + 15}, g(x) = x + 15$
   d) $f(x) = 11x^5, g(x) = 22x^2\log x$

7. State the domain of $(f \div g)(x)$ for each of your answers in the previous question.

Lesson 9.5

8. Let $f(x) = \dfrac{1}{\sqrt{x + 1}}$ and $g(x) = x^2 + 3$.
   a) What are the domain and range of $f(x)$ and $g(x)$?
   b) Find $f(g(x))$.
   c) Find $g(f(x))$.
   d) Find $f(g(0))$.
   e) Find $g(f(0))$.
   f) State the domain of each of the functions you found in parts b) and c).

9. Let $f(x) = x - 3$. Determine each of the following functions:
   a) $(f \circ f)(x)$
   b) $(f \circ f \circ f)(x)$
   c) $(f \circ f \circ f \circ f)(x)$
   d) f composed with itself n times

10. A circle has radius r.
   a) Write a function for the circle's area in terms of r.
   b) Write a function for the radius in terms of the circumference, C.
   c) Determine $A(r(C))$.
   d) A tree's circumference is 3.6 m. What is the area of the cross-section?

Lesson 9.6

11. In the graph shown below, $f(x) = 5 \sin x \cos x$ and $g(x) = 2x$. State the values of x in which $f(x) < g(x), f(x) = g(x)$, and $f(x) > g(x)$. Express the values to the nearest tenth.

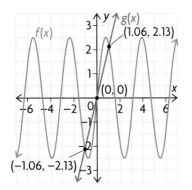

12. Solve each of the following equations for x in the given interval, using a guess and improvement strategy. Express your answers to the nearest tenth, and verify them using graphing technology.
   a) $-3 \csc x = x, \pi \leq x \leq \dfrac{3\pi}{2}$
   b) $\cos^2 x = 3 - 2\sqrt{x}, 0 \leq x \leq \pi$
   c) $8^x = x^8, -1 \leq x \leq 1$
   d) $7 \sin x = \dfrac{3}{x}, 0 \leq x \leq 2$

Lesson 9.7

13. Let P represent the size of the frog population in a marsh at time t, in years. At $t = 0$, a species of frog is released into a marsh. When $t = 5$, biologists estimate that there are 2000 frogs in the marsh. Two years later, the biologists estimate that there are 3200 frogs.
   a) Find a formula for $P = f(t)$, assuming linear growth. Interpret the slope and the P-intercept of your formula in terms of the frog population.
   b) Find a formula for $P = g(t)$, assuming exponential growth. Interpret the parameters of your formula in terms of the frog population.

14. The population of the world from 1950 to 2000 is shown. Create a scatter plot of the data, and determine an algebraic model for this situation. Use your model to estimate the world's population in 1963, 1983, and 2040.

Year	Population (millions)
1950	2555
1955	2780
1960	3039
1965	3346
1970	3708
1975	4088
1980	4457
1985	4855
1990	5284
1995	5691
2000	6080

Source: U.S. Census Bureau

1. A sphere has radius r.
   a) Write a function for the sphere's surface area in terms of r.
   b) Write a function for the radius in terms of the volume, V.
   c) Determine $A(r(V))$.
   d) A mother wrapped a ball in wrapping paper and gave it to her son on his birthday. The volume of the ball was 0.75 m^3. Assuming that she used the minimum amount of wrapping paper possible to cover the ball, how much wrapping paper did she use?

2. Solve $x \sin x \geq x^2 - 1$. Use any strategy.

3. Let $f(x) = (2x + 3)^7$. Find at least two different pairs of functions, $g(x)$ and $h(x)$, such that $f(x) = (g \circ h)(x)$.

4. In the table at the left, $N(n)$ is the number, in thousands, of Canadian home computers sold, where n is the number of years since 1990.
   a) Determine the equation that best models this relationship.
   b) How many home computers were sold in June 1993?

n	N(n)
0	400
2	520
4	752
6	1144
8	1744
10	2600
15	6175

5. The graph of the function $f(x)$ is a line passing through the point $(2, -3)$ with a slope of 6. The graph of the function $g(x)$ is the graph of the function $h(x) = x^2$ vertically stretched by a factor of 5, horizontally translated 8 units to the left, and vertically translated 1 unit down. Find $(f \times g)(x)$.

6. The height of a species of dwarf evergreen tree, in centimetres, as a function of time, in months, can be modelled by the logistic function $h(t) = \dfrac{275}{1 + 26(0.85)^t}$.
   a) If this function is graphed, are there any asymptotes? If so, name each asymptote and describe what it means.
   b) Determine when this tree will reach a height of 150 cm.

7. The cost, in dollars, to produce a product can be modelled by the function $C(x) = 5x + 18$, where x is the number of the product produced, in thousands. The revenue generated by producing and selling x units of this product can be modelled by the function $R(x) = 2x^2$. How much of the product must the company produce in order to break even?

8. Solve $\dfrac{\cot x}{x} = x^3 + 3$. Use any strategy. Round your answer(s) to the nearest tenth, if necessary.

9. Given $f(x) = \sin x$ and $g(x) = \cos x$, which of the following operations make it possible to combine the two functions into one function that is not sinusoidal: addition, subtraction, multiplication, or division?

Modelling a Situation Using a Combination of Functions

A mass is attached to a spring at one end and secured to a wall at the other end. When the mass is pulled away from the wall and released, it moves back and forth (oscillates) along the floor.

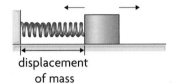

displacement of mass

If there is no friction between the mass and the floor, and no drag from the air, then the displacement of the mass versus time could be modelled by a sinusoidal function. Because of friction, however, the speed of the mass is reduced, which causes the displacement to decrease exponentially with each oscillation.

The displacement function $d(t)$ is a combination of functions:
$d(t) = f(t)g(t) + r$.

Consider the following situation:
- The mass is at a resting position of $r = 30$ cm.
- The spring provides a period of 2 s for the oscillations.
- The mass is pulled to $d = 50$ cm and released.
- After 10 s, the spring is at $d = 33$ cm.

?   How would the displacement and speed of the mass at time $t = 7.7$ s differ if there were no friction between the mass and the floor?

A.   Make a sketch of the displacement versus time graph to ensure that you understand this situation.

B.   Write the general equation of the function that models this situation, with the necessary parameters.

C.   Use the information provided to determine the values of the parameters, and write the equation of the model.

D.   Graph the function you determined in part C using graphing technology. Check that it models the motion of the mass correctly.

E.   Write the function for displacement that would be correct if there were no damping of the motion due to friction.

F.   Calculate the displacement at 7.7 s for each model you determined in parts C and E, and compare your results.

G.   Estimate the instantaneous speed of the mass at 7.7 s for each model, and compare your results.

Task | *Checklist*

✔ Did you draw and label your displacement versus time graph accurately?

✔ Did you show all your steps when determining both models?

✔ Did you show all your steps when determining the displacements and speeds?

✔ Did you discuss the difference between the displacements and speeds?

Multiple Choice

1. Which of these is an equivalent trigonometric ratio for $\sin \frac{2\pi}{5}$?

   a) $\cos \frac{\pi}{10}$

   c) $-\cos \frac{9\pi}{10}$

   b) $\sin \frac{3\pi}{5}$

   d) all of these

2. What is the exact value of $\cos \frac{\pi}{12}$?

   a) $\frac{\sqrt{3}}{4}$

   c) $\frac{\sqrt{6}}{4}$

   b) $\frac{\sqrt{2} + \sqrt{6}}{4}$

   d) $\frac{\sqrt{6} - \sqrt{2}}{4}$

3. If α and β are acute angles with $\sin \alpha = \frac{12}{13}$ and $\sin \beta = \frac{8}{17}$, what is the value of $\tan (\alpha + \beta)$?

   a) $-\frac{220}{21}$

   c) $\frac{220}{221}$

   b) $\frac{220}{21}$

   d) $\frac{220}{123}$

4. Given that $\sin \theta = \frac{3}{8}$ and θ is obtuse, what is the value of $\tan 2\theta$?

   a) $-\frac{3\sqrt{55}}{23}$

   c) $-\frac{3\sqrt{55}}{55}$

   b) $\frac{3\sqrt{55}}{46}$

   d) $\frac{3\sqrt{55}}{55}$

5. What is the exact value of $\cos \frac{\pi}{8}$?

   a) $\frac{2 + \sqrt{2}}{2}$

   c) $\frac{\sqrt{2 - \sqrt{2}}}{4}$

   b) $\frac{\sqrt{2 - \sqrt{2}}}{2}$

   d) $\frac{\sqrt{2 + \sqrt{2}}}{2}$

6. Which expression is equivalent to $\cos x$?

   a) $\frac{2 \cos^2 \left(\frac{1}{2}x\right) - 1}{\cos^2 \left(\frac{1}{2}x\right)}$

   c) $\frac{2 - \sec^2 \left(\frac{1}{2}x\right)}{\sec^2 \left(\frac{1}{2}x\right)}$

   b) $2 \cos^2 (2x) - 1$

   d) $1 - 2 \sin^2 (2x)$

7. Which of the following identities could you use to help you prove that $\frac{2 \tan x}{1 + \tan^2 x} = \sin 2x$?

   a) $1 + \tan^2 x = \sec^2 x$

   b) $\sin 2x = 2 \sin x \cos x$

   c) $\tan x = \frac{\sin x}{\cos x}$

   d) all of these

8. Which set of value(s), in radians, is the solution of $5 + 7 \sin \theta = 0$, where $-\pi \le \theta \le \pi$?

   a) $\theta = -0.80$

   b) $\theta = -0.80, -2.35$

   c) $\theta = 0.80, 2.35$

   d) $\theta = -0.80, 0.80$

9. The height of the tip of one blade of a wind turbine above the ground, $h(t)$, can be modelled by $h(t) = 18 \cos \left(\pi t + \frac{\pi}{4}\right) + 23$, where t is the time passed in seconds. Which time interval describes a period when the blade tip is at least 30 m above the ground?

   a) $5.24 \le t \le 7.33$ c) $1.37 \le t \le 2.12$

   b) $0.42 \le t \le 1.08$ d) $0.08 \le t \le 1.42$

10. Which set of values is the solution of $(2 \sin x + 1)(\cos x - 1) = 0$, where $0° \le x \le 360°$?

    a) $x = 180°, 210°, 330°$

    b) $x = 30°, 180°, 150°$

    c) $x = 0°, 150°, 210°, 360°$

    d) $x = 0°, 210°, 330°, 360°$

11. The equation $\cos 2\theta + d\cos\theta + e = 0$ has solutions $\theta = 0, \frac{\pi}{3}, \frac{5\pi}{3}, 2\pi$ in the interval $0 \le \theta \le 2\pi$. What are the values of d and e?
a) $d = -3, e = 2$ c) $d = 1, e = 3$
b) $d = 2, e = 3$ d) $d = -3, e = 1$

12. What is the exponential form of $y = \log_7 x$?
a) $x = \log_7 y$ c) $y = 7^x$
b) $x = 7^y$ d) $y = x^7$

13. The function $f(x) = \log_{10} x$ is reflected in the x-axis, stretched horizontally by a factor of 3, and translated up 2 units. Which of these functions is the result?
a) $g(x) = -\log_{10}(3x) - 2$
b) $g(x) = \log_{10}\left(-\frac{1}{3}x\right) + 2$
c) $g(x) = -\log_{10}\left(\frac{1}{3}(x-2)\right) + 2$
d) $g(x) = -\log_{10}\left(\frac{1}{3}x\right) + 2$

14. What is the value of $7^{\log_7 49}$?
a) 7   b) 2   c) 14   d) 49

15. The equation $\log_{10} T = 1.5\log_{10} d - 0.45$ describes the orbit of a planet around the star Gliese 581. In this equation, T is the length of the planet's year in days, and d is its average distance in millions of kilometres from Gliese 581. The earth-like planet Gliese 581c is 11 000 000 km from Gliese 581. How long is its year?
a) 16.1 days   c) 12.9 days
b) 1.1 days   d) 3.9 days

16. What is the solution of the equation $\log_4 x + 3 = \log_4 1024$?
a) 16   b) 4   c) 128   d) $\frac{16}{3}$

17. A transformation that takes the graph of $f(x) = \log_5 x$ to that of $g(x) = \log_5 25x$ is
a) horizontal translation 2 units left
b) vertical translation 2 units up
c) vertical stretch by a factor of 25
d) horizontal stretch by a factor of 25

18. Solve $x = \log_3 27\sqrt{3}$.
a) $2\frac{1}{2}$ b) $3\frac{1}{2}$ c) $3\frac{1}{3}$ d) $9\frac{1}{2}$

19. An investment of $1600 grows at a rate of 1% per month, compounded monthly. How long will it take for the investment to be worth more than $6400? Recall that the formula for compound interest is $A = P(1 + i)^n$.
a) 11 years 7 months   c) 11 years 8 months
b) 33 years 3 months   d) 33 years 4 months

20. The loudness of a sound in decibels, L, is $L = 10\log\left(\frac{I}{I_0}\right)$, where I is the intensity of the sound in watts per square metre (W/m^2) and $I_0 = 10^{-12}\ W/m^2$. If the loudness of a jet taking off is 133 dB, what is the intensity of this sound?
a) $2.00 \times 10^{13}\ W/m^2$ c) $10^{-1}\ W/m^2$
b) $10.0\ W/m^2$ d) $20.0\ W/m^2$

21. Solve the following:
$\log_a(x - 3) + \log_a(x - 2) = \log_a(5x - 15)$
a) $x = 3$ c) $x = -3$ or 7
b) $x = 7$ d) $x = 2$

22. Carbon-14 has a half-life of 5730 years. A fossil human jawbone that contains 0.017 g of carbon-14 is estimated to have contained 3.9 g when the person was alive. How old is the fossil?
a) 45 000 years   c) 1 300 000 years
b) 13 500 years   d) 12 000 years

23. Assume that the annual rate of inflation will average 3.1% over the next 5 years. For a product that currently costs P dollars, which is the best model for the approximate cost, C, of goods and services during any year in the next 5 years?
a) $C = P(1 + 0.031^t)$
b) $C = (1.031)^t$
c) $C = P(1.031)^t$
d) $C = P(1 + 3.1^t)$

24. The population of a city is currently 150 000 and is increasing at a rate of 2.3%/a. Predict the instantaneous rate of growth in the population 7 years from now.
   a) 175 900 people/a   c) 4000 people/a
   b) 25 900 people/a   d) 3700 people/a

25. Which combination of functions could result in this graph?

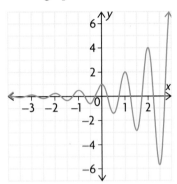

   a) $y = x^2 \cos(2\pi x)$
   b) $y = \sin(2\pi x) + \log x$
   c) $y = 2^x \cos(2\pi x)$
   d) $y = \sin(2\pi|x|)0.5^x$

26. If $f(x) = \log x$ and $g(x) = \dfrac{1}{x - 3}$, which set is the domain of $f - g$?
   a) $\{x \in \mathbf{R} \,|\, x > 3\}$
   b) $\{x \in \mathbf{R} \,|\, x > 0, x \neq 3\}$
   c) $\{x \in \mathbf{R} \,|\, x > 0, x \neq -3\}$
   d) $\{x \in \mathbf{R} \,|\, x < 3\}$

27. Which combination is always an odd function?
   a) the sum of two odd functions
   b) the difference of an odd function and an even function
   c) the sum of an odd function and an even function
   d) the difference of two even functions

28. For which pair of functions, $f(x)$ and $g(x)$, is the range of $f \times g$ equal to $\{y \in \mathbf{R} \,|\, y \geq 1\}$?
   a) $f(x) = g(x) = \sec x$
   b) $f(x) = \sec x, g(x) = \csc x$
   c) $f(x) = 2^x, g(x) = |x| + 1$
   d) $f(x) = 2^x, g(x) = x^2 + 1$

29. Given $f(x) = ax^2 + 3$ and $g(x) = bx - 1$, the graph of the product $f \times g$ passes through the points $(-1, -3)$ and $(1, 9)$. What are the values of a and b?
   a) $a = -6, b = 10$ c) $a = -8, b = 2$
   b) $a = 6, b = 2$ d) $a = -6, b = -2$

30. What is the domain of $f \div g$, where $f(x) = \log x$ and $g(x) = |x - 2|$?
   a) $\{x \in \mathbf{R} \,|\, x \neq 0, 2\}$
   b) $\{x \in \mathbf{R} \,|\, x > 2\}$
   c) $\{x \in \mathbf{R} \,|\, 0 < x < 2\}$
   d) $\{x \in \mathbf{R} \,|\, x > 0, x \neq 2\}$

31. If $f(x) = \sqrt{3 - x}$ and $g(x) = 3x^2$, what is the domain of $f \circ g$?
   a) $\{x \in \mathbf{R} \,|\, -3 \leq x \leq 3\}$
   b) $\{x \in \mathbf{R} \,|\, x \leq 3\}$
   c) $\{x \in \mathbf{R} \,|\, -1 \leq x \leq 1\}$
   d) $\{x \in \mathbf{R} \,|\, x \geq 0\}$

32. Which combination of the functions $f(x) = 2x, g(x) = x + 5$, and $h(x) = 3 - x$ has this graph?

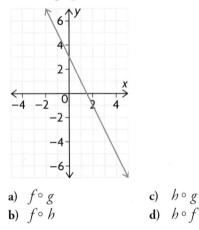

   a) $f \circ g$ c) $h \circ g$
   b) $f \circ h$ d) $h \circ f$

33. Which values are solutions of the equation $x^3 = \sqrt[3]{\tan x}$?
   a) $x = 0$ c) $x = 1.07$
   b) $x = -1.07$ d) all of these

34. Given $f(x) = 4 - x^2$, for which function $g(x)$ is $f(x) < g(x)$ when $x \in (-\infty, -1)$ or $(4, \infty)$?
   a) $g(x) = 4x$ c) $g(x) = 4x - 8$
   b) $g(x) = -3x$ d) $g(x) = -4x$

Investigations

Touchdown Pass

35. The horizontal distance, d, in metres, that a football can be thrown from its release point to the point where it hits the ground can be modelled by the equation $d = \dfrac{v^2}{9.8} \sin 2\theta + 1.8$, where v is the initial speed of the football in metres per second and θ is the angle relative to the horizontal at which the football leaves the quarterback's hand. If the football is thrown at 20 m/s and travels 35 m, determine the possible angles at which the football could be thrown. Give your answer to the nearest degree.

Projecting Populations

36. The data below were collected by the Ontario Ministry of Finance and released in July 2000. It shows the projected populations (in thousands) of the Regional Municipalities of Niagara and Waterloo.

	Historical		Projections						
Regional Municipality	**1996**	**1999**	**2001**	**2006**	**2011**	**2016**	**2021**	**2026**	**2028**
Niagara	414.8	421.7	426.4	435.9	445.3	455.1	464.9	473.8	476.8
Waterloo	418.3	438.4	452.1	483.6	512.6	541.4	569.8	596.3	606.1

a) Determine suitable models that the Ministry of Finance might have used to make these projections.

b) Use your models to estimate the doubling time of the population in each region.

c) Use your models to predict which region's population will be increasing the fastest in 2025. Support your answer with the necessary calculations.

It's Rocket Science

37. The mass of a rocket just before launch is 30 000 kg. During its ascent, the rocket burns 100 kg of fuel every second, and therefore decreases in mass at a rate of 100 kg/s. The mass m, acceleration a, and thrust T are related by the equation $T - 10m = ma$. The velocity v is related to the mass by the equation $m = 30\,000(2.72)^{-v-gt}$. Determine the functions $m(t)$, $a(t)$, and $v(t)$, in terms of the variable t (time measured in seconds) and the constants T and g. Use the fact that $a(0) > 0$ for the rocket to lift off, to determine the constraint on T.

PART 1 USING THE TI-83 PLUS AND TI-84 GRAPHING CALCULATORS

T–1 Preparing the Calculator

Before you graph a function, be sure to clear any information left on the calculator from the last time it was used. You should always do the following:

1. **Clear all data in the lists.**

   Press [2nd] [+] [4] [ENTER].

2. **Turn off all stat plots.**

   Press [2nd] [Y=] [4] [ENTER].

3. **Clear all equations in the equation editor.**

   Press [Y=], and then press [CLEAR] for each equation.

4. **Set the window so that the axes range from −10 to 10.**

   Press [ZOOM] [6]. Press [WINDOW] to verify.

T–2 Entering and Graphing a Function

1. **Enter the equation of the function in the equation editor.**

   To graph $y = 2x + 8$, press [Y=] [2] [X, T, Θ, n] [+] [8]

   [GRAPH]. The graph will be displayed as shown.

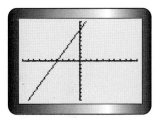

2. **Enter all linear equations in the form $y = mx + b$.**

   If m or b are fractions, enter them between brackets. For example, write

   $2x + 3y = 7$ in the form $y = -\frac{2}{3}x + \frac{7}{3}$, and enter it as shown.

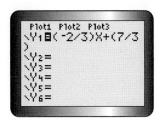

3. Press [GRAPH] to view the graph.

4. Press [TRACE] to find the coordinates of any point on the graph.

   Use the left and right arrow keys to cursor along the graph.
   Press [ZOOM] [8] [ENTER] [TRACE] to trace using integer intervals. If you are working with several graphs at the same time, use

   [▲] and [▼] to scroll between graphs.

T–3 Evaluating a Function

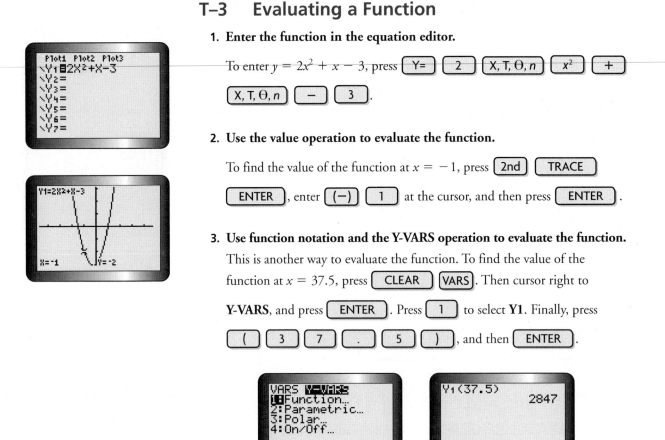

1. Enter the function in the equation editor.

To enter $y = 2x^2 + x - 3$, press Y=   2   X, T, Θ, n x^2 +   X, T, Θ, n −   3 .

2. Use the value operation to evaluate the function.

To find the value of the function at $x = -1$, press 2nd   TRACE   ENTER , enter (−)   1 at the cursor, and then press ENTER .

3. Use function notation and the Y-VARS operation to evaluate the function.

This is another way to evaluate the function. To find the value of the function at $x = 37.5$, press CLEAR   VARS . Then cursor right to **Y-VARS**, and press ENTER . Press 1 to select **Y1**. Finally, press (3   7   .   5   ) , and then ENTER .

T–4 Changing Window Settings

The window settings can be changed to show a graph for a given domain and range.

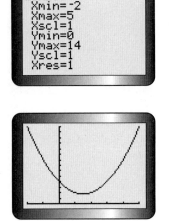

1. Enter the function in the equation editor.
For example, enter $y = x^2 - 3x + 4$ in the equation editor.

2. Use the WINDOW function to set the domain and range.

To display the function over the domain $\{x \mid -2 \le x \le 5\}$ and range $\{y \mid 0 \le y \le 14\}$, press WINDOW   (−)   2   ENTER , then 5   ENTER , then 1   ENTER , then 0   ENTER , then 1   4   ENTER , then 1   ENTER , and finally 1   ENTER .

3. Press GRAPH to show the function with this domain and range.

T–5 Using the Split Screen

1. **The split screen can be used to see a graph and the equation editor at the same time.**

   Press [MODE] and cursor to **Horiz**. Press [ENTER] to select this, and then press [2nd] [MODE] to return to the home screen. Enter $y = x^2$ in

   Y1 of the equation editor, and then press [GRAPH].

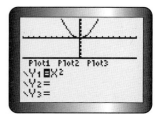

2. **The split screen can also be used to see a graph and a table at the same time.**

   Press [MODE], and move the cursor to **G–T** (Graph-Table). Press

   [ENTER] to select this, and then press [GRAPH].

   It is possible to view the table with different increments. For example, to see the table start at $x = 0$ and increase in increments of 0.5, press [2nd] [WINDOW] and adjust the settings as shown. Then press [GRAPH].

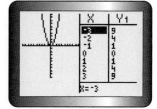

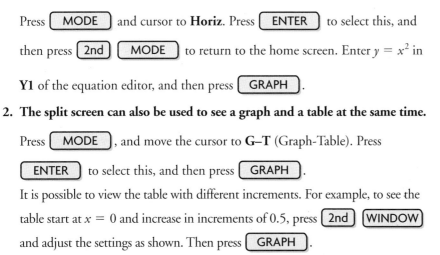

T–6 Using the TABLE Feature

A function can be displayed in a table of values.

1. **Enter the function in the equation editor.**

   To enter $y = -0.1x^3 + 2x + 3$, press [Y=] [(−)] [.] [1]
   [X, T, Θ, n] [∧] [3] [+] [2] [X, T, Θ, n] [+] [3].

2. **Set the start point and step size for the table.**

   Press [2nd] [WINDOW]. The cursor is beside "TblStart=." To start at

   $x = -5$, press [(−)] [5] [ENTER]. The cursor is now beside **ΔTbl=**.

   To increase the x-value in increments of 1, press [1] [ENTER].

3. **To view the table, press [2nd] [GRAPH].**

   Use [▲] and [▼] to move up and down the table. Notice that you can look

   at higher or lower x-values than those in the original range.

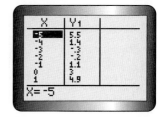

T–7 Making a Table of Differences

To make a table with the first and second differences for a function, use the STAT lists.

1. **Press** [STAT] [1] , **and enter the x-values into L1.**

   For the function $f(x) = 3x^2 - 4x + 1$, use x-values from -2 to 4.

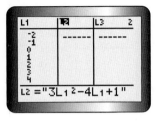

2. **Enter the function.**

   Scroll right and up to select **L2**. Enter the function $f(x)$, using **L1** as the variable x. Press

3. **Press** [ENTER] **to display the values of the function in L2.**

4. **Find the first differences.**

   Scroll right and up to select **L3**. Then press [2nd] [STAT] .
   Scroll right to **OPS** and press [7] to choose **ΔList(**.
   Enter **L2** by pressing [2nd] [2] [)] . Press [ENTER] to see the first differences displayed in **L3**.

5. **Find the second differences.**

   Scroll right and up to select **L4**. Repeat step 4, using **L3** instead of **L2**. Press [ENTER] to see the second differences displayed in **L4**.

T–8 Finding the Zeros of a Function

To find the zeros of a function, use the **zero** operation.

1. **Start by entering the function in the equation editor.**

   For example, enter $y = -(x + 3)(x - 5)$ in the equation editor. Then press [GRAPH] [ZOOM] [6] .

2. **Access the zero operation.**

   Press [2nd] [TRACE] [2] .

3. **Use the left and right arrow keys to cursor along the curve to any point that is left of the zero.**

   Press [ENTER] to set the left bound.

4. **Cursor along the curve to any point that is right of the zero.**

   Press [ENTER] to set the right bound.

5. **Press [ENTER] again to display the coordinates of the zero (the x-intercept).**

6. **Repeat to find the second zero.**

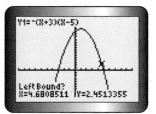

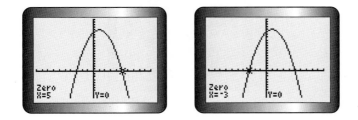

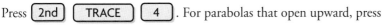

T–9 Finding the Maximum or Minimum Value of a Function

The least or greatest value can be found using the **minimum** operation or the **maximum** operation.

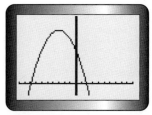

1. **Enter and graph the function.**
   For example, enter $y = -2x^2 - 12x + 30$.
   Graph the function, and adjust the window as shown. This graph opens downward, so it has a maximum.

2. **Use the maximum operation.**

   Press [2nd] [TRACE] [4]. For parabolas that open upward, press

   [2nd] [TRACE] [3] to use the **minimum** operation.

3. **Use [◄] and [►] to cursor along the curve to any point that is left of the maximum value.**

   Press [ENTER] to set the left bound.

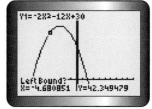

4. **Cursor along the curve to any point that is right of the maximum value.**

   Press [ENTER] to set the right bound.

5. **Press [ENTER] again to display the coordinates of the optimal value.**

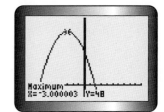

T–10 Graphing the Inverse of a Function

Parametric equations allow you to graph any function and its inverse.
For example, the function $y = 2 - x^2$, with domain $x \geq 0$, can be graphed using
parametric mode. For a parametric equation, both x and y must be expressed in
terms of a parameter, t. Replace x with t. Then $x = t$ and $y = 2 - t^2$. The inverse
of this function can now be graphed.

1. **Clear the calculator, and press** [MODE].

   Change the setting to the parametric mode by scrolling down to the fourth line
   and to the right to **Par**, as shown on the screen below. Press [ENTER].

2. **Enter the inverse function by changing the parametric equations $x = t$**
   and $y = 2 - t^2$ to $x = 2 - t^2$ and $y = t$.

   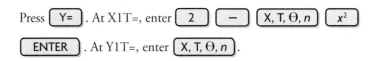

   Press [Y=]. At X1T=, enter [2] [−] [X, T, Θ, n] [x^2]

   [ENTER]. At Y1T=, enter [X, T, Θ, n].

3. **Press** [WINDOW].

   The original domain, $x \geq 0$, is also the domain of t. Use window settings,
   such as those shown below, to display the graph.

4. **Press** [GRAPH] **to display the inverse function.**

   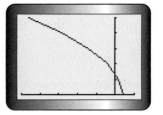

T–11 Creating a Scatter Plot and Determining a Line or Curve of Best Fit Using Regression

This table gives the height of a baseball above ground, from the time it was hit to the time it touched the ground.

Time (s)	0	1	2	3	4	5	6
Height (m)	2	27	42	48	43	29	5

1. **Start by entering the data into lists.**

   Press [STAT] [ENTER]. Move the cursor over to the first position in L_1, and enter the values for time. Press [ENTER] after each value. Repeat this for height in L_2.

2. **Create a scatter plot.**

   Press [2nd] [Y=] and [1] [ENTER]. Turn on Plot 1 by making sure that the cursor is over **On**, the **Type** is set to the graph type you prefer, and L_1 and L_2 appear after **Xlist** and **Ylist**.

3. **Display the graph.**

   Press [ZOOM] [9] to activate **ZoomStat**.

4. **Apply the appropriate regression analysis.**

   To determine the equation of the line or curve of best fit, press [STAT] and scroll over to **CALC**. Press

   - [4] to enable **LinReg(ax+b)**

   - [5] to enable **QuadReg**

   - [6] to enable **CubicReg**

   - [7] to enable **QuartReg**

   - [0] to enable **ExpReg**

   - [ALPHA] [C] to enable **SinReg**

   Then press [2nd] [1] [,] [2nd] [2] [,] [VARS]. Scroll over to **Y-VARS**. Press [1] twice. This action stores the equation of the line or curve of best fit into **Y1** of the equation editor.

5. **Display and analyze the results.**

Press $\boxed{\text{ENTER}}$. In this example, the letters a, b, and c are the coefficients of the general quadratic equation $y = ax^2 + bx + c$ for the curve of best fit.  R^2 is the percent of data variation represented by the model. The equation is about $y = -4.90x^2 + 29.93x + 1.98$.

Note: For linear regression, if r is not displayed, turn on the diagnostics function. Press $\boxed{\text{2nd}}$ $\boxed{0}$, and scroll down to **DiagnosticOn**. Press $\boxed{\text{ENTER}}$ twice. Repeat steps 4 to 6.

6. **Plot the curve.**

Press $\boxed{\text{GRAPH}}$

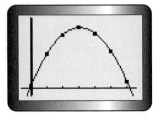

T–12 Finding the Points of Intersection of Two Functions

1. **Enter both functions in the equation editor.**
   For example, enter $y = 5x + 4$ and $y = -2x + 18$.

2. **Graph both functions.**

Press $\boxed{\text{GRAPH}}$. Adjust the window settings until one or more points of intersection are displayed.

3. **Use the intersect operation.**

Press $\boxed{\text{2nd}}$ $\boxed{\text{TRACE}}$ $\boxed{5}$.

4. **Determine a point of intersection.**
   You will be asked to verify the two curves and enter a guess (optional) for the point of intersection. Press $\boxed{\text{ENTER}}$ after each screen appears.

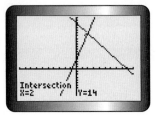

The point of intersection is exactly $(2, 14)$.

5. **Determine any additional points of intersection.**

Press $\boxed{\text{TRACE}}$, and move the cursor close to the other point you wish to identify. Repeat step 4.

T–13 Evaluating Trigonometric Ratios and Finding Angles

Working with Degrees

1. **Put the calculator in degree mode.**

   Press [MODE]. Scroll down and across to **Degree**. Press [ENTER].

2. **Use the [SIN], [COS], or [TAN] key to calculate a trigonometric ratio.**

   To find the value of sin 54°, press [SIN] [5] [4] [ )] [ENTER].

3. **Use SIN⁻¹, COS⁻¹, or TAN⁻¹ to calculate an angle.**

   To find the angle whose cosine is 0.6, press [2nd] [COS] [.] [6] [ )] [ENTER].

Working with Radians

1. **Put the calculator in radian mode.**

   Press [MODE]. Scroll down and across to **Radian**. Press [ENTER].

2. **Use the [SIN], [COS], or [TAN] key to calculate a trigonometric ratio.**

   To find the value of $\sin \frac{\pi}{4}$, press [SIN] [2nd] [^] [÷] [4] [ )] [ENTER].

3. **Use SIN⁻¹, COS⁻¹, or TAN⁻¹ to calculate an angle.**

   To find the angle whose cosine is 0.6, press [2nd] [COS] [.] [6] [ )] [ENTER].

T–14 Graphing a Trigonometric Function

Working with Degrees

You can graph a trigonometric function in degree measure using the TI-83 Plus or TI-84 calculator.

step 3

step 4

1. **Put the calculator in degree mode.**

   Press [MODE]. Scroll down and across to **Degree**. Press [ENTER].

2. **Enter the function in the equation editor.**

   For example, to graph the function $y = \sin x$, for $0° \leq x \leq 360°$, press

   [Y=] [SIN] [X, T, Θ, n] [ )].

3. **Adjust the window to correspond to the given domain.**

   Press [WINDOW]. Set **Xmin** $= 0$, **Xmax** $= 360$, and **Xscl** $= 90$. These settings display the graph from $0°$ to $360°$, using an interval of $90°$ on the x-axis. Then set **Ymin** $= -1$ and **Ymax** $= 1$, since the sine function being graphed lies between these values. If the domain is not known, this step can be omitted.

4. **Graph the function using ZoomFit.**

   Press [ZOOM] [0]. The graph is displayed over the domain, and the calculator determines the best values to use for **Ymax** and **Ymin** in the display window.

   Note: You can use **ZoomTrig** (press [ZOOM] [7]) to graph the function in step 4. **ZoomTrig** will always display the graph in a window where **Xmin** $= -360°$, **Xmax** $= 360°$, **Ymin** $= -4$, and **Ymax** $= 4$.

Working with Radians

You can also graph a trigonometric function in radians using the TI-83 Plus or TI-84 calculator.

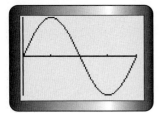

1. **Put the calculator in radian mode.**

   Press [MODE]. Scroll down and across to **Radian**. Press [ENTER].

2. **Enter the function in the equation editor.**

   For example, to graph the function $y = \sin x$, for $0 \leq x \leq 2\pi$, press

   [Y=] [SIN] [X, T, Θ, n] [ )].

3. **Adjust the window to correspond to the given domain.**

   Press [WINDOW]. Set **Xmin** $= 0$, **Xmax** $= 2\pi$, and **Xscl** $= \dfrac{\pi}{2}$. These settings display the graph from 0 to 2π, using an interval of $\dfrac{\pi}{2}$ on the x-axis. Then set **Ymin** $= -1$ and **Ymax** $= 1$, since the sine function being graphed lies between these values. If the domain is not known, this step can be omitted.

4. **Graph the function using ZoomFit.**

   Press ZOOM 0 . The graph is displayed over the domain, and the calculator determines the best values to use for **Ymax** and **Ymin** in the display window.

   Note: You can use **ZoomTrig** (press ZOOM 7) to graph the function in step 4. **ZoomTrig** will always display the graph in a window where $Xmin = -2\pi$, $Xmax = 2\pi$, $Ymin = -4$, and $Ymax = 4$.

T–15 Evaluating Powers and Roots

1. **Evaluate the power $(5.3)^2$.**

   Press 5 . 3 x^2 ENTER .

2. **Evaluate the power 7^5.**

   Press 7 ∧ 5 ENTER .

3. **Evaluate the power $8^{-\frac{2}{3}}$.**

   Press 8 ∧ (− 2 ÷ 3) ENTER .

4. **Evaluate the square root of 46.1.**

   Press 2nd x^2 4 6 . 1) ENTER .

5. **Evaluate $\sqrt[4]{256}$.**

   Press 4 MATH 5 2 5 6 ENTER .

T–16 Graphing a Piecewise Function

Follow these steps to graph the piecewise function defined by

$$f(x) = \begin{cases} -x + 1, & \text{if } x < 1 \\ x^2 - 5, & \text{if } x \geq 1 \end{cases}$$

1. **Enter the first equation.**

   In the equation editor for **Y1**, enter the first equation in brackets. Then enter its corresponding interval in brackets. The inequality signs can be accessed in the **Test** menu by pressing 2nd MATH .

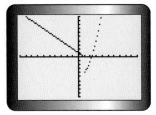

2. Enter the second equation.

Press $\boxed{+}$, and repeat step 1 for the second equation and its interval. Scroll to the left of **Y1**, and press $\boxed{\text{ENTER}}$ until the dotted graphing mode appears.

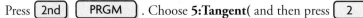

3. Display the graph.

Press $\boxed{\text{GRAPH}}$ to display the graph.
Each equation produces a different graph on each interval. This function is discontinuous at $x = 1$.

T–17 Drawing Tangent Lines

1. Enter the function, and display the graph.

Enter $y = (4 - x)^2$ into **Y1** of the equation editor, and display the graph.

2. Draw the tangent line, and estimate its slope.

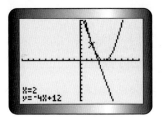

Use the **Tangent** command in the **Draw** menu to draw a tangent line at point $(2, 4)$ and estimate its slope.
Press $\boxed{\text{2nd}}$ $\boxed{\text{PRGM}}$. Choose **5:Tangent(** and then press $\boxed{2}$ and $\boxed{\text{ENTER}}$.
The tangent line is drawn, and its equation is displayed.

The slope of the tangent line is -4, and its y-intercept is 12.

3. Clear the tangent line.

Press $\boxed{\text{2nd}}$ $\boxed{\text{PRGM}}$ $\boxed{1}$ to clear the tangent line. The function will be graphed again, without the tangent line.

PART 2 USING A SPREADSHEET

T–18 Introduction to Spreadsheets

A spreadsheet is a computer program that can be used to create a table of values and then graph the values. It is made up of cells that are identified by column letter and row number, such as A2 or B5. A cell can hold a label, a number, or a formula.

Creating a Table

Use a spreadsheet to solve a problem like this:

> How long will it take to double your money if you invest $1000 at 5%/a, compounded quarterly?

To create a spreadsheet, label cell A1 as Number of Quarters, Cell B1 as Time (years), and cell C1 as Amount ($). Enter the initial values of 0 in A2, 0 in B2, and 1000 in C2. Enter the formula $= A2 + 1$ in A3, the formula $= A3/4$ in B3, and the formula $= 1000*(1.0.125)$^A3 in C3 to generate the next values in the table.

	A	B	C
	Number of Quarters	**Time (years)**	**Amount ($)**
2	0	0	1000
3	=A2+1	=A3/4	-1000*(1.0125^A3)
4			

Notice that an equal sign is in front of each formula, an asterisk (*) is used for multiplication, and a caret (^) is used for an exponent.

	A	B	C
	Number of Quarters	**Time (years)**	**Amount ($)**
2	0	0	1000
3	1	0.25	
4			

Use the cursor to select cells A3 to C3 and several rows of cells below them. Then use the **Fill Down** command to insert the appropriate formula into the selected cells. The computer will automatically calculate and enter the values in the cells, as shown in the screen on the left.

Continue to select the cells in the last row of the table. Use the **Fill Down** command to generate more values until the solution appears, as shown below in the screen on the right.

	A	B	C
	Number of Quarters	**Time (years)**	**Amount ($)**
2	0	0	1000
3	1	0.25	1012.50
4	2	0.5	1025.16
5	3	0.75	1037.97
6	4	1	1050.94

	A	B	C
	Number of Quarters	**Time (years)**	**Amount ($)**
2	0	0	1000
3	1	0.25	1012.50
4	2	0.5	1025.1563
:	:	:	:
56	54	13.5	1955.8328
57	55	13.75	1980.2807
58	56	14	2005.0342

Creating a Graph

Use the spreadsheet's graphing command to graph the results. Use the cursor to highlight the portion of the table you would like to graph. In this example, Time versus Amount is graphed.

	A	B	C
1	**Number of Quarters**	**Time (years)**	**Amount ($)**
2	0	0	1000
3	1	0.25	1012.50
4	2	0.5	1025.1563
⋮	⋮	⋮	⋮
56	54	13.5	1955.8328
57	55	13.75	1980.2807
58	56	14	2005.0342

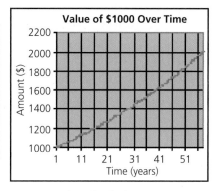

Different spreadsheets have different graphing commands. Check the instructions for your spreadsheet to find the proper command.

Determining the Equation of the Curve of Best Fit

Different spreadsheets have different commands for finding the equation of the curve of best fit using regression. Check the instructions for your spreadsheet to find the proper command for the type of regression that suits the data.

PART 3 USING THE GEOMETER'S SKETCHPAD

T–19   Graphing a Function

1. **Turn on the grid.**
   From the **Graph** menu, choose **Show Grid**.

2. **Enter the function.**
   From the **Graph** menu, choose **Plot New Function**. The function calculator should appear.

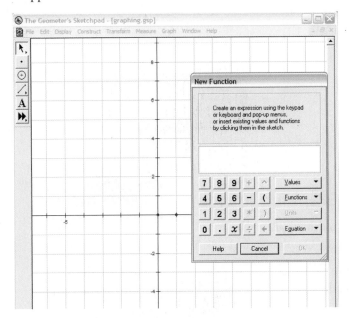

3. **Graph the function.**
   To graph $y = x^2 - 3x + 2$, use either the calculator keypad or the keyboard

   to enter **x ^ 2 − 3 * x + 2**. Then press ⬛ **OK** ⬛ on the calculator
   keypad. The graph of $y = x^2 - 3x + 2$ should appear on the grid.

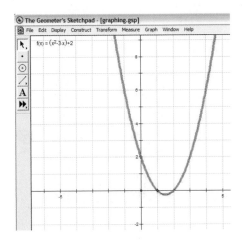

4. **Adjust the origin and/or scale.**

To adjust the origin, left-click on the point at the origin to select it. Then left-click and drag the origin as desired.

To adjust the scale, left-click in blank space to deselect the origin, and then left-click on the point at (1, 0) to select it. Left-click and drag this point to change the scale.

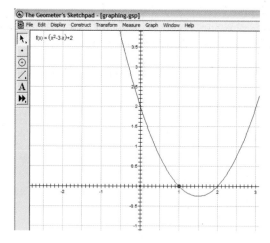

T–20 Graphing a Trigonometric Function

1. **Turn on the grid.**

   From the **Graph** menu, choose **Show Grid**.

2. **Graph the function $y = 2 \sin (30x) + 3$ using degrees.**

   From the **Graph** menu, choose **Plot New Function**. The function calculator should appear.

   Use either the calculator keypad or the keyboard to enter **$2 * \sin (30 * x) + 3$**. To enter sin, use the pull-down **Functions** menu on

   the calculator keypad. Click (**OK**) on the calculator keypad.

   Click on **No** in the pop-up panel to keep degrees as the unit. The graph of $y = 2 \sin (30x) + 3$ should appear on the grid.

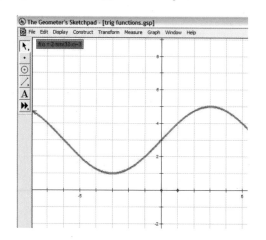

3. **Graph the function $y = 2 \cos (3x) - 1$ using radians.**

From the **Graph** menu, choose **Plot New Function**. The function calculator should appear.

Use either the calculator keypad or the keyboard to enter $2 * \cos (3 * x) - 1$. To enter cos, use the pull-down **Functions** menu on the calculator keypad.

Click [OK] on the calculator keypad.

Click on **Yes** in the pop-up panel to change the unit to radians. The graph of $y = 2 \cos (3x) - 1$ should appear on the grid.

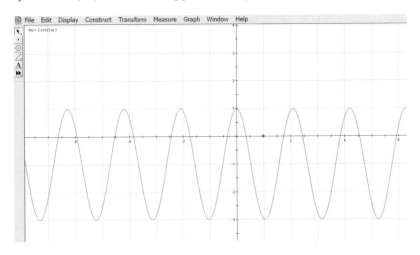

Note: Selecting **Preferences** from the **Edit** menu will also allow you to change from radians to degrees or from degrees to radians.

4. **Adjust the origin and/or scale.**

Left-click on and drag either the origin or the point $(1, 0)$.

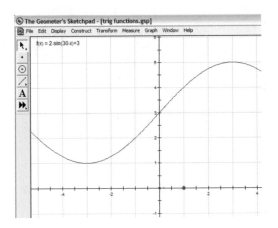

PART 4 USING FATHOM

T–21 Creating a Scatter Plot and Determining the Equation of a Line or Curve of Good Fit

1. **Create a case table.**

   Drag a case table from the object shelf, and drop it in the document.

   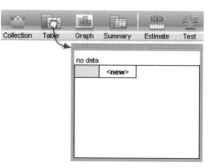

2. **Enter the Variables and Data.**

   Click on **<new>**, type a name for the new variable or attribute, and press
   [ENTER] . (If necessary, repeat this step to add more attributes. Pressing

   [TAB] instead of [ENTER] moves you to the next column.) When
   you name your first attribute, *Fathom* creates an empty collection to hold your
   data (a little, empty box). This is where your data are actually stored. Deleting
   the collection deletes your data. When you add cases by typing values, the
   collection icon fills with gold balls. To enter the data, click in the blank cell
   under the attribute name and begin typing values. (Press [TAB] to move
   from cell to cell.)

	time	height	<ne
1	0	2.0	
2	1	27.1	
3	2	42.4	
4	3	47.9	
5	4	43.6	
6	5	29.5	

3. Graph the data.

Drag a new graph from the object shelf at the top of the *Fathom* window, and drop it in a blank space in your document. Drag an attribute from the case table, and drop it on the prompt below and/or to the left of the appropriate axis in the graph.

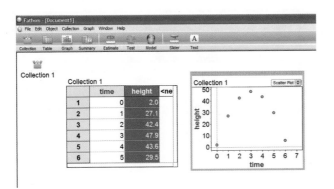

4. Create a function.

Right-click the graph, and select **Plot Function.** Enter your function using a parameter that can be adjusted to fit the curve to the scatter plot (**a** was used below).

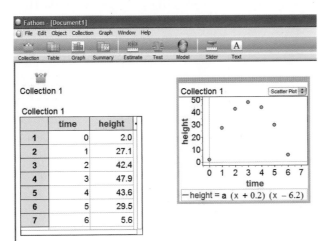

5. Create a slider for the parameter.

Drag a new slider from the object shelf at the top of the *Fathom* window, and drop it in a blank space below your graph. Over **V1**, type the letter of the parameter used in step 4. Click on the number, and then adjust the value of the slider until you are satisfied with the fit.

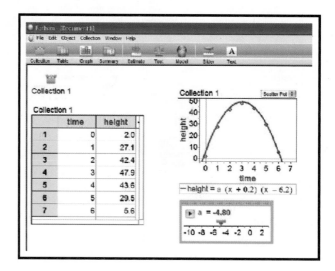

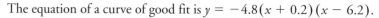

The equation of a curve of good fit is $y = -4.8(x + 0.2)(x - 6.2)$.

Glossary

Instructional Words

C

calculate: Figure out the number that answers a question; compute

clarify: Make a statement easier to understand; provide an example

classify: Put things into groups according to a rule and label the groups; organize into categories

compare: Look at two or more objects or numbers and identify how they are the same and how they are different (e.g., Compare the numbers 6.5 and 5.6. Compare the size of the students' feet. Compare two shapes.)

conclude: Judge or decide after reflection or after considering data

construct: Make or build a model; draw an accurate geometric shape (e.g., Use a ruler and a protractor to construct an angle.)

create: Make your own example

D

describe: Tell, draw, or write about what something is or what something looks like; tell about a process in a step-by-step way

determine: Decide with certainty as a result of calculation, experiment, or exploration

draw: 1. Show something in picture form (e.g., Draw a diagram.)
2. Pull or select an object (e.g., Draw a card from the deck. Draw a tile from the bag.)

E

estimate: Use your knowledge to make a sensible decision about an amount; make a reasonable guess (e.g., Estimate how long it takes to cycle from your home to school. Estimate how many leaves are on a tree. What is your estimate of 3210 + 789?)

evaluate: 1. Determine if something makes sense; judge
2. Calculate the value as a number

explain: Tell what you did; show your mathematical thinking at every stage; show how you know

explore: Investigate a problem by questioning, brainstorming, and trying new ideas

extend: 1. In patterning, continue the pattern
2. In problem solving, create a new problem that takes the idea of the original problem further

J

justify: Give convincing reasons for a prediction, an estimate, or a solution; tell why you think your answer is correct

M

measure: Use a tool to describe an object or determine an amount (e.g., Use a ruler to measure the height or distance around something. Use a protractor to measure an angle. Use balance scales to measure mass. Use a measuring cup to measure capacity. Use a stopwatch to measure the time in seconds or minutes.)

model: Show, represent, or demonstrate an idea or situation using a diagram, graph, table of values, equation, formula, physical model, or computer model

P

predict: Use what you know to work out what is going to happen (e.g., Predict the next number in the pattern 1, 2, 4, 7, ...)

R

reason: Develop ideas and relate them to the purpose of the task and to each other; analyze relevant information to show understanding

relate: Describe how two or more objects, drawings, ideas, or numbers are similar

represent: Show information or an idea in a different way that makes it easier to understand (e.g., Draw a graph. Make a model.)

S

show (your work): Record all calculations, drawings, numbers, words, or symbols that make up the solution

sketch: Make a rough drawing (e.g., Sketch a picture of the field with dimensions.)

solve: Develop and carry out a process for finding a solution to a problem

sort: Separate a set of objects, drawings, ideas, or numbers according to an attribute (e.g., Sort 2-D shapes by the number of sides.)

Mathematical Words

A

absolute maximum: The greatest value of a function for all values in its domain

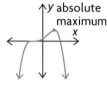

absolute minimum: The least value of a function for all values in its domain

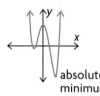

absolute value: Written as $|x|$; describes the distance of x from 0; equals x when $x \geq 0$ and equals $-x$ when $x < 0$; for example, $|3| = 3$ and $|-3| = -(-3) = 3$

amplitude: Half the difference between the maximum and minimum values of a sinusoidal function; also the vertical distance from the axis of a sinusoidal function to the maximum or minimum value

argument: The expression on which a function operates; for example, in $\sin(x + \pi)$, sin is the function and $x + \pi$ is the argument

asymptote: A line that the graph of a relation or function gets closer and closer to, but never meets, on some part of its domain

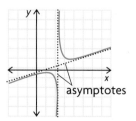

V

validate: Check an idea by showing that it works

verify: Work out an answer or solution again, usually in another way; show evidence of

visualize: Form a picture in your head of what something is like; imagine

average rate of change: In a relation, the change in the quantity represented by the dependent variable (Δy) divided by the corresponding change in the quantity represented by the independent variable (Δx); for a function $y = f(x)$, the average rate of change in the interval $x_1 \leq x \leq x_2$ is $\dfrac{\Delta y}{\Delta x} = \dfrac{f(x_2) - f(x_1)}{x_2 - x_1}$

C

centred interval: An interval of the independent variable of the form $a - h \leq x \leq a + h$, where h is a small positive value; used to determine an average rate of change

composite function: A function that is the composite of two other functions; the function $f(g(x))$, denoted by $(f \circ g)(x)$, is called the composition of f with g and is defined using the output of the function g as the input for the function f

compound angle: An angle that is created by adding or subtracting two or more angles

conjecture: A guess or prediction based on limited evidence

continuous function: A function that does not contain any holes or breaks over its entire domain

counterexample: An example that shows a general statement to be false

cubic function: A polynomial function whose degree is three; for example, $y = 5x^3 + 6x^2 - 4x + 7$

curve of best fit: The curve that best describes the distribution of points in a scatter plot; typically found using regression analysis

D

damped motion: Motion where a restriction is placed on an oscillating system that results in a decrease in amplitude over time

decreasing function: A function $f(x)$ whose y values get continually smaller as x gets continually larger

degree: The size of an angle that is subtended at the centre of a circle by an arc with a length equal to $\frac{1}{360}$ of the circumference of the circle

difference quotient: If $P(a, f(a))$ and $Q(a + h, f(a + h))$ are two points on the graph of $y = f(x)$, then the instantaneous rate of change of y with respect to x at P can be estimated using the average rate of change $\frac{\Delta y}{\Delta x} = \frac{f(a + h) - f(a)}{h}$, where h is a very small number; the expression $\frac{f(a + h) - f(a)}{h}$ is the difference quotient

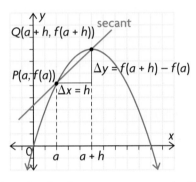

discontinuity: A value for x, on an x-y graph, for which a value for y is not defined. In the graph below the y-value is not defined when $x = a$

displacement: A translation from one position to another, without consideration of any intervening positions; the minimal distance between two points

domain: The set of all values of the independent variable of a relation

E

end behaviour: A description of the values of $f(x)$ as $x \to \infty$ or $x \to -\infty$

equation of the axis: The equation of the horizontal line that is halfway between the maximum value and minimum value of a sinusoidal function; determined using

$$y = \frac{\text{maximum value} + \text{minimum value}}{2}$$

even function: A function that is symmetric about the y-axis; algebraically, all even functions have the property $f(-x) = f(x)$

exponential function: A function of the form $y = a(b^x)$

extrapolation: The process of using a graphical or algebraic model to predict the value of a function beyond the known values

F

factor theorem: A theorem stating that $x - a$ is a factor of $f(x)$ if and only if $f(a) = 0$

family of polynomial functions: A set of polynomial functions whose equations have the same degree and whose graphs have common characteristics; for example, one quadratic family may have the same zeros and another quadratic family may have the same x-intercepts

finite difference: The difference between two consecutive values in a table that has a constant difference between the values of the independent variable; first differences are the differences between the values of the dependent variable, second differences are the differences between the first differences, and so on

following interval: An interval of the independent variable of the form $a \leq x \leq a + h$, where h is a small positive value; used to determine an average rate of change

function: A relation in which each value of the independent variable corresponds to only one value of the dependent variable

function notation: Notation, such as $f(x)$, that is used to represent the value of the dependent variable, y (the output) for a given value of the independent variable, x (the input)

H

half-life: The time that is required for a quantity to decay to half of its initial value

horizontal asymptote: An asymptote that takes the form of a horizontal line

I

identity: A mathematical statement that is true for all values of the given variables; any restrictions on the variables must be stated; for example, if an identity involves fractions, the denominator cannot be zero

increasing function: A function $f(x)$ whose y values get continually larger as x gets continually larger

independent variable: In an algebraic relation, a variable whose values may be freely chosen and upon which the values of the other variables depend; often represented by x

instantaneous rate of change: The exact rate of change of a function $y = f(x)$ at a specific value of the independent variable, $x = a$; estimated using average rates of change for small intervals of the independent variable that are very close to the value $x = a$

interpolation: The process of using a graphical or algebraic model to predict the value of a function between known values

intersection: A set that contains the elements that are common to both sets; the symbol for intersection is ∩

interval of decrease: The interval(s) within the domain of a function where the y values of the function get smaller, moving from left to right

interval of increase: The interval(s) within the domain of a function where the y values of the function get larger, moving from left to right

inverse of a function: The reverse of the original function; undoes what the original function has done

L

leading coefficient: The coefficient of the term with the highest degree in a polynomial

linear inequality: An inequality that contains an algebraic expression whose degree is one; for example, $5x + 3 > 6x - 2$

linear relation: A relation between two variables that appears as a straight line when graphed on a coordinate system; can be represented by an equation whose degree is one; also called a *linear function*

logarithm: The exponent required on base a to give the value x; written as $\log_a x$, where $a > 0$ and $a \neq 1$

logarithmic function: The inverse of the exponential function $y = a^x$ is the function with exponential equation $x = a^y$. We write y as a function of x using the logarithmic form of this equation, $y = \log_a x$. As with the exponential function, $a > 0$ and $a \neq 1$

lowest common denominator: The smallest multiple that is shared by two or more denominators

M

magnitude: The absolute value of a quantity

N

negative angle: An angle that is measured *clockwise* from the positive x-axis

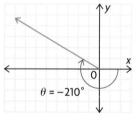

nonlinear relation: A relation whose graph is not a straight line

O

oblique asymptote: An asymptote that is neither vertical nor horizontal, but slanted

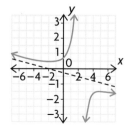

odd function: A function that has rotational symmetry about the origin; algebraically, all odd functions have the property $f(-x) = -f(x)$

order: The exponent to which each factor in an algebraic expression is raised; for example, in $f(x) = (x - 3)^2(x - 1)$, the order of $(x - 3)$ is 2 and the order of $(x - 1)$ is 1

P

parent function: The simplest, or base, function in a family; for example, $y = x^2$ is the parent function for all quadratic functions

period: The change in the independent variable (typically x) that corresponds to one cycle of a sinusoidal function; the cycle of a periodic function is the part of the graph that repeats

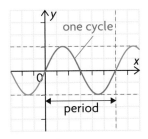

piecewise function: A function that is defined using two or more rules on two or more intervals; as a result, the graph consists of two or more pieces of similar or different functions

polynomial equation: An equation in which one polynomial expression is set equal to another polynomial expression; for example, $x^3 - 5x^2 = 4x - 3$ or $5x^4 - 3x^3 + x^2 - 6x = 9$

polynomial function: A function of the form $f(x) = a_nx^n + a_{n-1}x^{n-1} + \ldots + a_2x^2 + a_1x + a_0$, where $a_0, a_1, a_2, \ldots, a_{n-1}$, and a_n are real numbers and n is a whole number; the equation of a polynomial function is defined by a polynomial expression, as in $f(x) = 5x^3 + 6x^2 - 3x + 7$

polynomial inequality: An inequality that contains a polynomial expression; for example, $5x^3 + 3x^2 - 6x \le 2$

preceding interval: An interval of the independent variable of the form $a - h \le x \le a$, where h is a small positive value; used to determine an average rate of change

principal angle: The counterclockwise angle between the initial arm and terminal arm of an angle in standard position; its value is between $0°$ and $360°$ (0 and 2π)

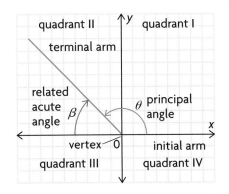

Q

quadratic function: A function that can be represented by a quadratic equation whose degree is two; for example, $y = x^2 + 3x - 2$

quartic function: a polynomial function whose degree is four; for example, $y = 8x^4 - 5x^3 + 6x^2 - 4x + 7$

quintic function: a polynomial function whose degree is five; for example, $y = -2x^5 + 8x^4 - 5x^3 + 6x^2 - 4x + 7$

R

radian: The size of an angle that is subtended at the centre of a circle by an arc with a length equal to the radius of the circle; both the arc length and the radius are measured in units of length (such as centimetres) and, as a result, the angle is a real number without any units

range: The set of all values of the dependent variable of a relation

rational expression: A quotient of polynomials; for example, $\frac{2x - 1}{3x}, x \ne 0$

rational function: A function that can be expressed as $f(x) = \frac{p(x)}{q(x)}$, where $p(x)$ and $q(x)$ are polynomial functions, $q(x) \ne 0$; for example, $f(x) = \frac{3x^2 - 1}{x + 1}$, $x \ne -1$, and $f(x) = \frac{1 - x}{x^2}, x \ne 0$, are rational functions, but $f(x) = \frac{1 + x}{\sqrt{2 - x}}, x \ne 2$, is not because its denominator is not a polynomial

rational inequality: A statement that one rational expression is less than or greater than (or as well as equal to in some cases) another rational expression; for example, $\dfrac{2x}{x+3} > \dfrac{x-1}{5x}$

rational number: a number that can be expressed exactly as the ratio of two integers; $\left\{\dfrac{a}{b} \,\middle|\, a, b \in I, b \neq 0\right\}$

real numbers: Numbers that are either rational or irrational; include positive and negative integers, zero, fractions, and irrational numbers such as $\sqrt{2}$ and π

related acute angle: The acute angle between the terminal arm of an angle in standard position and the x-axis, when the terminal arm lies in quadrant II, III, or IV.

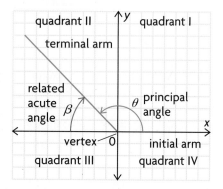

relation: A set of ordered pairs; values of the independent variable are paired with values of the dependent variable

remainder theorem: A theorem stating that when a polynomial $f(x)$ is divided by $x - a$, the remainder is equal to $f(a)$; if the remainder is zero, then $x - a$ is a factor of the polynomial; the remainder theorem can be used to factor polynomials

restrictions: The values of the variable(s) in a function or expression that cause the function or expression to be undefined; the zeros of the denominator, or the numbers that are not in the domain of the function

S

scatter plot: A graph that attempts to show a relationship between two variables using points plotted on a coordinate grid

secant line: A line that passes through two points on the graph of a relation

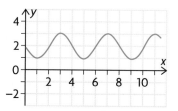

sinusoidal function: A periodic function whose graph looks like smooth symmetrical waves, if any part of the wave can be horizontally translated onto another part of the wave; a graph of a sinusoidal function can be created by transforming the graph of $y = \sin x$ or $y = \cos x$

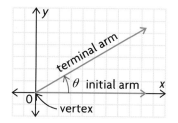

special triangle: A right triangle whose angles measure $45°$, $45°$, and $90°$ $\left(\dfrac{\pi}{4}, \dfrac{\pi}{4}, \text{ and } \dfrac{\pi}{2}\right)$ or $30°$, $60°$, and $90°$ $\left(\dfrac{\pi}{6}, \dfrac{\pi}{3}, \text{ and } \dfrac{\pi}{2}\right)$; used to determine the exact values of trigonometric ratios that include these as principal or related angles

standard position: An angle in the Cartesian plane whose vertex lies at the origin and whose initial arm (the arm that is fixed) lies on the positive x-axis; angle θ is measured from the initial arm to the terminal arm (the arm that rotates)

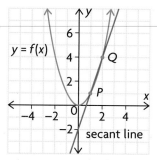

T

tangent line: A line that touches a graph at only one point, P, within a small interval of the relation; the tangent line could, but does not have to, cross the graph at another point outside this interval; it goes in the same direction as the relation at point P (called the point of tangency)

transformation: A geometric operation, such as a translation, a rotation, a dilation, or a reflection

turning point: A point on a curve where the function changes from increasing to decreasing, or vice versa; for example, A and B are turning points on the following curve

V

vertical asymptote: An asymptote that takes the form of a vertical line

vertical line test: A test that can be used to determine whether a relation is a function; if any vertical line intersects the graph of a relation more than once, then the relation is not a function

Chapter 1

Getting Started, p. 2

1. a) 6   **c)** $-\dfrac{51}{16}$

   b) -6 **d)** $a^2 + 5a$

2. a) $(x + y)(x + y)$

   b) $(5x - 1)(x - 3)$

   c) $(x + y + 8)(x + y - 8)$

   d) $(a + b)(x - y)$

3. a) horizontal translation 3 units to the right, vertical translation 2 units up;

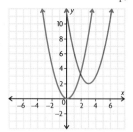

   b) horizontal translation 1 unit to the right, vertical translation 2 units up;

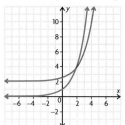

   c) horizontal stretch by a factor of 2, vertical stretch by a factor of 2, reflection across the x-axis;

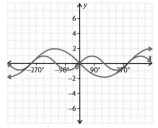

   d) horizontal compression by a factor of $\dfrac{1}{2}$, vertical stretch by a factor of 2, reflection across the x-axis;

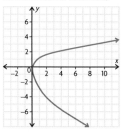

4. a) $D = \{x \in \mathbf{R} \mid -2 \le x \le 2\}$, $R = \{y \in \mathbf{R} \mid 0 \le y \le 2\}$

   b) $D = \{x \in \mathbf{R}\}$, $R = \{y \in \mathbf{R} \mid y \ge -19\}$

   c) $D = \{x \in \mathbf{R} \mid x \ne 0\}$, $R = \{y \in \mathbf{R} \mid y \ne 0\}$

   d) $D = \{x \in \mathbf{R}\}$, $R = \{y \in \mathbf{R} \mid -3 \le y \ge 3\}$

   e) $D = \{x \in \mathbf{R}\}$, $R = \{y \in \mathbf{R} \mid y > 0\}$

5. a) This is not a function; it does not pass the vertical line test.

   b) This is a function; for each x-value, there is exactly one corresponding y-value.

   c) This is not a function; for each x-value greater than 0, there are two corresponding y-values.

   d) This is a function; for each x-value, there is exactly one corresponding y-value.

   e) This is a function; for each x-value, there is exactly one corresponding y-value.

6. a) 8

   b) about 2.71

7. If a relation is represented by a set of ordered pairs, a table, or an arrow diagram, one can determine if the relation is a function by checking that each value of the independent variable is paired with no more than one value of the dependent variable. If a relation is represented using a graph or scatter plot, the vertical line test can be used to determine if the relation is a function. A relation may also be represented by a description/rule or by using function notation or an equation. In these cases, one can use reasoning to determine if there is more than one value of the dependent variable paired with any value of the independent variable.

Lesson 1.1, pp. 11–13

1. a) $D = \{x \in \mathbf{R}\}$; $R = \{y \in \mathbf{R} \mid -4 \le y \le -2\}$; This is a function because it passes the vertical line test.

   b) $D = \{x \in \mathbf{R} \mid -1 \le x \le 7\}$; $R = \{y \in \mathbf{R} \mid -3 \le y \le 1\}$; This is a function because it passes the vertical line test.

   c) $D = \{1, 2, 3, 4\}$; $R = \{-5, 4, 7, 9, 11\}$; This is not a function because 1 is sent to more than one element in the range.

   d) $D = \{x \in \mathbf{R}\}$; $R = \{y \in \mathbf{R}\}$; This is a function because every element in the domain produces exactly one element in the range.

   e) $D = \{-4, -3, 1, 2\}$; $R = \{0, 1, 2, 3\}$; This is a function because every element of the domain is sent to exactly one element in the range.

   f) $D = \{x \in \mathbf{R}\}$; $R = \{y \in \mathbf{R} \mid y \le 0\}$; This is a function because every element in the domain produces exactly one element in the range.

2. a) $D = \{x \in \mathbf{R}\}$; $R = \{y \in \mathbf{R} \mid y \le -3\}$; This is a function because every element in the domain produces exactly one element in the range.

   b) $D = \{x \in \mathbf{R} \mid x \ne -3\}$; $R = \{y \in \mathbf{R} \mid y \ne 0\}$; This is a function because every element in the domain produces exactly one element in the range.

   c) $D = \{x \in \mathbf{R}\}$; $R = \{y \in \mathbf{R} \mid y > 0\}$; This is a function because every element in the domain produces exactly one element in the range.

   d) $D = \{x \in \mathbf{R}\}$; $R = \{y \in \mathbf{R} \mid 0 \le y \le 2\}$; This is a function because every element in the domain produces exactly one element in the range.

   e) $D = \{x \in \mathbf{R} \mid -3 \le x \le 3\}$; $R = \{y \in \mathbf{R} \mid -3 \le y \le 3\}$; This is not a function because (0, 3) and (0, 3) are both in the relation.

   f) $D = \{x \in \mathbf{R}\}$; $R = \{y \in \mathbf{R} \mid -2 \le y \le 2\}$; This is a function because every element in the domain produces exactly one element in the range.

3. a) function; $D = \{1, 3, 5, 7\}$; $R = \{2, 4, 6\}$

   b) function; $D = \{0, 1, 2, 5\}$; $R = \{-1, 3, 6\}$

   c) function; $D = \{0, 1, 2, 3\}$; $R = \{2, 4\}$

   d) not a function; $D = \{2, 6, 8\}$; $R = \{1, 3, 5, 7\}$

   e) not a function; $D = \{1, 10, 100\}$; $R = \{0, 1, 2, 3\}$

   f) function; $D = \{1, 2, 3, 4\}$; $R = \{1, 2, 3, 4\}$

4. a) function; $D = \{x \in \mathbf{R}\}$; $R = \{y \in \mathbf{R} \mid y \ge 2\}$.

   b) not a function; $D = \{x \in \mathbf{R} \mid x \ge 2\}$; $R = \{y \in \mathbf{R}\}$

   c) function; $D = \{x \in \mathbf{R}\}$; $R = \{y \in \mathbf{R} \mid y \ge -0.5\}$

   d) not a function; $D = \{x \in \mathbf{R} \mid x \ge 0\}$; $R = \{y \in \mathbf{R}\}$

   e) function; $D = \{x \in \mathbf{R} \mid x \ne 0\}$; $R = \{y \in \mathbf{R} \mid y \ne 0\}$

   f) function; $D = \{x \in \mathbf{R}\}$; $R = \{y \in \mathbf{R}\}$

5. a) $y = x + 3$ **c)** $y = 3(x - 2)$

   b) $y = 2x - 5$ **d)** $y = -x + 5$

6. a) The length is twice the width.

b) $f(l) = \dfrac{3}{2}l$

c)
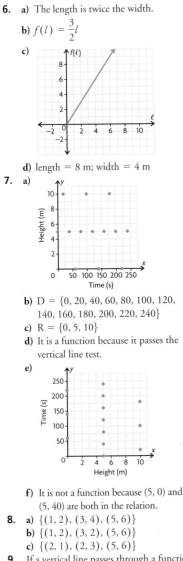

d) length = 8 m; width = 4 m

7. a)

b) D = {0, 20, 40, 60, 80, 100, 120, 140, 160, 180, 200, 220, 240}

c) R = {0, 5, 10}

d) It is a function because it passes the vertical line test.

e)

f) It is not a function because (5, 0) and (5, 40) are both in the relation.

8. a) {(1, 2), (3, 4), (5, 6)}

b) {(1, 2), (3, 2), (5, 6)}

c) {(2, 1), (2, 3), (5, 6)}

9. If a vertical line passes through a function and hits two points, those two points have identical x-coordinates and different y-coordinates. This means that one x-coordinate is sent to two different elements in the range, violating the definition of *function*.

10. a) Yes, because the distance from (4, 3) to (0, 0) is 5.

b) No, because the distance from (1, 5) to (0, 0) is not 5.

c) No, because (4, 3) and (4, −3) are both in the relation.

11. a) $g(x) = x^2 + 3$

b) $g(3) - g(2) = 12 - 7$
$= 5$
$g(3 - 2) = g(1)$
$= 4$
So, $g(3) - g(2) \neq g(3 - 2)$.

12. a) $f(6) = 12; f(7) = 8; f(8) = 15$

b) Yes, $f(15) = f(3) \times f(5)$

c) Yes, $f(12) = f(3) \times f(4)$

d) Yes, there are others that will work.
$f(a) \times f(b) = f(a \times b)$ whenever a and b have no common factors other than 1.

13. Answers may vary. For example:

14.

The first is not a function because it fails the vertical line test:
$D = \{x \in \mathbf{R} \mid -5 \le x \le 5\}$;
$R = \{y \in \mathbf{R} \mid -5 \le y \le 5\}$.
The second is a function because it passes the vertical line test:
$D = \{x \in \mathbf{R} \mid -5 \le x \le 5\}$;
$R = \{y \in \mathbf{R} \mid 0 \le y \le 5\}$.

15. x is a function of y if the graph passes the horizontal line test. This occurs when any horizontal line hits the graph at most once.

Lesson 1.2, p. 16

1. $|-5|, |12|, |-15|, |20|, |-25|$

2. a) 22   **c)** 18   **e)** −2
b) −35   **d)** 11   **f)** −2

3. a) $|x| > 3$ **c)** $|x| \ge 1$
b) $|x| \le 8$ **d)** $|x| \neq 5$

4. a)

b)

c) The absolute value of a number is always greater than or equal to 0. There are no solutions to this inequality.

d)

5. a) $|x| \le 3$ **c)** $|x| \ge 2$
b) $|x| > 2$ **d)** $|x| < 4$

6.
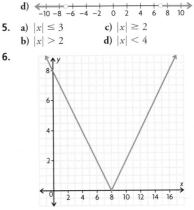

a) The graphs are the same.

b) Answers may vary. For example, $x - 8 = -(-x + 8)$, so they are negatives of each other and have the same absolute value.

7. a)
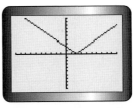

b)

c)

d)

8. When the number you are adding or subtracting is inside the absolute value signs, it moves the function to the left (when adding) or to the right (when subtracting) of the origin. When the number you are

adding or subtracting is outside the absolute value signs, it moves the function down (when subtracting) or up (when adding) from the origin.
The graph of the function will be the absolute value function moved to the left 3 units and up 4 units from the origin.

9. This is the graph of $g(x) = |x|$ horizontally compressed by a factor of $\frac{1}{2}$ and translated $\frac{1}{2}$ unit to the left.

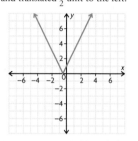

10. This is the graph of $g(x) = |x|$ horizontally compressed by a factor of $\frac{1}{2}$, reflected over the x-axis, translated $2\frac{1}{2}$ units to the right, and translated 3 units up.

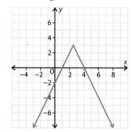

Lesson 1.3, pp. 23–25

1. Answers may vary. For example, domain because most of the parent functions have all real numbers as a domain.

2. Answers may vary. For example, the end behaviour because the only two that match are x^2 and $|x|$.

3. Given the horizontal asymptote, the function must be derived from 2^x. But the asymptote is at $y = 2$, so it must have been translated up two. Therefore, the function is $f(x) = 2^x + 2$.

4. **a)** Both functions are odd, but their domains are different.
b) Both functions have a domain of all real numbers, but $\sin(x)$ has more zeros.
c) Both functions have a domain of all real numbers, but different end behaviour.
d) Both functions have a domain of all real numbers, but different end behaviour.

5. **a)** even **d)** odd
b) odd **e)** neither even nor odd
c) odd **f)** neither even nor odd

6. **a)** $|x|$, because it is a measure of distance from a number

b) $\sin(x)$, because the heights are periodic
c) 2^x, because population tends to increase exponentially
d) x, because there is $1 on the first day, $2 on the second, $3 on the third, etc.

7. **a)** $f(x) = \sqrt{x}$ **c)** $f(x) = x^2$
b) $f(x) = \sin x$ **d)** $f(x) = x$

8. **a)** $f(x) = 2^x - 3$

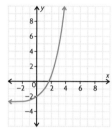

b) $g(x) = \sin x + 3$

c) $h(x) = \dfrac{1}{x - 5} - 3 = \dfrac{16 - 3x}{x - 5}$

9.

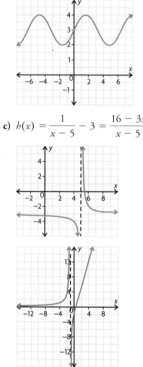

10. **a)** $f(x) = (x - 2)^2$
b) There is not only one function.
$f(x) = \frac{3}{4}(x - 2)^2 + 1$ works as well.
c) There is more than one function that satisfies the property.
$f(x) = |x - 2| + 2$ and $f(x) = 2|x - 2|$ both work.

11. x^2 is a smooth curve, while $|x|$ has a sharp, pointed corner at $(0, 0)$.

12. See next page.

13. It is important to name parent functions in order to classify a wide range of functions according to similar behaviour and characteristics.

14.

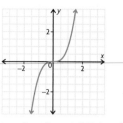

$D = \{x \in \mathbf{R}\}$, $R = \{f(x) \in \mathbf{R}\}$; interval of increase $= (-\infty, \infty)$, no interval of decrease, no discontinuities, x- and y-intercept at $(0, 0)$, odd, $x \to \infty$, $y \to \infty$, and $x \to -\infty$, $y \to -\infty$. It is very similar to $f(x) = x$. It does not, however, have a constant slope.

15. No, $\cos x$ is a horizontal translation of $\sin x$.

16. The graph can have 0, 1, or 2 zeros.
0 zeros:

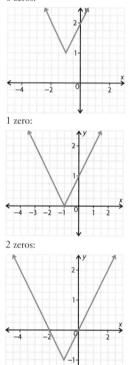

1 zero:

2 zeros:

Mid-Chapter Review, p. 28

1. **a)** function; $D = \{0, 3, 15, 27\}$, $R = \{2, 3, 4\}$
b) function; $D = \{x \in \mathbf{R}\}$, $R = \{y \in \mathbf{R}\}$
c) not a function; $D = \{x \in \mathbf{R} \mid -5 \le x \le 5\}$, $R = \{y \in \mathbf{R} \mid -5 \le y \le 5\}$
d) not a function; $D = \{1, 2, 10\}$, $R = \{-1, 3, 6, 7\}$

2. **a)** Yes. Every element in the domain gets sent to exactly one element in the range.
b) $D = \{0, 1, 2, 3, 4, 5, 6, 7, 8, 9, 10\}$
c) $R = \{10, 20, 25, 30, 35, 40, 45, 50\}$

12.

Parent Function	$f(x) = x$	$g(x) = x^2$	$h(x) = \frac{1}{x}$	$k(x) = |x|$	$m(x) = \sqrt{x}$	$p(x) = 2^x$	$r(x) = \sin x$
Sketch							
Domain	$\{x \in \mathbf{R}\}$	$\{x \in \mathbf{R}\}$	$\{x \in \mathbf{R} \mid x \neq 0\}$	$\{x \in \mathbf{R}\}$	$\{x \in \mathbf{R} \mid x \geq 0\}$	$\{x \in \mathbf{R}\}$	$\{x \in \mathbf{R}\}$
Range	$\{f(x) \in \mathbf{R}\}$	$\{f(x) \in \mathbf{R} \mid f(x) \geq 0\}$	$\{f(x) \in \mathbf{R} \mid f(x) \neq 0\}$	$\{f(x) \in \mathbf{R} \mid f(x) \geq 0\}$	$\{f(x) \in \mathbf{R} \mid f(x) \geq 0\}$	$\{f(x) \in \mathbf{R} \mid f(x) > 0\}$	$\{f(x) \in \mathbf{R} \mid -1 \leq f(x) \leq 1\}$
Intervals of Increase	$(-\infty, \infty)$	$(0, \infty)$	None	$(0, \infty)$	$(0, \infty)$	$(-\infty, \infty)$	$[90(4k + 1), 90(4k + 3)]$ $K \in \mathbf{Z}$
Intervals of Decrease	None	$(-\infty, 0)$	$(-\infty, 0)\ (0, \infty)$	$(-\infty, 0)$	None	None	$[90(4k + 3), 90(4k + 1)]$ $K \in \mathbf{Z}$
Location of Discontinuities and Asymptotes	None	None	$y = 0$ $x = 0$	None	None	$y = 0$	None
Zeros	$(0, 0)$	$(0, 0)$	None	$(0, 0)$	$(0, 0)$	None	$180k\ K \in \mathbf{Z}$
y-Intercepts	$(0, 0)$	$(0, 0)$	None	$(0, 0)$	$(0, 0)$	$(0, 1)$	$(0, 0)$
Symmetry	Odd	Even	Odd	Even	Neither	Neither	Odd
End Behaviours	$x \to \infty, y \to \infty$ $x \to -\infty, y \to -\infty$	$x \to \infty, y \to \infty$ $x \to -\infty, y \to \infty$	$x \to \infty, y \to 0$ $x \to -\infty, y \to 0$	$x \to \infty, y \to \infty$ $x \to -\infty, y \to \infty$	$x \to \infty, y \to \infty$	$x \to \infty, y \to \infty$ $x \to -\infty, y \to 0$	Oscillating

Answers

3. a) D = {x ∈ **R**}, R = {f(x) ∈ **R**};
function
b) D = {x ∈ **R** | −3 ≤ x ≤ 3},
R = {y ∈ **R** | −3 ≤ y ≤ 3}; not a
function
c) D = {x ∈ **R** | x ≤ 5},
R = {y ∈ **R** | y ≥ 0}; function
d) D = {x ∈ **R**}, R = {y ∈ **R** | y ≥ −2};
function
4. −|3|, |0|, |−3|, |−4|, |5|
5. a)

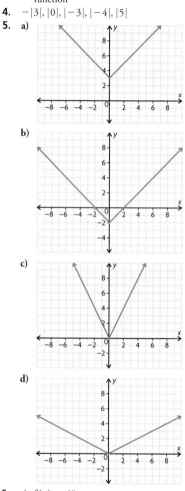

b)

c)

d)

6. a) $f(x) = 2^x$
b) $f(x) = \dfrac{1}{x}$
c) $f(x) = \sqrt{x}$
7. a) even   **c)** neither odd nor even
b) even   **d)** neither odd nor even
8. a) This is $f(x) = \dfrac{1}{x}$ translated right 1 and
up 3; discontinuous

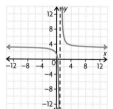

b) This if $f(x) = \sin x$ translated down 2;
continuous

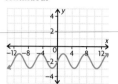

c) This is $f(x) = 2^x$ translated down 10;
continuous

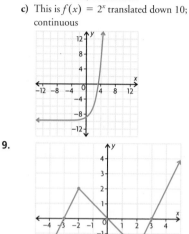

9.

Lesson 1.4, pp. 35–37

1. a) translation 1 unit down
b) horizontal compression by a factor of $\dfrac{1}{2}$,
translation 1 unit right
c) reflection over the x-axis, translation 2
units up, translation 3 units right
d) reflection over the x-axis, vertical stretch
by a factor of 2, horizontal compression
by a factor of $\dfrac{1}{4}$
e) reflection over the x-axis, translation 3
units down, reflection over the y-axis,
translation 2 units left
f) vertical compression by a factor of $\dfrac{1}{2}$,
translation 6 units up, horizontal
stretch by a factor of 4, translation 5
units right

2. a) $a = -1, k = \dfrac{1}{2}, d = 0, c = 3$
b) $a = 3, k = \dfrac{1}{2}, d = 0, c = -2$

3. (2, 3), (1, 3), (1, 6), (1, −6), (−4, −6),
(−4, −10)
4. a) (2, 6), (4, 14), (−2, 10), (−4, 12)
b) (5, 3), (7, 7), (1, 5), (−1, 6)
c) (2, 5), (4, 9), (−2, 7), (−4, 8)
d) (1, 0), (3, 4), (−3, 2), (−5, 3)
e) (2, 5), (4, 6), (−2, 3), (−4, 7)
f) (1, 2), (2, 6), (−1, 4), (−2, 5)

5. a) $f(x) = x^2$, translated left 1

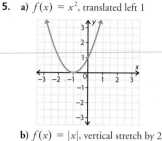

b) $f(x) = |x|$, vertical stretch by 2

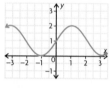

c) $f(x) = \sin x$, horizontal compression
of $\dfrac{1}{3}$, translation up 1

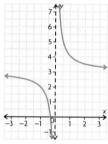

d) $f(x) = \dfrac{1}{x}$, translation up 3

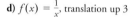

e) $f(x) = 2^x$, horizontal stretch by 2

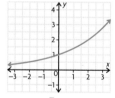

f) $f(x) = \sqrt{x}$, horizontal compression by
$\dfrac{1}{2}$, translation right 6

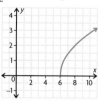

6. a) $D = \{x \in \mathbf{R}\}$,
   $R = \{f(x) \in \mathbf{R} \mid f(x) \geq 0\}$
b) $D = \{x \in \mathbf{R}\}$,
   $R = \{f(x) \in \mathbf{R} \mid f(x) \geq 0\}$
c) $D = \{x \in \mathbf{R}\}$,
   $R = \{f(x) \in \mathbf{R} \mid 0 \leq f(x) \leq 2\}$
d) $D = \{x \in \mathbf{R} \mid x \neq 0\}$,
   $R = \{f(x) \in \mathbf{R} \mid f(x) \neq 3\}$
e) $D = \{x \in \mathbf{R}\}$,
   $R = \{f(x) \in \mathbf{R} \mid f(x) > 0\}$
f) $D = \{x \in \mathbf{R} \mid x \geq 6\}$,
   $R = \{f(x) \in \mathbf{R} \mid f(x) \geq 0\}$

7. a)

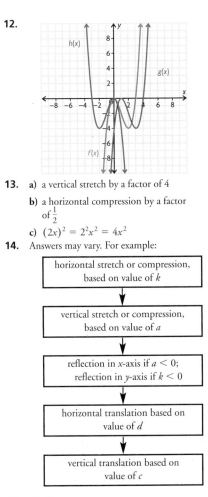

b) The domain remains unchanged at
   $D = \{x \in \mathbf{R}\}$. The range must now
   be less than 4:
   $R = \{f(x) \in \mathbf{R} \mid f(x) < 4\}$. It
   changes from increasing on $(-\infty, \infty)$
   to decreasing on $(-\infty, \infty)$. The end
   behaviour becomes as $x \to -\infty, y \to 4$,
   and as $x \to \infty, y \to -\infty$.

c) $g(x) = -2(2^{3(x-1)} + 4)$

8. $y = -3\sqrt{x - 5}$

9. a) $(3, 24)$ **d)** $(-0.75, -8)$
b) $(-0.5, 4)$ **e)** $(-1, -8)$
c) $(-1, 9)$ **f)** $(-1, 7)$

10. a) $D = \{x \in \mathbf{R} \mid x \geq 2\}$,
   $R = \{g(x) \in \mathbf{R} \mid g(x) \geq 0\}$
b) $D = \{x \in \mathbf{R} \mid x \geq 1\}$,
   $R = \{h(x) \in \mathbf{R} \mid h(x) \geq 4\}$
c) $D = \{x \in \mathbf{R} \mid x \leq 0\}$,
   $R = \{k(x) \in \mathbf{R} \mid k(x) \geq 1\}$
d) $D = \{x \in \mathbf{R} \mid x \geq 5\}$,
   $R = \{j(x) \in \mathbf{R} \mid j(x) \geq -3\}$

11. $y = 5(x^2 - 3)$ is the same as
   $y = 5x^2 - 15$, not $y = 5x^2 - 3$.

12.

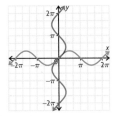

13. a) a vertical stretch by a factor of 4
b) a horizontal compression by a factor
   of $\frac{1}{2}$
c) $(2x)^2 = 2^2 x^2 = 4x^2$

14. Answers may vary. For example:

> horizontal stretch or compression,
> based on value of k
>
> ↓
>
> vertical stretch or compression,
> based on value of a
>
> ↓
>
> reflection in x-axis if $a < 0$;
> reflection in y-axis if $k < 0$
>
> ↓
>
> horizontal translation based on
> value of d
>
> ↓
>
> vertical translation based on
> value of c

15. $(4, 5)$
16. a) horizontal compression by a factor of $\frac{1}{3}$,
   translation 2 units to the left
b) because they are equivalent expressions:
   $3(x + 2) = 3x + 6$
c)

Lesson 1.5, pp. 43–45

1. a) $(5, 2)$ **c)** $(-8, 4)$ **e)** $(0, -3)$
b) $(-6, -5)$ **d)** $(2, 1)$ **f)** $(7, 0)$

2. a) $D = \{x \in \mathbf{R}\}$, $R = \{y \in \mathbf{R}\}$
b) $D = \{x \in \mathbf{R}\}$, $R = \{y \in \mathbf{R} \mid y \geq 2\}$
c) $D = \{x \in \mathbf{R} \mid x < 2\}$,
   $R = \{y \in \mathbf{R} \mid y \geq -5\}$
d) $D = \{x \in \mathbf{R} \mid -5 < x < 10\}$,
   $R = \{y \in \mathbf{R} \mid y < -2\}$

3. A and D match; B and F match; C and E
   match

4. a) $(4, 129)$
b) $(129, 4)$
c) $D = \{x \in \mathbf{R}\}$, $R = \{y \in \mathbf{R}\}$
d) $D = \{x \in \mathbf{R}\}$, $R = \{y \in \mathbf{R}\}$
e) Yes; it passes the vertical line test.

5. a) $(4, 248)$
b) $(248, 4)$
c) $D = \{x \in \mathbf{R}\}$, $R = \{y \in \mathbf{R} \mid y \geq -8\}$
d) $D = \{x \in \mathbf{R} \mid x \geq -8\}$ $R = \{y \in \mathbf{R}\}$
e) No; $(248, 4)$ and $(248, -4)$ are both
   on the inverse relation.

6. a) Not a function

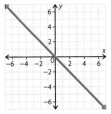

b) Not a function

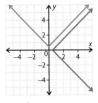

c) Function

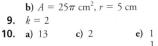

d) Not a function

7. a) $C = \frac{5}{9}(F - 32)$; this allows you to
   convert from Fahrenheit to Celsius.
b) $20\ °C = 68\ °F$

8. a) $r = \sqrt{\frac{A}{\pi}}$; this can be used to determine
   the radius of a circle when its area is
   known.
b) $A = 25\pi\ cm^2$, $r = 5\ cm$
9. $k = 2$
10. a) 13   **c)** 2   **e)** 1
b) 25   **d)** -2 **f)** $\frac{1}{2}$

11. No; several students could have the same grade point average.

12. **a)** $f^{-1}(x) = \dfrac{1}{3}(x - 4)$

    b) $h^{-1}(x) = -x$

    c) $g^{-1}(x) = \sqrt[3]{x + 1}$

    d) $m^{-1}(x) = -\dfrac{x}{2} - 5$

13. **a)** $x = 4(y - 3)^2 + 1$

    b) $y = \pm\sqrt{\dfrac{x - 1}{4}} + 3$

    c)

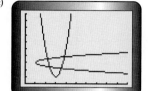

    d) (2.20, 3.55), (2.40, 2.40), (3.55, 2.20), (3.84, 3.84)

    e) $x \geq 3$ because a negative square root is undefined.

    f) $g(2) = 5$, but $g^{-1}(5) = 2$ or 4; the inverse is not a function if this is the domain of g.

14. For $y = -\sqrt{x + 2}$,
$D = \{x \in \mathbf{R} \mid x \geq -2\}$ and
$R = \{y \in \mathbf{R} \mid y \leq 0\}$. For $y = x^2 - 2$,
$D = \{x \in \mathbf{R}\}$ and $R = \{y \in \mathbf{R} \mid y \geq -2\}$.
The student would be correct if the domain of $y = x^2 - 2$ is restricted to
$D = \{x \in \mathbf{R} \mid x \leq 0\}$.

15. Yes; the inverse of $y = \sqrt{x + 2}$ is
$y = x^2 - 2$ so long as the domain of this second function is restricted to
$D = \{x \in \mathbf{R} \mid x \geq 0\}$.

16. John is correct.
Algebraic: $y = \dfrac{x^3}{4} + 2; y - 2 = \dfrac{x^3}{4};$
$4(y - 2) = x^3; x = \sqrt[3]{4(y - 2)}.$

Numeric: Let $x = 4$.
$y = \dfrac{4^3}{4} + 2 = \dfrac{64}{4} + 2 = 16 + 2 = 18;$
$x = \sqrt[3]{4(y - 2)} = \sqrt[3]{4(18 - 2)}$
$= \sqrt[3]{4(16)} = \sqrt[3]{64} = 4.$

Graphical:

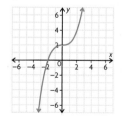

17. $f(x) = k - x$ works for all $k \in \mathbf{R}$.
$y = k - x$
Switch variables and solve for y: $x = k - y$
$y = k - x$
So the function is its own inverse.

18. If a horizontal line hits the function in two locations, that means there are two points with equal y-values and different x-values. When the function is reflected over the line $y = x$ to find the inverse relation, those two points become points with equal x-values and different y-values, thus violating the definition of a function.

Lesson 1.6, pp. 51–53

1. **a)**

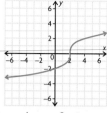

The graphs are reflections over the line $y = x$.

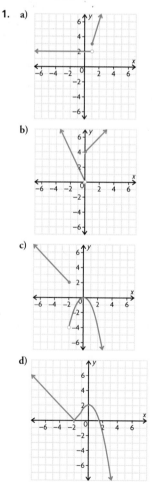

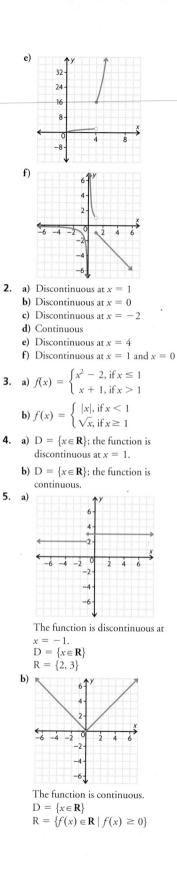

2. **a)** Discontinuous at $x = 1$

    b) Discontinuous at $x = 0$

    c) Discontinuous at $x = -2$

    d) Continuous

    e) Discontinuous at $x = 4$

    f) Discontinuous at $x = 1$ and $x = 0$

3. **a)** $f(x) = \begin{cases} x^2 - 2, & \text{if } x \leq 1 \\ x + 1, & \text{if } x > 1 \end{cases}$

    b) $f(x) = \begin{cases} |x|, & \text{if } x < 1 \\ \sqrt{x}, & \text{if } x \geq 1 \end{cases}$

4. **a)** $D = \{x \in \mathbf{R}\}$; the function is discontinuous at $x = 1$.

    b) $D = \{x \in \mathbf{R}\}$; the function is continuous.

5. **a)**

The function is discontinuous at $x = -1$.
$D = \{x \in \mathbf{R}\}$
$R = \{2, 3\}$

    b)

The function is continuous.
$D = \{x \in \mathbf{R}\}$
$R = \{f(x) \in \mathbf{R} \mid f(x) \geq 0\}$

c)

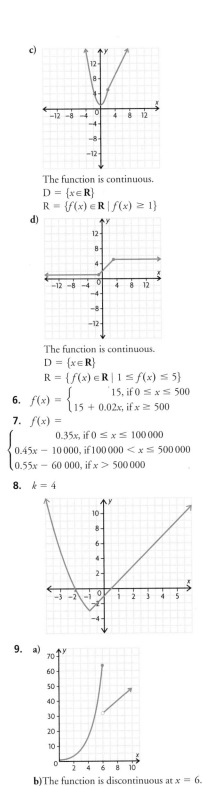

The function is continuous.
$D = \{x \in \mathbf{R}\}$
$R = \{f(x) \in \mathbf{R} \mid f(x) \geq 1\}$

d)

The function is continuous.
$D = \{x \in \mathbf{R}\}$
$R = \{f(x) \in \mathbf{R} \mid 1 \leq f(x) \leq 5\}$

6. $f(x) = \begin{cases} 15, \text{ if } 0 \leq x \leq 500 \\ 15 + 0.02x, \text{ if } x \geq 500 \end{cases}$

7. $f(x) =$
$\begin{cases} 0.35x, \text{ if } 0 \leq x \leq 100\,000 \\ 0.45x - 10\,000, \text{ if } 100\,000 < x \leq 500\,000 \\ 0.55x - 60\,000, \text{ if } x > 500\,000 \end{cases}$

8. $k = 4$

9. a)

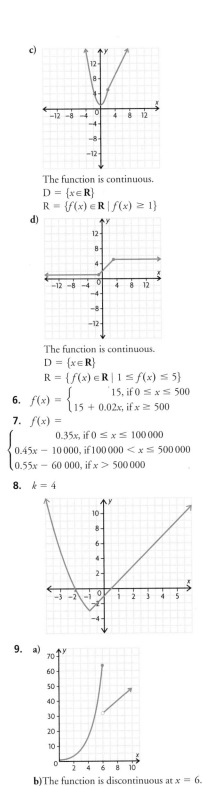

b) The function is discontinuous at $x = 6$.
c) 32 fish
d) $4x + 8 = 64; 4x = 56; x = 14$
e) Answers may vary. For example, three possible events are environmental changes, introduction of a new predator, and increased fishing.

10. Answers may vary. For example:

> Plot the function for the left interval.

$\downarrow$

> Plot the function for the right interval.

$\downarrow$

> Determine if the plots for the left and right intervals meet at the x-value that serves as the common end point for the intervals; if so, the function is continuous at this point.

$\downarrow$

> Determine continuity for the two intervals using standard methods.

11. $f(x) = |x + 3| = \begin{cases} x + 3, \text{ if } x \geq -3 \\ -x - 3, \text{ if } x < -3 \end{cases}$

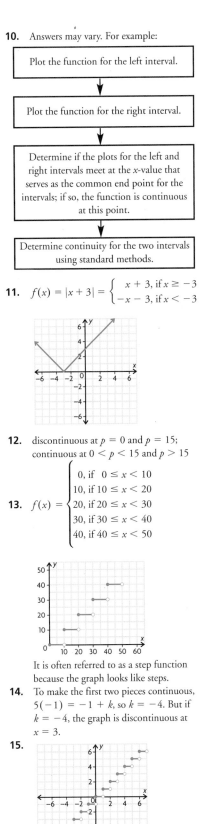

12. discontinuous at $p = 0$ and $p = 15$; continuous at $0 < p < 15$ and $p > 15$

13. $f(x) = \begin{cases} 0, \text{ if } 0 \leq x < 10 \\ 10, \text{ if } 10 \leq x < 20 \\ 20, \text{ if } 20 \leq x < 30 \\ 30, \text{ if } 30 \leq x < 40 \\ 40, \text{ if } 40 \leq x < 50 \end{cases}$

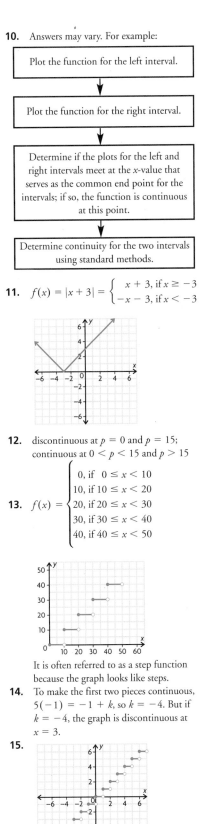

It is often referred to as a step function because the graph looks like steps.

14. To make the first two pieces continuous, $5(-1) = -1 + k$, so $k = -4$. But if $k = -4$, the graph is discontinuous at $x = 3$.

15.

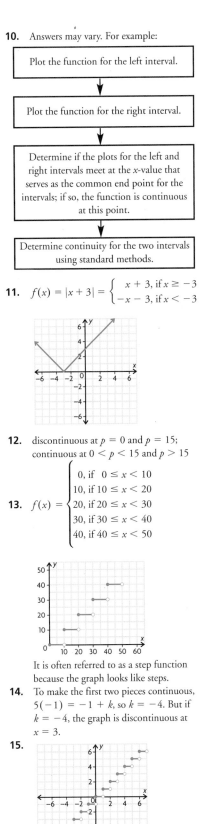

16. Answers may vary. For example:

a) $f(x) = \begin{cases} x + 3, \text{ if } x < -1 \\ x^2 + 1, \text{ if } -1 \leq x \leq 2 \\ \sqrt{x} + 1, \text{ if } x > 2 \end{cases}$

b)

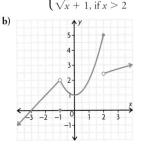

c) The function is not continuous. The last two pieces do not have the same value for $x = 2$.

d) $f(x) = \begin{cases} x + 3, \text{ if } x < -1 \\ x^2 + 1, \text{ if } -1 \leq x \leq 1 \\ \sqrt{x} + 1, \text{ if } x > 1 \end{cases}$

Lesson 1.7, pp. 56–57

1. a) $\{(-4, 6), (-2, 5), (1, 5), (4, 10)\}$
b) $\{(-4, 2), (-2, 3), (1, 1), (4, 2)\}$
c) $\{(-4, -2), (-2, -3), (1, -1), (4, -2)\}$
d) $\{(-4, 8), (-2, 4), (1, 6), (4, 24)\}$

2. a)

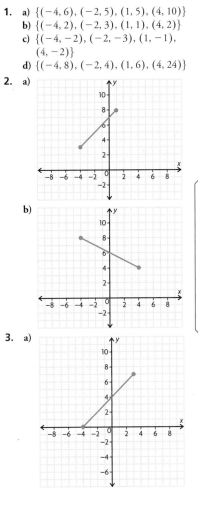

b)

3. a)

b)

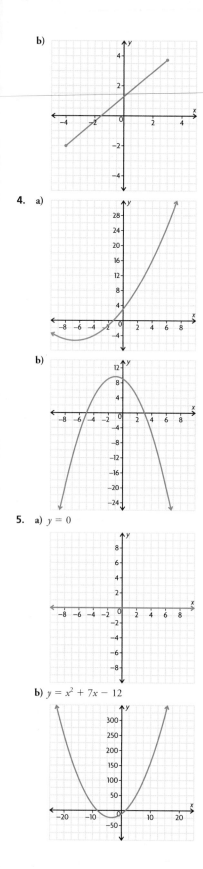

4. a)

b)

5. a) $y = 0$

b) $y = x^2 + 7x - 12$

c) $y = |x| + 2^x$

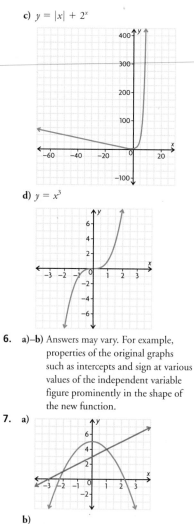

d) $y = x^3$

6. a)–b) Answers may vary. For example, properties of the original graphs such as intercepts and sign at various values of the independent variable figure prominently in the shape of the new function.

7. a)

b)

x	f(x)	g(x)	h(x) = f(x) × g(x)
−3	0	−4	0
−2	1	1	1
−1	2	4	8
0	3	5	15
1	4	4	16
2	5	1	5
3	6	−4	−24

c)

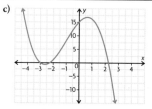

d) $h(x) = (x + 3)(-x^2 + 5)$
$= -x^3 - 3x^2 + 5x + 15$; degree is 3

e) $D = \{x \in \mathbf{R}\}$; this is the same as the domain of both f and g.

8. a)

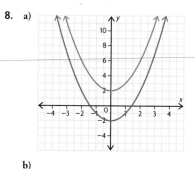

b)

x	f(x)	g(x)	h(x) = f(x) × g(x)
−3	11	7	77
−2	6	2	12
−1	3	−1	−3
0	2	−2	−4
1	3	−1	−3
2	6	2	12
3	11	7	77

c)

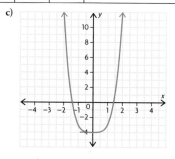

d) $h(x) = (x^2 + 2)(x^2 - 2) = x^4 - 4$; degree is 4

e) $D = \{x \in \mathbf{R}\}$

Chapter Review, pp. 60–61

1. a) function; $D = \{x \in \mathbf{R}\}$; $R = \{y \in \mathbf{R}\}$
b) function; $D = \{x \in \mathbf{R}\}$;
$R = \{y \in \mathbf{R} \mid y \le 3\}$
c) not a function;
$D = \{x \in \mathbf{R} \mid -1 \le x \le 1\}$;
$R = \{y \in \mathbf{R}\}$
d) function; $D = \{x \in \mathbf{R} \mid x > 0\}$;
$R = \{y \in \mathbf{R}\}$

2. a) $C(t) = 30 + 0.02t$
b) $D = \{t \in \mathbf{R} \mid t \ge 0\}$,
$R = \{C(t) \in \mathbf{R} \mid C(t) \ge 30\}$

3. $D = \{x \in \mathbf{R}\}$,
$R = \{f(x) \in \mathbf{R} \mid f(x) \ge 1\}$

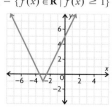

4. $|x| < 2$

5. a) Both functions have a domain of all real numbers, but the ranges differ.
  b) Both functions are odd but have different domains.
  c) Both functions have the same domain and range, but x^2 is smooth and $|x|$ has a sharp corner at $(0, 0)$.
  d) Both functions are increasing on the entire real line, but 2^x has a horizontal asymptote while x does not.

6. a) Increasing on $(-\infty, \infty)$; odd;
  $D = \{x \in \mathbf{R}\}$; $R = \{f(x) \in \mathbf{R}\}$
  b) Decreasing on $(-\infty, 0)$; increasing on $(0, \infty)$; even; $D = \{x \in \mathbf{R}\}$;
  $R = \{f(x) \in \mathbf{R} \mid f(x) \geq 2\}$
  c) Increasing on $(-\infty, \infty)$; neither even nor odd; $D = \{x \in \mathbf{R}\}$;
  $R = \{f(x) \in \mathbf{R} \mid f(x) > -1\}$

7. a) Parent: $y = |x|$; translated left 1

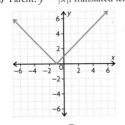

  b) Parent: $y = \sqrt{x}$; compressed vertically by a factor of 0.25, reflected across the x-axis, compressed horizontally by a factor of $\frac{1}{3}$, and translated left 7

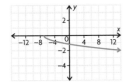

  c) Parent: $y = \sin x$; reflected across the x-axis, expanded vertically by a factor of 2, compressed horizontally by a factor of $\frac{1}{3}$, translated up by 1

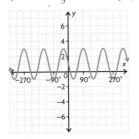

  d) Parent: $y = 2^x$; reflected across the y-axis, compressed horizontally by a factor of $\frac{1}{2}$, and translated down by 3

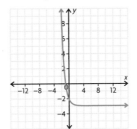

8. $y = -\left(\frac{1}{2}x\right)^2 - 3$

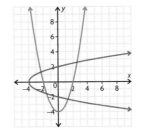

9. a) $(-2, 1)$
  b) $(-10, -6)$
  c) $(4, 3)$
  d) $\left(\dfrac{17}{5}, 0.3\right)$
  e) $(-1, 0)$
  f) $(9, -1)$

10. a) $(2, 1)$
  b) $(-9, -1)$
  c) $(7, 0)$
  d) $(7, 5)$
  e) $(-3, 0)$
  f) $(10, 1)$

11. a) $D = \{x \in \mathbf{R} \mid -2 < x < 2\}$,
  $R = \{y \in \mathbf{R}\}$
  b) $D = \{x \in \mathbf{R} \mid x < 12\}$,
  $R = \{y \in \mathbf{R} \mid y \geq 7\}$

12. a) The inverse relation is not a function.

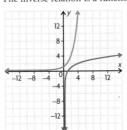

  b) The inverse relation is a function.

13. a) $f^{-1}(x) = \dfrac{x - 1}{2}$
  b) $g^{-1}(x) = \sqrt[3]{x}$

14.

The function is continuous; $D = \{x \in \mathbf{R}\}$, $R = \{y \in \mathbf{R}\}$

15. $f(x) = \begin{cases} 3x - 1, & \text{if } x \leq 2 \\ -x, & \text{if } x > 2 \end{cases}$;
  the function is discontinuous at $x = 2$.

16. In order for $f(x)$ to be continuous at $x = 1$, the two pieces must have the same value when $x = 1$.
  When $x = 1$, $x^2 + 1 = 2$ and $3x = 3$.
  The two pieces are not equal when $x = 1$, so the function is not continuous at $x = 1$.

17. a) $f(x) = \begin{cases} 30, & \text{if } x \leq 200 \\ 24 + 0.03, & \text{if } x > 200 \end{cases}$
  b) \$34.50
  c) \$30

18. a) $\{(1, 7), (4, 15)\}$
  b) $\{(1, -1), (4, -1)\}$
  c) $\{(1, 12), (4, 56)\}$

19. a)

  b)

  c)

Answers

d)

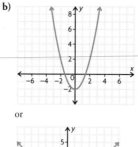

e)

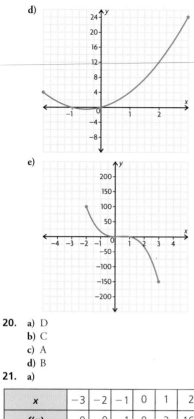

20. a) D
   b) C
   c) A
   d) B

21. a)

x	−3	−2	−1	0	1	2
f(x)	−9	0	1	0	3	16
g(x)	9	8	7	6	5	4
(f + g)(x)	0	8	8	6	8	20

b)–c)

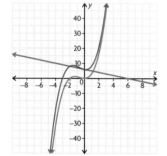

d) $x^3 + 2x^2 - x + 6$

e) Answers may vary. For example, (0, 0) belongs to f, (0, 6) belongs to g and (0, 6) belongs to $f + g$. Also, (1, 3) belongs to f, (1, 5) belongs to g and (1, 8) belongs to $f + g$.

Chapter Self-Test, p. 62

1. a) Yes. It passes the vertical line test.
   b) $D = \{x \in \mathbf{R}\}$; $R = \{y \in \mathbf{R} | y \geq 0\}$

2. a) $f(x) = x^2$ or $f(x) = |x|$

---

b)

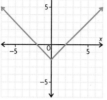

or

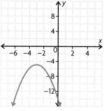

c) The graph was translated 2 units down.

3. $f(-x) = |3(-x)| + (-x)^2$
    $= |3x| + x^2 = f(x)$

4. 2^x has a horizontal asymptote while x^2 does not. The range of 2^x is $\{y \in \mathbf{R} | y > 0\}$ while the range of x^2 is $\{y \in \mathbf{R} | y \geq 0\}$. 2^x is increasing on the whole real line and x^2 has an interval of decrease and an interval of increase.

5. reflection over the x-axis, translation down 5 units, translation left 3 units

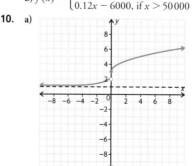

6. horizontal stretch by a factor of 2, translation 1 unit up;
    $f(x) = \text{if } \left|\frac{1}{2}x\right| + 1$

7. a) $(-4, 17)$
   b) $(5, 3)$

8. $f^{-1}(x) = -\frac{x}{2} - 1$

9. a) 9000
   b) $f(x) = \begin{cases} 0.05, & \text{if } x \leq 50\,000 \\ 0.12x - 6000, & \text{if } x > 50\,000 \end{cases}$

10. a)

---

b) $f(x)$ is discontinuous at $x = 0$ because the two pieces do not have the same value when $x = 0$. When $x = 0$, $2^x + 1 = 2$ and $\sqrt{x + 3} = 3$.
   c) Intervals of increase: $(-\infty, 0)$, $(0, \infty)$; no intervals of decrease
   d) $D = \{x \in \mathbf{R}\}$,
      $R = \{y \in \mathbf{R} | 0 < y < 2 \text{ or } y \geq 3\}$

Chapter 2

Getting Started, p. 66

1. a) $\dfrac{4}{3}$ **b)** $-\dfrac{6}{7}$

2. a) Each successive first difference is 2 times the previous first difference. The function is exponential.
   b) The second differences are all 6. The function is quadratic.

3. a) $-\dfrac{3}{2}, 2$ **c)** $45°, 225°$
   b) 0   **d)** $-270°, -90°$

4. a) vertical compression by a factor of $\dfrac{1}{2}$
   b) vertical stretch by a factor of 2, horizontal translation 4 units to the right
   c) vertical stretch by a factor of 3, reflection across x-axis, vertical translation 7 units up
   d) vertical stretch by a factor of 5, horizontal translation 3 units to the right, vertical translation 2 units down,

5. a) $A = 1000(1.08)^t$
   b) 1259.71
   c) No, since the interest is compounded each year, each year you earn more interest than the previous year.

6. a) 15 m; 1 m
   b) 24 s
   c) 15 m

7.

Linear relations	**Nonlinear relations**
constant; same as slope of line; positive for lines that *(Rates of Change)* slope up from left to right; negative for lines that slope down from left to right; 0 for horizontal lines.	variable; can be positive, negative, or 0 for different parts of the same relation

Lesson 2.1, pp. 76–78

1. a) 19   **c)** 13   **e)** 11.4
   b) 15   **d)** 12   **f)** 11.04

2. a) i) 15 m/s   **ii)** −5 m/s

---

b) During the first interval, the height is increasing at 15 m/s; during the second interval, the height is decreasing at 5 m/s.

3. $f(x)$ is always increasing at a constant rate. $g(x)$ is decreasing on $(-\infty, 0)$ and increasing on $(0, \infty)$, so the rate of change is not constant.

4. a) 352, 138, 286, 28, 60, -34 people/h
  b) the rate of growth of the crowd at the rally
  c) A positive rate of growth indicates that people were arriving at the rally. A negative rate of growth indicates that people were leaving the rally.

5. a) 203, 193, 165, 178.5, 218.5, 146 km/day
  b) No. Some days the distance travelled was greater than others.

6. 4; 4; the average rate of change is always 4 because the function is linear, with a slope of 4.

7. The rate of change is 0 for 0 to 250 min. After 250 min, the rate of change is $0.10/min.

8. a) i) 750 people/year
  ii) 3000 people/year
  iii) 12 000 people/year
  iv) 5250 people/year
  b) No; the rate of growth increases as the time increases.
  c) You must assume that the growth continues to follow this pattern, and that the population will be 5 120 000 people in 2050.

9. -2 m/s

10. a) i) $2.60/sweatshirt
  ii) $2.00/sweatshirt
  iii) $1.40/sweatshirt
  iv) $0.80/sweatshirt
  b) The rate of change is still positive, but it is decreasing. This means that the profit is still increasing, but at a decreasing rate.
  c) No; after 6000 sweatshirts are sold, the rate of change becomes negative. This means that the profit begins to decrease after 6000 sweatshirts are sold.

11. a)

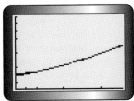

  b) The rate of change will be greater farther in the future. The graph is getting steeper as the values of t increase.

c) i) 1500 people/year
  ii) 1700 people/year
  iii) 2000 people/year
  iv) 2500 people/year
  d) The prediction was correct.

12. Answers may vary. For example:
  a) Someone might calculate the average increase in the price of gasoline over time. One might also calculate the average decrease in the price of computers over time.
  b) An average rate of change might be useful for predicting the behaviour of a relationship in the future.
  c) An average rate of change is calculated by dividing the change in the dependent variable by the corresponding change in the dependent variable.

13. -7.8%

14. Answers may vary. For example:

AVERAGE RATE OF CHANGE

Definition in your own words	Personal example	Visual representation
the change in one quantity divided by the change in a related quantity	I record the number of miles I run each week versus the week number. Then, I can calculate the average rate of change in the distance I run over the course of weeks.	Average rate of change $= \frac{\Delta y}{\Delta x}$

15. 80 km/h

Lesson 2.2, pp. 85–88

1. a)

Preceding Interval	$\Delta f(x)$	Δx	Average Rate of Change, $\frac{\Delta f(x)}{\Delta x}$
$1 \le x \le 2$	$13 - (-2) = 15$	$2 - 1 = 1$	15
$1.5 \le x \le 2$	8.75	0.5	17.5
$1.9 \le x \le 2$	1.95	0.1	19.5
$1.99 \le x \le 2$	0.1995	0.01	19.95

Following Interval	$\Delta f(x)$	Δx	Average Rate of Change, $\frac{\Delta f(x)}{\Delta x}$
$2 \le x \le 3$	$38 - 13 = 25$	$3 - 2 = 1$	25
$2 \le x \le 2.5$	11.25	0.5	22.5
$2 \le x \le 2.1$	2.05	0.1	20.5
$2 \le x \le 2.01$	0.2005	0.01	20.05

  b) 20

2. a) 5.4 m/s **b)** 5.4 m/s
  c) Answers may vary. For example: I prefer the centred interval method. Fewer calculations are required, and it takes into account points on each side of the given point in each calculation.

3. a) 200
  b) 40 raccoons/month
  c) 50 raccoons/month
  d) The three answers represent different things: the population at a particular time, the average rate of change prior to that time, and the instantaneous rate of change at that time.

4. a) -24 **b)** 0 **c)** 48 **d)** 96

5. -27 m/s

6. $11 610 per year

7. a) 0 people/year
  b) Answers may vary. For example: Yes, it makes sense. It means that the populations in 2000 and 2024 are the same, so their average rate of change is 0.
  c) The average rate of change from 2000 to 2012 is 18 000 people/year; the average rate of change from 2012 to 2024 is -18 000 people/year.
  d) $t = 12$

8. About $-$$960 per year; when the car turns five, it loses $960 of its value.

9. a) 1.65 s **b)** about 14 m/s

10. 100π cm³/cm

11. If David knows how far he has travelled and how long he has been driving, he can calculate his average speed from the beginning of the trip by dividing the distance travelled by the time he has been driving.

12. a) -22.5 °F/min
  b) Answers may vary. For example: -25.5 °F/min
  c) Answers may vary. For example, the first rate is using a larger interval to estimate the instantaneous rate.
  d) Answers may vary. For example, the second estimate is better, as it uses a much smaller interval to estimate the instantaneous rate.

13. Answers may vary. For example:

Method of Estimating Instantaneous Rate of Change	Advantage	Disadvantage
series of preceding intervals and following intervals	accounts for differences in the way that change occurs on either side of the given point	must do two sets of calculations
series of centred intervals	accounts for points on either side of the given interval in same calculation	to get a precise answer, numbers involved will need to have several decimal places
difference quotient	more precise	calculations can be tedious or messy

14. a) 100π cm^2/cm
b) 240π cm^2/cm
15. 36 cm^2/cm
16. 160π cm^2/cm

Lesson 2.3, pp. 91–92

1. a) about 7   **c)** about 0.25
b) about 10   **d)** 2

2. a)

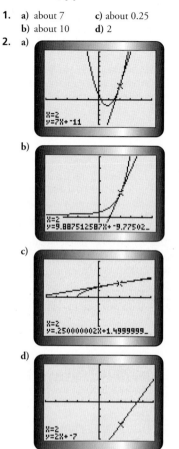

b)

c)

d)

3. a) Set A: 0, 0, 0, 0
Set B: 14, 1.4, 5, 0.009
Set C: $-4, -0.69, -3, -0.009$
b) Set A: All slopes are zero.
Set B: All slopes are positive.
Set C: All slopes are negative.

4. a) and b)

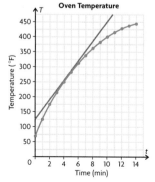

c) 31
d) Rate of change is about $30\,°\text{F}/\text{min}$ at $x = 5$.
e) Answers may vary. For example: The two answers are about the same. The slope of the tangent line at the point is the same as the instantaneous rate of change at the point.

5. Answers may vary. For example: Similarity: the calculation; difference: average rate of change is over an interval; instantaneous rate of change is at a point.

6. a)

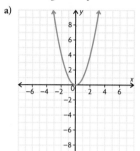

b)

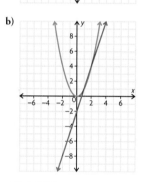

c) (1.5, 2.25)

Mid-Chapter Review, p. 95

1. a)

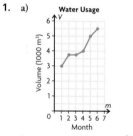

b) 750; 250; 1100; 400 m^3/month
c) April and May
d) 580 m^3/month
2. a) The equation models exponential growth. This means that the average rate of change between consecutive years will always increase.
b) The instantaneous rate of change in population in 2010 is about 950 people per year.

3. a) 10 m/s; -10 m/s
b) $t = 2$; Answers may vary. For example: The graph has a vertex at (2, 21). It appears that a tangent line at this point would be horizontal.
$$\frac{(f(2.01) - f(1.99))}{0.02}$$
4. 0.9 m/day
5. Answers may vary. For example:

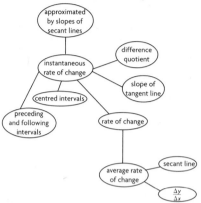

6. Answers may vary. For example:

Points	Slope of Secant
(2, 9) and (1, 2)	7
(2, 9) and (1.5, 4.375)	9.25
(2, 9) and (1.9, 7.859)	11.41
(2, 9) and (2.1, 10.261)	12.61
(2, 9) and (2.5, 16.625)	15.25
(2, 9) and (3, 28)	19

The slope of the tangent line at (2, 9) is about 12.
7. 4
8. The instantaneous rate of change of the function whose graph is shown is 4 at $x = 2$.
9. Answers may vary. For example:
a) 0   **b)** 4   **c)** 5   **d)** 8

Lesson 2.4, pp. 103–106

1. a) C   **b)** A   **c)** B
2. All of the graphs show that the speed is constant. In a), the speed is positive and constant. In b), the speed is negative and constant. In c), the speed is 0, which is constant.

3.

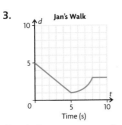
Jan's Walk

4. a) Answers may vary. For example:

Rachel's Climb

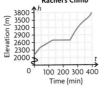

b) Average speed over first 40 min is 7.5 m/min, average speed over next 90 min is 3.3 m/min, average speed over next 120 min is 0 m/min, average speed over next 40 min is 10 m/min, average speed over next 45 min is 6.7 m/min, and average speed over last 60 min is 5.7 m/min.

c) Answers may vary. For example:

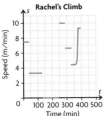
Rachel's Climb

5. a) Answers may vary. For example:

Water Level vs Time

b) Answers may vary. For example:

Water Level vs Time

6. a) Answers may vary. For example:

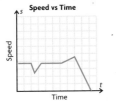
Speed vs Time

b) Answers may vary. For example:

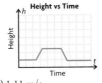
Height vs Time

7. a) 1.11 m/s

b) 0.91 m/s

c) The graph of the first length would be steeper, indicating a quicker speed. The graph of the second length would be less steep, indicating a slower speed.

d) Answers may vary. For example:

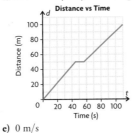
Distance vs Time

e) 0 m/s

f) Answers may vary. For example:

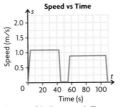
Speed vs Time

8. a) A   **b)** C   **c)** D   **d)** B

9. Answers may vary. For example:

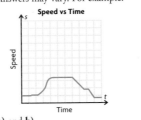
Speed vs Time

10. a) and **b)**

i) Start 5 m from sensor. Walk toward sensor at a constant rate of 1 m/s for 3 s. Walk away from sensor at a constant rate of 1 m/s for 3 s.

ii) Start 6 m from sensor. Walk toward sensor at a constant rate of 1 m/s for 2 s. Stand still for 1 s. Walk toward sensor at a constant rate of 1 m/s for 2 s. Walk away from sensor at a constant rate of 1.5 m/s.

11. a) Answers may vary. For example:

Marathon Training Program
(16, 10)
(17, 7)
(47, 7)
(11, 10)
(10, 5)
(0, 5)
(59, 3)
(49, 3)

b) 5 mph/min

c) −0.1842 mph/min

d) The answer to part c) is an average rate of change over a long period, but the runner does not slow down at a constant rate during this period.

12. Answers may vary. For example: Walk from (0, 0) to (5, 5) and stop for 5 s. Then run to (15, 30). Continue walking to (20, 5) and end at (25, 0). What is the maximum speed and minimum speed on an interval? Create the speed versus time graph from these data.

13. Answers may vary. For example:

Speed vs Time

14. If the original graph showed an increase in rate, it would mean that the distance travelled during each successive unit of time would be greater—meaning a graph that curves upward. If the original graph showed a straight, horizontal line, then it would mean that the distance travelled during each successive unit of time would be greater—meaning a steady increasing straight line on the second graph. If the original graph showed a decrease in rate, it would mean that the distance travelled during each successive unit of time would be less—meaning a line that curves down.

Lesson 2.5, pp. 111–113

1. Answers may vary. For example, I used the difference quotient when $a = 1.5$ and $h = 0.001$ and got an estimate for the instantaneous rate of change in cost that was close to 0.

2. 0

3. a) The slopes of the tangent lines are positive, but close to 0.

b) The slopes of the tangent lines are negative, but close to 0.

4. a) The slopes of the tangent lines are negative, but close to 0.

b) The slopes of the tangent lines are positive, but close to 0.

5. a) The slope is 0.

b) The slope is 0.

c) The slope is 0.

d) The slope is 0.

6. a) minimum

b) maximum

c) minimum

d) maximum

e) maximum

f) maximum

7. $t = 2.75$; Answers may vary. For example: The slopes of tangents for values of t less than about 2.75 would be positive, while slopes of tangents for values of t greater than about 2.75 would be negative.

8. a) $x = -5$; minimum
$x = 7.5$; maximum
$x = 3.25$; minimum
$x = 6$; maximum

b) i)

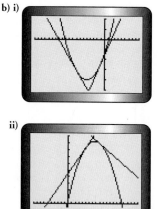

ii)

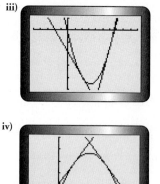

iii)

iv)

c) Answers may vary. For example, if the sign of the slope of the tangent changed from positive to negative, there was a maximum. If the sign of the slope of the tangent changed from negative to positive, there was a minimum.

9. a) i) maximum $= (0, 100)$;
minimum $= (5, 44.4)$
ii) maximum $= (10, 141.6)$;
minimum $= (0, 35)$
b) For an equation that represents exponential growth (where $r > 0$), the minimum value will always be at point a and the maximum value will always

be at point b, because y will always increase as x increases. For an equation that represents exponential decay (where $r < 0$), the minimum value will always be at point b and the maximum value will always be at point a, because y will always decrease as x increases.

10. Answers may vary. For example, the slope of the tangent at 0.5 s is 0. The slope of the tangent at 0 s is 5, and the slope of the tangent at 1 s is -5. So, the diver reaches her maximum height at 0.5 s.

11. Answers may vary. For example, yes, this observation is correct. The slope of the tangent at 1.5 s is 0. The slopes of the tangents between 1 s and 1.5 s are negative, and the slopes of the tangent lines between 1.5 s and 2 s are positive. So, the minimum of the function occurs at 1.5 s.

12. Answers may vary. For example, estimate the slope of the tangent line to the curve when $x = 5$ by writing an equation for the slope of any secant line on the graph of $R(x)$. If the slope of the tangent is 0, this will confirm there may be a maximum at $x = 5$. If the slopes of tangent lines to the left are positive and the slopes of tangent lines to the right are negative, this will confirm that a maximum occurs at $x = 5$.

13. Answers may vary. For example, because $\sin 90°$ gives a maximum value of 1, I know that a maximum occurs when $(k(x - d)) = 90°$. Solving this equation for x will tell me what types of x-values will give a maximum. For example, when $k = 2$ and $d = 3$,
$(2(x - 3°)) = 90°$
$(x - 3°) = 45°$
$x = 48°$

14. Myra is plotting (instantaneous) velocity versus time. The rates of change Myra calculates represent acceleration. When Myra's graph is increasing, the car is accelerating. When Myra's graph is decreasing, the car is decelerating. When Myra's graph is constant, the velocity of the car is constant; the car is neither accelerating nor decelerating.

15. $-4, -2, 4, 6$; The rule appears to be "multiply the x-coordinate by 2." 12, 3, 12, 27; The rule for $f(x) = x^3$ seems to be "square the x-coordinate and multiply by 3."

Chapter Review, pp. 116–117

1. a) Yes. Divide revenue by number of watches, and the slope is 17.5.

b) Answers may vary. For example:

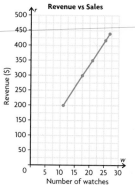

The data represent a linear relationship.
c) $17.50 per watch
d) $17.50; this is the slope of the line on the graph.

2. a) 1.5 m/s
b) -1.5 m/s
c) The time intervals have the same length. The amount of change is the same, but with opposite signs for the two intervals. So, the rates of change are the same for the two intervals, but with opposite signs.

3. a) $E = 2500m + 10\ 000$
b) $2500 per month
c) No; the equation that represents this situation is linear, and the rate of change over time for a linear equation is constant.

4. a) Answers may vary. For example, because the unit of the equation is years, you would not choose $3 \leq t \leq 4.25$ and $4 \leq t \leq 5$. A better choice would be $3.75 \leq t \leq 4.0$ and $4.0 \leq t \leq 4.25$.
b) Answers may vary. For example, find the average of the two interval values:
$\frac{(600.56 + 621.91)}{2} = \$611.24$

5. a) Answers may vary. For example, squeezing the interval.
b) 4.19 cm/s

6. a) -2 **b)** 0   **c)** 4
7. a) -37 **b)** -17 **c)** 0   **d)** 23
8. Answers may vary. For example:

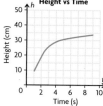

9. a) Answers may vary. For example:

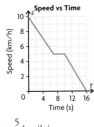

Speed vs Time

b) $-\dfrac{5}{7}$ km/h/s

c) From $(7, 5)$ to $(12, \frac{10}{3})$, the rate of change of speed in $-\frac{1}{3}$ km/h/s

d) $-\dfrac{5}{6}$ km/h/s

10. The roller coaster moves at a slow steady speed between A and B. At B, it begins to accelerate as it moves down to C. Going uphill from C to D it decelerates. At D, it starts to move down and accelerates to E, where the speed starts to decrease until F, where it maintains a slower speed to G, the end of the track.

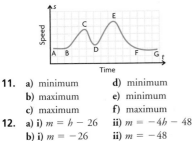

11. a) minimum   **d)** minimum
b) maximum   **e)** minimum
c) maximum   **f)** maximum

12. a) i) $m = h - 26$ **ii)** $m = -4h - 48$
    b) i) $m = -26$ **ii)** $m = -48$

13. a) To the left of a maximum, the instantaneous rates of change are positive. To the right, the instantaneous rates of change are negative.
b) To the left of a minimum, the instantaneous rates of change are negative. To the right, the instantaneous rates of change are positive.

14. a)

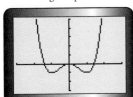

b) minimum: $x = -1$, $x = 1$
maximum: $x = 0$
c) The slopes of tangent lines for points to the left of a minimum will be negative, while the slopes of tangent lines for points to the right of a minimum will be positive. The slopes of tangent lines for points to the left of a maximum will be positive, while the slopes of tangent lines for points to the right of a minimum will be negative.

d)

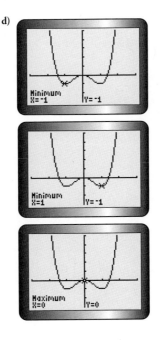

Chapter Self-Test, p. 118

1. a)

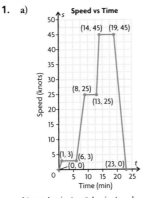

Speed vs Time

b) 11 kn/min; 0 kn/min; the two different average rates of change indicate that the boat was increasing its speed from $t = 6$ to $t = 8$ at a rate of 11knots/min and moving at a constant speed from $t = 8$ to $t = 13$.
c) 11 kn/min

2. a) -1
b) The hot cocoa is cooling by $1\ ^\circ$C/min on average.
c) -0.75
d) The hot cocoa is cooling by $0.75\ ^\circ$C/min after 30 min.
e) The rate decreases over the interval, until it is nearly 0 and constant.

3. a) $310 per dollar spent
b) $-$100 per dollar spent
c) The positive sign for part a) means that the company is increasing its profit when it spends between $8000 and $10 000 on advertising. The negative sign

means the company's profit is decreasing when it spends $50 000 on advertising.

4. a) -1; 0 (minimum); 7
b) 4.5; -4.5; 0 (maximum)

Chapter 3

Getting Started, p. 122

1. a) $6x^3 - 22x^2$
b) $x^2 + 2x - 24$
c) $24x^3 - 44x^2 - 40x$
d) $5x^3 + 31x^2 - 68x + 32$
2. a) $(x + 7)(x - 4)$
b) $2(x - 2)(x - 7)$
3. a) $x = -6$
b) $x = -3, 4.5$
c) $x = -3, -8$
d) $x = \dfrac{1}{3}, -4$
4. a) vertical compression by a factor of $\frac{1}{4}$; horizontal translation 3 units to the right; vertical translation 9 units up
b) vertical compression by a factor of $\frac{1}{4}$; vertical translation 7 units down
5. a) $y = 2(x - 5)^2 - 2$
b) $y = -2x^2 + 3$
6. a)

$y = 3(x + 5)^2 - 4$

b)

$y = 2x^2 - 12x + 5$

7. a) quadratic
b) other
c) other
d) linear

8.

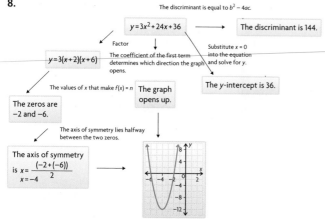

The discriminant is equal to $b^2 - 4ac$.

$y = 3x^2 + 24x + 36$ → The discriminant is 144.

Factor

The coefficient of the first term determines which direction the graph opens.

Substitute $x = 0$ into the equation and solve for y.

$y = 3(x + 2)(x + 6)$

The values of x that make $f(x) = n$

The y-intercept is 36.

The graph opens up.

The zeros are -2 and -6.

The axis of symmetry lies halfway between the two zeros.

The axis of symmetry is $x = \dfrac{(-2 + (-6))}{2}$
$x = -4$

Lesson 3.1, pp. 127–128

1. a) This represents a polynomial function because the domain is the set of all real numbers, the range does not have a lower bound, and the graph does not have horizontal or vertical asymptotes.
 b) This represents a polynomial function because the domain is the set of all real numbers, the range is the set of all real numbers, and the graph does not have horizontal or vertical asymptotes.
 c) This is not a polynomial function because it has a horizontal asymptote.
 d) This represents a polynomial function because the domain is the set of all real numbers, the range does not have an upper bound, and the graph does not have horizontal or vertical asymptotes.
 e) This is not a polynomial function because its domain is not all real numbers.
 f) This is not a polynomial function because it is a periodic function.

2. a) polynomial; the exponents of the variables are all natural numbers
 b) polynomial; the exponents of the variables are all natural numbers
 c) polynomial; the exponents of the variables are all natural numbers
 d) other; the variable is under a radical sign
 e) other; the function contains another function in the denominator
 f) polynomial; the exponents of the variables are all natural numbers

3. a) linear **c)** linear
 b) quadratic **d)** cubic

4.

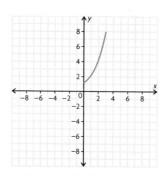

 a) The graph looks like one half of a parabola, which is the graph of a quadratic equation.
 b) There is a variable in the exponent.

5.

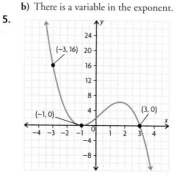

6. Answers may vary. For example, any equation of the form
$$y = a\left(-\frac{4}{3}x^2 + \frac{8}{3}x + 4\right)$$ will have the same zeros, but have a different y-intercept and a different value for
$f(-3)$. Any equation of the form
$$y = x\left(-\frac{4}{3}x^2 + \frac{8}{3}x + 4\right)$$ would have two of the same zeros, but a different value for $f(-3)$ and different positive/negative intervals.

7. $y = x + 5$, $y = x^2 + 5$,
$y = x^3 + 5$, $y = x^4 + 5$

8. Answers may vary. For example:

Definition	Characteristics
A polynomial is an expression of the form $a_n x^n + a_{n-1}x^{n-1} + \ldots + a_2 x^2 + a_1 x + a_0$, where $a_0, a_1, \ldots, a_n$ are real numbers and n is a whole number.	The domain of the function is all real numbers, but the range can have restrictions; except for polynomial functions of degree zero (whose graphs are horizontal lines), the graphs of polynomials do not have horizontal or vertical asymptotes. The shape of the graph depends on its degree.

Polynomials

Examples	Non-Examples
$x^2 + 4x + 6$	$\sqrt{x + 1}$

Lesson 3.2, pp. 136–138

1. a) $4; -4$; as $x \to +/-\infty$, $y \to -\infty$
 b) $5; 2$; as $x \to -\infty$, $y \to -\infty$ and as $x \to \infty$, $y \to \infty$
 c) $3; -3$; as $x \to -\infty$, $y \to \infty$ and as $x \to \infty$, $y \to -\infty$
 d) $4; 24$; as $x \to +/-\infty$, $y \to \infty$

2. a) Turning points
  a) minimum 1, maximum 3
  b) minimum 0, maximum 4
  c) minimum 0, maximum 2
  d) minimum 1, maximum 3
 b) Zeros
  a) minimum 0, maximum 4
  b) minimum 1, maximum 5
  c) minimum 1, maximum 3
  d) minimum 0, maximum 4

3. i) a) The degree is even.
   b) The leading coefficient is negative.
  ii) a) The degree is even.
   b) The leading coefficient is negative.
  iii) a) The degree is odd.
   b) The leading coefficient is negative.
  iv) a) The degree is even.
   b) The leading coefficient is positive.
  v) a) The degree is odd.
   b) The leading coefficient is negative.
  vi) a) The degree is odd.
   b) The leading coefficient is positive.

4. a) as $x \to +/-\infty$, $y \to \infty$
 b) as $x \to -\infty$, $y \to \infty$ and as $x \to \infty$, $y \to -\infty$
 c) as $x \to -\infty$, $y \to -\infty$ and as $x \to \infty$, $y \to \infty$
 d) as $x \to +/-\infty$, $y \to -\infty$

e) as $x \to +/-\infty$, $y \to \infty$

f) as $x \to -\infty$, $y \to \infty$ and as $x \to \infty$, $y \to -\infty$

5. a) D: The graph extends from quadrant III to quadrant I and the y-intercept is 2.

b) A: The graph extends from quadrant III to quadrant IV.

c) E: The graph extends from quadrant II to quadrant I and the y-intercept is -5.

d) C: The graph extends from quadrant II to quadrant I and the y-intercept is 0.

e) F: The graph extends from quadrant II to quadrant IV.

f) B: The graph extends from quadrant III to quadrant I and the y-intercept is 1.

6. a) Answers may vary. For example, $f(x) = 2x^3 + 5$.

b) Answers may vary. For example, $f(x) = 6x^2 + x - 4$.

c) Answers may vary. For example, $f(x) = -x^4 - x^3 + 7$.

d) Answers may vary. For example, $f(x) = -9x^5 + x^4 - x^3 - 2$.

7. a) Answers may vary. For example:

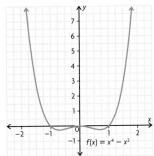
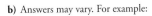

b) Answers may vary. For example:

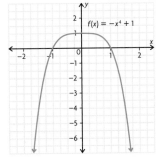

c) Answers may vary. For example:

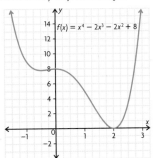

d) Answers may vary. For example:

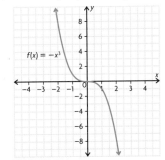

e) Answers may vary. For example:

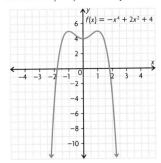

f) Answers may vary. For example:

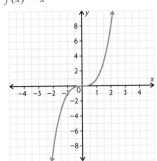

8. An odd-degree polynomial can have only local maximums and minimums because the y-value goes to $-\infty$ and ∞ at each end of the function. An even-degree polynomial can have absolute maximums and minimums because it will go to either $-\infty$ at both ends or ∞ at both ends of the function.

9. even number of turning points

10. a) Answers may vary. For example: $f(x) = x^3$

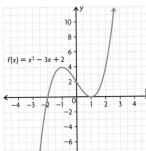

b) Answers may vary. For example: $f(x) = x^3 - 2x^2$

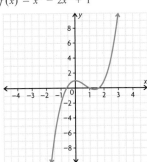

c) Answers may vary. For example: $f(x) = x^3 - 2x^2 + 1$

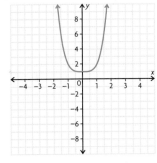

11. a) Answers may vary. For example: $f(x) = x^4 + 1$

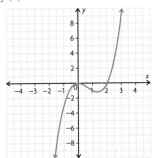

b) Answers may vary. For example: $f(x) = x^4$

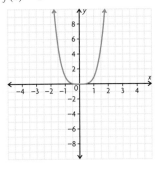

c) Answers may vary. For example:
$f(x) = x^4 - 1$

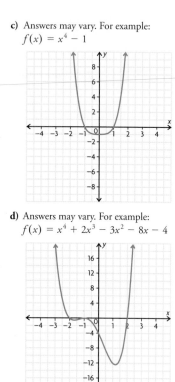

d) Answers may vary. For example:
$f(x) = x^4 + 2x^3 - 3x^2 - 8x - 4$

e) Answers may vary. For example:
$f(x) = x^4 - 5x^2 + 4$

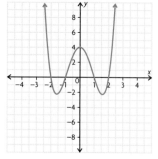

12. a) Answers may vary. For example:
$f(x) = \frac{1}{4}x^4 - \frac{1}{3}x^3 - 3x^2$

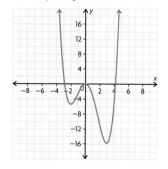

and $f(x) = \frac{1}{4}x^4 - \frac{1}{3}x^3 - 3x^2 - 1$

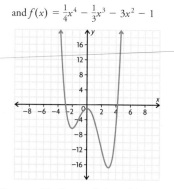

b) zero and leading coefficient of the function

13. a) 700 people
b) The population will decrease because the leading coefficient is negative.

14. a) False; Answers may vary. For example, $f(x) = x^2 + x$ is not an even function.
b) True
c) False; Answers may vary. For example, $f(x) = x^2 + 1$ has no zeros.
d) False; Answers may vary. For example, $f(x) = -x^2$ has end behaviour opposite the behaviour stated.

15. Answers may vary. For example, "What are the turning points of the function?", "What is the leading coefficient of the function?", and "What are the zeros of the function?" If the function has 0 turning points or an even number of turning points, then it must extend to the opposite side of the x-axis. If it has an odd number of turning points, it must extend to the same side of the x-axis. If the leading coefficient is known, it can be determined exactly which quadrants the function extends to/from and if the function has been vertically stretched. If the zeros are known, it can be determined if the function has been vertically translated up or down.

16. a) $b = 0$
b) $b = 0, d = 0$

Lesson 3.3, pp. 146–148

1. a) C: The graph has zeros of -1 and 3, and it extends from quadrant III to quadrant I.
b) A: The graph has zeros of -1 and 3, and it extends from quadrant II to quadrant III.
c) B: The graph has zeros of -1 and 3, and it extends from quadrant II to quadrant IV.
d) D: The graph has zeros of -1, 0, 3, and 5, and it extends from quadrant II to quadrant I.

2. a)

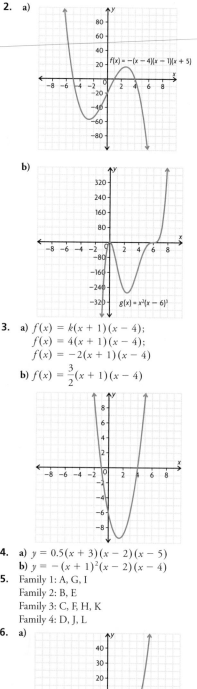

$f(x) = -(x-4)(x-1)(x+5)$

b)

$g(x) = x^2(x-6)^3$

3. a) $f(x) = k(x+1)(x-4)$;
$f(x) = 4(x+1)(x-4)$;
$f(x) = -2(x+1)(x-4)$
b) $f(x) = \frac{3}{2}(x+1)(x-4)$

4. a) $y = 0.5(x+3)(x-2)(x-5)$
b) $y = -(x+1)^2(x-2)(x-4)$

5. Family 1: A, G, I
Family 2: B, E
Family 3: C, F, H, K
Family 4: D, J, L

6. a)

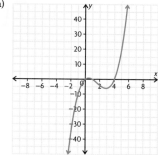

b)

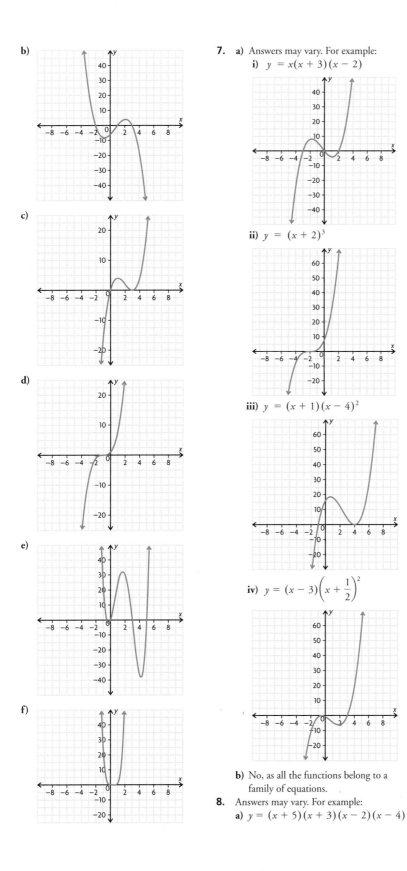

c)

d)

e)

f)

7. a) Answers may vary. For example:

i) $y = x(x + 3)(x - 2)$

ii) $y = (x + 2)^3$

iii) $y = (x + 1)(x - 4)^2$

iv) $y = (x - 3)\left(x + \dfrac{1}{2}\right)^2$

b) No, as all the functions belong to a family of equations.

8. Answers may vary. For example:

a) $y = (x + 5)(x + 3)(x - 2)(x - 4)$

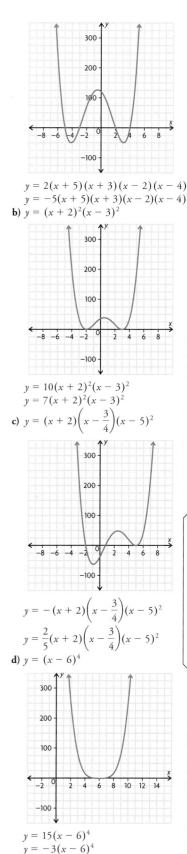

$y = 2(x + 5)(x + 3)(x - 2)(x - 4)$
$y = -5(x + 5)(x + 3)(x - 2)(x - 4)$

b) $y = (x + 2)^2(x - 3)^2$

$y = 10(x + 2)^2(x - 3)^2$
$y = 7(x + 2)^2(x - 3)^2$

c) $y = (x + 2)\left(x - \dfrac{3}{4}\right)(x - 5)^2$

$y = -(x + 2)\left(x - \dfrac{3}{4}\right)(x - 5)^2$

$y = \dfrac{2}{5}(x + 2)\left(x - \dfrac{3}{4}\right)(x - 5)^2$

d) $y = (x - 6)^4$

$y = 15(x - 6)^4$
$y = -3(x - 6)^4$

9. a)

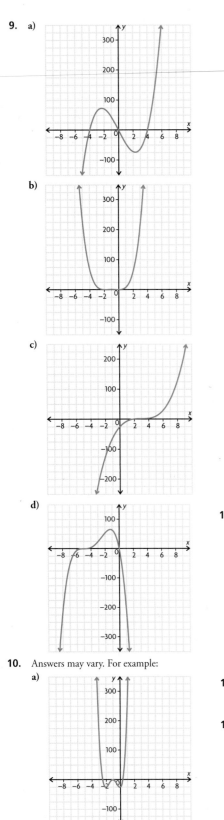

b)

c)

d)

10. Answers may vary. For example:

a)

11. a)

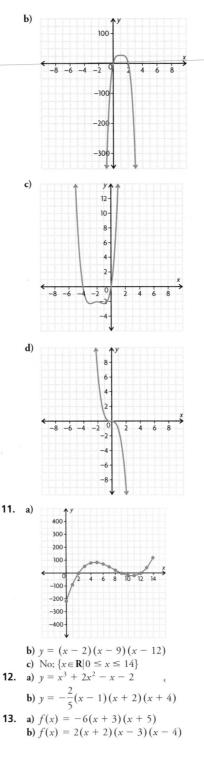

b) $y = (x - 2)(x - 9)(x - 12)$

c) No; $\{x \in \mathbf{R} \mid 0 \le x \le 14\}$

12. a) $y = x^3 + 2x^2 - x - 2$

b) $y = -\dfrac{2}{5}(x - 1)(x + 2)(x + 4)$

13. a) $f(x) = -6(x + 3)(x + 5)$

b) $f(x) = 2(x + 2)(x - 3)(x - 4)$

14. $k = 3$

The zeros are $\dfrac{5}{3}$, -1, and 2.

$f(x) = (3x - 5)(x + 1)(x - 2)$

15. a) It has zeros at 2 and 4, and it has turning points at 2, 3, and 4. It extends from quadrant II to quadrant I.

b) It has zeros at -4 and 3, and it has turning points at $-\dfrac{5}{3}$ and 3. It extends from quadrant III to quadrant I.

16. a) 832 cm^3

b) 2.93 cm by 24.14 cm by 14.14 cm or 5 cm by 20 cm by 10 cm

c) $0 < x < 10$; The values of x are the side lengths of squares that can be cut from the sheet of cardboard to produce a box with positive volume. Since the sheet of cardboard is 30 cm by 20 cm, the side lengths of a square cut from each corner have to be less than 10 cm, or an entire edge would be cut away, leaving nothing to fold up.

d) The square that is cut from each corner must be larger than 0 cm by 0 cm but smaller than 10 cm by 10 cm.

Lesson 3.4, pp. 155–158

1. a) B: $y = x^3$ has been vertically stretched by a factor of 2, horizontally translated 3 units to the right, and vertically translated 1 unit up.

b) C: $y = x^3$ has been reflected in the x-axis, vertically compressed by a factor of $\dfrac{1}{3}$, horizontally translated 1 unit to the left, and vertically translated 1 unit down.

c) A: $y = x^4$ has been vertically compressed by a factor of 0.2, horizontally translated 4 units to the right, and vertically translated 3 units down.

d) D: $y = x^4$ has been reflected in the x-axis, vertically stretched by a factor of 1.5, horizontally translated 3 units to the left, and vertically translated 4 units up.

2. a) $y = x^4$; vertical stretch by a factor of $\dfrac{5}{4}$ and vertical translation of 3 units up

b) $y = x$; vertical stretch by a factor of 3 and vertical translation of 4 units down

c) $y = x^3$; horizontal compression by a factor of $\dfrac{1}{3}$, horizontal translation of $\dfrac{4}{3}$ units to the left, and vertical translation of 7 units down

d) $y = x^4$; reflection in the x-axis and horizontal translation of 8 units to the left

e) $y = x^2$; reflection in the x-axis, vertical stretch by a factor of 4.8, and horizontal translation 3 units left

f) $y = x^3$; vertical stretch by a factor of 2, horizontal stretch by a factor of 5, horizontal translation of 7 units to the left, and vertical translation of 4 units down

3. a) $y = x^3$ has been translated 3 units to the left and 4 units down.
$y = (x + 3)^3 - 4$

b) $y = x^4$ has been reflected in the x-axis, vertically stretched by a factor of 2, horizontally translated 4 units to the left, and vertically translated 5 units up.
$y = -2(x + 4)^4 + 5$

c) $y = x^4$ has been vertically compressed by a factor of $\frac{1}{4}$, horizontally translated 1 unit to the right, and vertically translated 2 units down.
$y = \frac{1}{4}(x - 1)^4 - 2$

d) $y = x^3$ has been reflected in the x-axis, vertically stretched by a factor of 2, horizontally translated 3 units to the right, and vertically translated 4 units down.
$y = -2(x - 3)^3 - 4$

4. a) vertically stretched by a factor of 12, horizontally translated 9 units to the right, and vertically translated 7 units down

b) horizontally stretched by a factor of $\frac{8}{7}$, horizontally translated 1 unit to the left, and vertically translated 3 units up

c) vertically stretched by a factor of 2, reflected in the x-axis, horizontally translated 6 units to the right, and vertically translated 8 units down

d) horizontally translated 9 units to the left

e) reflected in the x-axis, vertically stretched by a factor of 2, reflected in the y-axis, horizontally compressed by a factor of $\frac{1}{3}$, horizontally translated 4 units to the right, and vertically translated 5 units down

f) horizontally stretched by a factor of $\frac{4}{3}$ and horizontally translated 10 units to the right

5. a) $y = 8x^2 - 11$
$y = x^2$ was vertically stretched by a factor of 8 and vertically translated 11 units down.

b) $y = -\frac{1}{4}x^2 + 1.25$
$y = x^2$ was reflected in the x-axis, vertically compressed by a factor of $\frac{1}{4}$, and vertically translated 1.25 units up.

6. a) $\left(-6\frac{1}{5}, -\frac{1}{2}\right), (-6, 0), \left(-5\frac{3}{5}, 4\right)$

b) $(2, 2), (0, 3), (-4, 11)$

c) $\left(3, 2\frac{1}{2}\right), \left(4, -\frac{1}{2}\right), \left(6, -24\frac{1}{2}\right)$

d) $\left(-7, -2\frac{1}{10}\right), (0, -2), \left(14, -1\frac{1}{5}\right)$

e) $\left(1, 1\frac{9}{10}\right), \left(0, \frac{9}{10}\right), \left(-2, -7\frac{1}{10}\right)$

f) $(-11, -8), (-4, -7), (10, 1)$

7. $y = -\frac{1}{4}(x - 1)^4 + 3$

8. $(-2, 8), (0, 0), (2, -8)$

9. a) -2 and -4

b) 4

c) -3 and 1

d) no x-intercepts

e) 6.68 and 9.32

f) -3.86

10. a) $1; 0 = 2(x - 4)^3 + 1$ has only one solution.

b) $0; 0 = 2(x - 4)^4 + 1$ has no solution.

c) 1 when n is odd, since an odd root results in only one value; 0 when n is even, since there is no value for an even root of a negative number.

11. a) The reflection of the function $y = x^n$ in the x-axis will be the same as its reflection in the y-axis for odd values of n.

b) The reflections will be different for even values of n. The reflection in the x-axis will be $y = -x^n$, and the reflection in the y-axis will be $y = (-x)^n$. For odd values of n, $-x^n$ equals $(-x)^n$. For even values of n, $-x^n$ does not equal $(-x)^n$.

12. a) Vertical stretch and compression:
$y = ax^3$

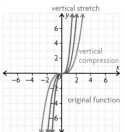
vertical stretch / vertical compression / original function

Horizontal stretch and compression:
$y = (kx)^3$

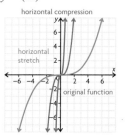
horizontal compression / horizontal stretch / original function

Vertical translation up or down:
$y = x^3 + c$

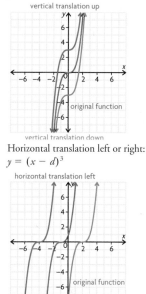
vertical translation up / original function / vertical translation down

Horizontal translation left or right:
$y = (x - d)^3$

horizontal translation left / original function / horizontal translation right

Reflection in the x-axis: $y = -x^3$

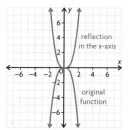
reflection in the x-axis / original function

Reflection in the y-axis: $y = (-x)^3$

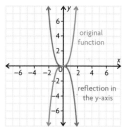
original function / reflection in the y-axis

b) When using a table of values to sketch the graph of a function, you may not select a large enough range of values for the domain to produce an accurate representation of the function.

13. Yes, you can. The zeros of the first function have the same spacing between them as the zeros of the second function. Also, the ratio of the distances of the two curves above or below the x-axis at similar distances between the zeros is always the same. Therefore, the two curves have the same general shape, and one can be transformed into the other.

14. $y = (x - 1)^2 (x + 1)^2$ has zeroes at $x = \pm1$ where the x-axis is tangent to these points. $y = 2(x - 1)^2(x + 1)^2 + 1$ is obtained by vertically stretching the original function by a factor of 2 and vertically translating up 1 unit. This results in a new graph that has no zeroes.

15. $f(x) = 5(2(x + 3))^2 + 1$

Mid-Chapter Review, p. 161

1. **a)** Yes
   b) No; it contains a rational exponent.
   c) Yes
   d) No; it is a rational function.

2. **a)** Answers may vary. For example,
   $f(x) = x^3 + 2x^2 - 8x + 1.$
   b) Answers may vary. For example,
   $f(x) = 5x^4 - x^2 - 7.$
   c) Answers may vary. For example,
   $f(x) = 7x^6 + 3.$
   d) Answers may vary. For example,
   $f(x) = -2x^5 - 4x^4 + 3x^3 - 2x^2 + 9.$

3. **a)** As $x \to -\infty, y \to \infty$ and as $x \to \infty$, $y \to -\infty.$
   b) As $x \to \pm\infty, y \to \infty.$
   c) As $x \to -\infty, y \to -\infty$ and as $x \to \infty$, $y \to \infty.$
   d) As $x \to \pm\infty, y \to -\infty.$

4. **a)** even   **c)** odd
   b) odd   **d)** even

5. Answers may vary. For example:
   a)

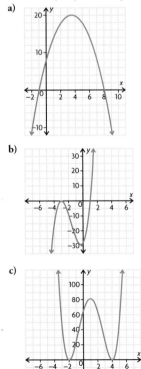

   b)

   c)

d)

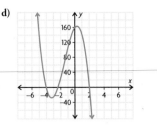

6. end behaviours
7. $y = 5(x - 2)(x + 3)^2(x - 5)$
8. **a)** reflection in the x-axis, vertical stretch by a factor of 25, horizontal compression by a factor of $\frac{1}{3}$, horizontal translation 4 units to the left, vertical translation 60 units down
   b) vertical stretch by a factor of 8, horizontal stretch by a factor of $\frac{4}{3}$, vertical translation 43 units up
   c) reflection in the y-axis, horizontal compression by a factor of $\frac{1}{13}$, horizontal translation 2 units to the right, vertical translation 13 units up
   d) vertical compression by a factor of $\frac{8}{11}$, reflection in the y-axis, vertical translation 1 unit down

9. vertically stretched by a factor of 5, horizontally translated 4 units to the left, and vertically translated 2 units down

Lesson 3.5, pp. 168–170

1. **a)** **i)** $x^3 - 14x^2 - 24x - 38$ remainder -87
      ii) $x^3 - 20x^2 + 84x - 326$ remainder 1293
      iii) $x^3 - 15x^2 - 11x - 1$ remainder -12
   b) No; because for each division problem there is a remainder.

2. **a)** 2   **b)** 2   **c)** 1   **d)** not possible

3. **a)** $x^2 - 15x + 6$ remainder $-48x + 14$
   b) $5x^2 - 19x + 60$ remainder -184
   c) $x - 6$ remainder $-6x^2 + 22x + 6$
   d) Not possible

4.

Dividend	Divisor	Quotient	Remainder
$2x^3 - 5x^2 + 8x + 4$	$x + 3$	$2x^2 - 11x + 41$	-119
$6x^4 + 12x^3 - 10x^2 - 4x + 29$	$2x + 4$	$3x^3 - 5x + 8$	-3
$6x^4 + 2x^3 + 3x^2 - 11x - 9$	$3x + 1$	$2x^3 + x - 4$	-5
$3x^3 + x^2 - 6x + 16$	$x + 2$	$3x^2 - 5x + 4$	8

5. **a)** $x^2 + 4x + 14$ remainder 57
   b) $x^2 - 6$ remainder 13

6. **c)** $x^2 + 2x - 3$ remainder -2
   d) $x^2 + 3x - 9$ remainder $-16x + 62$
   e) $x + 1$ remainder $8x^2 - 8x + 11$
   f) $x + 3$ remainder $-4x^3 - 4x^2 + 8x + 14$

6. **a)** $x^2 + 3x + 2$ no remainder
   b) $2x^2 - 5x - 12$ remainder 7
   c) $6x^3 - 5x^2 - 19x + 10$ remainder -2
   d) $x^2 + 2x - 8$ remainder -2
   e) $6x^3 - 31x^2 + 45x - 18$ no remainder
   f) $3x^2 - 1$ no remainder

7. **a)** $x^3 + 4x^2 - 51x + 89$
   b) $3x^4 - 2x^3 + 3x^2 - 38x + 39$
   c) $5x^4 + 22x^3 - 17x^2 + 21x + 10$
   d) $x^6 + 8x^5 + 5x^4 - 13x^3 - 72x^2 + 49x - 3$

8. **a)** $r = 20$ **c)** $r = 0$
   b) $r = x - 22$ **d)** $r = 2x^2 + 2$

9. **a)** $x + 3$ **c)** $x + 4$
   b) $x + 10$ **d)** $x - 2$

10. **a)** $x + 5$ is a factor since there is no remainder.
   b) $x + 2$ is a factor since there is no remainder.
   c) $x - 2$ is not a factor since there is a remainder of 2.
   d) $x - 1$ is not a factor since there is a remainder of 1.
   e) $3x + 5$ is not a factor since there is a remainder of $-\frac{13}{3}$.
   f) $5x - 1$ is not a factor since there is a remainder of -8.

11. $(x + 1)$ cm
12. **a)** 7   **b)** 3
13. 2
14. Yes, $f(x)$ is always divisible by $x - 1$. Regardless of the value of $n, f(x) = x^n - 1$ can always be written as $f(x) = x^n + 0x^{n-1} + 0x^{n-2} + \ldots 0x - 1.$ Therefore, the same pattern continues when dividing $x^n - 1$ by $x - 1$, regardless of how large n is, and there is never a remainder.
15. **a)** $f(x) = (x^3 - 3x^2 - 10x + 31)$
      $= (x - 4)(x^2 + x - 6)$
      remainder 7
   b) $f(x) = (x^3 - 3x^2 - 10x + 31)$
      $= (x - 4)(x + 3)(x - 2)$
      remainder 7
   c)

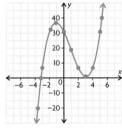

16. Answers may vary. For example:

$$
\begin{array}{r}
2x^3 + 9x^2 + 2x - 1 \\
x - 3 \overline{)\,2x^4 + 3x^3 - 25x^2 - 7x - 14}
\end{array}
$$

$2x^3(x - 3) \rightarrow \quad \underline{2x^4 - 6x^3}$

$ 9x^3 - 25x^2$

$9x^2(x - 3) \rightarrow \quad \underline{9x^3 - 27x^2}$

$ 2x^2 - 7x$

$2x(x - 3) \rightarrow \quad\quad \underline{2x^2 - 6x}$

$ -1x - 14$

$-1(x - 3) \rightarrow \quad\quad \underline{-1x + 3}$

$ -17$

17. $r = 2x + 5$ cm

18. **a)** $x^2 + xy + y^2$
b) $x^2 - 2xy + y^2$

19. $x - y$ is a factor because there is no remainder.

20. $[q(x) + 1](x + 5)$

Lesson 3.6, pp. 176–177

1. **a)** **i)** 64
ii) 22
iii) 12
b) No, according to the factor theorem, $x - a$ is a factor of $f(x)$ if and only if $f(a) = 0$.

2. **a)** not divisible by $x - 1$
b) divisible by $x - 1$
c) not divisible by $x - 1$
d) divisible $x - 1$

3. $(x + 1)(x + 3)(x - 2)$

4. **a)** -1 **c)** 0   **e)** 30
b) -5 **d)** -34 **f)** 0

5. **a)** yes   **c)** yes
b) no   **d)** no

6. **a)** $(x - 2)(x - 4)(x + 3)$
b) $(x - 1)(2x + 3)(2x + 5)$
c) $x(x - 2)(x + 4)(x + 6)$
d) $(x + 2)(x + 5)(4x - 9)(x - 3)$
e) $x(x + 2)(x + 1)(x - 3)(x - 5)$
f) $(x - 3)(x - 3)(x + 4)(x + 4)$

7. **a)** $(x - 2)(x + 5)(x + 6)$
b) $(x + 1)(x - 3)(x + 2)$
c) $(x + 1)(x - 1)(x - 2)(x + 2)$
d) $(x - 2)(x + 1)(x + 8)(x - 4)$
e) $(x - 1)(x^2 + 1)$
f) $(x - 1)(x^2 + 1)(x^2 + 1)$

8. **a)**

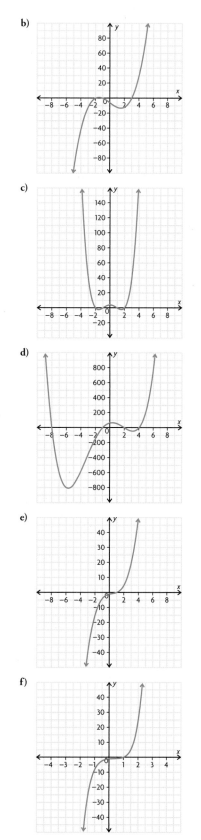

b)

c)

d)

e)

f)

9. 20

10. $a = 6$, $b = 3$

11. For $x^n - a^n$, if n is even, they're both factors. If n is odd, only $(x - a)$ is a factor. For $x^n + a^n$, if n is even, neither is a factor. If n is odd, only $(x + a)$ is a factor.

12. $a = -2$, $b = 22$;
The other factor is $-2x + 3$.

13. -6

14. $x^4 - a^4$
$= (x^2)^2 - (a^2)^2$
$= (x^2 + a^2)(x^2 - a^2)$
$= (x^2 + a^2)(x + a)(x - a)$

15. Answers may vary. For example: if $f(x) = k(x - a)$, then $f(a) = k(a - a)$ $= k(0) = 0$.

16. $x^2 - x - 2 = (x - 2)(x + 1)$;
If $f(x) = x^3 - 6x^2 + 3x + 10$, then $f(2) = 0$ and $f(-1) = 0$.

17. If $f(x) = (x + a)^5 + (x + c)^5 + (a - c)^5$, then $f(-a) = 0$

Lesson 3.7, p. 182

1. $(x + b)(x^2 - bx + b^2)$

2. **a)** $(x - 4)(x^2 + 4x + 16)$
b) $(x - 5)(x^2 + 5x + 25)$
c) $(x + 2)(x^2 - 2x + 4)$
d) $(2x - 3)(4x^2 + 6x + 9)$
e) $(4x - 5)(16x^2 + 20x + 25)$
f) $(x + 1)(x^2 - x + 1)$
g) $(3x + 2)(9x^2 - 6x + 4)$
h) $(10x + 9)(100x^2 - 90x + 81)$
i) $8(3x - 1)(9x^2 + 3x + 1)$

3. **a)** $(4x + 3y)(16x^2 - 12xy + 9y^2)$
b) $(-3x)(x - 2)(x^2 + 2x + 4)$
c) $(4 - x)(7x^2 + 25x + 31)$
d) $(x^2 + 4)(x^4 - 4x^2 + 16)$

4. **a)** $(x - 7)(x^2 + 7x + 49)$
b) $(6x - 1)(36x^2 + 6x + 1)$
c) $(x + 10)(x^2 - 10x + 100)$
d) $(5x - 8)(25x^2 + 40x + 64)$
e) $(4x - 11)(16x^2 + 44x + 121)$
f) $(7x + 3)(49x^2 - 21x + 9)$
g) $(8x + 1)(64x^2 - 8x + 1)$
h) $(11x + 12)(121x^2 - 132x + 144)$
i) $(8 - 11x)(64 + 88x + 121x^2)$

5. **a)** $\left(\dfrac{1}{3}x - \dfrac{2}{5}\right)\left(\dfrac{1}{9}x^2 + \dfrac{2}{15}x + \dfrac{4}{25}\right)$
b) $-16x^2(3x + 2)(9x^2 - 6x + 4)$
c) $7(4x - 5)(x^2 - x + 1)$
d) $\left(\dfrac{1}{2}x - 2\right)\left(\dfrac{1}{4}x^2 + x + 4\right)$
$\left(\dfrac{1}{64}x^6 + x^3 + 64\right)$

6. Agree; by the formulas for factoring the sum and difference of cubes, the numerator of the fraction is equivalent to $(a^3 + b^3) + (a^3 - b^3)$. Since $(a^3 + b^3) + (a^3 - b^3) = 2a^3$, the entire fraction is equal to 1.

Answers

7. a) $1^3 + 12^3 = (1 + 12)(1^2 - (1)(12)$
$\qquad\qquad + 12^2)$
$\qquad\quad = (13)(133) = 1729\cdot$
b) $9^3 + 10^3 = (9 + 10)(9^2 - (9)(10)$
$\qquad\qquad + 10^2)$
$\qquad\quad = (19)(91) = 1729$

8. $x^9 + y^9$
$= x^{18} + 2x^9y^9 + y^{18}$
$= (x^{18} + y^{18}) + 2x^9y^9$
$= (x^6 + y^6)(x^{12} - x^6y^6 + y^{12})$
$\quad + 2x^9y^9$
$= (x^2 + y^2)(x^4 - x^2y^2 + y^4)$
$\quad (x^{12} - x^6y^6 + y^{12}) + 2x^9y^9$

9. Answers may vary. For example, this statement is true because $a^3 - b^3$ is the same as $a^3 + (-b)^3$.

10. a) 1729 was the number of the taxicab that G. H. Hardy rode in when going to visit the mathematician Ramanujan. When Hardy told Ramanujan that the number of the taxicab he rode in was uninteresting, Ramanujan replied that the number was interesting because it was the smallest number that could be expressed as the sum of two cubes in two different ways. This is how such numbers came to be known as taxicab numbers.
b) Yes;
$TN(1) = 2$
$TN(2) = 1729$
$TN(3) = 87\ 539\ 319$
$TN(4) = 6\ 963\ 472\ 309\ 248$
$TN(5) = 48\ 988\ 659\ 276\ 962\ 496$
$TN(6) = 24\ 153\ 319\ 581\ 254\ 312\ 065\ 344$

Chapter Review, pp. 184–185

1.

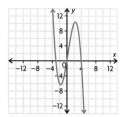

2. As $x \to -\infty$, $y \to +\infty$ and as $x \to \infty$, $y \to \infty$.
3. a) degree: $2 + 1$; leading coefficient: positive; turning points: 2
b) degree: $3 + 1$; leading coefficient: positive; turning points: 3
4. a) Answers may vary. For example,
$f(x) = (x + 3)(x - 6)(x - 4)$,
$f(x) = 10(x + 3)(x - 6)(x - 4)$,
$f(x) = -4(x + 3)(x - 6)(x - 4)$
b) Answers may vary. For example,
$f(x) = (x - 5)(x + 1)(x + 2)$,
$f(x) = -6(x - 5)(x + 1)(x + 2)$,
$f(x) = 9(x - 5)(x + 1)(x + 2)$

c) Answers may vary. For example,
$f(x) = (x + 7)(x - 2)(x - 3)$,
$f(x) = \dfrac{1}{4}(x + 7)(x - 2)(x - 3)$,
$f(x) = 3(x + 7)(x - 2)(x - 3)$
d) Answers may vary. For example,
$f(x) = (x - 9)(x + 5)(x + 4)$,
$f(x) = 7(x - 9)(x + 5)(x + 4)$,
$f(x) = -\dfrac{1}{3}(x - 9)(x + 5)(x + 4)$

5. a) Answers may vary. For example,
$f(x) = (x + 6)(x - 2)$
$\quad\ (x - 5)(x - 8)$,
$f(x) = 2(x + 6)(x - 2)$
$\quad\ (x - 5)(x - 8)$,
$f(x) = -8(x + 6)(x - 2)$
$\quad\ (x - 5)(x - 8)$
b) Answers may vary. For example,
$f(x) = (x - 4)(x + 8)$
$\quad\ (x - 1)(x - 2)$,
$f(x) = \dfrac{3}{4}(x - 4)(x + 8)$
$\quad\ (x - 1)(x - 2)$,
$f(x) = -12(x - 4)(x + 8)$
$\quad\ (x - 1)(x - 2)$
c) Answers may vary. For example,
$f(x) = x(x + 1)(x - 9)(x - 10)$,
$f(x) = 5x(x + 1)(x - 9)(x - 10)$,
$f(x) = -3x(x + 1)(x - 9)(x - 10)$
d) Answers may vary. For example,
$f(x) = (x + 3)(x - 3)$
$\quad\ (x + 6)(x - 6)$,
$f(x) = \dfrac{2}{5}(x + 3)(x - 3)$
$\quad\ (x + 6)(x - 6)$,
$f(x) = -10(x + 3)(x - 3)$
$\quad\ (x + 6)(x - 6)$

6.

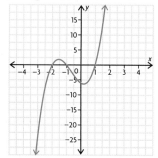

7. $y = 3(x - 1)(x + 1)(x + 2)$

8. a) reflected in the x-axis, vertically stretched by a factor of 2, horizontally translated 1 unit to the right, and vertically translated 23 units up
b) horizontally stretched by a factor of $\dfrac{13}{12}$, horizontally translated 9 units to the left, and vertically translated 14 units down
c) horizontally translated 4 units to the right
d) horizontally translated $\dfrac{3}{7}$ units to the left
e) vertically stretched by a factor of 40, reflected in the y-axis, horizontally compressed by a factor of $\dfrac{1}{7}$, horizontally translated 10 units to the right, and vertically translated 9 units up
9. a) Answers will vary. For example,
$(-2, -5400)$, $(3, 0)$, and $(8, 5400)$.
b) Answers will vary. For example,
$(-7, -18)$, $(0, -19)$, and $(7, -20)$.
c) Answers will vary. For example,
$\left(-6, \dfrac{182}{11}\right)$, $(-5, 16)$, and $\left(-4, \dfrac{170}{11}\right)$.
d) Answers will vary. For example,
$(-2, -86)$, $(0, 14)$, and $(2, 114)$.
e) Answers will vary. For example,
$(-1, -44)$, $(0, -45)$, and $(1, -46)$.
f) Answers will vary. For example,
$(5, 1006)$, $(12, 6)$, and $(19, -994)$.
10. a) $2x^2 - 5x + 28$ remainder -144
b) $x^2 + 4x + 5$ remainder $26x + 33$
c) $2x - 6$ remainder $10x^2 + 27x - 34$
d) $x - 4$ remainder
$\qquad 4x^3 + 17x^2 - 8x - 18$
11. a) $(x + 2)(2x^2 + x - 3)$ remainder 1
b) $(x + 2)(3x^2 + 7x + 3)$ remainder -3
c) $(x + 2)(2x^3 + x^2 - 18x - 9)$
$\qquad$ remainder 0
d) $(x + 2)(2x^2 - 5)$ remainder 6
12. a) $2x^3 - 7x^2 - 107x + 75$
b) $4x^4 + 3x^3 - 8x^2 + 22x + 17$
c) $3x^4 + 14x^3 - 42x^2 + 3x + 33$
d) $3x^6 - 11x^5 - 9x^4 + 47x^3$
$\qquad - 46x + 14$
13. 13
14. a) $(x + 1)(x - 8)(x + 2)$
b) $(x - 4)(2x + 3)(x + 3)$
c) $x(x - 2)(x - 3)(3x - 4)$
d) $(x - 1)(x + 4)(x + 4)(x + 4)$
15. a) $(x - 2)(4x + 5)(2x - 1)$
b) $(2x + 5)(x - 2)(x + 3)$
c) $(x - 3)(x - 3)(x - 3)(x + 2)$
d) $(2x + 1)(2x + 1)(x - 3)(x + 3)$
16. a) $(4x - 3)(16x^2 + 12x + 9)$
b) $(8x - 5)(64x^2 + 40x + 25)$
c) $(7x - 12)(49x^2 + 84x + 144)$
d) $(11x - 1)(121x^2 + 11x + 1)$
17. a) $(10x + 7)(100x^2 - 70x + 49)$
b) $(12x + 5)(144x^2 - 60x + 25)$
c) $(3x + 11)(9x^2 - 33x + 121)$
d) $(6x + 13)(36x^2 - 78x + 169)$
18. a) $(x - y)(x^2 + xy + y^2)(x + y)$
$\qquad (x^2 - xy + y^2)$

b) $(x - y)(x + y)(x^4 + x^2y^2 + y^4)$

c) Both methods produce factors of $(x - y)$ and $(x + y)$; however, the other factors are different. Since the two factorizations must be equal to each other, this means that $(x^4 + x^2y^2 + y^4)$ must be equal to $(x^2 + xy + y^2)(x^2 - xy + y^2)$.

Chapter Self-Test, p. 186

1. a) $f(x) = a_nx^n + a_{n-1}x^{n-1} + \ldots + a_1x + a_0$, where $a_0, a_1, \ldots, a_n$ are real numbers and n is a whole number. The degree of the function is n; the leading coefficient is a_n.

b) $n - 1$

c) n

d) odd degree function

e) even degree function with a negative leading coefficient

2. $y = (x + 4)(x + 2)(x - 2)$

3. a) $(x - 9)(x + 8)(2x - 1)$

b) $(3x - 4)(3x^2 + 9x + 79)$

4. more zeros

5. $-5 < x < -3; x > 1$

6. yes

7. a) $y = 5(2(x - 2))^3 + 4$

b) $(2.5, 9)$

8. $x + 5$

9. $a = -2$; zeros at $0, -2,$ and 2.

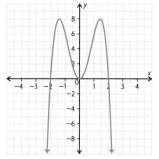

Cumulative Review Chapters 1–3, pp. 188–191

1. (b)	**9.** (c)	**17.** (a)	**25.** (c)
2. (a)	**10.** (d)	**18.** (d)	**26.** (c)
3. (c)	**11.** (a)	**19.** (b)	**27.** (d)
4. (b)	**12.** (a)	**20.** (c)	**28.** (b)
5. (b)	**13.** (c)	**21.** (b)	**29.** (c)
6. (d)	**14.** (d)	**22.** (b)	**30.** (c)
7. (d)	**15.** (c)	**23.** (b)	**31.** (c)
8. (a)	**16.** (c)	**24.** (a)	

32. a)

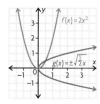

b) Answers may vary. For example, vertical translation up produces horizontal translation of the inverse to the right.

Vertical stretch produces horizontal stretch of inverse.

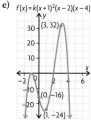

c) Answers may vary. For example, if the vertex of the inverse is (a, b), restrict the value of y to either $y \geq b$ or $y \leq b$.

33. Answers may vary. For example, average rates of change vary between -2 and 4, depending on the interval; instantaneous rates of change are 9 at $(0, 1)$, 0 at $(1, 5)$, -3 at $(2, 3)$, 0 at $(3, 1)$, 9 at $(4, 5)$; instantaneous rate of change is 0 at maximum $(1, 5)$ and at minimum $(3, 1)$.

34. a) $f(x) = -2(x + 1)^2(x - 2)(x - 4)$

b) $p = 32$

c) As $x \to \pm\infty, f(x) \to -\infty$; zeros: $-1, 2,$ and 4.

d) -16

e) $f(x) = k(x+1)^2(x - 2)(x - 4)$

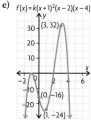

Chapter 4

Getting Started, pp. 194–195

1. a) 3

b) 5

c) 1

d) $\dfrac{64}{11}$

2. a) $x(x + 6)(x - 5)$

b) $(x - 4)(x^2 + 4x + 16)$

c) $3x(2x + 3)(4x^2 - 6x + 9)$

d) $(x + 3)(x - 3)(2x + 7)$

3. a)

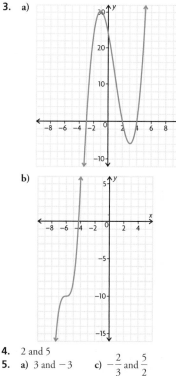

b)

4. 2 and 5

5. a) 3 and -3

c) $-\dfrac{2}{3}$ and $\dfrac{5}{2}$

b) -10 and 2

d) 0.3452 and -4.345

6. a) $(3, 7)$; Answers may vary. For example, the change in distance over time from $t = 3$ to $t = 7$ is greater than at other intervals of time.

b) $\dfrac{1}{3}$ m/s; $\dfrac{3}{4}$ m/s

c) Answers may vary. For example, away; Erika's displacement, or distance from the sensor, is increasing.

7. a) 2 s

b) 4.75 m/s

c) -10.245 m/s

8. a) Disagree; You could use the quadratic formula to solve $y = x^3 + 4x^2 + 3x$ because it equals $x(x^2 + 4x + 3)$.

b) Disagree; $y = (x + 3)^2(x - 2)$ is a cubic equation that will have two roots.

c) Disagree; The equation $y = x^3$ will only pass through two quadrants.

d) Agree; All polynomials are continuous and all polynomials have a y-intercept.

e) Disagree; $f(-3) = 9$

f) Agree; The instantaneous rates of change will tell you whether the graph is increasing, decreasing, or not changing at those points.

Lesson 4.1, pp. 204–206

1. a) $0, 1, -2, 2$

d) $-6, \dfrac{5}{2}$

b) $-\dfrac{3}{2}, \dfrac{5}{4}, -7$

e) $0, -3, 3$

c) $3, -5, 4$

f) $-5, -2, 6$

2. a) $0, -3, 3$ **d)** $0, \dfrac{2}{5}, 3$

b) ± 3 **e)** $-3\sqrt[3]{3}$

c) $0, 2, -2, -\dfrac{5}{3}$ **f)** $0, \pm 2\sqrt{6}$

3. a) $6, -1, \dfrac{7}{2}$

b) $2x^3 - 17x^2 + 23x + 42 = 0$ or $(x - 6)(x + 1)(2x - 7)$

4. Algebraically:
$x = -1, -3, 7, 0$
Graphically:

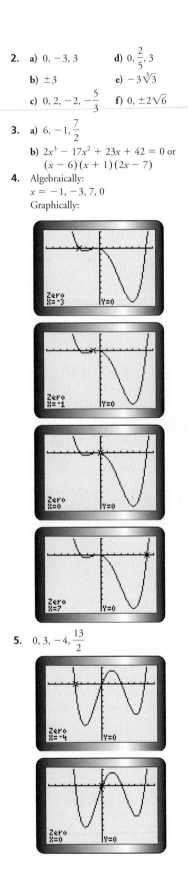

5. $0, 3, -4, \dfrac{13}{2}$

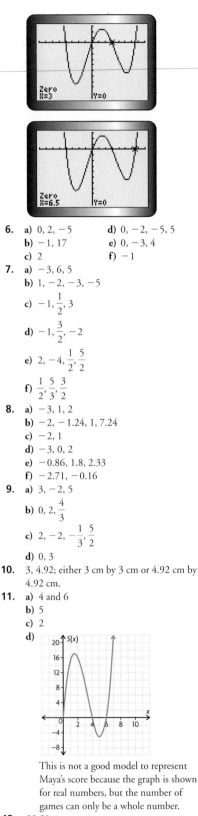

6. a) $0, 2, -5$ **d)** $0, -2, -5, 5$

b) $-1, 17$ **e)** $0, -3, 4$

c) 2 **f)** -1

7. a) $-3, 6, 5$

b) $1, -2, -3, -5$

c) $-1, \dfrac{1}{2}, 3$

d) $-1, \dfrac{3}{2}, -2$

e) $2, -4, \dfrac{1}{2}, \dfrac{5}{2}$

f) $\dfrac{1}{2}, \dfrac{5}{3}, \dfrac{3}{2}$

8. a) $-3, 1, 2$

b) $-2, -1.24, 1, 7.24$

c) $-2, 1$

d) $-3, 0, 2$

e) $-0.86, 1.8, 2.33$

f) $-2.71, -0.16$

9. a) $3, -2, 5$

b) $0, 2, \dfrac{4}{3}$

c) $2, -2, -\dfrac{1}{3}, \dfrac{5}{2}$

d) $0, 3$

10. $3, 4.92$; either 3 cm by 3 cm or 4.92 cm by 4.92 cm.

11. a) 4 and 6

b) 5

c) 2

d)

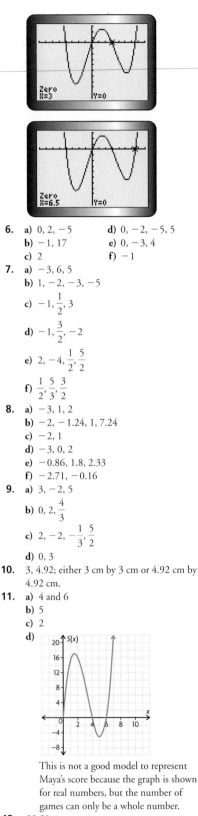

This is not a good model to represent Maya's score because the graph is shown for real numbers, but the number of games can only be a whole number.

12. 22.59 s

13. a) $d(t) = -3t(t + 2)(t - 3)$

b) 3 h after departure

c) -2, because time cannot be negative

d)

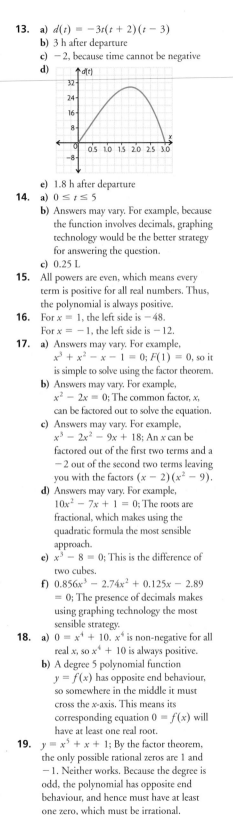

e) 1.8 h after departure

14. a) $0 \leq t \leq 5$

b) Answers may vary. For example, because the function involves decimals, graphing technology would be the better strategy for answering the question.

c) 0.25 L

15. All powers are even, which means every term is positive for all real numbers. Thus, the polynomial is always positive.

16. For $x = 1$, the left side is -48.
For $x = -1$, the left side is -12.

17. a) Answers may vary. For example, $x^3 + x^2 - x - 1 = 0$; $F(1) = 0$, so it is simple to solve using the factor theorem.

b) Answers may vary. For example, $x^2 - 2x = 0$; The common factor, x, can be factored out to solve the equation.

c) Answers may vary. For example, $x^3 - 2x^2 - 9x + 18$; An x can be factored out of the first two terms and a -2 out of the second two terms leaving you with the factors $(x - 2)(x^2 - 9)$.

d) Answers may vary. For example, $10x^2 - 7x + 1 = 0$; The roots are fractional, which makes using the quadratic formula the most sensible approach.

e) $x^3 - 8 = 0$; This is the difference of two cubes.

f) $0.856x^3 - 2.74x^2 + 0.125x - 2.89 = 0$; The presence of decimals makes using graphing technology the most sensible strategy.

18. a) $0 = x^4 + 10$. x^4 is non-negative for all real x, so $x^4 + 10$ is always positive.

b) A degree 5 polynomial function $y = f(x)$ has opposite end behaviour, so somewhere in the middle it must cross the x-axis. This means its corresponding equation $0 = f(x)$ will have at least one real root.

19. $y = x^5 + x + 1$; By the factor theorem, the only possible rational zeros are 1 and -1. Neither works. Because the degree is odd, the polynomial has opposite end behaviour, and hence must have at least one zero, which must be irrational.

Lesson 4.2, pp. 213–215

1. a) $x \le 4; \{x \in \mathbf{R} \mid x \le 4\}$
b) $x < 7; \{x \in \mathbf{R} \mid x < 7\}$
c) $x < -5; \{x \in \mathbf{R} \mid x < 5\}$
d) $x \ge -3; \{x \in \mathbf{R} \mid x \ge -3\}$
e) $x > -10; \{x \in \mathbf{R} \mid x > -10\}$
f) $x \ge 7; \{x \in \mathbf{R} \mid x \ge 7\}$

2. a) $x \in [-3, \infty)$
b) $x \in \left(-\infty, -\dfrac{2}{3}\right)$
c) $x \in [18, \infty)$
d) $x \in [1, \infty)$
e) $x \in (-\infty, 0)$
f) $x \in [-10, \infty)$

3. $-1 \le x < 6$

4. a) yes   **c)** no   **e)** yes
b) no   **d)** no   **f)** no

5. a) $x \le 7$ **c)** $x < -10$ **e)** $x < 6$
b) $x < 0$ **d)** $x \ge 5$ **f)** $x \ge \dfrac{7}{5}$

6. a) yes   **c)** no   **e)** yes
b) yes   **d)** no   **f)** no

7. a) $-6 < x < 2$
b) $4 < x < 8$
c) $-4 \le x \le 10$
d) $-7 \le x \le -4$
e) $7 < x < 9$
f) $-3 \le x \le -\dfrac{1}{2}$

8. a) Answers may vary. For example,
$3x + 1 > 9 + x$
b) Answers may vary. For example,
$3x + 1 \le 4 + x$

9. a) $\{x \in \mathbf{R} \mid -6 \le x \le 4\}$
b) $-13 \le 2x - 1 \le 7$

10. Attempting to solve $x - 3 < 3 - x < x - 5$ yields $3 > x > 4$, which has no solution. Solving $x - 3 > 3 - x > x - 5$ yields $3 < x < 4$.

11. a) $\dfrac{1}{2}x + 1 < 3$
b) $x < 4$
c) $\dfrac{1}{2}x + 1 < 3$
$\dfrac{1}{2}x < 2$
$x < 4$

12. a) $18 \le \dfrac{5}{9}(F - 32) \le 22$
b) $64.4 \le F \le 71.6$

13. 18 min

14. a) $\dfrac{9}{5}C + 32 = F$
b) $C > -40$

15. a)

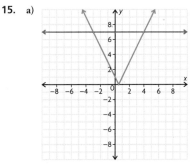

b) $-3 < x < 4$

16. The solution will always have an upper and lower bound due to the manner in which the inequality is solved. The only exception to this is when there is no solution set.

17. a) Isolating x is very hard.
b) A graphical approach as described in the lesson yields a solution of $x > 2.75$ (rounded to two places).

18. a) Maintained
b) Maintained if both positive; switched if both negative; varies if one positive and one negative.
c) Maintained
d) Switched
e) Switched unless one is positive and the other is negative, in which case it is maintained. (If either side is zero, it becomes undefined.)
f) Maintained, except that $<$ and $>$ become $\le$ and $\ge$, respectively.
g) Maintained, but it is undefined for negative numbers.

19. a) $\{x \in \mathbf{R} \mid -2 < x < 2\}; \ (-2, 2)$
b) $\{x \in \mathbf{R} \mid -3 \le x \ge 3\}; \ (-\infty, -3)$ or $(3, \infty)$
c) $\{x \in \mathbf{R} \mid -5 < x < 3\}; \ (-5, 3)$
d) $\{x \in \mathbf{R} \mid x \le 3\}; \ (-\infty, 3)$

Mid-Chapter Review, p. 218

1. a) $0, \dfrac{5}{2}, 4$ **d)** $-4, 6, 5, -5$
b) -2 **e)** $0, -2, -9$
c) $1, -2, 5$ **f)** $3, -3, 2, -2$

2. a) $h(t) = -5t^2 + 3t + 24.55$
b) 24.55 m
c) 2.5 s after jumping
d) $t > 2.5$ s; Jude is below sea level (in the water)

3. either 10 cm by 10 cm or 1.34 cm by 1.34 cm

4. a) $x > -11$
b) $x \ge -4$
c) $x \le -4$
d) $x < -\dfrac{1}{3}$

5. $x \in [-2, 6)$

6. a) Answers may vary. For example,
$2x + 1 > 15$
b) Answers may vary. For example,
$4x - 1 < -33$
c) Answers may vary. For example,
$-3 \le 2x - 1 \le 13$
d) Answers may vary. For example,
$x - 2 \le 3x - 8$

7. a) $f(x) = -x + 1; g(x) = 2x - 5$
b) $x > 2$
c) $f(x) < g(x)$
$-x + 1 < 2x - 5$
$-3x < -6$
$x > 2$

8. a) $N(t) = 20 + 0.02t;$
$M(t) = 15 + 0.03t$
b) $20 + 0.02t > 15 + 0.03t$
c) $0 \le t < 500$
d) Negative time has no meaning.

Lesson 4.3, pp. 225–228

1. a) $-2 \le x \le -1$ or $x \ge 3$
b) $-3 < x < 2$ or $x > 4$
c) $x < -\dfrac{2}{5}$ or $\dfrac{3}{4} < x < 3$
d) $-\dfrac{1}{4} \le x \le \dfrac{5}{2}$ or $x \ge 5$

2. a) $(-\infty, -5], [-2, 0],$ and $[3, \infty)$
b) $x = 1$
c) $[-7, -3]$ and $[0, 4]$
d) $(-\infty, -4]$ and $[2, 7]$

3. $-1 < x < 2$ or $x > 3$

4. $-1.14 < x < 3$ and $x > 6.14$

5. a) $(-1, 2), (4, \infty)$
b) $(-2, 2), (2, \infty)$
c) $(-\infty, -2), (0, 1)$
d) $(-\infty, 2), (2, \infty)$

6. a) $x < -1$ or $x > 1$
b) $-3 < x < 4$
c) $x \le -\dfrac{1}{2}$ or $x \ge 5$
d) $-7 < x < 0$ or $x > 2$
e) $-\dfrac{3}{2} < x < 3$ or $x > 3$
f) $-4 \le x \le \dfrac{3}{2}$

Answers

7. a) $x \le -1$ or $x \ge 7$
b) $0 < x < 2$
c) $x \le -3$ or $-2 \le x \le 1$
d) $x < -2$, $-1 < x < 1$ or $x > 2$
e) $x \le -1$ or $0 \le x \le 3$
f) $-1 < x < -\dfrac{1}{2}$ or $x > 2$

8. $(-1, 1)$ and $(2, \infty)$

9. a) $x^3 + 11x^2 + 18x = 0$
b) Any values of x for which the graph of the corresponding function is above the x-axis ($y = 0$) are solutions to the original inequality.
c) $-9 < x < -2$ or $x > 0$

10. $f(x) = -3(x + 2)(x - 1)(x - 3)^2$

11. a)

b) $0 < v < 154.77\,°C$
c) $133.78\,°C$ to $139.56\,°C$

12. a) 14 m   **c)** $0.3 < t < 2.1$
b) 3.3 s   **d)** 1.8 s

13. $V(x) = x(50 - 2x)(30 - 2x)$;
$5 < x < 7.19$

14. a) Since all the powers are even and the coefficients are positive, the polynomial on the left is always positive.
b) Since all the powers are even and all the coefficients are negative (once all terms are brought to the left), the polynomial on the left is always negative.

15. You cannot divide by a variable expression because you do not know whether it is positive, negative, or zero.
The correct solution is $x < -1$ or $x > 4$.

16. Answers may vary. For example:

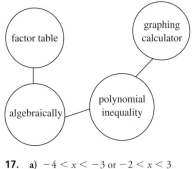

17. a) $-4 < x < -3$ or $-2 < x < 3$
b) $-1 < x < 0$ or $x > 5$

18. $x < -1$ or $x > 2$

Lesson 4.4, pp. 235–237

1. a) positive on $(0, 1)$, $(4, 7)$, $(10, 15.5)$, $(19, 20)$; negative on $(1, 4)$, $(7, 10)$, $(15.5, 19)$; zero at $x = 1, 4, 7, 10, 15.5,$ and 19

b) A positive slope means the cyclist's elevation is increasing, a negative slope means it is decreasing, and a zero slope means the cyclist's elevation is transitioning from increasing to decreasing or vice versa.

2. a) i) 6   **ii)** 12   **iii)** 18
b) about 12
c) The graph is increasing on $(2, 6)$.
d) -6
e) about -6

3. a) about 0
b) It indicates that $x = 2$ is a turning point in the graph.
c)
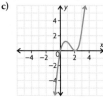

4. a) 3
b) Answers may vary. For example, $x = 4.5, 3$.

5. a) 3   **c)** $-\dfrac{1}{10}$ **e)** $\dfrac{28}{3}$
b) 17   **d)** -7 **f)** 0

6. a) 3   **c)** about $-\dfrac{1}{9}$ **e)** about 5.5
b) about 14   **d)** about -6 **f)** 0

7.
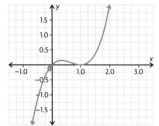
Rate of change is positive on $\left(-\infty, \dfrac{1}{3}\right)$ and $(1, \infty)$, negative on $\left(\dfrac{1}{3}, 1\right)$, and zero at $x = \dfrac{1}{3}$ and 1.

8. a) -55 m/s
b) about -20 m/s

9. a) about 2
b) -2
c) $y = 2x - 4$

10. a) about 10 m/s
b) about -50 m/s
c) 0 m/s

11. a)
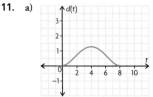

The rate is positive for $t \in (0, 4)$, negative for $t \in (4, 8)$, and zero at $t = 0, 4$ and 8.
b) When the rate of change is zero, the boat stops.
c) When the rate of change is negative, the boat is headed back to the dock.

12. At $(-3, 0)$, instantaneous rate $\doteq -96$; at $(1, 0)$, instantaneous rate $\doteq 0$; at $(3, 0)$, instantaneous rate $\doteq 24$; at $(-1, 0)$, instantaneous rate $\doteq 24$

13. a) about 5   **c)** $2x + 3$
b) $2x + 3 + h$ **d)** $2(1) + 3 = 5$

14. When the instantaneous rate of change is zero, the function potentially has a local maximum or a local minimum. If the rate is positive to the left and negative to the right, it has a local maximum. If the rate is negative to the left and positive to the right, it has a local minimum.

15. a) Rate of change and $f(5)$ are both approximately 148.4.
b) Answers may vary. For example, the instantaneous rate of change at $x = 1$ is 2.7; at $x = 3$, it is 20.1; and at $x = 4$, it is 54.6.
c) The instantaneous rate of change of e^x for any value of x is e^x.

16. a) about -1
b) $y = -x - 2$
c) $(-2, 0)$
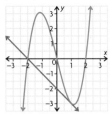

17. $x = -0.53, 2.53$

Chapter Review, pp. 240–241

1. a) ± 3 **c)** $0, -2, 1$
b) $\dfrac{1}{2}, -2$ **d)** $\pm 1, 2$

2. $0, 2, \dfrac{2}{3}, \dfrac{4}{5}$

3. a) $f(x) = (x - 1)(x - 2)(x + 1)(x + 2)$
or $f(x) = x^4 - 5x^2 + 4$
b) 48, 3.10

4. 2 cm by 2 cm or 7.4 cm by 7.4 cm

5. a) The given information states that the model is valid between 1985 and 1995, so it can be used for 1993, but not 2005.
b) Set $C(t) = 1500$ (since the units are in thousands) and solve using a graphing calculator.
c) Sales reach 1.5 million in the 8th year after 1985, so in 1993.

6. **a)** Answers may vary. For example,
$2x + 1 > 17$
b) Answers may vary. For example,
$3x - 4 \geq -16$
c) Answers may vary. For example,
$2x + 3 \leq -21$
d) Answers may vary. For example,
$-19 < 2x - 1 < -3$

7. **a)** $x \in \left(\dfrac{25}{2}, \infty\right)$
b) $x \in \left[-\dfrac{23}{8}, \infty\right)$
c) $x \in (-\infty, 2)$
d) $x \in (-\infty, 3]$

8. **a)** $\{x \in \mathbf{R} \mid -2 < x < 4\}$
b) $\{x \in \mathbf{R} \mid -1 \leq x \leq 0\}$
c) $\{x \in \mathbf{R} \mid -3 \leq x \leq 5\}$
d) $\{x \in \mathbf{R} \mid -6 < x < -2\}$

9. **a)** The second plan is better if one calls more than 350 min per month.
b)
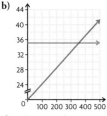

10. **a)** $-1 < x < 2$
b) $x \leq -\dfrac{3}{2}$ or $x \geq 5$
c) $x < -\dfrac{5}{2}$ or $1 < x < 7$
d) $x \leq -4$ or $1 \leq x \leq 5$

11. negative when $x \in (0, 5)$, positive when $x \in (-\infty, -2), (-2, 0), (5, \infty)$

12. $x \leq -3.81$

13. between January 1993 and March 1994 and between October 1995 and October 1996

14. **a)** average $= 7$, instantaneous $\doteq 8$
b) average $= 13$, instantaneous $\doteq 15$
c) average $= 129$, instantaneous $\doteq 145$
d) average $= -464$, instantaneous $\doteq -485$

15. positive when $-1 < x < 1$, negative when $x < -1$ or $x > 1$, and zero at $x = -1, 1$

16. **a)** $t \doteq 2.2$ s
b) -11 m/s
c) about -22 m/s

17. **a)** about 57.002
b) about 56.998
c) Both approximate the instantaneous rate of change at $x = 3$.

18. **a)** male:
$f(x) = 0.001x^3 - 0.162x^2 + 3.394x + 72.365$;
female:
$g(x) = 0.0002x^3 - 0.026x^2 + 1.801x + 14.369$
b) More females than males will have lung cancer in 2006.

c) The rate was changing faster for females, on average. Looking only at 1975 and 2000, the incidence among males increased only 5.5 per 100 000, while the incidence among females increased by 31.7.
d) Between 1995 and 2000, the incidence among males decreased by 6.1 while the incidence among females increased by 5.6. Since 1998 is about halfway between 1995 and 2000, an estimate for the instantaneous rate of change in 1998 is the average rate of change from 1995 to 2000. The two rates of change are about the same in magnitude, but the rate for females is positive, while the rate for males is negative.

Chapter Self-Test, p. 242

1. $1, \dfrac{3}{2}, -2$

2. **a)** positive when $x < -2$ and $0 < x < 2$, negative when $-2 < x < 0$ and $x > 2$, and zero at $-2, 0, 2$
b) positive when $-1 < x < 1$, negative when $x < -1$ or $1 < x$, and zero at $x = -1, 1$
c) -1

3. **a)** Cost with card: $50 + 5n$;
Cost without card: $12n$
b) at least 8 pizzas

4. **a)** $x < \dfrac{1}{2}$
b) $-2 \leq x \leq 1$
c) $-2 < x < -1$ or $x > 5$
d) $x \geq -3$

5. **a)** 15 m
b) 4.6 s
c) -3 m/s

6. **a)** about 5 **b)** $(1, 3)$ **c)** $y = 5x - 2$

7. Since all the exponents are even and all the coefficients are positive, all values of the function are positive and greater than or equal to 4 for all real numbers x.

8. **a)** $\{x \in \mathbf{R} \mid -2 \leq x \leq 7\}$
b) $-2 < x < 7$

9. 2 cm by 2 cm by 15 cm

Chapter 5

Getting Started, pp. 246–247

1. **a)** $(x - 5)(x + 2)$
b) $3(x + 5)(x - 1)$
c) $(4x - 7)(4x + 7)$
d) $(3x - 2)(3x - 2)$
e) $(a - 3)(3a + 10)$
f) $(2x + 3y)(3x - 7y)$

2. **a)** $3 - 2s$
b) $\dfrac{n^3}{3m}$, $m, n \neq 0$

c) $3x^2 - 4x - 1$, $x \neq 0$
d) $\dfrac{1}{5x - 2}$, $x \neq \dfrac{2}{5}$
e) $-\dfrac{x + 6}{3 + x}$, $x \neq -3, 3$
f) $\dfrac{a - b}{a - 3b}$, $a \neq -5b, \dfrac{3b}{2}$

3. **a)** $\dfrac{7}{15}$
b) $\dfrac{6}{x}$, $x \neq 0$
c) $\dfrac{-4x^2 + 20x - 6}{x - 3}$, $x \neq -2, 3$
d) $\dfrac{x^3 + 2x - 8x}{x^2 - 1}$, $x \neq -1, 0, 1, 3$

4. **a)** $1\dfrac{11}{21}$
b) $\dfrac{19x}{12}$
c) $\dfrac{4 + x}{x^2}$, $x \neq 0$
d) $\dfrac{3x - 6}{x^2 - 3x}$, $x \neq 0, 3$
e) $\dfrac{2x + 10 + y}{x^2 - 25}$, $x \neq 5, -5$
f) $\dfrac{-2a + 50}{(a + 3)(a - 5)(a + 3)}$, $x \neq -3, 4, 5$

5. **a)** $x = 6$
b) $x = 2$
c) $x = 3$
d) $x = \dfrac{-12}{7}$

6.
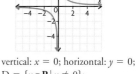
vertical: $x = 0$; horizontal: $y = 0$;
$D = \{x \in \mathbf{R} \mid x \neq 0\}$;
$R = \{y \in \mathbf{R} \mid y \neq 0\}$

7. **a)** translated three units to the left
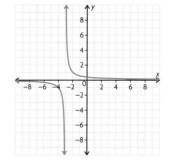

b) vertical stretch by a factor of 2 and a horizontal translation 1 unit to the right

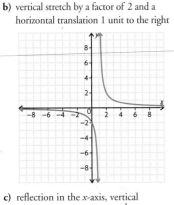

c) reflection in the x-axis, vertical compression by a factor of $\frac{1}{2}$, and a vertical translation 3 units down

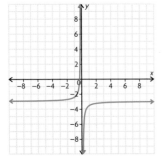

d) reflection in the x-axis, vertical compression by a factor of $\frac{2}{3}$, horizontal translation 2 units right, and a vertical translation 1 unit up

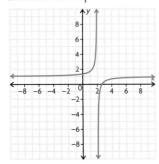

8. Factor the expressions in the numerator and the denominator. Simplify each expression as necessary. Multiply the first expression by the reciprocal of the second.

$$\frac{-3(3y - 2)}{2(3y + 2)}$$

Lesson 5.1, pp. 254–257

1. a) C; The reciprocal function is F.
b) A; The reciprocal function is E.
c) D; The reciprocal function is B.
d) F; The reciprocal function is C.
e) B; The reciprocal function is D.
f) E; The reciprocal function is A.

2. a) $x = 6$
b) $x = -\frac{4}{3}$
c) $x = 5$ and $x = -3$
d) $x = -\frac{5}{2}$ and $x = \frac{5}{2}$
e) no asymptotes
f) $x = -1.5$ and $x = -1$

3. a)

b)

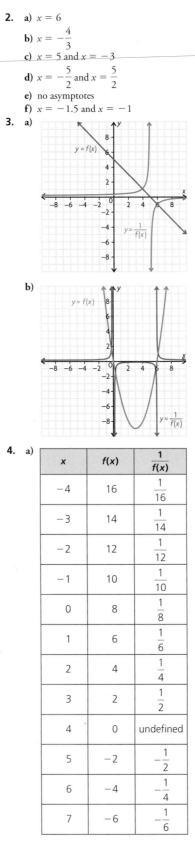

4. a)

x	f(x)	$\dfrac{1}{f(x)}$
−4	16	$\dfrac{1}{16}$
−3	14	$\dfrac{1}{14}$
−2	12	$\dfrac{1}{12}$
−1	10	$\dfrac{1}{10}$
0	8	$\dfrac{1}{8}$
1	6	$\dfrac{1}{6}$
2	4	$\dfrac{1}{4}$
3	2	$\dfrac{1}{2}$
4	0	undefined
5	−2	$-\dfrac{1}{2}$
6	−4	$-\dfrac{1}{4}$
7	−6	$-\dfrac{1}{6}$

b)

c) $f(x) = -2x + 8$, $y = \dfrac{1}{-2x + 8}$

5. a) $y = \dfrac{1}{2x}$; vertical asymptote at $x = 0$

b) $y = \dfrac{1}{x + 5}$; vertical asymptote at $x = -5$

c) $y = \dfrac{1}{x - 4}$; vertical asymptote at $x = 4$

d) $y = \dfrac{1}{2x + 5}$; vertical asymptote at $x = -\dfrac{5}{2}$

e) $y = \dfrac{1}{-3x + 6}$; vertical asymptote at $x = 2$

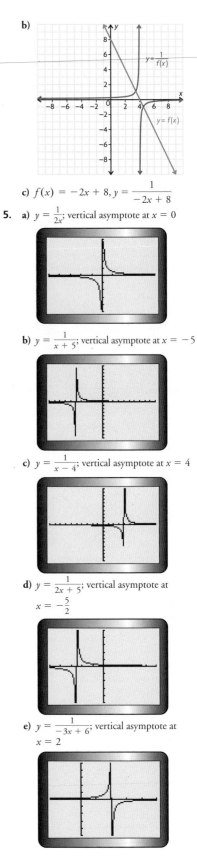

f) $y = \dfrac{1}{(x-3)^2}$; vertical asymptote at $x = 3$

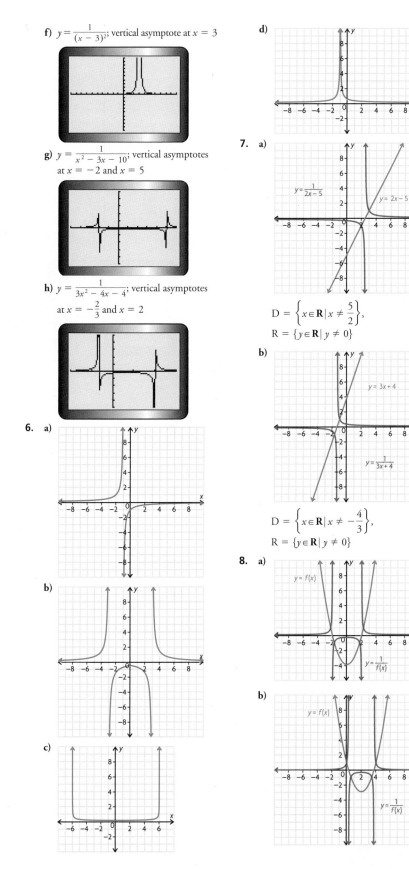

g) $y = \dfrac{1}{x^2 - 3x - 10}$; vertical asymptotes at $x = -2$ and $x = 5$

h) $y = \dfrac{1}{3x^2 - 4x - 4}$; vertical asymptotes at $x = -\dfrac{2}{3}$ and $x = 2$

6. a)

b)

c)

7. a)

$D = \left\{ x \in \mathbf{R} \,\middle|\, x \neq \dfrac{5}{2} \right\}$,
$R = \{ y \in \mathbf{R} \,|\, y \neq 0 \}$

b)

$D = \left\{ x \in \mathbf{R} \,\middle|\, x \neq -\dfrac{4}{3} \right\}$,
$R = \{ y \in \mathbf{R} \,|\, y \neq 0 \}$

8. a)

b)

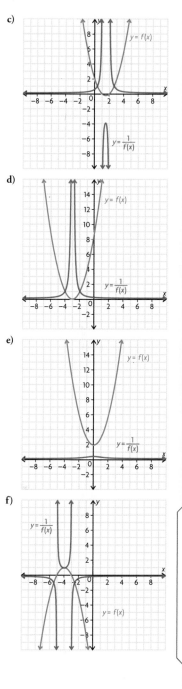

d)

c)

d)

e)

f)

9. a) $D = \{x \in \mathbf{R}\}$
$R = \{y \in \mathbf{R}\}$
y-intercept $= 8$
x-intercept $= -4$
negative on $(-\infty, -4)$
positive on $(-4, \infty)$
increasing on $(-\infty, \infty)$
equation of reciprocal $= \dfrac{1}{2x + 8}$

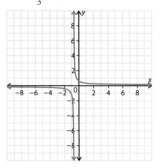

b) $D = \{x \in \mathbf{R}\}$
$R = \{y \in \mathbf{R}\}$
y-intercept $= -3$
x-intercept $= -\dfrac{3}{4}$
positive on $\left(-\infty, -\dfrac{3}{4}\right)$
negative on $\left(-\dfrac{3}{4}, \infty\right)$
decreasing on $(-\infty, \infty)$
equation of reciprocal $= \dfrac{1}{-4x - 3}$

c) $D = \{x \in \mathbf{R}\}$
$R = \{y \in \mathbf{R} \mid y \geq -12.25\}$
y-intercept $= 12$
x-intercepts $= 4, -3$
decreasing on $(-\infty, 0.5)$
increasing on $(0.5, \infty)$
positive on $(-\infty, -3)$ and $(4, \infty)$
negative on $(-3, 4)$
equation of reciprocal $= \dfrac{1}{x^2 - x - 12}$

d) $D = \{x \in \mathbf{R}\}$
$R = \{y \in \mathbf{R} \mid y \leq 2.5\}$
y-intercept $= -12$
x-intercepts $= 3, 2$
increasing on $(-\infty, 2.5)$
decreasing on $(2.5, \infty)$
negative on $(-\infty, 2)$ and $(3, \infty)$
positive on $(2, 3)$
equation of
reciprocal $= \dfrac{1}{-2x^2 + 10x - 12}$

10. Answers may vary. For example, a reciprocal function creates a vertical asymptote when the denominator is equal to 0 for a specific value of x. Consider $\dfrac{1}{ax + b}$. For this expression, there is always some value of x that is $\dfrac{-b}{a}$ that will result in a vertical asymptote for the function. This is a graph of $y = \dfrac{1}{3x + 2}$ and the vertical asymptote is at $x = -\dfrac{2}{3}$.

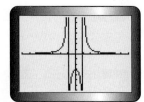

Consider the function $\dfrac{1}{(x - 3)(x - 4)}$. The graph of the quadratic function in the denominator crosses the x-axis at 3 and 4 and therefore will have vertical asymptotes at 3 and 4 in the graph of the reciprocal function.

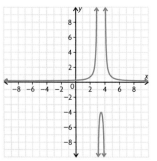

However, a quadratic function, such as $x^2 + c$, which has no real zeros, will not have a vertical asymptote in the graph of its reciprocal function. For example, this is the graph of $y = \dfrac{1}{x^2 + 2}$.

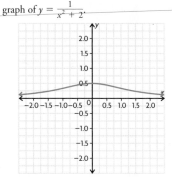

11. $y = \dfrac{3}{x^2 - 1}$

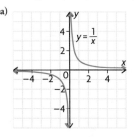

12. a) 500
b) $t = 2$
c) $t = 10\,000$
d) If you were to use a value of t that was less than one, the equation would tell you that the number of bacteria was increasing as opposed to decreasing. Also, after time $t = 10\,000$, the formula indicates that there is a smaller and smaller fraction of 1 bacteria left.
e) $D = \{x \in \mathbf{R} \mid 1 < x < 10\,000\}$,
$R = \{y \in \mathbf{R} \mid 1 < y < 10\,000\}$

13. a)

$D = \{x \in \mathbf{R} \mid x \neq -n\}$,
$R = \{y \in \mathbf{R} \mid y \neq 0\}$
b) The vertical asymptote occurs at $x = -n$. Changes in n in the $f(x)$ family cause changes in the y-intercept— an increase in n causes the intercept to move up the y-axis and a decrease causes it to move down the y-axis. Changes in n in the $g(x)$ family cause changes in the vertical asymptote of the function—an increase in n causes the asymptote to move down the x-axis and a decrease in n causes it to move up the x-axis.
c) $x = 1 - n$ and $x = -1 - n$

14. Answers may vary. For example:
1) Determine the zero(s) of the function $f(x)$—these will be the asymptote(s) for the reciprocal function $g(x)$.
2) Determine where the function $f(x)$ is positive and where it is negative—the reciprocal function $g(x)$ will have the same characteristics.
3) Determine where the function $f(x)$ is increasing and where it is decreasing—the reciprocal function $g(x)$ will have opposite characteristics.

15. a)

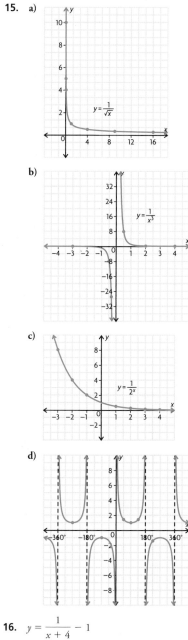

b)

c)

d)

16. $y = \dfrac{1}{x + 4} - 1$

Lesson 5.2, p. 262

1. a) A; The function has a zero at 3 and the reciprocal function has a vertical asymptote at $x = 3$. The function is positive for $x < 3$ and negative for $x > 3$.

b) C; The function in the numerator factors to $(x + 3)(x - 3)$. $(x - 3)$ factors out of both the numerator and the denominator. The equation simplifies to $y = x + 3$, but has a hole at $x = 3$.

c) F; The function in the denominator has a zero at $x = -3$, so there is a vertical asymptote at $x = -3$. The function is always positive.

d) D; The function in the denominator has zeros at $y = 1$ and $y = -3$. The rational function has vertical asymptotes at $x = 1$ and $x = -3$.

e) B; The function has no zeros and no vertical asymptotes or holes.

f) E; The function in the denominator has a zero at $x = 3$ and the rational function has a vertical asymptote at $x = 3$. The degree of the numerator is exactly 1 more than the degree of the denominator, so the graph has an oblique asymptote.

2. a) vertical asymptote at $x = -4$; horizontal asymptote at $y = 1$

b) vertical asymptote at $x = -\dfrac{3}{2}$; horizontal asymptote at $y = 0$

c) vertical asymptote at $x = 6$; horizontal asymptote at $y = 2$

d) hole at $x = -3$

e) vertical asymptotes at $x = -3$ and 5; horizontal asymptote at $y = 0$

f) vertical asymptote at $x = -1$; horizontal asymptote at $y = -1$

g) hole at $x = 2$

h) vertical asymptote at $x = \dfrac{5}{2}$; horizontal asymptote at $y = -2$

i) vertical asymptote at $x = -\dfrac{1}{4}$; horizontal asymptote at $y = 1$

j) vertical asymptote at $x = 4$; hole at $x = -4$; horizontal asymptote at $y = 0$

k) vertical asymptote at $x = \dfrac{3}{5}$; horizontal asymptote at $y = \dfrac{1}{5}$

l) vertical asymptote at $x = 4$; horizontal asymptote at $y = -\dfrac{3}{2}$

3. Answers may vary. For example:

a) $y = \dfrac{x - 1}{x^2 + x - 2}$

b) $y = \dfrac{1}{x^2 - 4}$

c) $y = \dfrac{x^2 - 4}{x^2 + 3x + 2}$

d) $y = \dfrac{2x}{x + 1}$

e) $y = \dfrac{x^3}{x^2 + 5}$

Lesson 5.3, pp. 272–274

1. a) A **c)** D
   b) C **d)** B

2. a) $x = 2$

b) As $x \to 2$ from the right, the values of $f(x)$ get larger. As $x \to 2$ from the left, the values become larger in magnitude but are negative.

c) $y = 0$

d) As $x \to -\infty$ and as $x \to \infty$, $f(x) \to 0$.

e) $D = \{x \in \mathbf{R} \mid x \neq 3\}$
   $R = \{y \in \mathbf{R} \mid y \neq 0\}$

f) positive: $(2, \infty)$
   negative: $(-\infty, 2)$

g)

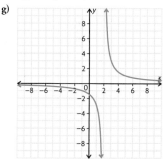

3. a) $x = -1$

b) As $x \to -1$ from the left, $y \to \infty$. As $x \to -1$ from the right, $y \to -\infty$.

c) $y = 4$

d) As $x \to \pm\infty$, $f(x)$ gets closer and closer to 4.

e) $D = \{x \in \mathbf{R} \mid x \neq -1\}$
   $R = \{y \in \mathbf{R} \mid y \neq 4\}$

f) positive: $(-\infty, -1)$ and $\left(\dfrac{3}{4}, -\infty\right)$
   negative: $\left(-1, \dfrac{3}{4}\right)$

g)

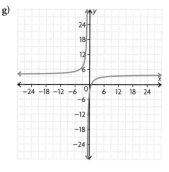

4. a) $x = -3$; As $x = -3$, $y = -\infty$ on the left.
As $x = -3$, $y = \infty$ on the right.

b) $x = 5$; As $x = 5$, $y = -\infty$ on the left.
As $x = 5$, $y = \infty$ on the right.

c) $x = \dfrac{1}{2}$; As $x = \dfrac{1}{2}$, $y = -\infty$ on the left.
As $x = \dfrac{1}{2}$, $y = \infty$ on the right.

d) $x = -\dfrac{1}{4}$; As $x = -\dfrac{1}{4}$, $y = -\infty$ on the left.
As $x = -\dfrac{1}{4}$, $y = \infty$ on the right.

5. a) vertical asymptote at $x = -5$
horizontal asymptote at $y = 0$
$D = \{x \in \mathbf{R} \mid x \neq -5\}$
$R = \{y \in \mathbf{R} \mid y \neq 0\}$
y-intercept $= \dfrac{3}{5}$
$f(x)$ is negative on $(-\infty, -5)$ and positive on $(-5, \infty)$.

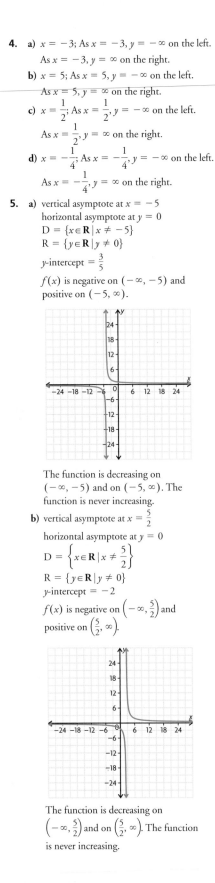

The function is decreasing on $(-\infty, -5)$ and on $(-5, \infty)$. The function is never increasing.

b) vertical asymptote at $x = \dfrac{5}{2}$
horizontal asymptote at $y = 0$
$D = \left\{x \in \mathbf{R} \mid x \neq \dfrac{5}{2}\right\}$
$R = \{y \in \mathbf{R} \mid y \neq 0\}$
y-intercept $= -2$
$f(x)$ is negative on $\left(-\infty, \dfrac{5}{2}\right)$ and positive on $\left(\dfrac{5}{2}, \infty\right)$.

The function is decreasing on $\left(-\infty, \dfrac{5}{2}\right)$ and on $\left(\dfrac{5}{2}, \infty\right)$. The function is never increasing.

c) vertical asymptote at $x = \dfrac{1}{4}$
horizontal asymptote at $y = \dfrac{1}{4}$
$D = \left\{x \in \mathbf{R} \mid x \neq \dfrac{1}{4}\right\}$
$R = \left\{y \in \mathbf{R} \mid y \neq \dfrac{1}{4}\right\}$
x-intercept $= -5$
y-intercept $= -1$
$f(x)$ is positive on $(-\infty, -5)$ and $\left(\dfrac{1}{4}, \infty\right)$ and negative on $\left(-5, \dfrac{1}{4}\right)$.

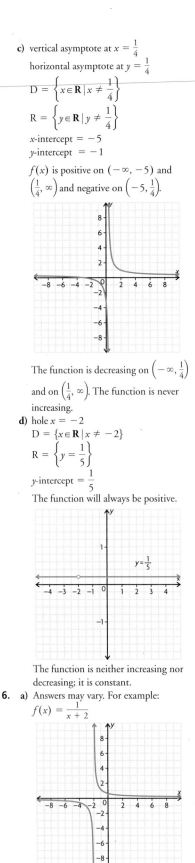

The function is decreasing on $\left(-\infty, \dfrac{1}{4}\right)$ and on $\left(\dfrac{1}{4}, \infty\right)$. The function is never increasing.

d) hole $x = -2$
$D = \{x \in \mathbf{R} \mid x \neq -2\}$
$R = \left\{y = \dfrac{1}{5}\right\}$
y-intercept $= \dfrac{1}{5}$
The function will always be positive.

The function is neither increasing nor decreasing; it is constant.

6. a) Answers may vary. For example:
$$f(x) = \dfrac{1}{x + 2}$$

b) Answers may vary. For example:
$$y = \dfrac{x}{x + 2}$$

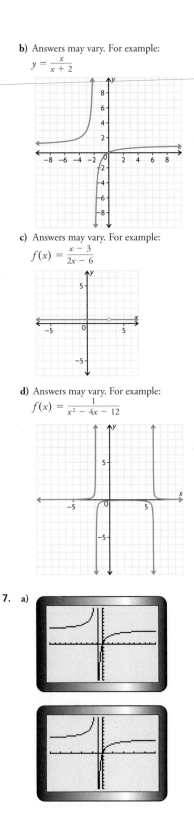

c) Answers may vary. For example:
$$f(x) = \dfrac{x - 3}{2x - 6}$$

d) Answers may vary. For example:
$$f(x) = \dfrac{1}{x^2 - 4x - 12}$$

7. a)

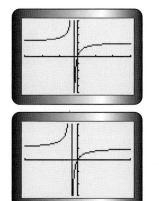

The equation has a general vertical asymptote at $x = -\frac{1}{n}$. The function has a general horizontal asymptote at $y = \frac{8}{n}$. The vertical asymptotes are $-\frac{1}{8}$, $-\frac{1}{4}$, $-\frac{1}{2}$, and -1. The horizontal asymptotes are $8, 4, 2,$ and 1. The function contracts as n increases. The function is always increasing. The function is positive on $\left(-\infty, -\frac{17}{n}\right)$ and $\left(\frac{3}{10}, \infty\right)$. The function is negative on $\left(-\frac{17}{n}, \frac{3}{10}\right)$.

b) The horizontal and vertical asymptotes both approach 0 as the value of n increases; the x- and y-intercepts do not change, nor do the positive and negative characteristics or the increasing and decreasing characteristics.

c) The vertical asymptote becomes $x = \frac{17}{n}$ and the horizontal becomes $x = -\frac{10}{n}$. The function is always increasing. The function is positive on $\left(-\infty, \frac{3}{10}\right)$ and $\left(\frac{17}{n}, \infty\right)$. The function is negative on $\left(\frac{3}{10}, \frac{17}{n}\right)$. The rest of the characteristics do not change.

8. $f(x)$ will have a vertical asymptote at $x = 1$; $g(x)$ will have a vertical asymptote at $x = -\frac{3}{2}$. $f(x)$ will have a horizontal asymptote at $x = 3$; $g(x)$ will have a vertical asymptote at $x = \frac{1}{2}$.

9. a) \$27 500
b) \$40 000
c) \$65 000
d) No, the value of the investment at $t = 0$ should be the original value invested.
e) The function is probably not accurate at very small values of t because as $t \to 0$ from the right, $x \to \infty$.
f) \$15 000

10. The concentration increases over the 24 h period and approaches approximately 1.89 mg/L.

11. Answers may vary. For example, the rational functions will all have vertical asymptotes at $x = -\frac{d}{c}$. They will all have horizontal asymptotes at $y = \frac{a}{c}$. They will intersect the y-axis at $y = \frac{b}{d}$. The rational functions will have an x-intercept at $x = -\frac{b}{a}$.

12. Answers may vary. For example, $f(x) = \frac{2x^2}{2 + x}$.

13. $f(x) = 2x^2 - 5x + 3 - \frac{2}{x - 1}$
As $x \to \pm\infty$, $f(x) \to \infty$.

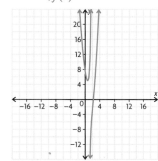

vertical asymptote: $x = 1$; oblique asymptote: $y = 2x^2 - 5x + 3$

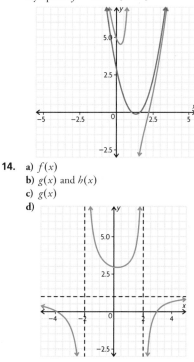

14. a) $f(x)$
b) $g(x)$ and $h(x)$
c) $g(x)$
d)

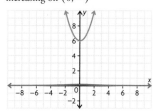

Mid-Chapter Review, p. 277

1. a) $\frac{1}{x - 3}$; $x = 3$

b) $\frac{1}{-4q + 6}$; $q = \frac{3}{2}$

c) $\frac{1}{z^2 + 4z - 5}$; $z = -5$ and 1

d) $\frac{1}{6d^2 + 7d - 3}$; $d = \frac{1}{3}$ and $-\frac{3}{2}$

2. a) $D = \{x \in \mathbf{R}\}$; $R = \{x \in \mathbf{R}\}$; y-intercept $= 6$; x-intercept $= -\frac{3}{2}$; negative on $\left(-\infty, -\frac{3}{2}\right)$; positive on $\left(-\frac{3}{2}, \infty\right)$; increasing on $(-\infty, \infty)$

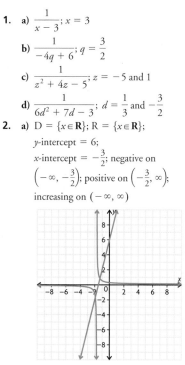

b) $D = \{x \in \mathbf{R}\}$; $R = \{y \in \mathbf{R} \,|\, y > -4\}$; y-intercept $= -4$; x-intercepts are 2 and -2; decreasing on $(-\infty, 0)$; increasing $(0, \infty)$; positive on $(-\infty, -2)$ and $(2, \infty)$; negative on $(-2, 2)$

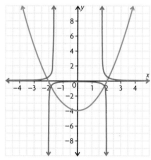

c) $D = \{x \in \mathbf{R}\}$; $R = \{y \in \mathbf{R} \,|\, y > 6\}$; no x-intercepts; function will never be negative; decreasing on $(-\infty, 0)$; increasing on $(0, \infty)$

d) $D = \{x \in \mathbf{R}\}$; $R = \{y \in \mathbf{R}\}$; x-intercept $= -2$; function is always decreasing; positive on $(-\infty, -2)$; negative on $(-2, \infty)$

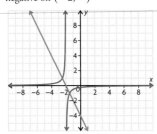

3. Answers may vary. For example: (1) Hole: Both the numerator and the denominator contain a common factor, resulting in $\frac{0}{0}$ for a specific value of x. (2) Vertical asymptote: A value of x causes the denominator of a rational function to be 0. (3) Horizontal asymptote: A horizontal asymptote is created by the ratio between the numerator and the denominator of a rational function as the function $\to \infty$ and $-\infty$. A continuous rational function is created when the denominator of the rational function has no zeros.

4. **a)** $x = 2$; vertical asymptote
   b) hole at $x = 1$
   c) $x = -\frac{1}{2}$; horizontal asymptote
   d) $x = 6$; oblique asymptote
   e) $x = -5$ and $x = 3$; vertical asymptotes

5. $y = \dfrac{x}{x-2}, y = 1; y = \dfrac{-7x}{4x+2}, y = \dfrac{-7}{4};$ $y = \dfrac{1}{x^2+2x-15}, x = 0$

6. **a)** vertical asymptote: $x = 6$; horizontal asymptote: $y = 0$; no x-intercept; y-intercept: $-\frac{5}{6}$; negative when the denominator is negative; positive when the numerator is positive; $x - 6$ is negative on $x < 6$; $f(x)$ is negative on $(-\infty, 6)$ and positive on $(6, \infty)$; function is always decreasing

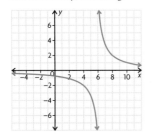

   b) vertical asymptote: $x = -4$; horizontal asymptote: $y = 3$; x-intercept: $x = 0$;

y-intercept: $f(0) = 0$; function is always increasing; positive on $(-\infty, -4)$ and $(0, \infty)$; negative on $(-4, 0)$

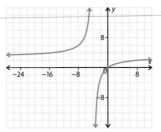

   c) straight, horizontal line with a hole at $x = -2$; always positive and never increases or decreases

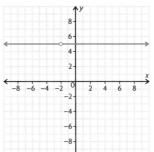

   d) vertical asymptote: $x = \frac{1}{2}$; horizontal asymptote: $y = \frac{1}{2}$; x-intercept: $x = 2$; y-intercept: $f(0) = 5$; function is always increasing

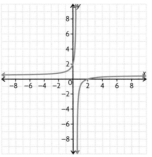

7. Answers may vary. For example: Changing the function to $y = \dfrac{7x+6}{x+1}$ changes the graph. The function now has a vertical asymptote at $x = -1$ and still has a horizontal asymptote at $y = 7$. However, the function is now constantly increasing instead of decreasing. The new function still has an x-intercept at $x = -\frac{6}{7}$, but now has a y-intercept at $y = 6$.

8. $n = \frac{1}{3}$; $m = 35$

9. Answers may vary. For example, $f(x) = \dfrac{4x+8}{x+2}$.
The graph of the function will be a horizontal line at $y = 4$ with a hole at $x = -2$.

Lesson 5.4, pp. 285–287

1. $3; -2$; Answers may vary. For example, substituting each value for x in the equation produces the same value on each side of the equation, so both are solutions.

2. **a)** $x = -3$ **c)** $x = -1$ and 2
   b) $x = 5$ **d)** $x = -4$

3. **a)** $f(x) = \dfrac{x-3}{x+3} - 2$

   b) $f(x) = \dfrac{3x-1}{x} - \dfrac{5}{2}$

   c) $f(x) = \dfrac{x-1}{x} - \dfrac{x+1}{x+3}$

   d) $f(x) = \dfrac{x-2}{x+3} - \dfrac{x-4}{x+5}$

4. **a)** $x = -9$ **c)** $x = 3$
   b) $x = 2$ **d)** $x = -\dfrac{1}{2}$

5. **a)** $x = 3$ **d)** $x = 0$
   b) $x = \dfrac{3}{4}$ **e)** $x = \dfrac{1}{4}$
   c) $x = -9$ **f)** $x = -23$

6. **a)** The function will have no real solutions.
   b) $x = 3$ and $x = -0.5$
   c) $x = -5$
   d) $x = 0$ and $x = -1$
   e) The original equation has no real solutions.
   f) $x = 5$ and $x = 2$

7. **a)** $x = 6$ **d)** $x = 3.25, 20.75$
   b) $x = 1.30, 7.70$ **e)** $x = -1.71, 2.71$
   c) $x = 10$ **f)** $x = -0.62, 1.62$

8. **a)** $\dfrac{x+1}{x-2} = \dfrac{x+3}{x-4}$
   Multiply both sides of the equation by the LCD, $(x-2)(x-4)$.
   $(x-2)(x-4)\left(\dfrac{x+1}{x-2}\right)$
   $= (x-2)(x-4)\left(\dfrac{x+3}{x-4}\right)$
   $(x-4)(x+1) = (x-2)(x+3)$
   Simplify. $x^2 - 3x - 4 = x^2 + x - 6$
   Simplify the equation so that 0 is on one side of the equation.
   $x^2 - x^2 - 3x - x - 4 + 6$
   $= x^2 - x^2 + x - x - 6 + 6$
   $-4x + 2 = 0$
   $-2(2x-1) = 0$
   Since the product is equal to 0, one of the factors must be equal to 0. It must be $2x - 1$ because 2 is a constant.
   $2x - 1 = 0$
   $2x - 1 + 1 = 0 + 1$
   $2x = 1$
   $\dfrac{2x}{2} = \dfrac{1}{2}$
   $x = \dfrac{1}{2}$

b) $\dfrac{\frac{1}{2}+1}{\frac{1}{2}-2}=-1$ and $\dfrac{\frac{1}{2}+3}{\frac{1}{2}-4}=-1$

c)
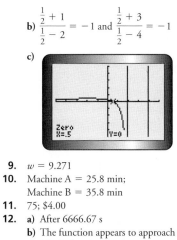

9. $w = 9.271$
10. Machine A $= 25.8$ min;
Machine B $= 35.8$ min
11. 75; \$4.00
12. **a)** After 6666.67 s
b) The function appears to approach
9 kg/m^3 as time increases.
13. **a)** Tom $= 4$ min; Carl $= 5$ min;
Paco $= 2$ min
b) 6.4 min
14. Answers may vary. For example, you can
use either algebra or graphing technology
to solve a rational equation. With algebra,
solving the equation takes more time, but
you get an exact answer. With graphing
technology, you can solve the equation
quickly, but you do not always get an exact
answer.
15. $x = -3.80, -1.42, 0.90, 4.33$
16. **a)** $x = 0.438$ and 1.712
b) $(0, 0.438)$ and $(1.712, \infty)$

Lesson 5.5, pp. 295–297

1. **a)** $(\infty, 1)$ and $(3, \infty)$
b) $(-0.5, 1)$ and $(2, \infty)$
2. **a)** Solve the inequality for x.

$$\frac{6x}{x+3} \le 4$$

$$\frac{6x}{x+3} - 4 \le 0$$

$$\frac{6x}{x+3} - 4\frac{x+3}{x+3} \le 0$$

$$\frac{6x - 4x - 12}{x+3} \le 0$$

$$\frac{2x - 12}{x+3} \le 0$$

$$\frac{2(x-6)}{x+3} \le 0$$

b) (number line from -4 to 6)
c) $(-3, 6]$

3. **a)**
$$x + 2 > \frac{15}{x}$$

$$x + 2 - \frac{15}{x} > 0$$

$$\frac{x^2}{x} + \frac{2x}{x} - \frac{15}{x} > 0$$

$$\frac{x^2 + 2x - 15}{x} > 0$$

$$\frac{(x+5)(x-3)}{x} > 0$$

b) negative: $x < -5$ and $0 < x < 3$;
positive: $-5 < x < 0, x > 3$
c) $\{x \in \mathbf{R} \mid -5 < x < 0 \text{ or } x > 3\}$ or
$(-5, 0)$ or $(3, \infty)$
4. **a)** $5 < x < -4.5$
b) $-7 < x < -5$ and $x > -3$
c) $0 < x < 2$ and $x > 8$
d) $-6.8 \le x < -4$ and $x > 3$
e) $x < -1$ and $-\dfrac{1}{7} < x < 0$
f) $-1 < x < \dfrac{7}{8}$ and $x < 4$
5. **a)** $t < -3$ or $1 < t < 4$
b) $-3 \le t \le 2$ or $t > 4$
c) $-\dfrac{1}{2} < t < \dfrac{1}{3}$ or $t > \dfrac{1}{2}$
d) $t < -2$ and $-2 < t < 3$
e) $t < -5$ and $-2 < t < 0$
f) $-1 \le t < 0.25$ and $2 \le t < 9$
6. **a)** $x \in (-\infty, -6)$ or $x \in (-1, 4)$
b) $x \in (3, \infty)$
c) $x \in (-4, -2)$ or $x \in (-1, 2)$
d) $x \in (-\infty, -9)$ or $x \in [-3, -1)$ or
$x \in [3, \infty)$
e) $x \in (-2, 0)$ or $x \in (4, \infty)$
f) $x \in (-\infty, -4)$ or $x \in (4, \infty)$
7. **a)** $x < -1, -0.2614 < x < 0.5,$
$x > 3.065$
b) (number line from -2 to 4)
c) Interval notation: $(-\infty, -1)$,
$(-0.2614, 0.5)$, $(3.065, \infty)$
Set notation: $\{x \in \mathbf{R} \mid x < -1,$
$-0.2614 < x < 0.5, \text{ or } x > 3.065\}$
8. **a)** $t < 2$ and $t > 5$.
b)
(graph)
c) It would be difficult to find a situation
that could be represented by these
rational expressions because very few
positive values of x yield a positive
value of y.
9. The only values that make the expression
greater than 0 are negative. Because the
values of t have to be positive, the bacteria
count in the tap water will never be greater
than that of the pond water.

---

10. **a)** $\dfrac{(x^2 - 4x - 5)}{2x} < 0$
b)

	$x < -1$	$-1 < x$ < 0	$0 < x$ < 5	$x > 5$
$(x - 5)$	$-$	$-$	$-$	$+$
$(x + 1)$	$-$	$+$	$+$	$+$
$2x$	$-$	$-$	$+$	$+$
$\dfrac{(x-5)(x+1)}{2x}$	$-$	$+$	$-$	$+$

The inequality is true for $x < -1$ and
$0 < x < 5$
11. when $x > 5$
12. **a)** The first inequality can be manipulated
algebraically to produce the second
inequality.
b) Graph the equation $y = \dfrac{x+1}{x-1} - \dfrac{x+3}{x+2}$
and determine when it is negative.
c) The values that make the factors of the
second inequality zero are $-5, -2,$
and 1. Determine the sign of each
factor in the intervals corresponding to
the zeros. Determine when the entire
expression is negative by examining the
signs of the factors.
13. $[2, 4)$ and $(4, \infty)$
14. $14.48 < x < 165.52$ and $180 < x < 360$
15. $0 < x < 2$

Lesson 5.6, pp. 303–305

1. **a)** -0.5
b) $y = -3x + 10$
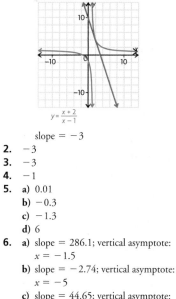
$$y = \frac{x+2}{x-1}$$
slope $= -3$
2. -3
3. -3
4. -1
5. **a)** 0.01
b) -0.3
c) -1.3
d) 6
6. **a)** slope $= 286.1$; vertical asymptote:
$x = -1.5$
b) slope $= -2.74$; vertical asymptote:
$x = -5$
c) slope $= 44.65$; vertical asymptote:
$x = -\dfrac{5}{3}$
d) slope $= -1.26$; vertical asymptote:
$x = 6$

7. a) 0.01
   b) 0.34

8. a) $R(x) = \dfrac{15x}{2x^2 + 11x + 5}$
   b) 0.3, −0.03

9. a) \$5.67
   b) −2

10. a) 68.46
   b) 94.54
   c)

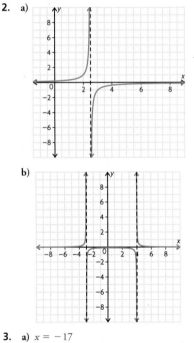

The number of houses that were built increases slowly at first, but rises rapidly between the third and sixth months. During the last six months, the rate at which the houses were built decreases.

11. Answers may vary. For example:
   $14 \leq x \leq 15; x = 14.5$

12. a) Find $s(0)$ and $s(6)$, and then solve $\dfrac{s(6) - s(0)}{6 - 0}$.
   b) The average rate of change over this interval gives the object's speed.
   c) To find the instantaneous rate of change at a specific point, you could find the slope of the line that is tangent to the function $s(t)$ at the specific point. You could also find the average rate of change on either side of the point for smaller and smaller intervals until it stabilizes to a constant. It is generally easier to find the instantaneous rate using a graph, but the second method is more accurate.
   d) The instantaneous rate of change for a specific time, t, is the acceleration of the object at this time.

13. $y = -0.5x - 2.598$;
   $y = -0.5x + 2.598; y = 4x$

14. The instantaneous rate of change at $(0, 0) = 4$. The rate of change at this rate of change will be 0.

Chapter Review, pp. 308–309

1. a) $D = \{x \in \mathbf{R}\}; R = \{y \in \mathbf{R}\}$;
   x-intercept $= -\dfrac{2}{3}; y$-intercept $= 2$;
   always increasing;
   negative on $\left(-\infty, -\dfrac{2}{3}\right)$;
   positive on $\left(-\dfrac{2}{3}, \infty\right)$

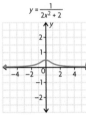

b) $D = \{x \in \mathbf{R}\}$;
   $R = \{y \in \mathbf{R} \mid y > -10.125\}$;
   x-intercept $= 0.5$ and -4;
   positive on $(-\infty, -4)$ and $(0.5, \infty)$;
   negative on $(-4, 0.5)$;
   decreasing on $(-\infty, -10.125)$;
   increasing on $(-10.125, \infty)$

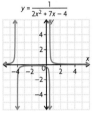
$y = \dfrac{1}{2x^2 + 7x - 4}$

c) $D = \{x \in \mathbf{R}\}; R = \{y \in \mathbf{R} \mid y > 2\}$; no
   x-intercepts; y-intercept $= 2$;
   decreasing on $(-\infty, 0)$;
   increasing on $(0, \infty)$; always positive,
   never negative

$y = \dfrac{1}{2x^2 + 2}$

2. a)

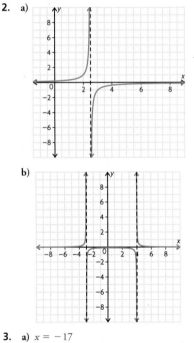

b)

3. a) $x = -17$
   b) $x = -\dfrac{3}{5}$; horizontal asymptote; $y = \dfrac{2}{5}$
   c) $x = 0.5$; hole at $x = -11$
   d) $x = 1$; oblique asymptote; $y = 3x + 3$

4. The locust population increased during the first 1.75 years, to reach a maximum of 1 248 000. The population gradually decreased until the end of the 50 years, when the population was 128 000.

5. a) x-intercept $= 2$:
   horizontal asymptote: $y = 0$;
   y-intercept $= \dfrac{2}{5}$:
   vertical asymptote: $x = -5$;

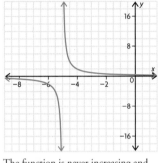

The function is never increasing and is decreasing on $(-\infty, -5)$ and $(-5, \infty)$.
$D = \{x \in \mathbf{R} \mid x \neq -5\}$;
negative for $x < -5$;
positive for $x > -5$

b) $D = \{x \in \mathbf{R} \mid x \neq 2\}$; no x-intercept;
   y-intercept $= 4$; positive for $x \neq 2$;

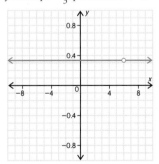

never increasing or decreasing

c) $D = \{x \in \mathbf{R} \mid x \neq 6\}$; no x-intercept;
   y-intercept $= \dfrac{1}{3}$; positive for $x \neq 6$;

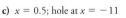

never increasing or decreasing

d) $x = -0.5$; vertical asymptote:
$x = -0.5$; D $= \{x \in \mathbf{R} \mid x \neq -0.5\}$;
x-intercept $= 0$; y-intercept $= 0$;
horizontal asymptote $= 2$;
R $= \{y \in \mathbf{R} \mid x \neq 2\}$; positive on
$x < -0.5$ and $x > 0$; negative on
$-0.5 < x < 0$

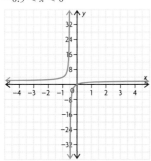

The function is never decreasing and is
increasing on $(-\infty, -0.5)$ and
$(-0.5, \infty)$.

6. Answers may vary. For example, consider
the function $f(x) = \dfrac{1}{x - 6}$. You know that
the vertical asymptote would be $x = 6$. If
you were to find the value of the function
very close to $x = 6$ (say $f(5.99)$ or
$f(6.01)$) you would be able to determine
the behaviour of the function on either
side of the asymptote.

$$f(5.99) = \frac{1}{(5.99) - 6} = -100$$

$$f(6.01) = \frac{1}{(6.01) - 6} = 100$$

To the left of the vertical asymptote, the
function moves toward $-\infty$. To the right
of the vertical asymptote, the function
moves toward ∞.

7. a) $x = 6$

b) $x = 0.2$ and $x = -\dfrac{2}{3}$

c) $x = -6$ or $x = 2$
d) $x = -1$ and $x = 3$
8. about 12 min
9. $x = 1.82$ days and 3.297 days
10. a) $x < -3$ and $-2.873 < x < 4.873$
b) $-16 < x < -11$ and $-5 < x$
c) $-2 < x < -1.33$ and $-1 < x < 0$
d) $0 < x < 1.5$
11. $-0.7261 < t < 0$ and $t > 64.73$
12. a) -6; $x = 3$
b) 0.2; $x = -2$ and $x = -1$
13. a) 0.455 mg/L/h
b) -0.04 mg/L/h
c) The concentration of the drug in the
blood stream appears to be increasing
most rapidly during the first hour and a
half; the graph is steep and increasing
during this time.
14. $x = 5$ and $x = 8$; $x = 6.5$

---

15. a) As the x-coordinate approaches the
vertical asymptote of a rational function, the line tangent to graph will get
closer and closer to being a vertical
line. This means that the slope of the
line tangent to the graph will get
larger and larger, approaching positive
or negative infinity depending on the
function, as x gets closer to the vertical
asymptote.
b) As the x-coordinate grows larger and
larger in either direction, the line
tangent to the graph will get closer and
closer to being a horizontal line. This
means that the slope of the line tangent
to the graph will always approach zero
as x gets larger and larger.

Chapter Self-Test, p. 310

1. a) B
b) A
2. a) If $f(n)$ is very large, then that would
make $\dfrac{1}{f(n)}$ a very small fraction.
b) If $f(n)$ is very small (less than 1), then
that would make $\dfrac{1}{f(n)}$ very large.
c) If $f(n) = 0$, then that would make
$\dfrac{1}{f(n)}$ undefined at that point because
you cannot divide by 0.
d) If $f(n)$ is positive, then that would
make $\dfrac{1}{f(n)}$ also positive because you are
dividing two positive numbers.
3.

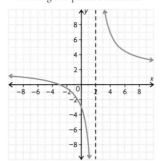

4. 4326 kg; \$0.52/kg
5. a) Algebraic; $x = -1$ and $x = -3$
b) Algebraic with factor table
The inequality is true on $(-10, -5.5)$
and on $(-5, 1.2)$.
6. a) To find the vertical asymptotes of
the function, find the zeros of the
expression in the denominator. To
find the equation of the horizontal
asymptotes, divide the first two terms
of the expressions in the numerator and
denominator.
b) This type of function will have a hole
when both the numerator and the
denominator share the same factor
$(x + a)$.

Chapter 6

Getting Started, p. 314

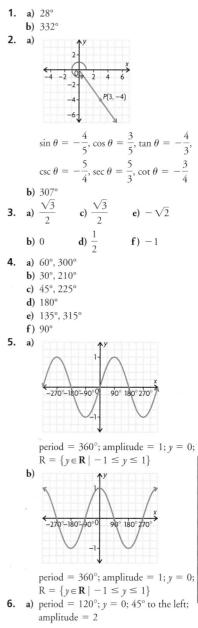

1. a) $28°$
b) $332°$
2. a)

$\sin \theta = -\dfrac{4}{5}$, $\cos \theta = \dfrac{3}{5}$, $\tan \theta = -\dfrac{4}{3}$,

$\csc \theta = -\dfrac{5}{4}$, $\sec \theta = \dfrac{5}{3}$, $\cot \theta = -\dfrac{3}{4}$

b) $307°$
3. a) $\dfrac{\sqrt{3}}{2}$ **c)** $\dfrac{\sqrt{3}}{2}$ **e)** $-\sqrt{2}$

b) 0 **d)** $\dfrac{1}{2}$ **f)** -1

4. a) $60°, 300°$
b) $30°, 210°$
c) $45°, 225°$
d) $180°$
e) $135°, 315°$
f) $90°$
5. a)

period $= 360°$; amplitude $= 1$; $y = 0$;
R $= \{y \in \mathbf{R} \mid -1 \leq y \leq 1\}$
b)

period $= 360°$; amplitude $= 1$; $y = 0$;
R $= \{y \in \mathbf{R} \mid -1 \leq y \leq 1\}$
6. a) period $= 120°$; $y = 0$; $45°$ to the left;
amplitude $= 2$

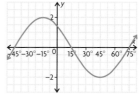

b) period $= 720°$; $y = -1$; 60° to the right; amplitude $= 1$

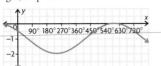

7. a is the amplitude, which determines how far above and below the axis of the curve of the function rises and falls; k defines the period of the function, which is how often the function repeats itself; d is the horizontal shift, which shifts the function to the right or the left; and c is the vertical shift of the function.

Lesson 6.1, pp. 320–322

1. a) π radians; 180°

   b) $\dfrac{\pi}{2}$ radians; 90°

   c) $-\pi$ radians; $-180°$

   d) $-\dfrac{3\pi}{2}$ radians; $-270°$

   e) -2π radians; $-360°$

   f) $\dfrac{3\pi}{2}$ radians; 270°

   g) $-\dfrac{4\pi}{3}$ radians $= -240°$

   h) $\dfrac{2\pi}{3}$ radians; 120°

2. a)

b)

c)

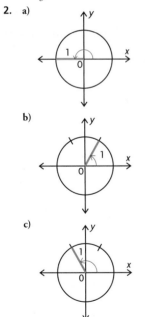

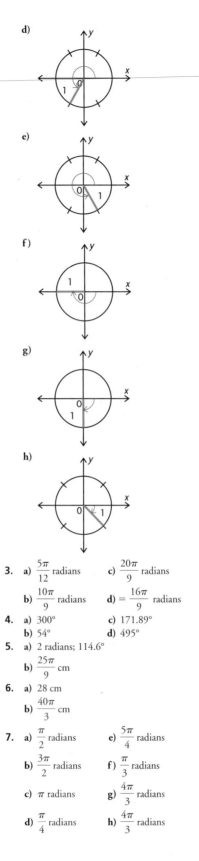

3. a) $\dfrac{5\pi}{12}$ radians   **c)** $\dfrac{20\pi}{9}$ radians

   b) $\dfrac{10\pi}{9}$ radians   **d)** $= \dfrac{16\pi}{9}$ radians

4. a) 300°   **c)** 171.89°

   b) 54°   **d)** 495°

5. a) 2 radians; 114.6°

   b) $\dfrac{25\pi}{9}$ cm

6. a) 28 cm

   b) $\dfrac{40\pi}{3}$ cm

7. a) $\dfrac{\pi}{2}$ radians   **e)** $\dfrac{5\pi}{4}$ radians

   b) $\dfrac{3\pi}{2}$ radians   **f)** $\dfrac{\pi}{3}$ radians

   c) π radians   **g)** $\dfrac{4\pi}{3}$ radians

   d) $\dfrac{\pi}{4}$ radians   **h)** $\dfrac{4\pi}{3}$ radians

8. a) 120°   **e)** 210°

   b) 60°   **f)** 90°

   c) 45°   **g)** 330°

   d) 225°   **h)** 270°

9. a) $\dfrac{247\pi}{4}$ m

   b) 162.5 m

   c) $\dfrac{325\pi}{6}$ cm

10. $4.50\sqrt{2}$ cm

11. a) $\doteq 0.418\ 88$ radians/s

   b) $\doteq 377.0$ m

12. a) 36

   b) 0.8 m

13. a) equal to

   b) greater than

   c) stay the same

14.

$0° = 0$ radians; $30° = \dfrac{\pi}{6}$ radians;

$45° = \dfrac{\pi}{4}$ radians; $60° = \dfrac{\pi}{3}$ radians;

$90° = \dfrac{\pi}{2}$ radians; $120° = \dfrac{2\pi}{3}$ radians;

$135° = \dfrac{3\pi}{4}$ radians; $150° = \dfrac{5\pi}{6}$ radians;

$180° = \pi$ radians; $210° = \dfrac{7\pi}{6}$ radians;

$225° = \dfrac{5\pi}{4}$ radians; $240° = \dfrac{4\pi}{3}$ radians;

$270° = \dfrac{3\pi}{2}$ radians; $300° = \dfrac{5\pi}{3}$ radians;

$315° = \dfrac{7\pi}{4}$ radians; $330° = \dfrac{11\pi}{6}$ radians;

$360° = 2\pi$ radians

15. Circle B, Circle A, and Circle C

16. about 144.5 radians/s

Lesson 6.2, pp. 330–332

1. a) second quadrant; $\dfrac{\pi}{4}$; positive

   b) fourth quadrant; $\dfrac{\pi}{3}$; positive

   c) third quadrant; $\dfrac{\pi}{3}$; positive

   d) second quadrant; $\dfrac{\pi}{6}$; negative

   e) second quadrant; $\dfrac{\pi}{3}$; negative

   f) fourth quadrant; $\dfrac{\pi}{4}$; negative

2. a) i)

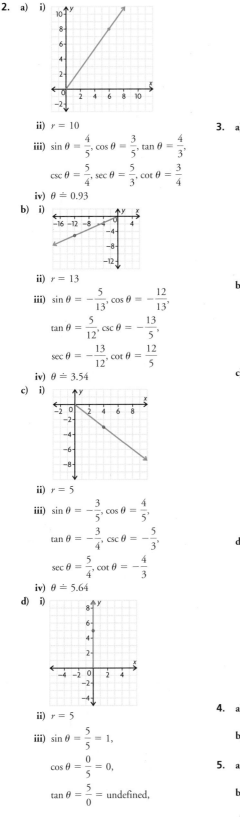

ii) $r = 10$

iii) $\sin \theta = \dfrac{4}{5}$, $\cos \theta = \dfrac{3}{5}$, $\tan \theta = \dfrac{4}{3}$,

$\csc \theta = \dfrac{5}{4}$, $\sec \theta = \dfrac{5}{3}$, $\cot \theta = \dfrac{3}{4}$

iv) $\theta \doteq 0.93$

b) i)

ii) $r = 13$

iii) $\sin \theta = -\dfrac{5}{13}$, $\cos \theta = -\dfrac{12}{13}$,

$\tan \theta = \dfrac{5}{12}$, $\csc \theta = -\dfrac{13}{5}$,

$\sec \theta = -\dfrac{13}{12}$, $\cot \theta = \dfrac{12}{5}$

iv) $\theta \doteq 3.54$

c) i)

ii) $r = 5$

iii) $\sin \theta = -\dfrac{3}{5}$, $\cos \theta = \dfrac{4}{5}$,

$\tan \theta = -\dfrac{3}{4}$, $\csc \theta = -\dfrac{5}{3}$,

$\sec \theta = \dfrac{5}{4}$, $\cot \theta = -\dfrac{4}{3}$

iv) $\theta \doteq 5.64$

d) i)

ii) $r = 5$

iii) $\sin \theta = \dfrac{5}{5} = 1$,

$\cos \theta = \dfrac{0}{5} = 0$,

$\tan \theta = \dfrac{5}{0} =$ undefined,

$\csc \theta = \dfrac{5}{5} = 1$,

$\sec \theta = \dfrac{5}{0} =$ undefined,

$\cot \theta = \dfrac{0}{5} = 0$

iv) $\theta \doteq \dfrac{\pi}{2}$

3. a) $\sin\left(-\dfrac{\pi}{2}\right) = -1$,

$\cos\left(-\dfrac{\pi}{2}\right) = 0$,

$\tan\left(-\dfrac{\pi}{2}\right) =$ undefined,

$\csc\left(-\dfrac{\pi}{2}\right) = -1$,

$\sec\left(-\dfrac{\pi}{2}\right) =$ undefined,

$\cot\left(-\dfrac{\pi}{2}\right) = 0$

b) $\sin(-\pi) = 0$,

$\cos(-\pi) = -1$,

$\tan(-\pi) = 0$,

$\csc(-\pi) =$ undefined,

$\sec(-\pi) = -1$,

$\cot(-\pi) =$ undefined

c) $\sin\left(\dfrac{7\pi}{4}\right) = -\dfrac{\sqrt{2}}{2}$,

$\cos\left(\dfrac{7\pi}{4}\right) = \dfrac{\sqrt{2}}{2}$,

$\tan\left(\dfrac{7\pi}{4}\right) = -1$,

$\csc\left(\dfrac{7\pi}{4}\right) = -\sqrt{2}$,

$\sec\left(\dfrac{7\pi}{4}\right) = \sqrt{2}$,

$\cot\left(\dfrac{7\pi}{4}\right) = -1$

d) $\sin\left(-\dfrac{\pi}{6}\right) = -\dfrac{1}{2}$,

$\cos\left(-\dfrac{\pi}{6}\right) = \dfrac{\sqrt{3}}{2}$,

$\tan\left(-\dfrac{\pi}{6}\right) = -\dfrac{\sqrt{3}}{3}$,

$\csc\left(-\dfrac{\pi}{6}\right) = -2$,

$\sec\left(-\dfrac{\pi}{6}\right) = \dfrac{2\sqrt{3}}{3}$,

$\cot\left(-\dfrac{\pi}{6}\right) = -\sqrt{3}$

4. a) $\sin \dfrac{\pi}{6}$ **c)** $\cot \dfrac{3\pi}{4}$

b) $\cos \dfrac{\pi}{3}$ **d)** $\sec \dfrac{5\pi}{6}$

5. a) $\dfrac{\sqrt{3}}{2}$ **d)** $-\dfrac{\sqrt{2}}{2}$

b) $-\dfrac{\sqrt{2}}{2}$ **e)** 2

c) $-\dfrac{\sqrt{3}}{3}$ **f)** 2

6. a) $\dfrac{4\pi}{3}$ **d)** $\dfrac{7\pi}{6}$

b) $\dfrac{11\pi}{6}$ **e)** $\dfrac{3\pi}{2}$

c) $\dfrac{5\pi}{4}$ **f)** π

7. a) $\theta \doteq 2.29$ **d)** $\theta \doteq 3.61$
b) $\theta \doteq 0.17$ **e)** $\theta \doteq 0.84$
c) $\theta \doteq 1.30$ **f)** $\theta \doteq 6.12$

8. a) $\cos \dfrac{5\pi}{4}$ **d)** $\cot \dfrac{5\pi}{3}$

b) $\tan \dfrac{5\pi}{6}$ **e)** $\sin \dfrac{7\pi}{6}$

c) $\csc \dfrac{4\pi}{3}$ **f)** $\sec \dfrac{\pi}{4}$

9. $\pi - 0.748 \doteq 2.39$
10. $x \doteq 5.55$ cm
11. $x \doteq 4.5$ cm
12. Draw the angle and determine the measure of the reference angle. Use the CAST rule to determine the sign of each of the ratios in the quadrant in which the angle terminates. Use this sign and the value of the ratios of the reference angle to determine the values of the primary trigonometric ratios for the given angle.
13. a) second or third quadrant

b) $\sin \theta = \dfrac{12}{13}$ or $-\dfrac{12}{13}$,

$\tan \theta = \dfrac{12}{5}$ or $-\dfrac{12}{5}$,

$\sec \theta = -\dfrac{13}{5}$,

$\csc \theta = \dfrac{13}{12}$ or $-\dfrac{13}{12}$,

$\cot \theta = \dfrac{5}{12}$ or $-\dfrac{5}{12}$

c) $\theta \doteq 1.97$ or 4.32
14.

By examining the special triangles, we see
$$\cos\left(\frac{5\pi}{6}\right) = \cos(-150°) = -\frac{\sqrt{3}}{2}$$

15. $2\left(\sin^2\left(\frac{11\pi}{6}\right)\right) - 1 = 2\left(-\frac{1}{2}\right)^2 - 1$

$$= 2\left(\frac{1}{4}\right) - 1$$

$$= -\frac{1}{2}$$

$$\left(\sin^2\frac{11\pi}{6}\right) - \left(\cos^2\frac{11\pi}{6}\right)$$

$$= \left(-\frac{1}{2}\right)^2 - \left(\frac{\sqrt{3}}{2}\right)^2$$

$$= \frac{1}{4} - \frac{3}{4}$$

$$= -\frac{1}{2}$$

$2\left(\sin^2\left(\frac{11\pi}{6}\right)\right) - 1$

$$= \left(\sin^2\frac{11\pi}{6}\right) - \left(\cos^2\frac{11\pi}{6}\right)$$

16. $AB = 16$;

$\sin D = \frac{8}{8\sqrt{2}} = \frac{\sqrt{2}}{2}$;

$\cos D = \frac{8}{8\sqrt{2}} = \frac{\sqrt{2}}{2}$;

$\tan D = \frac{8}{8} = 1$

17. a) The first and second quadrants both have a positive y-value.
  b) The first quadrant has a positive y-value, and the fourth quadrant has a negative y-value.
  c) The first quadrant has a positive x-value, and the second quadrant has a negative x-value.
  d) The first quadrant has a positive x-value and a positive y-value, and the third quadrant has a negative x-value and a negative y-value.

18. 1

19. $\cos 150° \doteq -0.26$

20. The ranges of the cosecant and secant functions are both $\{y \in \mathbf{R} \mid -1 \geq y$ or $y \geq 1\}$. In other words, the values of these functions can never be between -1 and 1. For the values of these functions to be between -1 and 1, the values of the sine and cosine functions would have to be greater than 1 and less than -1, which is never the case.

21. $\frac{2\sqrt{3} - 3}{4}$

Lesson 6.3, p. 336

1. a) $y = \sin\theta$ and $y = \cos\theta$ have the same period, axis, amplitude, maximum value, minimum value, domain, and range. They have different y- and θ-intercepts.

b) $y = \sin\theta$ and $y = \tan\theta$ have no characteristics in common except for their y-intercept and zeros.

2. a)

b) $\theta = -5.50, \theta = -2.36, \theta = 0.79, \theta = 3.93$

c) i) $t_n = n\pi, n \in \mathbf{I}$
  ii) $t_n = \frac{\pi}{2} + 2n\pi, n \in \mathbf{I}$
  iii) $t_n = \frac{3\pi}{2} + 2n\pi, n \in \mathbf{I}$

3. a) $t_n = \frac{\pi}{2} + n\pi, n \in \mathbf{I}$
  b) $t_n = 2n\pi, n \in \mathbf{I}$
  c) $t_n = -\pi + 2n\pi, n \in \mathbf{I}$

4. The two graphs appear to be identical.

5. a) $t_n = n\pi, n \in \mathbf{I}$
  b) $t_n = \frac{\pi}{2} + n\pi, n \in \mathbf{I}$

Lesson 6.4, pp. 343–346

1. a) period: $\frac{\pi}{2}$
    amplitude: 0.5
    horizontal translation: 0
    equation of the axis: $y = 0$
  b) period: 2π
    amplitude: 1
    horizontal translation: $\frac{\pi}{4}$
    equation of the axis: $y = 3$
  c) period: $\frac{2\pi}{3}$
    amplitude: 2
    horizontal translation: 0
    equation of the axis: $y = -1$
  d) period: π
    amplitude: 5
    horizontal translation: $\frac{\pi}{6}$
    equation of the axis: $y = -2$

2. Only the last one is cut off.

3.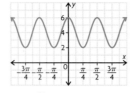

period: $\frac{\pi}{2}$
amplitude: 2
horizontal translation: $\frac{\pi}{4}$ to the left
equation of the axis: $y = 4$

4. a) $f(x) = 25\sin(2x) - 4$
  b) $f(x) = \frac{2}{5}\sin\left(\frac{\pi}{5}x\right) + \frac{1}{15}$
  c) $f(x) = 80\sin\left(\frac{1}{3}x\right) - \frac{9}{10}$
  d) $f(x) = 11\sin(4\pi x)$

5. a) period $= 2\pi$, amplitude $= 18$, equation of the axis is $y = 0$;
    $y = 18\sin x$
  b) period $= 4\pi$, amplitude $= 6$, equation of the axis is $y = -2$;
    $y = -6\sin(0.5x) - 2$
  c) period $= 6\pi$, amplitude $= 2.5$, equation of the axis is $y = 6.5$;
    $y = -2.5\cos\left(\frac{1}{3}x\right) + 6.5$
  d) period $= 4\pi$, amplitude $= 2$, equation of the axis is $y = -1$;
    $y = -2\cos\left(\frac{1}{2}x\right) - 1$

6. a) vertical stretch by a factor of 4, vertical translation 3 units up
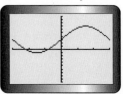

  b) reflection in the x–axis, horizontal stretch by a factor of 4
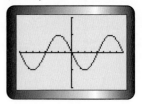

  c) horizontal translation π to the right, vertical translation 1 unit down
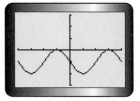

  d) horizontal compression by a factor of $\frac{1}{4}$, horizontal translation $\frac{\pi}{6}$ to the left
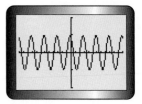

7. a) $f(x) = \dfrac{1}{2}\cos x + 3$

b) $f(x) = \cos\left(-\dfrac{1}{2}x\right)$

c) $f(x) = 3\cos\left(x - \dfrac{\pi}{2}\right)$

d) $f(x) = \cos\left(2\left(x + \dfrac{\pi}{2}\right)\right)$

8. a)
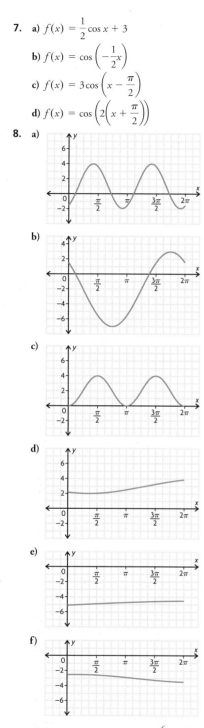

b)

c)

d)

e)

f)

9. a) The period of the function is $\dfrac{6}{5}$. This represents the time between one beat of a person's heart and the next beat.

b) 80

c)
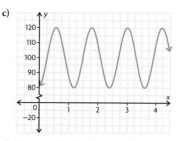

d) The range for the function is between 80 and 120. The range means the lowest blood pressure is 80 and the highest blood pressure is 120.

10. a)
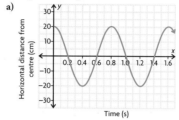

b) There is a vertical stretch by a factor of 20, followed by a horizontal compression by a of factor of $\dfrac{2}{5\pi}$, and then a horizontal translation 0.2 to the left.

c) $y = 20\sin\left(\dfrac{5\pi}{2}(x + 0.2)\right)$

11. a)
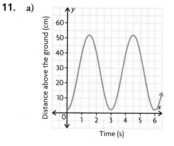

b) vertical stretch by a factor of 25, reflection in the x-axis, vertical translation 27 units up, horizontal compression by a factor of $\dfrac{1}{|k|} = \dfrac{3}{2\pi}$

c) $y = -25\cos\left(\dfrac{2\pi}{3}x\right) + 27$

12. $\dfrac{2\pi}{7}$

13. Answers may vary. For example, $\left(\dfrac{14\pi}{13}, 5\right)$.

14. a) $y = \cos(4\pi x)$

b) $y = -2\sin\left(\dfrac{\pi}{4}x\right)$

c) $y = 4\sin\left(\dfrac{\pi}{20}(x - 10)\right) - 1$

15.

Start with graph of $y = \sin x$.

↓

Reflect in the x-axis and stretch vertically by a factor of 2 to produce graph of $y = -2\sin x$.

↓

Stretch horizontally by a factor of 2 to produce graph of $y = -2\sin(0.5x)$.

↓

Translate $\dfrac{\pi}{4}$ units to the right to produce graph of $y = -2\sin\left(0.5\left(x - \dfrac{\pi}{4}\right)\right)$.

↓

Translate 3 units up to produce graph of $y = -2\sin\left(0.5\left(x - \dfrac{\pi}{4}\right)\right) + 3$.

16. a) 100 m

b) 400 m

c) 300 m

d) 80 s

e) about 23.561 94 m/s

Mid-Chapter Review, p. 349

1. a) 22.5°

b) 720°

c) 286.5°

d) 165°

2. a) $125° \doteq 2.2$ radians

b) $450° \doteq 7.9$ radians

c) $5° \doteq 0.1$ radians

d) $330° \doteq 5.8$ radians

e) $215° \doteq 3.8$ radians

f) $-140° \doteq -2.4$ radians

3. a) 20π

b) 4π radians/s

c) 380π cm

4. a) $\dfrac{\sqrt{2}}{2}$

b) $-\dfrac{1}{2}$

c) $-\sqrt{3}$

d) $-\dfrac{\sqrt{3}}{3}$

e) 0

f) $-\dfrac{1}{2}$

5. a) about 1.78

b) about 0.86

c) about 1.46

d) about 4.44

e) about 0.98

f) about 4.91

6. a) $\sin \dfrac{\pi}{6}$

  b) $\cot \dfrac{3\pi}{4}$

  c) $\sec \dfrac{\pi}{2}$

  d) $\cos \dfrac{5\pi}{6}$

7. a) $x = 0, \pm\pi, \pm2\pi, \ldots ; y = 0$

  b) $x = \pm\dfrac{\pi}{2}, \pm\dfrac{3\pi}{2}, \pm\dfrac{5\pi}{2}, \ldots ; y = 1$

  c) $x = 0, \pm\pi, \pm2\pi, \ldots ; y = 0$

8. a)

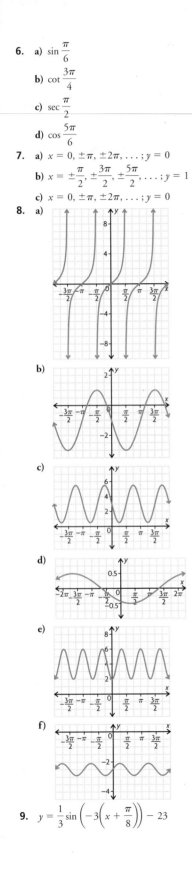

b)

c)

d)

e)

f)

9. $y = \dfrac{1}{3}\sin\left(-3\left(x + \dfrac{\pi}{8}\right)\right) - 23$

Lesson 6.5, p. 353

1. a) $t_n = n\pi,\ n \in \mathbf{I}$
  b) no maximum value
  c) no minimum value

2. a) $t_n = \dfrac{\pi}{2} + n\pi,\ n \in \mathbf{I}$
  b) no maximum value
  c) no minimum value

3. a) $t_n = n\pi,\ n \in \mathbf{I}$

  b) $t_n = \dfrac{\pi}{2} + n\pi,\ n \in \mathbf{I}$

4.

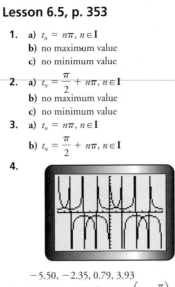

$-5.50, -2.35, 0.79, 3.93$

5. Yes, the graphs of $y = \csc\left(x + \dfrac{\pi}{2}\right)$ and $y = \sec x$ are identical.

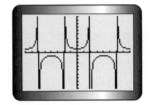

6. Answers may vary. For example, reflect the graph of $y = \tan x$ across the y-axis and then translate the graph $\dfrac{\pi}{2}$ units to the left.

7. a) period $= 2\pi$

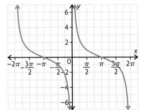

  b) period $= \pi$

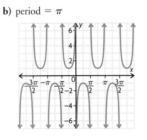

  c) period $= 2\pi$

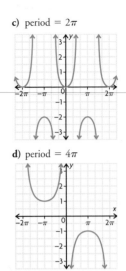

  d) period $= 4\pi$

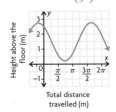

Lesson 6.6, pp. 360–362

1. $y = 3\cos\left(\dfrac{2}{3}\left(x + \dfrac{\pi}{4}\right)\right) + 2$

2. $2, 0.5, y \doteq 0.973\,94$

3.

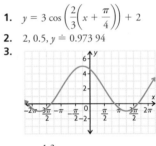

$x = 1.3$

4. amplitude and equation of the axis

5. a) the radius of the circle in which the tip of the sparkler is moving
  b) the time it takes Mike to make one complete circle with the sparkler
  c) the height above the ground of the centre of the circle in which the tip of the sparkler is moving
  d) cosine function

6. $y = 90\sin\left(\dfrac{\pi}{12}x\right) + 30$

7. $y = 250\cos\left(\dfrac{2\pi}{3}x\right) + 750$

8. $y = -1.25\sin\left(\dfrac{4}{5}x\right) + 1.5$

9. 0.98 min $< t <$ 1.52 min,
3.48 min $< t <$ 4.02 min,
5.98 min $< t <$ 6.52 min

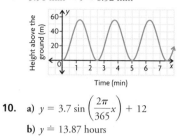

10. a) $y = 3.7 \sin\left(\dfrac{2\pi}{365}x\right) + 12$

b) $y \doteq 13.87$ hours

11. $T(t) = 16.2 \sin\left(\dfrac{2\pi}{365}(t - 116)\right) + 1.4$,
$0 < t < 111$ and $304 < t < 365$

12. The student should graph the height of
the nail above the ground as a function
of the total distance travelled by the nail,
because the nail would not be travelling at
a constant speed. If the student graphed
the height of the nail above the ground as
a function of time, the graph would not
be sinusoidal.

13. minute hand:
$$D(t) = 15 \cos\left(\dfrac{\pi}{30}t\right) + 300;$$
second hand:
$$D(t) = 15 \cos(2\pi t) + 300;$$
hour hand:
$$D(t) = 8 \cos\left(\dfrac{\pi}{360}t\right) + 300$$

Lesson 6.7, pp. 369–373

1. a) $0 < x < \pi, \pi < x < 2\pi$

b) $-\dfrac{\pi}{2} < x < \dfrac{\pi}{2}, \dfrac{3\pi}{2} < x < \dfrac{5\pi}{2}$

c) $\dfrac{\pi}{2} < x < \dfrac{3\pi}{2}, \dfrac{5\pi}{2} < x < 3\pi$

2. a) $x = \dfrac{\pi}{4}, x = \dfrac{5\pi}{4}$

b) $x = \dfrac{\pi}{2}, x = \dfrac{5\pi}{2}$

c) $x = 0, x = 2\pi$

3. 0

4. a) about 0.465

b) 0

c) about -0.5157

d) about -1.554

5. a) $0 < x < \dfrac{\pi}{2}, \pi < x < \dfrac{3\pi}{2}$

b) $0 < x < \dfrac{\pi}{4}, \pi < x < \dfrac{5\pi}{4}$

c) $\dfrac{\pi}{4} < x < \dfrac{\pi}{2}, \dfrac{5\pi}{4} < x < \dfrac{3\pi}{2}$

6. a) $x = \dfrac{1}{4}, x = \dfrac{3}{4}$

b) $x = 0, x = 1$

c) $x = \dfrac{1}{2}, x = \dfrac{3}{2}$

7. a) about -0.7459

b) about -1.310

c) 0

8. negative

9. a) $R(t) = 4.5 \cos\left(\dfrac{\pi}{12}t\right) + 20.2$

b) fastest: $t = 6$ months, $t = 18$ months,
$t = 30$ months, $t = 42$ months;
slowest: $t = 0$ months, $t = 12$ months,
$t = 24$ months, $t = 36$ months,
$t = 48$ months

c) about 1.164 mice per owl/s

10. a) **i)** 0.25 t/h
ii) about 0.2588 t/h
iii) 0.2612 t/h

b) The estimate calculated in part iii) is
the most accurate. The smaller the
interval, the more accurate the estimate.

11. a)

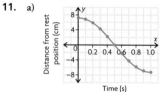

b) half of one cycle

c) -14.4 cm/s

d) The bob is moving the fastest when it
passes through its rest position. You can
tell because the images of the balls are
farthest apart at this point.

e) The pendulum's rest position is halfway
between the maximum and minimum
values on the graph. Therefore, at this
point, the pendulum's instantaneous
rate of change is at its maximum.

12. a) 0

b) -0.5 m/s

13. a)

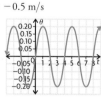

b) 0.2 radians/s

c) Answers may vary. For example,
about $-\frac{2}{3}$ radians/s.

d) $t = 0, 2, 4, 6,$ and 8

14. Answers may vary. For example, for $x = 0$,
the instantaneous rate of change of
$f(x) = \sin x$ is approximately 0.9003,
while the instantaneous rate of change of
$f(x) = 3\sin x$ is approximately 2.7009.

(The interval $-\dfrac{\pi}{4} < x < \dfrac{\pi}{4}$ was used.)
Therefore, the instantaneous rate of change
of $f(x) = 3\sin x$ is at its maximum three
times more than the instantaneous rate of
change of $f(x) = \sin x$. However, there
are points where the instantaneous rate of
change is the same for the two functions.
For example, at $x = \dfrac{\pi}{2}$, it is 0 for both
functions.

15. a) $-1, 0, 1, 0,$ and -1

b)

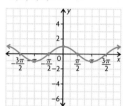

The function is $f(x) = \cos x$. Based on
this information, the derivative of
$f(x) = \sin x$ is $\cos x$.

16. a) $0, 1, 0, -1,$ and 0

b)

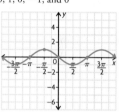

The function is $f(x) = -\sin x$. Based
on this information, the derivative of
$f(x) = \cos x$ is $-\sin x$.

Chapter Review, pp. 376–377

1. $\dfrac{33}{16}$

2. 70π

3. a) $\dfrac{\pi}{9}$ radians

b) $\dfrac{-5\pi}{18}$ radians

c) $\dfrac{8\pi}{9}$ radians

d) $\dfrac{7\pi}{3}$ radians

4. a) $45°$ **c)** $480°$
b) $-225°$ **d)** $-120°$

5. a) $\dfrac{5\pi}{6}$ **c)** $\dfrac{3\pi}{4}$

b) $\dfrac{4\pi}{3}$ **d)** $\dfrac{7\pi}{6}$

6. a) $\tan \theta = \dfrac{12}{13}$

b) $\sec \theta = -\dfrac{13}{5}$

c) about 5.14

7. 2.00

8. a) 2π radians
b) 2π radians
c) π radians

9. $y = 5 \sin\left(x + \dfrac{\pi}{3}\right) + 2$

10. $y = -3 \cos\left(2\left(x + \dfrac{\pi}{4}\right)\right) - 1$

11. a) reflection in the x-axis, vertical stretch by a factor of 19, vertical translation 9 units down
b) horizontal compression by a factor of $\dfrac{1}{10}$, horizontal translation $\dfrac{\pi}{12}$ to the left
c) vertical compression by a factor of $\dfrac{10}{11}$, horizontal translation $\dfrac{\pi}{9}$ to the right, vertical translation 3 units up
d) reflection in the x-axis, reflection in the y-axis, horizontal translation π to the right

12. a)

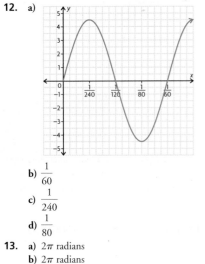

b) $\dfrac{1}{60}$

c) $\dfrac{1}{240}$

d) $\dfrac{1}{80}$

13. a) 2π radians
b) 2π radians
c) π radians

14. a) the radius of the circle in which the bumblebee is flying
b) the time that the bumblebee takes to fly one complete circle
c) the height, above the ground, of the centre of the circle in which the bumblebee is flying
d) cosine function

15. $P(m) = 7250 \cos\left(\dfrac{\pi}{6}m\right) + 7750$

16. $h(t) = 30 \sin\left(\dfrac{5\pi}{3}t - \dfrac{\pi}{2}\right) + 150$

17. a) $0 < x < 5\pi$, $10\pi < x < 15\pi$
b) $2.5\pi < x < 7.5\pi$, $12.5\pi < x < 17.5\pi$
c) $0 < x < 2.5\pi$, $7.5\pi < x < 12.5\pi$

18. a) $x = 0$, $x = \dfrac{1}{2}$
b) $x = \dfrac{1}{8}$, $x = \dfrac{5}{8}$
c) $x = \dfrac{3}{8}$, $x = \dfrac{7}{8}$

19. a) $x = \dfrac{3}{4}$ s
b) the time between one beat of a person's heart and the next beat
c) 140
d) -129

Chapter Self-Test, p. 378

1. $y = \sec x$
2. $\sec 2\pi$
3. $y \doteq 108.5$
4. about $0.31\ °C$ per day
5. $\dfrac{3\pi}{5}$, $110°$, $\dfrac{5\pi}{8}$, $113°$, and $\dfrac{2\pi}{3}$
6. $y = \sin\left(x + \dfrac{5\pi}{8}\right)$
7. $y \doteq -30$
8. a) $-3 \cos\left(\dfrac{\pi}{12}x\right) + 22$
b) about $0.5\ °C$ per hour
c) about $0\ °C$ per hour

Cumulative Review Chapters 4–6, pp. 380–383

1. (d) **9.** (c) **17.** (d) **25.** (b)
2. (b) **10.** (c) **18.** (b) **26.** (d)
3. (a) **11.** (d) **19.** (b) **27.** (a)
4. (c) **12.** (a) **20.** (b) **28.** (c)
5. (a) **13.** (d) **21.** (d) **29.** (b)
6. (b) **14.** (c) **22.** (c)
7. (a) **15.** (d) **23.** (a)
8. (c) **16.** (a) **24.** (d)

30. a) If x is the length in centimetres of a side of one of the corners that have been cut out, the volume of the box is $(50 - 2x)(40 - 2x)x$ cm^3.
b) 5 cm or 10 cm
c) $x \doteq 7.4$ cm
d) $3 < x < 12.8$

31. a) The zeros of $f(x)$ are $x = 2$ or $x = 3$. The zero of $g(x)$ is $x = 3$. The zero of $\dfrac{f(x)}{g(x)}$ is $x = 2$. $\dfrac{g(x)}{f(x)}$ does not have any zeros.
b) $\dfrac{f(x)}{g(x)}$ has a hole at $x = 3$; no asymptotes. $\dfrac{g(x)}{f(x)}$ has an asymptote at $x = 2$ and $y = 0$.
c) $x = 1$; $\dfrac{f(x)}{g(x)}$: $y = x - 2$, $\dfrac{g(x)}{f(x)}$: $y = -x$

32. a) Vertical compressions and stretches do not affect location of zeros; maximum and minimum values are multiplied by the scale factor, but locations are unchanged; instantaneous rates of change are multiplied by the scale factor.

Horizontal compressions and stretches move locations of zeros, maximums, and minimums toward or away from the y-axis by the reciprocal of the scale factor; instantaneous rates of change are multiplied by the reciprocal of scale factor.

Vertical translations change location of zeros or remove them; maximum and minimum values are increased or decreased by the amount of the translation, but locations are unchanged; instantaneous rates of change are unchanged.

Horizontal translations move location of zeros by the same amount as the translation; maximum and minimum values are unchanged, but locations are moved by the same amount as the translation; instantaneous rates of change are unchanged, but locations are moved by the same amount as the translation.

b) For $y = \cos x$, the answer is the same as in part **a)**, except that a horizontal reflection does not affect instantaneous rates of change. For $y = \tan x$, the answer is also the same as in part **a)**, except that nothing affects the maximum and minimum values, since there are no maximum or minimum values for $y = \tan x$.

Chapter 7

Getting Started, p. 386

1. a) 1
b) $-\dfrac{22}{7}$
c) 8 or -3
d) $\dfrac{2}{3}$ or $-\dfrac{5}{2}$
e) $-1 \pm \sqrt{2}$
f) $\dfrac{3 \pm \sqrt{21}}{6}$

2. To do this, you must show that the two distances are equal:
$$D_{AB} = \sqrt{(2 - 1)^2 + \left(\dfrac{1}{2} - 0\right)^2} = \dfrac{\sqrt{5}}{2};$$
$$D_{CD} = \sqrt{\left(0 - \dfrac{1}{2}\right)^2 + (6 - 5)^2} \doteq \dfrac{\sqrt{5}}{2}.$$
Since the distances are equal, the line segments are the same length.

3. a) $\sin A = \dfrac{8}{17}$, $\cos A = \dfrac{15}{17}$, $\tan A = \dfrac{8}{15}$, $\csc A = \dfrac{17}{8}$, $\sec A = \dfrac{17}{15}$, $\cot A = \dfrac{15}{8}$
b) 0.5 radians
c) $61.9°$

4. a)

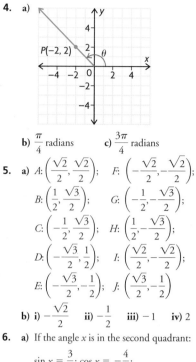

P(−2, 2)

b) $\dfrac{\pi}{4}$ radians **c)** $\dfrac{3\pi}{4}$ radians

5. a) $A: \left(\dfrac{\sqrt{2}}{2}, \dfrac{\sqrt{2}}{2}\right);$ $F: \left(-\dfrac{\sqrt{2}}{2}, -\dfrac{\sqrt{2}}{2}\right);$

$B: \left(\dfrac{1}{2}, \dfrac{\sqrt{3}}{2}\right);$ $G: \left(-\dfrac{1}{2}, -\dfrac{\sqrt{3}}{2}\right);$

$C: \left(-\dfrac{1}{2}, \dfrac{\sqrt{3}}{2}\right);$ $H: \left(\dfrac{1}{2}, -\dfrac{\sqrt{3}}{2}\right);$

$D: \left(-\dfrac{\sqrt{3}}{2}, \dfrac{1}{2}\right);$ $I: \left(\dfrac{\sqrt{2}}{2}, -\dfrac{\sqrt{2}}{2}\right);$

$E: \left(-\dfrac{\sqrt{3}}{2}, -\dfrac{1}{2}\right);$ $J: \left(\dfrac{\sqrt{3}}{2}, -\dfrac{1}{2}\right)$

b) i) $-\dfrac{\sqrt{2}}{2}$ **ii)** $-\dfrac{1}{2}$ **iii)** -1 **iv)** 2

6. a) If the angle x is in the second quadrant:

$\sin x = \dfrac{3}{5}; \cos x = -\dfrac{4}{5};$

$\csc x = \dfrac{5}{3}; \sec x = -\dfrac{5}{4}; \cot x = -\dfrac{4}{3}.$

If the angle x is in the fourth quadrant:

$\sin x = -\dfrac{3}{5}; \cos x = \dfrac{4}{5}; \csc x = -\dfrac{5}{3};$

$\sec x = \dfrac{5}{4}; \cot x = -\dfrac{4}{3}$

b) If x is in the second quadrant, $x = 2.5$.
If x is in the fourth quadrant, $x = 5.6$.

7. a) true **d)** false
b) true **e)** true
c) false **f)** true

8.

Perform a vertical stretch/compression by a factor of $|a|$.

↓

Use $\left|\dfrac{1}{k}\right|$ to determine the horizontal stretch/compression.

↓

Use a and k to determine whether the function is reflected in the y-axis or the x-axis.

↓

Perform a vertical translation of c units up or down.

↓

Perform a horizontal translation of d units to the right or the left.

Lesson 7.1, pp. 392–393

1. a) Answers may vary. For example:
$y = \cos(\theta + 2\pi), y = \cos(\theta + 4\pi),$
$y = \cos(\theta - 2\pi)$

b) $y = \sin\left(\theta + \dfrac{\pi}{2}\right), y = \sin\left(\theta - \dfrac{3\pi}{2}\right),$

$y = \sin\left(\theta + \dfrac{5\pi}{2}\right)$

2. a) $y = \csc\theta$ is odd, $\csc(-\theta) = -\csc\theta;$
$y = \sec\theta$ is even, $\sec(-\theta) = \sec\theta;$
$y = \cot\theta$ is odd, $\cot(-\theta) = -\cot\theta$

b) $y = \cot(-\theta)$ is the graph of $y = \cot\theta$ reflected across the y-axis; $y = -\cot\theta$ is the graph of $y = \cot\theta$ reflected across the x-axis. Both of these transformations result in the same graph. $y = \csc(-\theta)$ is the graph of $y = \csc\theta$ reflected across the y-axis; $y = -\csc\theta$ is the graph of $y = \csc\theta$ reflected across the x-axis. Both of these transformations result in the same graph. $y = \sec(-\theta)$ is the graph of $y = \sec\theta$ reflected across the y-axis. This results in the same graph as $y = \sec\theta$.

3. a) $\cos\dfrac{\pi}{3}$ **c)** $\cot\dfrac{\pi}{8}$ **e)** $\cos\dfrac{3\pi}{8}$

b) $\sin\dfrac{\pi}{12}$ **d)** $\sin\dfrac{3\pi}{16}$ **f)** $\cot\dfrac{\pi}{3}$

4. a) $\csc\theta = \sec\left(\dfrac{\pi}{2} - \theta\right);$

$\sec\theta = \csc\left(\dfrac{\pi}{2} - \theta\right);$

$\cot\theta = \tan\left(\dfrac{\pi}{2} - \theta\right)$

b) $y = \tan\left(\dfrac{\pi}{2} - \theta\right) = \tan\left(-\left(\theta - \dfrac{\pi}{2}\right)\right);$
This is the graph of $y = \tan\theta$ reflected across the y-axis and translated $\dfrac{\pi}{2}$ to the right, which is identical to the graph of $y = \cot\theta$.

$y = \csc\left(\dfrac{\pi}{2} - \theta\right) = \csc\left(-\left(\theta - \dfrac{\pi}{2}\right)\right);$
This is the graph of $y = \csc\theta$ reflected across the y-axis and translated $\dfrac{\pi}{2}$ to the right, which is identical to the graph of $y = \sec\theta$.

$y = \sec\left(\dfrac{\pi}{2} - \theta\right) = \sec\left(-\left(\theta - \dfrac{\pi}{2}\right)\right);$
This is the graph of $y = \sec\theta$ reflected across the y-axis and translated $\dfrac{\pi}{2}$ to the right, which is identical to the graph of $y = \csc\theta$.

5. a) $\sin\dfrac{\pi}{8}$ **d)** $\cos\dfrac{\pi}{6}$

b) $-\cos\dfrac{\pi}{12}$ **e)** $-\sin\dfrac{3\pi}{8}$

c) $\tan\dfrac{\pi}{4}$ **f)** $-\tan\dfrac{\pi}{3}$

6. a) Assume the circle is a unit circle. Let the coordinates of Q be (x, y). Since P and Q are reflections of each other in the line $y = x$, the coordinates of P are (y, x). Draw a line from P to the positive x-axis. The hypotenuse of the new right triangle makes an angle of $\left(\dfrac{\pi}{2} - \theta\right)$ with the positive x-axis. Since the x-coordinate of P is y, $\cos\left(\dfrac{\pi}{2} - \theta\right) = y$. Also, since the y-coordinate of Q is y, $\sin\theta = y$. Therefore, $\cos\left(\dfrac{\pi}{2} - \theta\right) = \sin\theta$.

b) Assume the circle is a unit circle. Let the coordinates of the vertex on the circle of the right triangle in the first quadrant be (x, y). Then $\sin\theta = y$, so $-\sin\theta = -y$. The point on the circle that results from rotating the vertex by $\dfrac{\pi}{2}$ counterclockwise about the origin has coordinates $(-y, x)$, so $\cos\left(\dfrac{\pi}{2} + \theta\right) = -y$. Therefore, $\cos\left(\dfrac{\pi}{2} + \theta\right) = -\sin\theta$.

7. a) true

b) false; Answers may vary. For example: Let $\theta = \dfrac{\pi}{2}$. Then the left side is $\sin\dfrac{\pi}{2}$, or 1. The right side is $-\sin\dfrac{\pi}{2}$, or -1.

c) false; Answers may vary. For example: Let $\theta = \pi$. Then the left side is $\cos\pi$, or -1. The right side is $-\cos 5\pi$, or 1.

d) false; Answers may vary. For example: Let $\theta = \dfrac{\pi}{4}$. Then the left side is $\tan\dfrac{3\pi}{4}$, or $-\dfrac{\sqrt{2}}{2}$. The right side is $\tan\dfrac{\pi}{4}$, or $\dfrac{\sqrt{2}}{2}$.

e) false; Answers may vary. For example: Let $\theta = \pi$. Then the left side is $\cot\dfrac{3\pi}{4}$, or -1. The right side is $\tan\dfrac{\pi}{4}$, or 1.

f) false; Answers may vary. For example: Let $\theta = \dfrac{\pi}{2}$. Then the left side is $\sin\dfrac{5\pi}{2}$, or 1. The right side is $\sin\left(-\dfrac{\pi}{2}\right)$, or -1.

Lesson 7.2, pp. 400–401

1. a) $\sin 3a$ **b)** $\cos 7x$

2. a) $\tan 60°; \sqrt{3}$ **b)** $\cos\dfrac{\pi}{3}; \dfrac{1}{2}$

3. a) $30° + 45°$ **d)** $\dfrac{\pi}{4} - \dfrac{\pi}{6}$

b) $30° - 45°$ **e)** $60° + 45°$

c) $\dfrac{\pi}{6} - \dfrac{\pi}{3}$ **f)** $\dfrac{\pi}{2} + \dfrac{\pi}{3}$

4. a) $\dfrac{\sqrt{2} + \sqrt{6}}{4}$ **d)** $\dfrac{\sqrt{2} - \sqrt{6}}{4}$

b) $\dfrac{\sqrt{2} + \sqrt{6}}{4}$ **e)** $\dfrac{\sqrt{2} - \sqrt{6}}{4}$

c) $2 + \sqrt{3}$ **f)** $-2 + \sqrt{3}$

5. a) $-\dfrac{1}{2}$ **d)** $-\dfrac{1}{2}$

b) $-\dfrac{\sqrt{2}}{2}$ **e)** $\dfrac{\sqrt{3}}{3}$

c) 1 **f)** $-\dfrac{\sqrt{3}}{2}$

6. a) $-\sin x$ **d)** $\tan x$
b) $\sin x$ **e)** $-\sin x$
c) $-\sin x$ **f)** $-\tan x$

7. a) $\sin(\pi + x)$ is equivalent to $\sin x$ translated π to the left, which is equivalent to $-\sin x$.

b) $\cos\left(x + \dfrac{3\pi}{2}\right)$ is equivalent to $\cos x$ translated $\dfrac{3\pi}{2}$ to the left, which is equivalent to $\sin x$.

c) $\cos\left(x + \dfrac{\pi}{2}\right)$ is equivalent to $\cos x$ translated $\dfrac{\pi}{2}$ to the left, which is equivalent to $-\sin x$.

d) $\tan(x + \pi)$ is equivalent to $\tan x$ translated π to the left, which is equivalent to $\tan x$.

e) $\sin(x - \pi)$ is equivalent to $\sin x$ translated π to the right, which is equivalent to $-\sin x$.

f) $\tan(2\pi - x)$ is equivalent to $\tan(-x)$, which is equivalent to $\tan x$ reflected in the y-axis, which is equivalent to $-\tan x$.

8. a) $\dfrac{\sqrt{6} - \sqrt{2}}{4}$ **d)** $\dfrac{\sqrt{2} - \sqrt{6}}{4}$

b) $-2 + \sqrt{3}$ **e)** $-2 - \sqrt{3}$

c) $\dfrac{-\sqrt{2} - \sqrt{6}}{4}$ **f)** $-2 - \sqrt{3}$

9. a) $\dfrac{63}{65}$ **d)** $\dfrac{56}{65}$

b) $-\dfrac{16}{65}$ **e)** $-\dfrac{16}{63}$

c) $-\dfrac{33}{65}$ **f)** $-\dfrac{56}{33}$

10. $\dfrac{323}{325}; \dfrac{323}{36}$

11. a) $\cos\left(\dfrac{\pi}{2} - x\right)$
$= \cos\dfrac{\pi}{2}\cos x + \sin\dfrac{\pi}{2}\sin x$
$= (0)(\cos x) + (1)(\sin x)$
$= 0 + \sin x$
$= \sin x$

b) $\sin\left(\dfrac{\pi}{2} - x\right)$
$= \sin\dfrac{\pi}{2}\cos x - \cos\dfrac{\pi}{2}\sin x$
$= (1)(\cos x) - (0)(\sin x)$
$= \cos x - 0$
$= \cos x$

12. a) 0 **b)** $-\sqrt{3}\sin x$

13. $\tan f, \cos f \neq 0, \cos g \neq 0$

14.

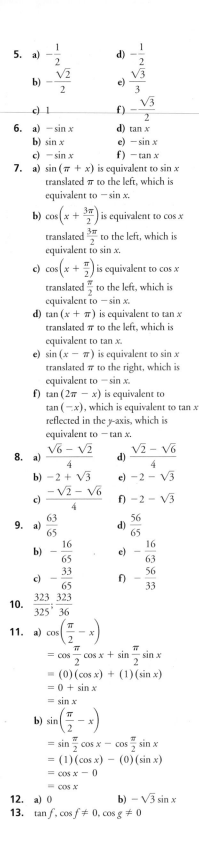

15. See compound angle formulas listed on p. 399.
The two sine formulas are the same, except for the operators. Remembering that the same operator is used on both the left and right sides in both equations will help you remember the formulas.
Similarly, the two cosine formulas are the same, except for the operators. Remembering that the operator on the left side is the opposite of the operator on the right side in both equations will help you remember the formulas.
The two tangent formulas are the same, except for the operators in the numerator and the denominator on the right side. Remembering that the operators in the numerator and the denominator are opposite in both equations, and that the operator in the numerator is the same as the operator on the left side, will help you remember the formulas.

16. $2\sin\left(\dfrac{C+D}{2}\right)\cos\left(\dfrac{C-D}{2}\right)$

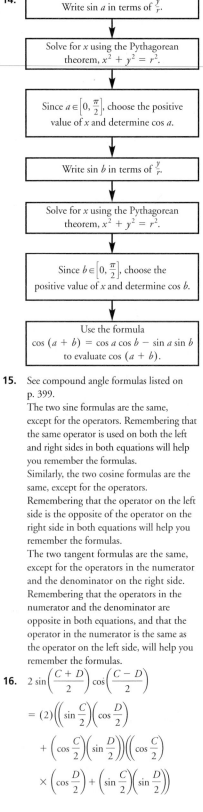

$= (2)\left(\left(\sin\dfrac{C}{2}\right)\left(\cos\dfrac{C}{2}\right)\left(\cos^2\dfrac{D}{2}\right)\right.$
$\quad + \left(\sin\dfrac{D}{2}\right)\left(\cos\dfrac{D}{2}\right)\left(\cos^2\dfrac{C}{2}\right)$
$\quad + \left(\sin\dfrac{D}{2}\right)\left(\cos\dfrac{D}{2}\right)\left(\sin^2\dfrac{C}{2}\right)$
$\quad + \left.\left(\sin\dfrac{C}{2}\right)\left(\cos\dfrac{C}{2}\right)\left(\sin^2\dfrac{D}{2}\right)\right)$

$= (2)\left(\sin\dfrac{C}{2}\right)\left(\cos\dfrac{C}{2}\right)\left(\cos^2\dfrac{D}{2} + \sin^2\dfrac{D}{2}\right)$
$\quad + 2\left(\sin\dfrac{D}{2}\right)\left(\cos\dfrac{D}{2}\right)\left(\cos^2\dfrac{C}{2} + \sin^2\dfrac{C}{2}\right)$

$= (2)\left(\sin\dfrac{C}{2}\right)\left(\cos\dfrac{C}{2}\right)$
$\quad + 2\left(\sin\dfrac{D}{2}\right)\left(\cos\dfrac{D}{2}\right)$

$= \sin\left(2\left(\dfrac{C}{2}\right)\right) + \sin\left(2\left(\dfrac{D}{2}\right)\right)$
$= \sin C + \sin D$

17. $\cot(x + y) = \dfrac{\cot x \cot y - 1}{\cot x + \cot y}$

18. Let $C = x + y$ and let $D = x - y$.
$\cos C + \cos D$
$= \cos(x + y) + \cos(x - y)$
$= \cos x \cos y - \sin x \sin y$
$\quad + \cos x \cos y + \sin x \sin y$
$= 2\cos x \cos y$
$\dfrac{C + D}{2} = \dfrac{x + y + x - y}{2} = x$
$\dfrac{C - D}{2} = \dfrac{x + y - x + y}{2} = y$
So $\cos C + \cos D$
$= 2\cos\left(\dfrac{C + D}{2}\right)\cos\left(\dfrac{C - D}{2}\right)$

19. Let $C = x + y$ and let $D = x - y$.
$\cos C - \cos D$
$= \cos(x + y) - \cos(x - y)$
$= \cos x \cos y - \sin x \sin y$
$\quad - (\cos x \cos y - \sin x \sin y)$
$= -2\sin x \sin y$
$\dfrac{C + D}{2} = \dfrac{x + y + x - y}{2} = x$
$\dfrac{C - D}{2} = \dfrac{x + y - x + y}{2} = y$
So $\cos C - \cos D$
$= -2\sin\left(\dfrac{C + D}{2}\right)\sin\left(\dfrac{C - D}{2}\right)$

Lesson 7.3, pp. 407–408

1. a) $\sin 10x$ **d)** $\tan 8x$
b) $\cos 2\theta$ **e)** $2\sin 2\theta$
c) $\cos 6x$ **f)** $\cos\theta$

2. a) $\sin 90°; 1$ **d)** $\cos\dfrac{\pi}{6}; \dfrac{\sqrt{3}}{2}$

b) $\cos 60°; \dfrac{1}{2}$ **e)** $\cos\dfrac{3\pi}{4}; -\dfrac{\sqrt{2}}{2}$

c) $\sin\dfrac{\pi}{6}; \dfrac{1}{2}$ **f)** $\sin 120°; \dfrac{\sqrt{3}}{2}$

3. **a)** $2 \sin 2\theta \cos 2\theta$
b) $2 \sin^2 (1.5x) - 1$
c) $\dfrac{2 \tan (0.5x)}{1 - \tan^2 (0.5x)}$
d) $\cos^2 3\theta - \sin^2 3\theta$
e) $2 \sin (0.5x) \cos (0.5x)$
f) $\dfrac{2 \tan (2.5\theta)}{1 - \tan^2 (2.5\theta)}$

4. $\sin 2\theta = \dfrac{24}{25}$, $\cos 2\theta = -\dfrac{7}{25}$,
$\tan 2\theta = -\dfrac{24}{7}$

5. $\sin 2\theta = -\dfrac{336}{625}$, $\cos 2\theta = \dfrac{527}{625}$,
$\tan 2\theta = -\dfrac{336}{527}$

6. $\sin 2\theta = -\dfrac{120}{169}$, $\cos 2\theta = -\dfrac{119}{169}$,
$\tan 2\theta = \dfrac{120}{119}$

7. $\sin 2\theta = -\dfrac{24}{25}$, $\cos 2\theta = \dfrac{7}{25}$,
$\tan 2\theta = -\dfrac{24}{7}$

8. $a = \dfrac{1}{2}$

9. Jim can find the sine of $\dfrac{\pi}{8}$ by using
the formula $\cos 2x = 1 - 2 \sin^2 x$ and
isolating $\sin x$ on one side of the equation.
When he does this, the formula becomes
$\sin x = \pm \sqrt{\dfrac{1 - \cos 2x}{2}}$. The cosine of $\dfrac{\pi}{4}$
is $\dfrac{\sqrt{2}}{2}$, so $\sin \dfrac{\pi}{8} = \pm \sqrt{\dfrac{1 - \cos \frac{\pi}{4}}{2}}$
$= \pm \dfrac{\sqrt{2 - \sqrt{2}}}{2}$.
Since $\dfrac{\pi}{8}$ is in the first quadrant, the sign of
$\sin \dfrac{\pi}{8}$ is positive.

10. Marion can find the cosine of $\dfrac{\pi}{12}$ by using
the formula $\cos 2x = 2 \cos^2 x - 1$ and
isolating $\cos x$ on one side of the equation.
When she does this, the formula becomes
$\cos x = \pm \sqrt{\dfrac{1 + \cos 2x}{2}}$. The cosine of $\dfrac{\pi}{6}$ is
$\dfrac{\sqrt{3}}{2}$, so $\cos \dfrac{\pi}{12} = \pm \sqrt{\dfrac{1 + \cos \frac{\pi}{6}}{2}}$
$= \pm \dfrac{\sqrt{2 + \sqrt{3}}}{2}$.
Since $\dfrac{\pi}{12}$ is in the first quadrant, the sign of
$\cos \dfrac{\pi}{12}$ is positive.

11. **a)** $\sin 4x$
$= (2)(2 \sin x \cos x)(\cos 2x)$
$= (2)(2 \sin x \cos x)(1 - 2 \sin^2 x)$
$= (4 \sin x \cos x)(1 - 2 \sin^2 x)$
$= 4 \sin x \cos x - 8 \sin^3 x \cos x$

b) $\sin \dfrac{2\pi}{3} = \dfrac{\sqrt{3}}{2}$
$\sin 4\left(\dfrac{2\pi}{3}\right) = 4 \sin \dfrac{2\pi}{3} \cos \dfrac{2\pi}{3}$
$\quad - 8 \sin^3 \dfrac{2\pi}{3} \cos \dfrac{2\pi}{3}$
$\sin \dfrac{8\pi}{3} = (4)\left(\dfrac{\sqrt{3}}{2}\right)\left(-\dfrac{1}{2}\right)$
$\quad - (8)\left(\dfrac{\sqrt{3}}{2}\right)^3\left(-\dfrac{1}{2}\right)$
$\sin \dfrac{8\pi}{3} = -\dfrac{4\sqrt{3}}{4} - (-4)\left(\dfrac{3\sqrt{3}}{8}\right)$
$\sin \dfrac{8\pi}{3} = -\dfrac{4\sqrt{3}}{4} - \left(-\dfrac{3\sqrt{3}}{2}\right)$
$\sin \dfrac{8\pi}{3} = -\dfrac{4\sqrt{3}}{4} - \left(-\dfrac{6\sqrt{3}}{4}\right)$
$\sin \dfrac{8\pi}{3} = -\dfrac{4\sqrt{3}}{4} + \dfrac{6\sqrt{3}}{4}$
$\sin \dfrac{8\pi}{3} = \dfrac{2\sqrt{3}}{4}$
$\sin \dfrac{8\pi}{3} = \dfrac{\sqrt{3}}{2}$

12. **a)** $\cos 2\theta = \cos^2 \theta - \sin^2 \theta$
$\sin 2\theta = 2 \cos \theta \sin \theta$
$\sin 3\theta = (\sin 2\theta + \theta)$
$\quad = (2 \cos \theta \sin \theta)(\cos \theta)$
$\quad \quad + (\cos^2 \theta - \sin^2 \theta)(\sin \theta)$
$\quad = 2 \cos^2 \theta \sin \theta + \cos^2 \theta \sin \theta$
$\quad \quad - \sin^3 \theta$
$\quad = 3 \cos^2 \theta \sin \theta - \sin^3 \theta$

b) $\cos 2\theta = \cos^2 \theta - \sin^2 \theta$
$\sin 2\theta = 2 \cos \theta \sin \theta$
$\cos 3\theta = (\cos 2\theta + \theta)$
$\quad = (\cos^2 \theta - \sin^2 \theta)(\cos \theta)$
$\quad \quad - (2 \cos \theta \sin \theta)(\sin \theta)$
$\quad = \cos^3 \theta - \cos x \sin^2 \theta$
$\quad \quad - 2 \cos \theta \sin^2 \theta$
$\quad = \cos^3 \theta - 3 \cos \theta \sin^2 \theta$

c) $\tan 2\theta = \dfrac{2 \tan \theta}{1 - \tan^2 \theta}$
$\tan 3\theta = (\tan 2\theta + \theta)$
$\quad = \dfrac{\frac{2 \tan \theta}{1 - \tan^2 \theta} + \tan \theta}{1 - \left(\frac{2 \tan \theta}{1 - \tan^2 \theta}\right) \tan \theta}$
$\quad = \dfrac{\frac{2 \tan \theta + \tan \theta - \tan^3 \theta}{1 - \tan^2 \theta}}{\frac{1 - \tan^2 \theta - 2 \tan^2 \theta}{1 - \tan^2 \theta}}$
$\quad = \dfrac{3 \tan \theta - \tan^3 \theta}{1 - 3 \tan^2 \theta}$

13. **a)** $-\dfrac{4\sqrt{2}}{9}$ **c)** $\dfrac{\sqrt{3}}{3}$
b) $-\dfrac{7}{9}$ **d)** $-\dfrac{10\sqrt{2}}{27}$

14.

Write $\sin a$ in terms of $\dfrac{y}{r}$.

↓

Solve for x using the Pythagorean theorem, $x^2 + y^2 = r^2$.

↓

Choose the negative value of x since $a \in \left[\dfrac{\pi}{2}, \pi\right]$, and determine $\cos a$.

↓

Write $\cos a$ in terms of $\dfrac{x}{r}$.

↓

Use the formula $\sin 2a = 2 \sin a \cos a$ to evaluate $\sin 2a$.

15. **a)** Use the formula $\sin 2x = 2 \sin x \cos x$
to determine that
$\sin x \cos x = \dfrac{\sin 2x}{2}$.
Then graph the function $f(x) = \dfrac{\sin 2x}{2}$
by vertically compressing $f(x) = \sin x$
by a factor of $\dfrac{1}{2}$ and horizontally
compressing it by a factor of $\dfrac{1}{2}$.

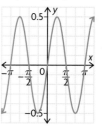

b) Use the formula $\cos 2x = 2 \cos^2 x - 1$
to determine that
$2 \cos^2 x = \cos 2x + 1$.
Then graph the function
$f(x) = \cos 2x + 1$ by horizontally
compressing $f(x) = \cos x$ by a factor of
$\dfrac{1}{2}$ and vertically translating it 1 unit up.

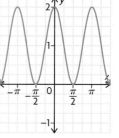

c) Use the formula $\tan 2x = \dfrac{2 \tan x}{1 - \tan^2 x}$
to determine that $\dfrac{\tan x}{1 - \tan^2 x} = \dfrac{\tan 2x}{2}$.

Then graph the function $f(x) = \frac{\tan 2x}{2}$ by vertically compressing $f(x) = \tan x$ by a factor of $\frac{1}{2}$ and horizontally compressing it by a factor of $\frac{1}{2}$.

16. a) $\dfrac{\tan^{-1} x}{2} = \tan^{-1} y$

b) $\dfrac{\cos^{-1} x}{2} = \cos^{-1} y$

c) $\dfrac{\cos^{-1} x}{2} = \csc^{-1} y$ or

$\dfrac{\cos^{-1} x}{2} = \sin^{-1}\left(\dfrac{1}{y}\right)$

d) $\dfrac{\sin^{-1} x}{2} = \dfrac{\sec^{-1} y}{4}$ or

$\dfrac{\sin^{-1} x}{2} = \dfrac{\cos^{-1}\left(\frac{1}{y}\right)}{4}$

17. a) $x = \dfrac{\pi}{6}, \dfrac{5\pi}{6},$ or $\dfrac{3\pi}{2}$

b) $x = \dfrac{\pi}{4}, \dfrac{\pi}{2}, \dfrac{5\pi}{4},$ or $\dfrac{3\pi}{2}$

18. a) $\dfrac{2\tan\theta}{1+\tan^2\theta}$

b) $\dfrac{1-\tan^2\theta}{1+\tan^2\theta}$

c) $\tan\theta$

d) $\tan\theta$

Mid-Chapter Review, p. 411

1. a) $\cos\dfrac{31\pi}{16}$ d) $\cos\dfrac{7\pi}{5}$

b) $\sin\dfrac{2\pi}{9}$ e) $\sin\dfrac{2\pi}{7}$

c) $\tan\dfrac{19\pi}{10}$ f) $\tan\dfrac{7\pi}{4}$

2. $y = 6\sin x + 4$

3. a) $\dfrac{1}{2}\cos x + \dfrac{\sqrt3}{2}\sin x$

b) $\dfrac{1}{2}\cos x - \dfrac{\sqrt3}{2}\sin x$

c) $\dfrac{1 + \tan x}{1 - \tan x}$

d) $\dfrac{\sqrt3}{2}\sin x - \dfrac{1}{2}\cos x$

4. a) $\dfrac{1}{2}\cos x + \dfrac{\sqrt3}{2}\sin x$

b) $\dfrac{\tan x - \sqrt3}{1 + \sqrt3\tan x}$

c) $\dfrac{\sqrt2}{2}\cos x - \dfrac{\sqrt2}{2}\sin x$

d) $-\dfrac{1}{2}\sin x - \dfrac{\sqrt3}{2}\cos x$

5. a) $\sqrt3$ c) $\dfrac{1}{2}$

b) 0 d) 1

6. a) $\tan 2x$ d) $\cos x$

b) $\sin x$ e) $\sqrt2(\cos x - \sin x)$

c) $\sin x$ f) $\dfrac{\tan x - 1}{1 + \tan x}$

7. $2\sqrt3\cos\left(x + \dfrac{\pi}{3}\right)$

8. a) $-\dfrac{1}{2}$ c) $\dfrac{\sqrt2}{2}$

b) $-\dfrac{1}{2}$ d) -1

9. a) $-\dfrac{\sqrt{11}}{11}$ c) $\dfrac{2\sqrt{10}}{11}$

b) $-\dfrac{\sqrt{110}}{11}$ d) $\dfrac{9}{11}$

10. $\sin 2x = \dfrac{24}{25}$; $\cos 2x = \dfrac{7}{25}$

11. $\sin 2x = \dfrac{120}{169}$

12. $\tan 2x = \dfrac{24}{7}$

Lesson 7.4, pp. 417–418

1. Answers may vary. For example,
$\sin\dfrac{\pi}{6} = \dfrac{1}{2}$; $\cos\dfrac{\pi}{6} = \dfrac{\sqrt3}{2}$.

2. a) $f(x) = \sin x$

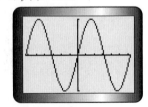

$g(x) = \tan x \cos x$

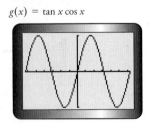

b) $\sin x = \tan x \cos x$

c) $\tan x \cos x = \left(\dfrac{\sin x}{\cos x}\right)\cos x$

$= \dfrac{\sin x \cos x}{\cos x} = \sin x$

d) The identity is not true when $\cos x = 0$ because when $\cos x = 0$, $\tan x$, or $\dfrac{\sin x}{\cos x}$, is undefined.

3. a) C; $\sin x \cot x = \cos x$

b) D; $1 - 2\sin^2 x = 2\cos^2 x - 1$

c) B; $(\sin x + \cos x)^2 = 1 + 2\sin x \cos x$

d) A; $\sec^2 x = \sin^2 x + \cos^2 x + \tan^2 x$

4. a) $\sin x \cot x = \cos x$

$\text{LS} = \sin x \cot x$

$= (\sin x)\left(\dfrac{\cos x}{\sin x}\right)$

$= \dfrac{\sin x \cos x}{\sin x}$

$= \cos x$

$= \text{RS}$

b) $1 - 2\sin^2 x = 2\cos^2 x - 1$

$1 - 2\sin^2 x - 2\cos^2 x + 1 = 0$

$2 - 2\sin^2 x - 2\cos^2 x = 0$

$2 - 2(\sin^2 x + \cos^2 x) = 0$

$2 - 2(1) = 0$

$2 - 2 = 0$

$0 = 0$

c) $(\sin x + \cos x)^2 = 1 + 2\sin x \cos x$

$\text{LS} = (\sin x + \cos x)^2$

$= \sin^2 x + 2\sin x \cos x$

$\quad + \cos^2 x$

$= (\sin^2 x + \cos^2 x)$

$\quad + 2\sin x \cos x$

$= 1 + 2\sin x \cos x$

$= \text{RS}$

d) $\sec^2 x = \sin^2 x + \cos^2 x + \tan^2 x$

$\text{RS} = \sin^2 x + \cos^2 x + \tan^2 x$

$= (\sin^2 x + \cos^2 x) + \tan^2 x$

$= 1 + \tan^2 x$

$= \dfrac{\cos^2 x}{\cos^2 x} + \dfrac{\sin^2 x}{\cos^2 x}$

$= \dfrac{\sin^2 x + \cos^2 x}{\cos^2 x}$

$= \dfrac{1}{\cos^2 x}$

$= \sec^2 x$

$= \text{LS}$

5. a) Answers may vary. For example,

$\cos\dfrac{\pi}{6} = \dfrac{\sqrt3}{2}$; $\dfrac{1}{\cos\frac{\pi}{6}} = \dfrac{2\sqrt3}{3}$.

b) Answers may vary. For example,

$1 - \tan^2\left(\dfrac{\pi}{4}\right) = 1 - (1)^2$

$= 1 - 1 = 0$;

$\sec^2\left(\dfrac{\pi}{4}\right) = (\sqrt2)^2 = 2$

c) Answers may vary. For example,

$\sin\left(\dfrac{\pi}{2} + \pi\right) = \sin\left(\dfrac{3\pi}{2}\right) = -1$;

$\cos\left(\dfrac{\pi}{2}\right)\cos\pi + \sin\left(\dfrac{\pi}{2}\right)\sin\pi$

$= (0)(-1) + (1)(0)$

$= 0 + 0 = 0$

d) Answers may vary. For example,

$$\cos\left(2\left(\frac{\pi}{3}\right)\right) = \cos\left(\frac{2\pi}{3}\right) = -\frac{1}{2}$$

$$1 + 2\sin^2\left(\frac{\pi}{3}\right) = 1 + (2)\left(\frac{\sqrt{3}}{2}\right)^2$$

$$= 1 + (2)\left(\frac{3}{4}\right)$$

$$= 1 + \frac{6}{4} = \frac{10}{4}$$

$$= \frac{5}{2}$$

6. Answers may vary. For example, $\cos 2x$.

7. $\dfrac{1 - \tan^2 x}{1 + \tan^2 x} = \dfrac{\dfrac{\cos^2 x - \sin^2 x}{\cos^2 x}}{\sec^2 x}$

$$= \frac{\cos^2 x - \sin^2 x}{\cos^2 x} \times \cos^2 x$$

$$= \cos^2 x - \sin^2 x$$

$$= \cos 2x$$

8. $\text{LS} = \dfrac{1 + \tan x}{1 + \cot x}$ $\quad$ $\text{RS} = \dfrac{1 - \tan x}{\cot x - 1}$

$$= \frac{1 + \tan x}{1 + \dfrac{1}{\tan x}} \qquad = \frac{1 - \tan x}{\dfrac{1}{\tan x} - 1}$$

$$= \frac{1 + \tan x}{\dfrac{\tan x + 1}{\tan x}} \qquad = \frac{1 - \tan x}{\dfrac{1 - \tan x}{\tan x}}$$

$$= \tan x \qquad = \tan x$$

Since the right side and the left side are equal, $\dfrac{1 + \tan x}{1 + \cot x} = \dfrac{1 - \tan x}{\cot x - 1}$.

9. a) $\dfrac{\cos^2 \theta - \sin^2 \theta}{\cos^2 \theta + \sin \theta \cos \theta}$

$$= \frac{(\cos \theta - \sin \theta)(\cos \theta + \sin \theta)}{(\cos \theta)(\cos \theta + \sin \theta)}$$

$$= \frac{\cos \theta - \sin \theta}{\cos \theta}$$

$$= \frac{\cos \theta}{\cos \theta} - \frac{\sin \theta}{\cos \theta}$$

$$= 1 - \tan \theta$$

b) $\text{LS} = \tan^2 x - \sin^2 x$

$$= \frac{\sin^2 x}{\cos^2 x} - \sin^2 x$$

$$= \sin^2 x \left(\frac{1}{\cos^2 x} - 1\right)$$

$$= \sin^2 x (\sec^2 x - 1)$$

$$= \sin^2 x \tan^2 x$$

$$= \text{RS}$$

So $\tan^2 x - \sin^2 x = \sin^2 x \tan^2 x$.

c) $\tan^2 x - \cos^2 x = \dfrac{1}{\cos^2 x} - 1$

$$\qquad\qquad - \cos^2 x$$

$$\tan^2 x - \cos^2 x + \cos^2 x$$

$$= \frac{1}{\cos^2 x} - 1 - \cos^2 x$$

$$+ \cos^2 x$$

$$\tan^2 x = \frac{1}{\cos^2 x} - 1$$

$$\tan^2 x = \frac{1}{\cos^2 x} - \frac{\cos^2 x}{\cos^2 x}$$

$$\tan^2 x = \frac{1 - \cos^2 x}{\cos^2 x}$$

$$\tan^2 x = \frac{\sin^2 x}{\cos^2 x}$$

$$\tan^2 x = \tan^2 x$$

d) $\dfrac{1}{1 + \cos \theta} + \dfrac{1}{1 - \cos \theta}$

$$= \frac{1 - \cos \theta}{(1 + \cos \theta)(1 - \cos \theta)}$$

$$+ \frac{1 + \cos \theta}{(1 - \cos \theta)(1 + \cos \theta)}$$

$$= \frac{1 - \cos \theta}{1 - \cos^2 \theta} + \frac{1 + \cos \theta}{1 - \cos^2 \theta}$$

$$= \frac{1 - \cos \theta + 1 + \cos \theta}{1 - \cos^2 \theta}$$

$$= \frac{2}{1 - \cos^2 \theta}$$

$$= \frac{2}{\sin^2 \theta}$$

10. a) $\cos x \tan^3 x = \sin x \tan^2 x$

$$\frac{\cos x \tan^3 x}{\tan^2 x} = \frac{\sin x \tan^2 x}{\tan^2 x}$$

$$\cos x \tan x = \sin x$$

$$\cos x \left(\frac{\sin x}{\cos x}\right) = \sin x$$

$$\sin x = \sin x$$

b) $\sin^2 \theta + \cos^4 \theta = \cos^2 \theta + \sin^4 \theta$

$$\sin^2 \theta + \cos^4 \theta - \sin^4 \theta = \cos^2 \theta$$

$$\qquad + \sin^4 \theta - \sin^4 \theta$$

$$\sin^2 \theta + \cos^4 \theta - \sin^4 \theta = \cos^2 \theta$$

$$\sin^2 \theta + \cos^4 \theta - \sin^4 \theta - \sin^2 \theta = \cos^2 \theta - \sin^2 \theta$$

$$\cos^4 \theta - \sin^4 \theta = \cos^2 \theta - \sin^2 \theta$$

$$(\cos^2 \theta + \sin^2 \theta)(\cos^2 \theta - \sin^2 \theta) = \cos^2 \theta - \sin^2 \theta$$

$$\cos^2 \theta + \sin^2 \theta = 1$$

$$1 = 1$$

c) $(\sin x + \cos x)\left(\dfrac{\tan^2 x + 1}{\tan x}\right)$

$$= \frac{1}{\cos x} + \frac{1}{\sin x}$$

$$(\sin x + \cos x)\left(\frac{\sec^2 x}{\tan x}\right)$$

$$= \frac{\sin x}{\cos x \sin x} + \frac{\cos x}{\sin x \cos x}$$

$$(\sin x + \cos x)\left(\frac{1}{\cos^2 x}\right)\left(\frac{1}{\tan x}\right)$$

$$= \frac{\sin x + \cos x}{\cos x \sin x}$$

$$(\sin x + \cos x)\left(\frac{1}{\cos^2 x}\right)\left(\frac{\cos x}{\sin x}\right)$$

$$= \frac{\sin x + \cos x}{\cos x \sin x}$$

$$(\sin x + \cos x)\left(\frac{1}{\cos x \sin x}\right)$$

$$= \frac{\sin x + \cos x}{\cos x \sin x}$$

$$\frac{\sin x + \cos x}{\cos x \sin x} = \frac{\sin x + \cos x}{\cos x \sin x}$$

d) $\tan^2 \beta + \cos^2 \beta + \sin^2 \beta = \dfrac{1}{\cos^2 \beta}$

$$\tan^2 \beta + 1 = \frac{1}{\cos^2 \beta}$$

$$\tan^2 \beta + 1 = \sec^2 \beta$$

Since $\tan^2 \beta + 1 = \sec^2 \beta$ is a known identity, $\tan^2 \beta + \cos^2 \beta + \sin^2 \beta$ must equal $\dfrac{1}{\cos^2 \beta}$.

e) $\sin\left(\dfrac{\pi}{4} + x\right) + \sin\left(\dfrac{\pi}{4} - x\right)$

$$= \sqrt{2}\cos x;$$

$$\sin\frac{\pi}{4}\cos x + \cos\frac{\pi}{4}\sin x$$

$$+ \sin\frac{\pi}{4}\cos x - \cos\frac{\pi}{4}\sin x$$

$$= \sqrt{2}\cos x;$$

$$2\sin\frac{\pi}{4}\cos x = \sqrt{2}\cos x;$$

$$(2)\left(\frac{\sqrt{2}}{2}\right)(\cos x) = \sqrt{2}\cos x;$$

$$\sqrt{2}\cos x = \sqrt{2}\cos x$$

f) $\sin\left(\dfrac{\pi}{2} - x\right)\cot\left(\dfrac{\pi}{2} + x\right) = -\sin x;$

$$\sin\left(\frac{\pi}{2} - x\right)\left(\frac{\cos\left(\frac{\pi}{2} + x\right)}{\sin\left(\frac{\pi}{2} + x\right)}\right) = -\sin x;$$

$$\left(\sin\frac{\pi}{2}\cos x - \cos\frac{\pi}{2}\sin x\right)$$

$$\times \left(\frac{\cos\frac{\pi}{2}\cos x - \sin\frac{\pi}{2}\sin x}{\sin\frac{\pi}{2}\cos x + \cos\frac{\pi}{2}\sin x}\right) = -\sin x;$$

$$((1)(\cos x) - (0)(\sin x))$$

$$\times \left(\frac{(0)(\cos x) - (1)(\sin x)}{(1)(\cos x) + (0)(\sin x)}\right) = -\sin x;$$

$$(\cos x - 0)\left(\frac{0 - \sin x}{\cos x + 0}\right) = -\sin x;$$

$$(\cos x)\left(-\frac{\sin x}{\cos x}\right) = -\sin x;$$

$$-\sin x = -\sin x$$

11. a) $\dfrac{\cos 2x + 1}{\sin 2x} = \cot x$

$$\frac{2\cos^2 x - 1 + 1}{2\sin x \cos x} = \cot x$$

$$\frac{2\cos^2 x}{2\sin x \cos x} = \cot x$$

$$\frac{\cos x}{\sin x} = \cot x$$

$$\cot x = \cot x$$

b)
$$\frac{\sin 2x}{1 - \cos 2x} = \cot x$$
$$\frac{2\sin x \cos x}{1 - (1 - 2\sin^2 x)} = \cot x$$
$$\frac{2\sin x \cos x}{1 - 1 + 2\sin^2 x} = \cot x$$
$$\frac{2\sin x \cos x}{2\sin^2 x} = \cot x$$
$$\frac{\cos x}{\sin x} = \cot x$$
$$\cot x = \cot x$$

c) $(\sin x + \cos x)^2 = 1 + \sin 2x$;
$\sin^2 x + \sin x \cos x + \sin x \cos x$
$\quad + \cos^2 x = 1 + 2\sin x \cos x$;
$\sin^2 x + 2\sin x \cos x + \cos^2 x$
$\quad = 1 + 2\sin x \cos x$;
$(\cos^2 x + \sin^2 x) + 2\sin x \cos x$
$\quad = 1 + 2\sin x \cos x$;
$1 + 2\sin x \cos x = 1 + 2\sin x \cos x$

d) $\cos^4\theta - \sin^4\theta = \cos 2\theta$
$(\cos^2\theta + \sin^2\theta)(\cos^2\theta - \sin^2\theta)$
$\quad = \cos^2\theta - \sin^2\theta$
$(1)(\cos^2\theta - \sin^2\theta) = \cos^2\theta - \sin^2\theta$
$\cos^2\theta - \sin^2\theta = \cos^2\theta - \sin^2\theta$

e) $\cot\theta - \tan\theta = 2\cot 2\theta$
$$\frac{\cos\theta}{\sin\theta} - \frac{\sin\theta}{\cos\theta} = 2\frac{\cos 2\theta}{\sin 2\theta}$$
$$\frac{\cos^2\theta}{\sin\theta\cos\theta} - \frac{\sin^2\theta}{\cos\theta\sin\theta}$$
$$= (2)\left(\frac{\cos 2\theta}{2\cos\theta\sin\theta}\right)$$
$$\frac{\cos^2\theta - \sin^2\theta}{\sin\theta\cos\theta} = \frac{\cos 2\theta}{\cos\theta\sin\theta}$$
$$\frac{\cos 2\theta}{\cos\theta\sin\theta} = \frac{\cos 2\theta}{\cos\theta\sin\theta}$$

f) $\cot\theta + \tan\theta = 2\csc 2\theta$
$$\frac{\cos\theta}{\sin\theta} + \frac{\sin\theta}{\cos\theta} = 2\frac{1}{\sin 2\theta}$$
$$\frac{\cos^2\theta}{\sin\theta\cos\theta} + \frac{\sin^2\theta}{\cos\theta\sin\theta}$$
$$= (2)\left(\frac{1}{2\cos\theta\sin\theta}\right)$$
$$\frac{\cos^2\theta + \sin^2\theta}{\sin\theta\cos\theta} = \frac{1}{\cos\theta\sin\theta}$$
$$\frac{1}{\cos\theta\sin\theta} = \frac{1}{\cos\theta\sin\theta}$$

g) $\dfrac{1 + \tan x}{1 - \tan x} = \tan\left(x + \dfrac{\pi}{4}\right)$
$$\frac{1 + \tan x}{1 - \tan x} = \frac{\tan x + \tan\frac{\pi}{4}}{1 - \tan x \tan\frac{\pi}{4}}$$
$$\frac{1 + \tan x}{1 - \tan x} = \frac{\tan x + 1}{1 - (\tan x)(1)}$$
$$\frac{1 + \tan x}{1 - \tan x} = \frac{1 + \tan x}{1 - \tan x}$$

h) $\csc 2x + \cot 2x = \cot x$;
$$\frac{1}{\sin 2x} + \frac{1}{\tan 2x} = \cot x;$$
$$\frac{1}{2\sin x \cos x} + \frac{1}{\frac{2\tan x}{1 - \tan^2 x}} = \cot x;$$
$$\frac{1}{2\sin x \cos x} + \frac{1 - \tan^2 x}{2\tan x} = \cot x;$$
$$\frac{1}{2\sin x \cos x} + \frac{1 - \tan^2 x}{2\frac{\sin x}{\cos x}} = \cot x;$$
$$\frac{1}{2\sin x \cos x} + \frac{(\cos x)(1 - \tan^2 x)}{2\sin x}$$
$$= \frac{\cos x}{\sin x};$$
$$\frac{1}{2\sin x \cos x} + \frac{(\cos x)(1 - \tan^2 x)(\cos x)}{2\sin x \cos x}$$
$$= \frac{(\cos x)(2\cos x)}{(\sin x)(2\cos x)};$$
$$\frac{1}{2\sin x \cos x} + \frac{(\cos^2 x)(1 - \tan^2 x)}{2\sin x \cos x}$$
$$= \frac{2\cos^2 x}{2\sin x \cos x};$$
$$\frac{1}{2\sin x \cos x} + \frac{\cos^2 x - (\tan^2 x)(\cos^2 x)}{2\sin x \cos x}$$
$$= \frac{2\cos^2 x}{2\sin x \cos x};$$
$$\frac{1}{2\sin x \cos x} + \frac{\cos^2 x - \sin^2 x}{2\sin x \cos x}$$
$$= \frac{2\cos^2 x}{2\sin x \cos x};$$
$$\frac{1 + \cos^2 x - \sin^2 x}{2\sin x \cos x} = \frac{2\cos^2 x}{2\sin x \cos x};$$
$$\frac{1 + \cos^2 x - \sin^2 x}{2\sin x \cos x} - \frac{2\cos^2 x}{2\sin x \cos x}$$
$$= \frac{2\cos^2 x}{2\sin x \cos x} - \frac{2\cos^2 x}{2\sin x \cos x};$$
$$\frac{1 + \cos^2 x - \sin^2 x - 2\cos^2 x}{2\sin x \cos x} = 0;$$
$$\frac{1 - \sin^2 x - \cos^2 x}{2\sin x \cos x} = 0;$$
$$\frac{1 - (\sin^2 x + \cos^2 x)}{2\sin x \cos x} = 0;$$
$$\frac{1 - 1}{2\sin x \cos x} = 0;$$
$$\frac{0}{2\sin x \cos x} = 0;$$
$$0 = 0$$

i)
$$\frac{2\tan x}{1 + \tan^2 x} = \sin 2x$$
$$\frac{2\tan x}{\sec^2 x} = \sin 2x$$
$$\frac{2\tan x}{\frac{1}{\cos^2 x}} = \sin 2x$$
$$(2\tan x)(\cos^2 x) = \sin 2x$$
$$\left(\frac{2\sin x}{\cos x}\right)(\cos^2 x) = \sin 2x$$
$$\sin 2x = 2\sin x \cos x$$

Since $\sin 2x = 2\sin x \cos x$ is a known identity, $\dfrac{2\tan x}{1 - \tan^2 x}$ must equal $\sin 2x$.

j) $\sec 2t = \dfrac{\csc t}{\csc t - 2\sin t}$
$$\frac{1}{\cos 2t} = \frac{\frac{1}{\sin t}}{\frac{1}{\sin t} - 2\sin t}$$
$$\frac{1}{\cos 2t} = \frac{\frac{1}{\sin t}}{\frac{1}{\sin t} - \frac{2\sin^2 t}{\sin t}}$$
$$\frac{1}{\cos 2t} = \frac{\frac{1}{\sin t}}{\frac{1 - 2\sin^2 t}{\sin t}}$$
$$\frac{1}{\cos 2t} = \frac{1}{\sin t} \times \frac{\sin t}{1 - 2\sin^2 t}$$
$$\frac{1}{\cos 2t} = \frac{1}{1 - 2\sin^2 t}$$
$$\frac{1}{\cos 2t} = \frac{1}{\cos 2t}$$

k) $\csc 2\theta = \dfrac{1}{2}\sec\theta\csc\theta$
$$\frac{1}{\sin 2\theta} = \left(\frac{1}{2}\right)\left(\frac{1}{\cos\theta}\right)\left(\frac{1}{\sin\theta}\right)$$
$$\frac{1}{\sin 2\theta} = \frac{1}{2\cos\theta\sin\theta}$$
$$\frac{1}{2\sin\theta\cos\theta} = \frac{1}{2\sin\theta\cos\theta}$$

l)
$$\frac{1}{\cos t} = \frac{2\sin t\cos t}{\sin t} - \frac{2\cos^2 t - 1}{\cos t}$$
$$\frac{\sin t}{\cos t\sin t} = \frac{2\sin t\cos^2 t}{\sin t\cos t}$$
$$- \frac{(\sin t)(2\cos^2 t - 1)}{\cos t\sin t}$$
$$\frac{\sin t}{\cos t\sin t} = \frac{2\sin t\cos^2 t}{\sin t\cos t}$$
$$- \frac{2\cos^2 t\sin t - \sin t}{\cos t\sin t}$$
$$\frac{\sin t}{\cos t\sin t} = \frac{2\sin t\cos^2 t}{\sin t\cos t}$$
$$- \frac{2\cos^2 t\sin t - \sin t}{\sin t\cos t}$$
$$\frac{\sin t}{\cos t\sin t} = \frac{2\sin t\cos^2 t}{\sin t\cos t}$$
$$+ \frac{-2\sin t\cos^2 t + \sin t}{\sin t\cos t}$$
$$\frac{\sin t}{\cos t\sin t} = \frac{\sin t}{\cos t\sin t}$$

12. Answers may vary. For example, an equivalent expression is tan x.

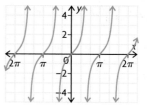

13.

$$\frac{\sin x + \sin 2x}{1 + \cos x + \cos 2x} = \tan x$$

$$\frac{\sin x + 2 \sin x \cos x}{1 + \cos x + \cos 2x} = \tan x$$

$$\frac{\sin x(1 + 2 \cos x)}{1 + \cos x + \cos 2x} = \tan x$$

$$\frac{\sin x(1 + 2 \cos x)}{\cos x + (1 + \cos 2x)} = \tan x$$

$$\frac{\sin x(1 + 2 \cos x)}{\cos x + 2 \cos^2 x} = \tan x$$

$$\frac{\sin x(1 + 2 \cos x)}{\cos x(1 + 2 \cos x)} = \tan x$$

$$\frac{\sin x}{\cos x} = \tan x$$

$$\tan x = \tan x$$

14.

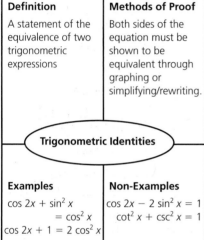

Definition	Methods of Proof
A statement of the equivalence of two trigonometric expressions	Both sides of the equation must be shown to be equivalent through graphing or simplifying/rewriting.

Trigonometric Identities

Examples	Non-Examples
$\cos 2x + \sin^2 x$ $= \cos^2 x$ $\cos 2x + 1 = 2 \cos^2 x$	$\cos 2x - 2 \sin^2 x = 1$ $\cot^2 x + \csc^2 x = 1$

15. She can determine whether the equation $2 \sin x \cos x = \cos 2x$ is an identity by trying to simplify and/or rewrite the left side of the equation so that it is equivalent to the right side of the equation. Alternatively, she can graph the functions $y = 2 \sin x \cos x$ and $y = \cos 2x$ and see if the graphs are the same. If they're the same, it's an identity, but if they're not the same, it's not an identity. By doing this she can determine it's not an identity, but she can make it an identity by changing the equation to $2 \sin x \cos x = \sin 2x$.

16. a) $a = 2, b = 1, c = 1$
b) $a = -1, b = 2, c = -2$

17. $\cos 4x + 4 \cos 2x + 3$; $a = 1$, $b = 4, c = 3$

Lesson 7.5, pp. 426–428

1. a) $\dfrac{\pi}{2}$ **d)** $\dfrac{7\pi}{6}$ or $\dfrac{11\pi}{6}$

b) $\dfrac{3\pi}{2}$ **e)** $0, \pi,$ or 2π

---

c) $\dfrac{\pi}{6}$ or $\dfrac{5\pi}{6}$ **f)** $\dfrac{\pi}{3}$ or $\dfrac{2\pi}{3}$

2. a) 0 or 2π **d)** $\dfrac{2\pi}{3}$ or $\dfrac{4\pi}{3}$

b) π **e)** $\dfrac{\pi}{2}$ or $\dfrac{3\pi}{2}$

c) $\dfrac{\pi}{3}$ or $\dfrac{5\pi}{3}$ **f)** $\dfrac{\pi}{6}$ or $\dfrac{11\pi}{6}$

3. a) 2 **c)** $x = \dfrac{\pi}{3}$

b) quadrants I and II **d)** $x = \dfrac{\pi}{3}$ and $\dfrac{2\pi}{3}$

4. a) 2
b) quadrants II and III
c) $30°$
d) $x = 150°$ or $210°$

5. a) 2
b) quadrants I and III
c) 1.22
d) $\theta = 1.22$ or 4.36

6. a) $\theta = \dfrac{\pi}{4}$ or $\dfrac{5\pi}{4}$

b) $\theta = \dfrac{\pi}{4}$ or $\dfrac{3\pi}{4}$

c) $\theta = \dfrac{\pi}{6}$ or $\dfrac{11\pi}{6}$

d) $\theta = \dfrac{4\pi}{3}$ or $\dfrac{5\pi}{3}$

e) $\theta = \dfrac{3\pi}{4}$ or $\dfrac{5\pi}{4}$

f) $\theta = \dfrac{\pi}{3}$ or $\dfrac{4\pi}{3}$

7. a) $\theta = 210°$ or $330°$
b) $\theta = 131.8°$ or $228.2°$
c) $\theta = 56.3°$ or $236.3°$
d) $\theta = 221.8°$ or $318.2°$
e) $\theta = 78.5°$ or $281.5°$
f) $\theta = 116.6°$ or $296.6°$

8. a) $x = 0.52$ or 2.62
b) $x = 0.52$ or 5.76
c) $x = 1.05$ or 5.24
d) $x = 3.67$ or 5.76

9. a) $x = 0.79$ or 3.93
b) $x = 0.52$ or 2.62
c) $x = 0$ or 6.28
d) $x = 3.67$ or 5.76
e) $x = 1.16$ or 5.12
f) $x = 1.11$ or 4.25

10. a) $x = 0.39, 1.18, 3.53,$ or 4.32
b) $x = 0.13, 0.65, 1.70, 2.23, 3.27, 3.80,$ $4.84,$ or 5.37
c) $x = 1.40, 1.75, 3.49, 3.84, 5.59,$ or 5.93
d) $x = 0.59, 0.985, 2.16, 2.55, 3.73,$ $4.12, 5.304,$ or 5.697
e) $x = 1.05, 2.09, 4.19,$ or 5.24
f) $x = 1.05$

11. from about day 144 to about day 221
12. $1.86 \text{ s} < t < 4.14 \text{ s};$
$9.86 \text{ s} < t < 12.14 \text{ s};$
$17.86 \text{ s} < t < 20.14 \text{ s}$

---

13. $x = \dfrac{\pi}{4}$ or $\dfrac{5\pi}{4}$

14.

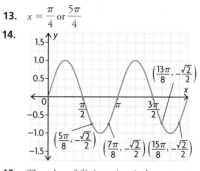

15. The value of $f(x) = \sin x$ is the same at x and $\pi - x$. In other words, it is the same at x and half the period minus x. Since the period of $f(x) = 25 \sin \dfrac{\pi}{50}(x + 20) - 55$ is 100, if the function were not horizontally translated, its value at x would be the same as at $50 - x$. The function is horizontally translated 20 units to the left, however, so it goes through half its period from $x = -20$ to $x = 30$. At $x = 3$, the function is 23 units away from the left end of the range, so it will have the same value at $x = 30 - 23$ or $x = 7$, which is 23 units away from the right end of the range.

16. To solve a trigonometric equation **algebraically**, first isolate the trigonometric function on one side of the equation. For example, the trigonometric equation $5 \cos x - 3 = 2$ would become $5 \cos x = 5$, which would then become $\cos x = 1$. Next, apply the inverse of the trigonometric function to both sides of the equation. For example, the trigonometric equation $\cos x = 1$ would become $x = \cos^{-1} 1$. Finally, simplify the equation. For example, $x = \cos^{-1} 1$ would become $x = 0 + 2n\pi$, where $n \in \mathbf{I}$. To solve a trigonometric equation **graphically**, first isolate the trigonometric function on one side of the equation. For example, the trigonometric equation $5 \cos x - 3 = 2$ would become $5 \cos x = 5$, which would then become $\cos x = 1$. Next, graph both sides of the equation. For example, the functions $f(x) = \cos x$ and $f(x) = 1$ would both be graphed. Finally, find the points where the two graphs intersect. For example, $f(x) = \cos x$ and $f(x) = 1$ would intersect at $x = 0 + 2n\pi$, where $n \in \mathbf{I}$. **Similarity:** Both trigonometric functions are first isolated on one side of the equation. **Differences:** The inverse of a trigonometric function is not applied in the graphical method, and the points of intersection are not obtained in the algebraic method.

17. $x = 0 + n\pi, \dfrac{2\pi}{3} + 2n\pi,$ and

$\dfrac{4\pi}{3} + n\pi,$ where $n \in \mathbf{I}$

18. a) $x = \dfrac{\pi}{4}, \dfrac{\pi}{2}, \dfrac{5\pi}{4},$ or $\dfrac{3\pi}{4}$

b) $x = \dfrac{\pi}{6}, \dfrac{\pi}{2},$ or $\dfrac{5\pi}{6}$

Lesson 7.6, pp. 435–437

1. a) $(\sin \theta)(\sin \theta - 1)$
   b) $(\cos \theta - 1)(\cos \theta - 1)$
   c) $(3 \sin \theta + 2)(\sin \theta - 1)$
   d) $(2 \cos \theta - 1)(2 \cos \theta + 1)$
   e) $(6 \sin x - 2)(4 \sin x + 1)$
   f) $(7 \tan x + 8)(7 \tan x - 8)$

2. a) $y = \pm\dfrac{\sqrt{3}}{3}, x = \dfrac{\pi}{6}, \dfrac{5\pi}{6}, \dfrac{7\pi}{6},$ or $\dfrac{11\pi}{6}$

   b) $y = 0$ or $-1, x = 0, \pi, \dfrac{3\pi}{2},$ or 2π

   c) $y = 0$ or $z = \dfrac{1}{2}, x = \dfrac{\pi}{6}, \dfrac{\pi}{2}, \dfrac{5\pi}{6},$ or $\dfrac{3\pi}{2}$

   d) $y = 0$ or $z = 1, x = 0, \pi,$ or 2π

3. a) $y = \dfrac{1}{3}$ or $\dfrac{1}{2}$

   b) $x = 1.05, 1.91, 4.37,$ or 5.24

4. a) $\theta = 90°$ or $270°$
   b) $\theta = 0°, 180°,$ or $360°$
   c) $\theta = 45°, 135°, 225°,$ or $315°$
   d) $\theta = 60°, 120°, 240°,$ or $300°$
   e) $\theta = 30°, 150°, 210°,$ or $330°$
   f) $\theta = 45°, 135°, 225°,$ or $315°$

5. a) $x = 0°, 90°, 180°, 270°,$ or $360°$
   b) $x = 0°, 180°,$ or $360°$
   c) $x = 90°$ or $270°$
   d) $x = 60°, 90°, 120°,$ or $270°$
   e) $x = 45°, 135°, 225°,$ or $315°$
   f) $x = 90°$ or $180°$

6. a) $x = \dfrac{\pi}{6}, \dfrac{\pi}{2}, \dfrac{5\pi}{6},$ or $\dfrac{3\pi}{2}$

   b) $x = \dfrac{3\pi}{2}$

   c) $x = 0, \dfrac{5\pi}{6}, \pi, \dfrac{7\pi}{6},$ or 2π

   d) $x = \dfrac{\pi}{3}, \dfrac{4\pi}{3},$ or $\dfrac{5\pi}{3}$

   e) $x = \dfrac{\pi}{4}, \dfrac{3\pi}{4}, \dfrac{5\pi}{4},$ or $\dfrac{7\pi}{4}$

   f) $x = 0, \dfrac{3\pi}{2},$ or 2π

7. a) $\theta = \dfrac{\pi}{3}, \pi,$ or $\dfrac{5\pi}{3}$

   b) $\theta = \dfrac{\pi}{6}, \dfrac{5\pi}{6},$ or $\dfrac{3\pi}{2}$

   c) $\theta = \pi$

   d) $\theta = \dfrac{\pi}{6}$ or $\dfrac{5\pi}{6}$

   e) $\theta = \dfrac{\pi}{4}, 2.82, \dfrac{5\pi}{4},$ or 5.96

   f) $\theta = 0.73, 2.41, 3.99,$ or 5.44

---

8. a) $x = \dfrac{\pi}{3}$ or $\dfrac{5\pi}{3}$

   b) $x = \dfrac{\pi}{6}, \dfrac{5\pi}{6}, \dfrac{7\pi}{6},$ or $\dfrac{11\pi}{6}$

   c) $x = 0, 0.96\,\pi, 5.33,$ or 2π

   d) $x = \dfrac{3\pi}{4}$ or $\dfrac{7\pi}{4}$

   e) $x = \dfrac{\pi}{4}, \dfrac{\pi}{2}, \dfrac{3\pi}{4}, \dfrac{5\pi}{4}, \dfrac{3\pi}{2},$ or $\dfrac{7\pi}{4}$

   f) $x = 0, \dfrac{\pi}{6}, \dfrac{5\pi}{6}, \pi, \dfrac{7\pi}{6}, \dfrac{11\pi}{6},$ or 2π

9. a) $x = \dfrac{\pi}{3}, 1.98, 4.30,$ or $\dfrac{5\pi}{3}$

   b) $x = 0.45, \dfrac{2\pi}{3}, \dfrac{4\pi}{3},$ or 5.83

   c) $x = \dfrac{\pi}{6}, 0.85, \dfrac{5\pi}{6},$ or 2.29

   d) $x = \dfrac{\pi}{2}, \dfrac{7\pi}{6},$ or $\dfrac{11\pi}{6}$

10. $x = 0.15, 1.02, 2.12,$ or 2.99
11. $b = 1 + \sqrt{3}, c = \sqrt{3}$

12. $c = \dfrac{1}{2}$

13. $\dfrac{\pi}{3} \text{ km} < d < \dfrac{2\pi}{3} \text{ km},$

$\dfrac{4\pi}{3} \text{ km} < d < \dfrac{5\pi}{3} \text{ km}$

14. $x = 1.91$ or 4.37

15. a) $x = \dfrac{3\pi}{4}$ or $\dfrac{5\pi}{4}$

   b) $x = \dfrac{3\pi}{4} + 2n\pi$ or $\dfrac{5\pi}{4} + 2n\pi,$ where

   $n \in \mathbf{I}$

16. It is possible to have different numbers of solutions for quadratic trigonometric equations because, when factored, a quadratic trigonometric equation can be one expression multiplied by another expression or it can be a single expression squared. For example, the equation $\cos^2 x + \dfrac{3}{2}\cos x + \dfrac{1}{2}$ becomes

$\left(\cos x + 1\right)\left(\cos x + \dfrac{1}{2}\right)$ when

factored, and it has the solutions $\dfrac{2\pi}{3}, \pi,$

and $\dfrac{4\pi}{3}$ in the interval $0 \le x \le 2\pi$.
In comparison, the equation
$\cos^2 x + 2\cos x + 1 = 0$ becomes
$(\cos x + 1)^2$ when factored, and it has only one solution, π, in the interval
$0 \le x \le 2\pi$. Also, different expressions produce different numbers of solutions. For example, the expression $\cos x + \dfrac{1}{2}$ produces two solutions in the interval $0 \le x \le 2\pi$

$\left(\dfrac{2\pi}{3} \text{ and } \dfrac{4\pi}{3}\right)$ because $\cos x = -\dfrac{1}{2}$ for two

different values of x. The expression
$\cos x + 1$, however, produces only one

---

solution in the interval $0 \le x \le 2\pi$ (π),
because $\cos x = -1$ for only one value of x.

17. $a = \dfrac{\pi}{4}, \dfrac{5\pi}{4}$

18. $x = 0.72, \dfrac{\pi}{2}, \pi, \dfrac{3\pi}{2},$ or 5.56

19. $x = 15°, 75°, 105°, 165°, 195°, 255°,$
   $285°,$ or $345°$

20. $\theta = 0.96$

Chapter Review, p. 440

1. a) Answers may vary. For example, $\sin \dfrac{7\pi}{10}$.

   b) Answers may vary. For example, $\cos \dfrac{8\pi}{7}$.

   c) Answers may vary. For example, $\sin \dfrac{6\pi}{7}$.

   d) Answers may vary. For example, $\cos \dfrac{\pi}{7}$.

2. $y = 5\cos(x) - 8$

3. a) $\dfrac{\sqrt{3}}{2}\cos x - \dfrac{1}{2}\sin x$

   b) $-\dfrac{\sqrt{2}}{2}\cos x - \dfrac{\sqrt{2}}{2}\sin x$

   c) $\dfrac{\tan x + \sqrt{3}}{1 - \sqrt{3}\tan x}$

   d) $-\dfrac{\sqrt{2}}{2}\cos x - \dfrac{\sqrt{2}}{2}\sin x$

4. a) $-\dfrac{\sqrt{3}}{3}$ **b)** $-\dfrac{\sqrt{3}}{2}$

5. a) $\dfrac{1}{2}$ **c)** $-\dfrac{\sqrt{2}}{2}$

   b) $\dfrac{\sqrt{3}}{2}$ **d)** $\sqrt{3}$

6. a) $\sin 2x = \dfrac{24}{25}, \cos 2x = \dfrac{7}{25},$

   $\tan 2x = \dfrac{24}{7}$

   b) $\sin 2x = -\dfrac{336}{625}, \cos 2x = -\dfrac{527}{625},$

   $\tan 2x = \dfrac{336}{527}$

   c) $\sin 2x = -\dfrac{120}{169}, \cos 2x = \dfrac{119}{169},$

   $\tan 2x = -\dfrac{120}{119}$

7. a) trigonometric identity
   b) trigonometric equation
   c) trigonometric identity
   d) trigonometric equation

8. $\dfrac{\cos^2 x}{\cot^2 x} = 1 - \cos^2 x$

$\dfrac{\cos^2 x}{\dfrac{\cos^2 x}{\sin^2 x}} = 1 - \cos^2 x$

$\dfrac{(\cos^2 x)(\sin^2 x)}{\cos^2 x} = 1 - \cos^2 x$

$\sin^2 x = 1 - \cos^2 x$

$1 - \cos^2 x = 1 - \cos^2 x$

9. $\dfrac{2(\sec^2 x - \tan^2 x)}{\csc x} = \sin 2x \sec x$

$\dfrac{2(1)}{\csc x} = \sin 2x \sec x$

$\dfrac{2}{\csc x} = \sin 2x \sec x$

$2 \sin x = \sin 2x \sec x$

$\dfrac{2 \sin x \cos x}{\cos x} = \sin 2x \sec x$

$\dfrac{\sin 2x}{\cos x} = \sin 2x \sec x$

$\sin 2x \sec x = \sin 2x \sec x$

10. **a)** $x = \dfrac{7\pi}{6}$ or $\dfrac{11\pi}{6}$

b) $x = \dfrac{\pi}{4}$ or $\dfrac{5\pi}{4}$

c) $x = \dfrac{2\pi}{3}$ or $\dfrac{4\pi}{3}$

11. **a)** $y = -2$ or 2

b) $x = \dfrac{\pi}{6}, \dfrac{5\pi}{6}, \dfrac{7\pi}{6},$ or $\dfrac{11\pi}{6}$

12. **a)** $x = \dfrac{\pi}{2}, \dfrac{7\pi}{6},$ or $\dfrac{11\pi}{6}$

b) $x = 0, \dfrac{\pi}{6}, \dfrac{5\pi}{6}, \pi, \dfrac{7\pi}{6}, \dfrac{11\pi}{6},$ or 2π

c) $x = \dfrac{\pi}{4}, \dfrac{2\pi}{3}, \dfrac{4\pi}{3},$ or $\dfrac{7\pi}{4}$

d) $x = 0.95$ or 4.09

13. $x = \dfrac{\pi}{2}, \pi,$ or $\dfrac{3\pi}{2}$

Chapter Self-Test, p. 441

1. $\dfrac{1 - 2\sin^2 x}{\cos x + \sin x} + \sin x = \cos x$

$\dfrac{1 - 2\sin^2 x}{\cos x + \sin x} + \sin x - \sin x$

$= \cos x - \sin x$

$\dfrac{1 - 2\sin^2 x}{\cos x + \sin x} = \cos x - \sin x$

$1 - 2\sin^2 x = (\cos x - \sin x)$
$\qquad\qquad\qquad \times (\cos x + \sin x)$

$\cos 2x = (\cos x - \sin x)$
$\qquad\qquad \times (\cos x + \sin x)$

$\cos 2x = \cos^2 x - \sin^2 x$

$\cos 2x = \cos 2x$

2. all real numbers x, where $0 \le x \le 2\pi$

3. **a)** $x = \dfrac{\pi}{6}$ or $x = \dfrac{11\pi}{6}$

b) $x = \dfrac{2\pi}{3}$ or $x = \dfrac{5\pi}{3}$

c) $x = \dfrac{5\pi}{4}$ or $x = \dfrac{7\pi}{4}$

4. $a = 2, b = 1$

5. $t = 7, 11, 19,$ and 23

6. Nina can find the cosine of $\dfrac{11\pi}{4}$ by using

the formula
$\cos(x + y) = \cos x \cos y - \sin x \sin y$.
The cosine of π is -1, and the

cosine of $\dfrac{7\pi}{4}$ is $\dfrac{\sqrt{2}}{2}$. Also, the sine of π is 0,

and the sine of $\dfrac{7\pi}{4}$ is $-\dfrac{\sqrt{2}}{2}$. Therefore,

$\cos \dfrac{11\pi}{4} = \cos\left(\pi + \dfrac{7\pi}{4} \right)$

$= \left(-1 \times \dfrac{\sqrt{2}}{2} \right) - \left(0 \times -\dfrac{\sqrt{2}}{2} \right)$

$= -\dfrac{\sqrt{2}}{2} - 0$

$= -\dfrac{\sqrt{2}}{2}$

7. $x = 3.31$ or 6.12

8. $-\dfrac{33}{65}, -\dfrac{16}{65}$

9. **a)** $-\dfrac{4\sqrt{5}}{9}$ **c)** $\sqrt{\dfrac{3 - \sqrt{5}}{6}}$

b) $\dfrac{1}{9}$ **d)** $\dfrac{22}{27}$

10. **a)** $x = -\dfrac{5\pi}{3}, -\dfrac{\pi}{3}, \dfrac{\pi}{3},$ or $\dfrac{5\pi}{3}$

b) $x = -\dfrac{4\pi}{3}, -\dfrac{2\pi}{3}, \dfrac{2\pi}{3},$ or $\dfrac{4\pi}{3}$

c) $x = -\pi$ and π

Chapter 8

Getting Started, p. 446

1. **a)** $\dfrac{1}{5^2} = \dfrac{1}{25}$ **d)** $\sqrt[3]{125} = 5$

b) 1 **e)** $-\sqrt{121} = -11$

c) $\sqrt{36} = 6$ **f)** $\left(\sqrt[3]{\dfrac{27}{8}} \right)^2 = \dfrac{9}{4}$

2. **a)** $3^7 = 2187$ **d)** $7^4 = 2401$

b) $(-2)^2 = 4$ **e)** $8^{\frac{2}{3}} = 4$

c) $10^3 = 1000$ **f)** $4^{\frac{1}{2}} = \sqrt{4} = 2$

3. **a)** $8m^3$ **d)** $x^3 y$

b) $\dfrac{1}{a^8 b^{10}}$ **e)** $-d^2 c^2$

c) $4|x|^3$ **f)** x

4. **a)**

$D = \{x \in \mathbf{R}\}$, $R = \{y \in \mathbf{R}\,|\,y > 0\}$, y-intercept 1, horizontal asymptote $y = 0$

b)

$D = \{x \in \mathbf{R}\}$, $R = \{y \in \mathbf{R}\,|\,y > 0\}$, y-intercept 1, horizontal asymptote $y = 0$

c)

$D = \{x \in \mathbf{R}\}$, $R = \{y \in \mathbf{R}\,|\,y > -2\}$, y-intercept -1, horizontal asymptote $y = -2$

5. **a)** **i)** $y = \dfrac{x + 6}{3}$

ii) $y = \pm\sqrt{x + 5}$

iii) $y = \sqrt[3]{\dfrac{x}{6}}$

iv)

b) The inverses of (i) and (iii) are functions.

6. **a)** 800 bacteria

b) 6400 bacteria

c) 209 715 200

d) 4.4×10^{15}

7. 12 515 people

8.

Similarities	Differences
• same y-intercept • same shape • same horizontal asymptote • both are always positive	• one is always increasing, the other is always decreasing • different end behaviour • reflections of each other across the y-axis

Lesson 8.1, p. 451

1. **a)** $x = 4^y$ or $f^{-1}(x) = \log_4 x$

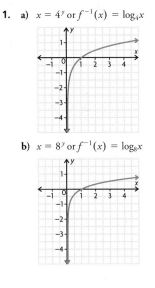

b) $x = 8^y$ or $f^{-1}(x) = \log_8 x$

c) $x = \left(\frac{1}{3}\right)^y$ or $f^{-1}(x) = \log_{\left(\frac{1}{3}\right)}x$

d) $x = \left(\frac{1}{5}\right)^y$ or $f^{-1}(x) = \log_{\left(\frac{1}{5}\right)}x$

2. a) i) $x = 4^y$
    ii) $\log_4 x = y$
  b) i) $x = 8^y$
    ii) $\log_8 x = y$
  c) i) $x = \left(\frac{1}{3}\right)^y$
    ii) $\log_{\frac{1}{3}} x = y$
  d) i) $x = \left(\frac{1}{5}\right)^y$
    ii) $\log_{\frac{1}{5}} x = y$

3. All the graphs have the same basic shape, but the last two are reflected over the x-axis, compared with the first two. All the graphs have the same x-intercept, 1. All have the same vertical asymptote, $x = 0$.

4. Locate the point on the graph that has 8 as its x-coordinate. This point is $(8, 3)$. The y-coordinate of this point is the solution to $2^y = 8$, $y = 3$.

5. a) $x = 3^y$ **c)** $x = \left(\frac{1}{4}\right)^y$
  b) $x = 10^y$ **d)** $x = m^y$
6. a) $\log_3 x = y$ **c)** $\log_{\frac{1}{4}} x = y$
  b) $\log_{10} x = y$ **d)** $\log_m x = y$
7. a) $x = 5^y$ **c)** $x = 3^y$
  b) $x = 10^y$ **d)** $x = \frac{1}{4}^y$
8. a) $y = 5^x$ **c)** $y = 3^x$
  b) $y = 10^x$ **d)** $y = \frac{1}{4}^x$
9. a) 2   **d)** 0
  b) 3   **e)** -1
  c) 4   **f)** $\frac{1}{2}$
10. Since 3 is positive, no exponent for 3^x can produce -9.
11. a) $\left(\frac{1}{4}, -2\right), \left(\frac{1}{2}, -1\right)$, $(1, 0)$, $(2, 1)$, $(4, 2)$
  b) $\left(\frac{1}{100}, -2\right), \left(\frac{1}{10}, -1\right)$, $(1, 0)$, $(10, 1)$, $(100, 2)$

Lesson 8.2, pp. 457–458

1. a) vertical stretch by a factor of 3
  b) horizontal compression by a factor of $\frac{1}{2}$
  c) vertical translation 5 units down
  d) horizontal translation 4 units left

2. a) (a) $\left(\frac{1}{10}, -3\right)$, $(1, 0)$, $(10, 3)$
    (b) $\left(\frac{1}{20}, -1\right), \left(\frac{1}{2}, 0\right)$, $(5, 1)$
    (c) $\left(\frac{1}{10}, -6\right)$, $(1, -5)$, $(10, -4)$
    (d) $\left(-3\frac{9}{10}, -1\right)$, $(-3, 0)$, $(6, 1)$
  b) (a) $D = \{x \in \mathbf{R} \mid x > 0\}$,
       $R = \{y \in \mathbf{R}\}$
    (b) $D = \{x \in \mathbf{R} \mid x > 0\}$,
       $R = \{y \in \mathbf{R}\}$
    (c) $D = \{x \in \mathbf{R} \mid x > 0\}$,
       $R = \{y \in \mathbf{R}\}$
    (d) $D = \{x \in \mathbf{R} \mid x > -4\}$,
       $R = \{y \in \mathbf{R}\}$

3. a) $f(x) = 5\log_{10}x + 3$
  b) $f(x) = -\log_{10}(3x)$
  c) $f(x) = \log_{10}(x + 4) - 3$
  d) $f(x) = -\log_{10}(x - 4)$

4. i) a) reflection in the x-axis and a vertical stretch by a factor of 4; $c = 5$ resulting in a translation 5 units up
  b) $(1, 5), (10, 1)$
  c) vertical asymptote is $x = 0$
  d) $D = \{x \in \mathbf{R} \mid x > 0\}$,
    $R = \{y \in \mathbf{R}\}$
  ii) a) vertical compression by a factor of $\frac{1}{2}$; $d = 6$ resulting in a horizontal translation 6 units to the right; $c = 3$ resulting in a vertical translation 3 units up
  b) $(7, 3), \left(16, 3\frac{1}{2}\right)$
  c) vertical asymptote is $x = 6$
  d) $D = \{x \in \mathbf{R} \mid x > 6\}$,
    $R = \{y \in \mathbf{R}\}$
  iii) a) horizontal compression by a factor of $\frac{1}{3}$; $c = -4$ resulting in a vertical shift 4 units down
  b) $\left(\frac{1}{3}, -4\right), \left(3\frac{1}{3}, -3\right)$
  c) vertical asymptote is $x = 0$
  d) $D = \{x \in \mathbf{R} \mid x > 6\}$,
    $R = \{y \in \mathbf{R}\}$
  iv) a) vertical stretch by a factor of 2; $k = -2$ resulting in a horizontal compression by a factor of $\frac{1}{2}$ and a reflection in the y-axis; $d = -2$ resulting in a horizontal translation 2 units to the left.
  b) $\left(-2\frac{1}{2}, 0\right), (-7, 2)$

c) vertical asymptote is $x = -2$
d) $D = \{x \in \mathbf{R} \mid x < -2\}$,
   $R = \{y \in \mathbf{R}\}$
v) a) horizontal compression by a factor of $\frac{1}{2}$; $d = -2$ resulting in a horizontal translation 2 units to the left
  b) $\left(-1\frac{1}{2}, 0\right)$, $(3, 1)$
  c) vertical asymptote is $x = -2$
  d) $D = \{x \in \mathbf{R} \mid x > -2\}$,
    $R = \{y \in \mathbf{R}\}$
vi) a) reflection in the x-axis; $d = -2$, resulting in a horizontal translation 2 units to the right
  b) $(-3, 0)$, $(-12, 1)$
  c) vertical asymptote is $x = -2$
  d) $D = \{x \in \mathbf{R} \mid x < -2\}$,
    $R = \{y \in \mathbf{R}\}$
5. a) $D = \{x \in \mathbf{R} \mid x > 0\}$,
   $R = \{y \in \mathbf{R}\}$

  b) $D = \{x \in \mathbf{R} \mid x > -6\}$,
   $R = \{y \in \mathbf{R}\}$

  c) $D = \{x \in \mathbf{R} \mid x > 0\}$,
   $R = \{y \in \mathbf{R}\}$

d) $D = \{x \in \mathbf{R} \mid x > 0\}$,
$R = \{y \in \mathbf{R}\}$

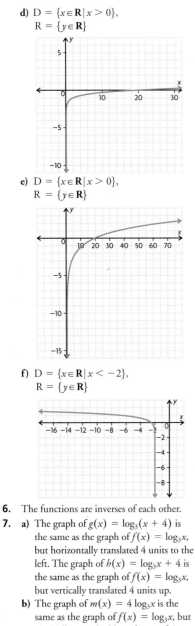

e) $D = \{x \in \mathbf{R} \mid x > 0\}$,
$R = \{y \in \mathbf{R}\}$

f) $D = \{x \in \mathbf{R} \mid x < -2\}$,
$R = \{y \in \mathbf{R}\}$

6. The functions are inverses of each other.

7. a) The graph of $g(x) = \log_3(x + 4)$ is the same as the graph of $f(x) = \log_3 x$, but horizontally translated 4 units to the left. The graph of $h(x) = \log_3 x + 4$ is the same as the graph of $f(x) = \log_3 x$, but vertically translated 4 units up.

b) The graph of $m(x) = 4\log_3 x$ is the same as the graph of $f(x) = \log_3 x$, but vertically stretched by a factor of 4. The graph of $n(x) = \log_3 4x$ is the same as the graph of $f(x) = \log_3 x$, but horizontally compressed by a factor of $\frac{1}{4}$.

8. a) $f(x) = -3\log_{10}\left(\frac{1}{2}x - 5\right) + 2$

b) $(30, -1)$

c) $D = \{x \in \mathbf{R} \mid x > 5\}$,
$R = \{y \in \mathbf{R}\}$

9. vertical compression by a factor of $\frac{1}{2}$, reflection in the x-axis, horizontal translation 5 units to the left

10. domain, range, and vertical asymptote

11.

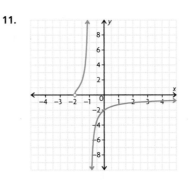

Lesson 8.3, pp. 466–468

1. a) $\log_4 16 = 2$ **d)** $\log_6 \frac{1}{36} = -2$

b) $\log_3 81 = 4$ **e)** $\log_{\frac{1}{3}} \frac{1}{27} = 3$

c) $\log_8 1 = 0$ **f)** $\log_8 2 = \frac{1}{3}$

2. a) $2^3 = 8$ **d)** $\left(\frac{1}{6}\right)^{-3} = 216$

b) $5^{-2} = \frac{1}{25}$ **e)** $6^{\frac{1}{2}} = \sqrt{6}$

c) $3^4 = 81$ **f)** $10^0 = 1$

3. a) 1   **d)** $\frac{1}{2}$

b) 0   **e)** 3

c) -2 **f)** $\frac{1}{3}$

4. a) -1 **d)** about 25

b) 0   **e)** 1.78

c) 6   **f)** 0.01

5. a) $\frac{1}{2}$ **d)** -2

b) 1   **e)** $\frac{1}{3}$

c) 7   **f)** $\frac{3}{2}$

6. a) 125   **d)** 16

b) 3   **e)** $\sqrt{5}$

c) -3 **f)** 8

7. a) about 2.58   **c)** about 4.29

b) about 3.26   **d)** about 4.52

8. a) about 2.50   **c)** about 4.88

b) about 2.65   **d)** about 2.83

9. a) 5   **d)** n

b) 25   **e)** b

c) $\frac{1}{16}$ **f)** 0

10. $\frac{4}{3}$

11. about 1.7 weeks or 12 days

12. a) $4.68\ g$ **b)** 522 years

13. $A{:}(0.0625) = 0.017$; $B{:}(1) = 0.159$; B has a steeper slope.

14. a) about 233 mph   **b)** 98 miles

15. $\log 365 = 2.562$

$\frac{3}{2}\log 150 - 0.7 = 2.564$

16. a) about 83 years

b) about 164 years

17. a) $y = 100(2)^{\frac{x}{0.32}}$

b)

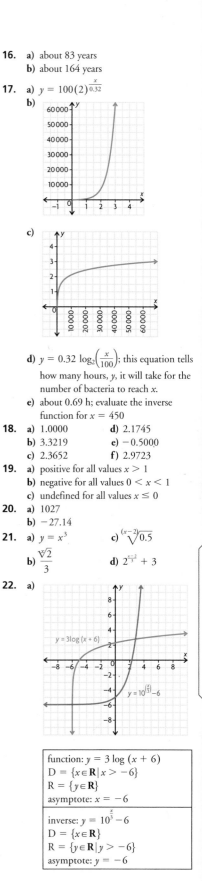

c)

d) $y = 0.32\log_2\left(\frac{x}{100}\right)$; this equation tells how many hours, y, it will take for the number of bacteria to reach x.

e) about 0.69 h; evaluate the inverse function for $x = 450$

18. a) 1.0000   **d)** 2.1745

b) 3.3219   **e)** -0.5000

c) 2.3652   **f)** 2.9723

19. a) positive for all values $x > 1$

b) negative for all values $0 < x < 1$

c) undefined for all values $x \le 0$

20. a) 1027

b) -27.14

21. a) $y = x^3$ **c)** $\sqrt[(x-2)]{0.5}$

b) $\frac{\sqrt[5]{2}}{3}$ **d)** $2^{\frac{x-2}{3}} + 3$

22. a)

$y = 3\log(x + 6)$
$y = 10^{\left(\frac{x}{3}\right)} - 6$

function: $y = 3\log(x + 6)$
$D = \{x \in \mathbf{R} \mid x > -6\}$
$R = \{y \in \mathbf{R}\}$
asymptote: $x = -6$

inverse: $y = 10^{\frac{x}{3}} - 6$
$D = \{x \in \mathbf{R}\}$
$R = \{y \in \mathbf{R} \mid y > -6\}$
asymptote: $y = -6$

b)

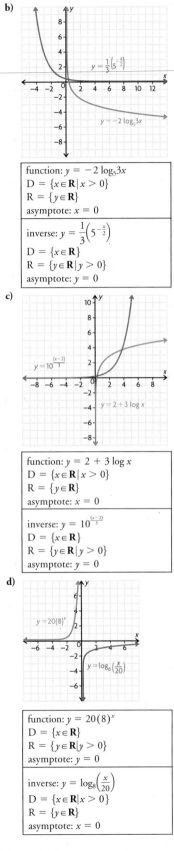

function: $y = -2 \log_5 3x$
$D = \{x \in \mathbf{R} \mid x > 0\}$
$R = \{y \in \mathbf{R}\}$
asymptote: $x = 0$

inverse: $y = \dfrac{1}{3}\left(5^{-\frac{x}{2}}\right)$

$D = \{x \in \mathbf{R}\}$
$R = \{y \in \mathbf{R} \mid y > 0\}$
asymptote: $y = 0$

c)

function: $y = 2 + 3 \log x$
$D = \{x \in \mathbf{R} \mid x > 0\}$
$R = \{y \in \mathbf{R}\}$
asymptote: $x = 0$

inverse: $y = 10^{\frac{(x-2)}{3}}$
$D = \{x \in \mathbf{R}\}$
$R = \{y \in \mathbf{R} \mid y > 0\}$
asymptote: $y = 0$

d)

function: $y = 20(8)^x$
$D = \{x \in \mathbf{R}\}$
$R = \{y \in \mathbf{R} \mid y > 0\}$
asymptote: $y = 0$

inverse: $y = \log_8\left(\dfrac{x}{20}\right)$
$D = \{x \in \mathbf{R} \mid x > 0\}$
$R = \{y \in \mathbf{R}\}$
asymptote: $x = 0$

e)

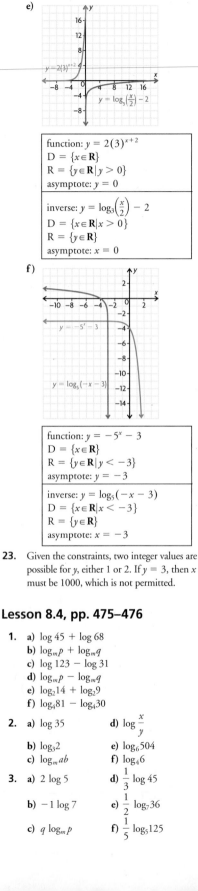

function: $y = 2(3)^{x+2}$
$D = \{x \in \mathbf{R}\}$
$R = \{y \in \mathbf{R} \mid y > 0\}$
asymptote: $y = 0$

inverse: $y = \log_3\left(\dfrac{x}{2}\right) - 2$
$D = \{x \in \mathbf{R} \mid x > 0\}$
$R = \{y \in \mathbf{R}\}$
asymptote: $x = 0$

f)

function: $y = -5^x - 3$
$D = \{x \in \mathbf{R}\}$
$R = \{y \in \mathbf{R} \mid y < -3\}$
asymptote: $y = -3$

inverse: $y = \log_5(-x - 3)$
$D = \{x \in \mathbf{R} \mid x < -3\}$
$R = \{y \in \mathbf{R}\}$
asymptote: $x = -3$

23. Given the constraints, two integer values are possible for y, either 1 or 2. If $y = 3$, then x must be 1000, which is not permitted.

Lesson 8.4, pp. 475–476

1.
a) $\log 45 + \log 68$
b) $\log_m p + \log_m q$
c) $\log 123 - \log 31$
d) $\log_m p - \log_m q$
e) $\log_2 14 + \log_2 9$
f) $\log_4 81 - \log_4 30$

2.
a) $\log 35$
b) $\log_3 2$
c) $\log_m ab$
d) $\log \dfrac{x}{y}$
e) $\log_6 504$
f) $\log_4 6$

3.
a) $2 \log 5$
b) $-1 \log 7$
c) $q \log_m p$
d) $\dfrac{1}{3} \log 45$
e) $\dfrac{1}{2} \log_7 36$
f) $\dfrac{1}{5} \log_5 125$

4.
a) $\log_3 27; 3$
b) $\log_5 25; 2$
c) $\log 100; 2$
d) $7 \log_4 4; 7$
e) $\log_2 32; 5$
f) $\dfrac{1}{2} \log 10; \dfrac{1}{2}$

5. $y = \log_2(4x) = \log_2 x + \log_2 4$
$= \log_2 x + 2$, so $y = \log_2(4x)$ vertically
shifts $y = \log_2 x$ up 2 units;
$y = \log_2(8x) = \log_2 x + \log_2 8$
$= \log_2 x + 3$, so $y = \log_2(4x)$ vertically
shifts $y = \log_2 x$ up 3 units;
$y = \log_2\left(\dfrac{x}{2}\right) = \log_2 x - \log_2 2$
$= \log_2 x - 1$, so $y = \log_2(4x)$ vertically
shifts $y = \log_2 x$ down 1 unit

6.
a) 1.5
b) 2
c) 1.5
d) -0.5
e) 4
f) 2

7.
a) $\log_b x + \log_b y + \log_b z$
b) $\log_b z - (\log_b x + \log_b y)$
c) $2 \log_b x + 3 \log_b y$
d) $\dfrac{1}{2}\left(5 \log_b x + \log_b y + 3 \log_b z\right)$

8. $\log_5 3$ means $5^x = 3$ and $\log_5 \dfrac{1}{3}$ means
$5^y = \dfrac{1}{3}$; since $\dfrac{1}{3} = 3^{-1}$, $5^y = 5^{x(-1)}$;
therefore $\log_5 3 + \log_5 \dfrac{1}{3} = x + x(-1) = 0$

9.
a) $\log_5 56$
b) $\log_3 2$
c) $\log_2 45$
d) $\log_3 4$
e) $\log_4(3\sqrt{2})$
f) $\log 16$

10.
a) $\log_2 x = \log_2 245; x = 245$
b) $\log x = \log 432; x = 432$
c) $\log_4 x = \log_7 5; x = 5$
d) $\log_7 x = \log_7 5; x = 5$
e) $\log_3 x = \log_3 4; x = 4$
f) $\log_5 x = \log_5 384; x = 384$

11.
a) $\log_2 xyz$
b) $\log_5 \dfrac{uw}{v}$
c) $\log_6 \dfrac{a}{bc}$
d) $\log_2 xy$
e) $\log_3 3x^2$
f) $\log_4 \dfrac{x^5}{v}$

12. $\log_a \dfrac{\sqrt{x}\sqrt{y}}{\sqrt[4]{z^3}}$

13. vertical stretch by a factor of 3, and vertical shift 3 units up

14. Answers may vary. For example,
$f(x) = 2 \log x - \log 12$
$g(x) = \log \dfrac{x^2}{12}$
$2 \log x - \log 12 = \log x^2 - \log 12$
$= \log \dfrac{x^2}{12}$

15. Answers may vary. For example, any number can be written as a power with a given base. The base of the logarithm is 3. Write each term in the quotient as a power of 3. The laws of logarithms make it possible to evaluate the expression by simplifying the quotient and noting the exponent.

16. $\log_x x^{m-1} + 1 = m - 1 + 1 = m$

17. $\log_b x \sqrt{x} = \log_b x + \log_b \sqrt{x}$

$\qquad = \log_b x + \dfrac{1}{2}\log_b x$

$\qquad = 0.3 + 0.3\left(\dfrac{1}{2}\right)$

$\qquad = 0.45$

18. The two functions have different domains. The first function has a domain of $x > 0$. The second function has a domain of all real numbers except 0, since x is squared.

19. Answers may vary; for example,
Product law
$\log_{10}10 + \log_{10}10 = 1 + 1$
$\qquad = 2$
$\qquad = \log_{10}100$
$\qquad = \log_{10}(10 \times 10)$

Quotient law
$\log_{10}10 - \log_{10}10 = 1 - 1$
$\qquad = 0$
$\qquad = \log_{10}1$
$\qquad = \log_{10}\left(\dfrac{10}{10}\right)$

Power law
$\log_{10}10^2 = \log_{10}100$
$\qquad = 2$
$\qquad = 2\log_{10}10$

Mid-Chapter Review, p. 479

1. a) $\log_5 y = x$ c) $\log x = y$
b) $\log_{\frac{1}{3}} y = x$ d) $\log_p m = q$
2. a) $3^y = x$ c) $10^k = m$
b) $10^y = x$ d) $s^t = r$
3. a) vertical stretch by a factor of 2, vertical translation 4 units down
b) reflection in the x-axis, horizontal compression by a factor of $\dfrac{1}{3}$
c) vertical compression by a factor of $\dfrac{1}{4}$, horizontal stretch by a factor of 4
d) horizontal compression by a factor of $\dfrac{1}{2}$, horizontal translation 2 units to the right
e) horizontal translation 5 units to the left, vertical translation 1 unit up
f) vertical stretch by a factor of 5, reflection in the y-axis, vertical translation 3 units down
4. a) $y = -4\log_3 x$
b) $y = \log_3(x + 3) + 1$
c) $y = \dfrac{2}{3}\log_3\left(\dfrac{1}{2}x\right)$
d) $y = 3\log_3[-(x - 1)]$
5. a) $(9, -8)$
b) $(6, 3)$
c) $\left(18, \dfrac{4}{3}\right)$
d) $(-8, 6)$
6. It is vertically stretched by a factor of 2 and vertically shifted up 2.

7. a) 4   c) 0
b) -2 d) -3
8. a) 0.602   c) 2.130
b) 1.653   d) 2.477
9. a) $x \doteq 4.392$ c) $x \doteq 2.543$
b) $x \doteq 2.959$ d) $x \doteq 2.450$
10. a) $\log 28$ c) $\log_3 \dfrac{22}{3}$
b) $\log 2.5$ d) $\log_p q^2$
11. a) 1   d) -3
b) 2   e) $\dfrac{2}{3}$
c) 2   f) 3.5
12. Compared with the graph of $y = \log x$, the graph of $y = \log x^3$ is vertically stretched by a factor of 3.
13. a) 4.82   d) 1.69
b) 1.35   e) 3.82
c) 0.80   f) 3.49

Lesson 8.5, pp. 485–486

1. a) 4   d) $\dfrac{13}{9}$
b) 1   e) $-\dfrac{1}{3}$
c) $\dfrac{11}{4}$ f) -1
2. a) 4.088   d) 4.092
b) 3.037   e) -0.431
c) 1   f) 5.695
3. a) 5   d) $\dfrac{3}{5}$
b) 3   e) -2
c) 1.5   f) $-\dfrac{1}{2}$
4. a) 4.68 h   c) 16 h
b) 12.68 h   d) 31.26 h
5. a) 1.75   d) -4
b) $\dfrac{2}{3}$ e) 2
c) -4.75 f) 2
6. a) 9.12 years
b) 13.5 years
c) 16.44 quarters or 4.1 years
d) 477.9 weeks or 9.2 years
7. 13 quarter hours or 3.25 h
8. a) 2.5   d) 3
b) 6   e) 1
c) 5   f) 0
9. a) Solve using logarithms. Both sides can be divided by 225, leaving only a term with a variable in the exponent on the left. This can be solved using logarithms.
b) Solve by factoring out a power of 3 and then simplifying. Logarithms may still be necessary in a situation like this, but the factoring must be done first because logarithms cannot be used on the equation in its current form.
10. a) 1.849   c) 3.606
b) 2.931   d) 5.734

11. a) $I_f = I_o(0.95)^t$, where I_f is the final intensity, I_o is the original intensity, and t is the thickness
b) 10 mm
12. 1; 0.631
13. $a^y = x$, so $\log a^y = \log x$; $y\log a = \log x$;
$y = \dfrac{\log x}{\log a}$
A graphing calculator does not allow logarithms of base 5 to be entered directly. However, $y = \log_5 x$ can be entered for graphing, as $y = \dfrac{\log x}{\log 5}$.
14. a) $x = 2.5$
b) $x = 5$ or $x = 4$
c) $x = -2.45$
15. Let $\log_a 2 = x$. Then $a^x = 2$. $(a^x)^3 = 2^3$, or $a^{3x} = 8$. Since $\log_a 2 = \log_b 8$, $\log_b 8 = x$. So $b^x = 8$. Since each equation is equal to 8, $a^{3x} = b^x$ and $a^3 = b$.
16. $x = -0.737$; $y = 0.279$
17. a) $x = -1.60$
b) $x = -4.86$
c) $x = -0.42$
18. ±1.82

Lesson 8.6, pp. 491–492

1. a) 25   d) 15
b) 81   e) 3
c) 8   f) $\sqrt{3}$
2. a) 5   d) 200.4
b) $\dfrac{1}{36}$ e) 5
c) 13   f) 20
3. 201.43
4. a) 9   d) 10 000
b) $\sqrt{5}$ e) -3
c) $\dfrac{25}{3}$ f) 4
5. a) $\dfrac{8}{3}$ d) 32
b) $\dfrac{10}{3}$ e) 3
c) $\dfrac{25}{6}$ f) 8.1
6. $x = 9$ or $x = -4$
Restrictions: $x > 5$ ($x - 5$ must be positive) so $x = 9$
7. a) $x = 6$ d) $x = 2.5$
b) $x = 3$ e) $x = 3$
c) $x = \dfrac{6}{5}$ f) $x = 16$
8. a) Use the rules of logarithms to obtain $\log_9 20 = \log_9 x$. Then, because both sides of the equation have the same base, $20 = x$.
b) Use the rules of logarithms to obtain $\log\dfrac{x}{2} = 3$. Then use the definition of a logarithm to obtain $10^3 = \dfrac{x}{2}$; $1000 = \dfrac{x}{2}$; $2000 = x$.

c) Use the rules of logarithms to obtain $\log x = \log 64$. Then, because both sides of the equation have the same base, $x = 64$.

9. a) 10^{-7}
b) $10^{-3.6}$

10. $x = 2.5$ or $x = 2$

11. a) $x = 0.80$ **c)** $x = 3.16$
b) $x = -6.91$ **d)** $x = 0.34$

12. $x = 4.83$

13. $\log_3(-8) = x$; $3^x = -8$; Raising positive 3 to any power produces a positive value. If $x \geq 1$, then $3^x \geq 3$. If $0 \leq x < 1$, then $1 \leq 3^x < 3$. If $x < 0$, then $0 < 3^x < 1$.

14. a) $x > 3$
b) If x is 3, we are trying to take the logarithm of 0. If x is less than 3, we are trying to take the logarithm of a negative number.

15. $\frac{1}{2}(\log x + \log y) = \frac{1}{2}\log xy = \log \sqrt{xy}$ so $\frac{x+y}{5} = \sqrt{xy}$ and $x + y = 5\sqrt{xy}$. Squaring both sides gives $(x + y)^2 = 25xy$. Expanding gives $x^2 + 2xy + y = 25xy$; therefore, $x + y = 23xy$.

16. $x = 3$ or $x = 2$

17. 1 and 16, 2 and 8, 4 and 4, 8 and 2, and 16 and 1

18. $x = 4$, $y = 4.58$

19. a) $x = 3$
b) $x = 16$

20. $x = -1.75$, $y = -2.25$

Lesson 8.7, pp. 499–501

1. First earthquake: $5.2 = \log x$; $10^{5.2} = 158\,489$
Second earthquake; $6 = \log x$; $10^6 = 1\,000\,000$
Second earthquake is 6.3 times stronger than the first.

2. 7.2

3. 60 dB

4. 7.9 times

5. a) 0.000 000 001
b) 0.000 000 251
c) 0.000 000 016
d) 0.000 000 000 000 1

6. a) 3.49
b) 3.52
c) 4.35
d) 2.30

7. a) 7
b) Tap water is more acidic than distilled water as it has a lower pH than distilled water (pH 7).

8. 7.98 times

9. a) $y = 5000(1.0642)^t$

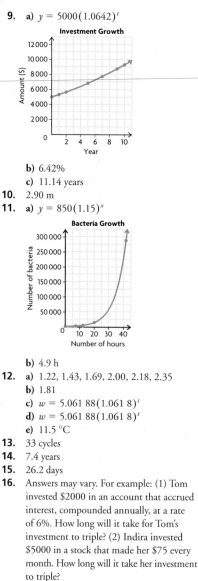

b) 6.42%
c) 11.14 years

10. 2.90 m

11. a) $y = 850(1.15)^x$

b) 4.9 h

12. a) 1.22, 1.43, 1.69, 2.00, 2.18, 2.35
b) 1.81
c) $w = 5.061\,88(1.061\,8)^t$
d) $w = 5.061\,88(1.061\,8)^t$
e) 11.5 °C

13. 33 cycles

14. 7.4 years

15. 26.2 days

16. Answers may vary. For example: (1) Tom invested $2000 in an account that accrued interest, compounded annually, at a rate of 6%. How long will it take for Tom's investment to triple? (2) Indira invested $5000 in a stock that made her $75 every month. How long will it take her investment to triple?
The first problem could be modelled using an exponential function. Solving this problem would require the use of logarithms. The second problem could be modelled using a linear equation. Solving the second problem would not require the use of logarithms.

17. 73 dB

18. a) $C = P(1.038)^t$
b) $580.80
c) $33.07

Lesson 8.8, pp. 507–508

1. a) -7.375
b) -23.25
c) -2

2. The instantaneous rate of decline was greatest in year 1. The negative change from year 1 to year 2 was 50, which is greater than the negative change in any other two-year period.

3. a) -12.378
b) -4.867
c) -1.914

4. a) $A(t) = 6000(1.075)^t$
b) 894.35
c) 461.25

5. a) i) 61.80
ii) 67.65
iii) 79.08
b) The rate of change is not constant because the value of the account each year is determined by adding a percent of the previous year's value.

6. a) 20.40 g
b) -0.111 g/h

7. a) 1.59 g/day
b) $y = 0.0017(1.7698)^x$, where x is the number of days after the egg is laid
c) i) 0.0095 g/day
ii) 0.917 g/day
iii) 88.25 g/day
d) 14.3 days

8. a) 3.81 years
b) 9.5%/year

9. a) $y = 12\,000(0.982)^t$
b) -181.7 people/year
c) -109 people/year

10. Both functions approach a horizontal asymptote. Each change in x yields a smaller and smaller change in y. Therefore, the instantaneous rate of change grows increasingly small, toward 0, as x increases.

11. a)

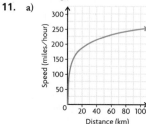

b) 1.03 miles/hour/hour
c) 4.03 miles/hour/hour and 0.403 miles/hour/hour
d) The rate at which the wind changes during shorter distances is much greater than the rate at which the wind changes at farther distances. As the distance increases, the rate of change approaches 0.

12. To calculate the instantaneous rate of change for a given point, use the exponential function to calculate the values of y that approach the given value of x. Do this for values on either side of the given value of x. Determine the average rate of change for these values of x and y. When the average rate of change has stabilized to a constant value, this is the instantaneous rate of change.

13. a) and **b)** Only a and k affect the instantaneous rate of change. Increases in the absolute value of either parameter tend to increase the instantaneous rate of change.

Chapter Review, pp. 510–511

1. a) $y = \log_4 x$ **c)** $y = \log_{\frac{1}{4}} x$
    b) $y = \log_a x$ **d)** $m = \log_p q$

2. a) vertical stretch by a factor of 3, reflection in the x-axis, horizontal compression by a factor of $\frac{1}{2}$
    b) horizontal translation 5 units to the right, vertical translation 2 units up
    c) vertical compression by a factor of $\frac{1}{2}$, horizontal compression by a factor of $\frac{1}{5}$
    d) horizontal stretch by a factor of 3, reflection in the y-axis, vertical shift 3 units down

3. a) $y = \dfrac{2}{5} \log x - 3$

    b) $y = -\log\left[\dfrac{1}{2}(x - 3)\right]$

    c) $y = 5 \log(-2x)$
    d) $y = \log(-x - 4) - 2$

4. Compared to $y = \log x$, $y = 3 \log(x - 1) + 2$ is vertically stretched by a factor of 3, horizontally translated 1 unit to the right, and vertically translated 2 units up.

5. a) 3   **c)** 0
    b) -2 **d)** -4

6. a) 3.615   **c)** 2.829
    b) -1.661 **d)** 2.690

7. a) $\log 55$ **c)** $\log_5 4$
    b) $\log 5$ **d)** $\log 128$

8. a) 1   **c)** $\dfrac{2}{3}$
    b) 2   **d)** 3

9. It is shifted 4 units up.

10. a) 5   **c)** -2
    b) 3.75   **d)** -0.2

11. a) 2.432   **c)** 2.553
    b) 3.237   **d)** 4.799

12. a) 0.79; 0.5
    b) -0.43

13. 5.45 days

14. a) 63   **c)** 9
    b) $\dfrac{10\,000}{3}$ **d)** 1.5

15. a) 1   **c)** 3
    b) 5   **d)** $\pm\sqrt{10\,001}$

16. 10^{-2} W/m^2
17. $10^{-3.8}$ W/m^2
18. 5 times

19. 3.9 times

20. $\dfrac{10^{4.7}}{10^{2.3}} = 251.2$

    $\dfrac{10^{12.5}}{10^{10.1}} = 251.2$

    The relative change in each case is the same. Each change produces a solution with concentration 251.2 times the orignial solution.

21. Yes; $y = 3(2.25^x)$
22. 17.8 years
23. a) 8671 people per year
    b) 7114; The rate of growth for the first 30 years is slower than the rate of growth for the entire period.
    c) $y = 134\,322(1.03^x)$, where x is the number of years after 1950
    d) i) 7171 people per year
      ii) 12 950 people per year

24. a) exponential; $y = 23(1.17^x)$, where x is the number of years since 1998
    b) 331 808
    c) Answers may vary. For example, I assumed that the rate of growth would be the same through 2015. This is not reasonable. As more people buy the players, there will be fewer people remaining to buy them, or newer technology may replace them.
    d) about 5300 DVD players per year
    e) about 4950 DVD players per year
    f) Answers may vary. For example, the prediction in part e) makes sense because the prediction is for a year covered by the data given. The prediction made in part b) does not make sense because the prediction is for a year that is beyond the data given, and conditions may change, making the model invalid.

Chapter Self-Test, p. 512

1. a) $x = 4^y$; $\log_4 x = y$
    b) $y = 6^x$; $\log_6 y = x$

2. a) horizontal compression by a factor of $\frac{1}{2}$, horizontal translation 4 units to the right, vertical translation 3 units up
    b) vertical compression by a factor of $\frac{1}{2}$, reflection in the x-axis, horizontal translation 5 units to the left, vertical translation 1 unit down

3. a) -2 **b)** 5
4. a) 2   **b)** 7
5. $\log_4 xy$
6. 7.85
7. a) 2   **b)** $1\frac{3}{4}$
8. a) 50 g
    b) $A(t) = 100(0.5)^{\frac{t}{5730}}$
    c) 1844 years
    d) -0.015 g/year
9. a) 6 min
    b) $97°$

Chapter 9

Getting Started, p. 516

1. a) $f(-1) = 30$,
      $f(4) = 0$
    b) $f(-1) = -2$,
      $f(4) = -5\frac{1}{3}$
    c) $f(-1)$ is undefined,
      $f(4) \doteq 1.81$
    d) $f(-1) = -20$,
      $f(4) = -0.625$

2. $D = \{x \in \mathbf{R} \mid x \neq 1\}$
    $R = \{y \in \mathbf{R} \mid y \neq 2\}$
    There is no minimum or maximum value; the function is never increasing; the function is decreasing from $(-\infty, 1)$ and $(1, \infty)$;
    the function approaches $-\infty$ as x approaches 1 from the left and ∞ as x approaches 1 from the right;
    vertical asymptote is $x = 1$;
    horizontal asymptote is $y = 2$

3. a) $y = 2|x - 3|$
    b) $y = -\cos(2x)$
    c) $y = \log_3(-x - 4) - 1$
    d) $y = -\dfrac{4}{x} - 5$

4. a) $x = -1, \frac{1}{2}$, and 4
    b) $x = -\dfrac{5}{3}$ or $x = 3$
    c) $x = 5$ or $x = -2$
      Cannot take the log of a negative number, so $x = 5$.
    d) $x = -\dfrac{3}{4}$
    e) $x = -3$
    f) $\sin x = \dfrac{3}{2}$ or $\sin x = -1$. Since $\sin x$ cannot be greater than 1, the first equation does not give a solution; $x = 270°$

5. a) $(-\infty, -4) \cup (2, 3)$
    b) $\left(-2, \dfrac{3}{2}\right) \cup [4, \infty)$

6. a) odd   **c)** even
    b) neither   **d)** neither

7. Polynomial, logarithmic, and exponential functions are continuous. Rational and trigonometric functions are sometimes continuous and sometimes not.

Lesson 9.1, p. 520

1. Answers may vary. For example, the graph of $y = \left(\left(\dfrac{1}{2}\right)^x\right)(2x)$ is

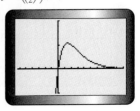

2. a) Answers may vary. For example,
$y = (2^x)(2x)$;

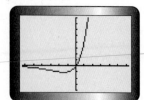

b) Answers may vary. For example,
$y = (2x)(\cos(2\pi x))$;

c) Answers may vary. For example,
$y = (2x)(\sin(2\pi x))$;

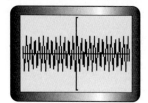

d) Answers may vary. For example,
$y = (\sin 2\pi x)(\cos 2\pi x)$;

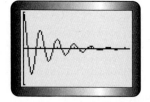

e) Answers may vary. For example,
$y = \left(\dfrac{1}{2}\right)^x (\cos 2\pi x)$,

where $0 \le x \le 2\pi$;

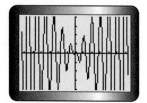

f) Answers may vary. For example,
$y = 2x \sin 2\pi x$, where $0 \le x \le 2\pi$;

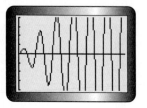

3. Answers will vary. For example,
$y = x^2$
$y = \log x$
The product will be $y = x^2 \log x$.

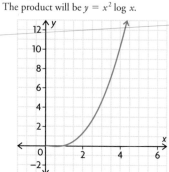

Lesson 9.2, pp. 528–530

1. a) $\{(-4, 6), (-2, 5), (1, 5), (4, 10)\}$
b) $\{(-4, 6), (-2, 5), (1, 5), (4, 10)\}$
c) $\{(-4, 2), (-2, 3), (1, 1), (4, 2)\}$
d) $\{(-4, -2), (-2, -3), (1, -1),$
$(4, -2)\}$
e) $\{(-4, 8), (-2, 8), (1, 6), (3, 10),$
$(4, 12)\}$
f) $\{(-4, 0), (-2, 0), (0, 0), (1, 0),$
$(2, 0), (4, 0)\}$
2. a) 10
b) 2; $(f + g)(x)$ is undefined at $x = 2$
because $g(x)$ is undefined at $x = 2$.
c) $\{x \in \mathbf{R} \mid x \ne 2\}$
3. $\{x \in \mathbf{R} \mid -1 \le x < 1\}$
4. Graph of $f + g$:

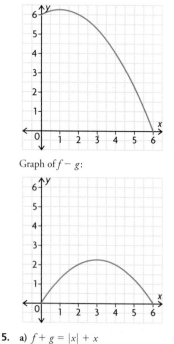

Graph of $f - g$:

5. a) $f + g = |x| + x$
b) The function is neither even nor odd.

6. a) $\{(-6, 7), (-3, 10)\}$
b) $\{(-6, 7), (-3, 10)\}$
c) $\{(-6, -5), (-3, 4)\}$
d) $\{(-6, 5), (-3, -4)\}$
e) $\{(-9, 0), (-8, 0), (-6, 0), (-3, 0),$
$(-1, 0), (0, 0)\}$
f) $\{(-7, 14), (-6, 12), (-5, 10),$
$(-4, 8), (-3, 6)\}$
7. a) $\dfrac{2(2x + 1)}{3x^2 - 2x - 8}$
b) $\left\{x \in \mathbf{R} \mid x \ne -\dfrac{4}{3} \text{ or } 2\right\}$
c) $\dfrac{17}{84}$
d) $-\dfrac{11}{84}$
8. The graph of $(f + g)(x)$:

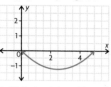

The graph of $(f - g)(x)$:

9. a) $f(x) + g(x) = 2^x + x^3$
The function is not symmetric.
The function is always increasing.
zero at $x = -0.8262$
no maximum or minimum
period: N/A
The domain is all real numbers. The
range is all real numbers.
$f(x) - g(x) = 2^x - x^3$
The function is not symmetric.
The function is always decreasing.
zero at $x = 1.3735$
no maximum or minimum
period: N/A
The domain is all real numbers. The
range is all real numbers.
b) $f(x) + g(x) = \cos(2\pi x) + x^4$
The function is symmetric across the
line $x = 0$.
The function is decreasing from $-\infty$ to
-0.4882 and 0 to 0.4882 and increasing
from -0.4882 to 0 and 0.4882 to ∞.
zeros at $x = -0.7092, -0.2506,$
$0.2506, 0.7092$

relative maximum at $x = 0$ and relative minimums at $x = -0.4882$ and $x = 0.4882$
period: N/A
The domain is all real numbers. The range is all real numbers greater than -0.1308.
$f(x) - g(x) = \cos{(2\pi x)} - x^4$
The function is symmetric across the line $x = 0$.
The function is increasing from $-\infty$ to -0.9180 and -0.5138 to 0 and 0.5138 to 0.9180; decreasing from -0.9180 to -0.5138 and 0 to 0.5138 and 0.9180 to ∞.
zeros at $x = -1, -0.8278, -0.2494, 0.2494, 0.8278, 1$
relative maxima at -0.9180, 0, and 0.9180; relative minima at -0.5138 and 0.5138
period: N/A
The domain is all real numbers. The range is all real numbers less than 1.
c) $f(x) + g(x) = \log(x) + 2x$
The function is not symmetric.
The function is increasing from 0 to ∞.
no zeros
no maximum or minimum
period: N/A
The domain is all real numbers greater than 0. The range is all real numbers.
$f(x) - g(x) = \log(x) - 2x$
The function is not symmetric.
The function is increasing from 0 to approximately 0.2 and decreasing from approximately 0.2 to ∞.
no zeros
maximum at $x \doteq 0.2$
period: N/A
The domain is all real numbers greater than 0. The range is all real numbers less than or equal to approximately -1.1.
d) $f(x) + g(x) = \sin{(2\pi x)} + 2\sin{(\pi x)}$
The function is symmetric about the origin.
The function is increasing from $-0.33 + 2k$ to $0.33 + 2k$ and decreasing from $0.33 + 2k$ to $1.67 + 2k$.
zero at k
minimum at $x = -0.33 + 2k$
maximum at $x = 0.33 + 2k$
period: 2
The domain is all real numbers. The range is all real numbers between -2.598 and 2.598.
$f(x) - g(x) = \sin{(2\pi x)} - 2\sin{(\pi x)}$
The function is symmetric about the origin, increasing from $0.67 + 2k$ to $1.33 + 2k$ and decreasing from

$-0.67 + 2k$ to $0.67 + 2k$
zero at k
minimum at $0.67 + 2k$ and maximum at $1.33 + 2k$
period: 2
The domain is all real numbers. The range is all real numbers between -2.598 to 2.598.
e) $f(x) + g(x) = \sin{(2\pi x)} + \frac{1}{x}$
The function is not symmetric.
The function is increasing and decreasing at irregular intervals.
The zeros are changing at irregular intervals.
The maximums and minimums are changing at irregular intervals.
period: N/A
The domain is all real numbers except 0.
The range is all real numbers.
$f(x) - g(x) = \sin{(2\pi x)} - \frac{1}{x}$
The function is not symmetric.
The function is increasing and decreasing at irregular intervals.
The zeros are changing at irregular intervals.
The maximums and minimums are changing at irregular intervals.
period: N/A
The domain is all real numbers except 0.
The range is all real numbers.
f) $f(x) + g(x) = \sqrt{x - 2} + \frac{1}{x - 2}$
The function is not symmetric.
The function is increasing from 3.5874 to ∞ and decreasing from 2 to 3.5874.
zeros: none
minimum at $x = 3.5874$
period: N/A
The domain is all real numbers greater than 2. The range is all real numbers greater than 1.8899.
$f(x) - g(x) = \sqrt{x - 2} - \frac{1}{x - 2}$
The function is not symmetric.
The function is increasing from 2 to ∞.
zero at $x = 3$
no maximum or minimum
period: N/A
The domain is all real numbers greater than 2. The range is all real numbers.
10. a) The sum of two even functions will be even because replacing x with $-x$ will still result in the original function.
b) The sum of two odd functions will be odd because replacing x with $-x$ will still result in the opposite of the original function.
c) The sum of an even and an odd function will result in neither an even nor an odd function because replacing x with $-x$ will not result in the same function or in the opposite of the function.

11. a) $R(t) = 5000 - 25t - 1000 \cos{\left(\frac{\pi}{6}t\right)}$; it is neither odd nor even; it is increasing during the first 6 months of each year and decreasing during the last 6 months of each year; it has one zero, which is the point at which the deer population has become extinct; it has a maximum value of 3850 and a minimum value of 0, so its range is $\{R(t) \in \mathbf{R} \mid 0 \le R(t) \le 3850\}$.
b) after about 167 months, or 13 years and 11 months
12. The stopping distance can be defined by the function $s(x) = 0.006x^2 + 0.21x$. If the vehicle is travelling at 90 km/h, the stopping distance is 67.5 m.
13. $f(x) = \sin{(\pi x)}; g(x) = \cos{(\pi x)}$
14. The function is neither even nor odd; it is not symmetrical with respect to the y-axis or with respect to the origin; it extends from the third quadrant to the first quadrant; it has a turning point between $-n$ and 0 and another turning point at 0; it has zeros at $-n$ and 0; it has no maximum or minimum values; it is increasing when $x \in (-\infty, -n)$ and when $x \in (0, \infty)$; when $x \in (-n, 0)$, it increases, has a turning point, and then decreases; its domain is $\{x \in \mathbf{R}\}$, and its range is $\{y \in \mathbf{R}\}$.
15. a) $f(x) = 0; g(x) = 0$
b) $f(x) = x^2; g(x) = x^2$
c) $f(x) = \frac{1}{x - 2}; g(x) = \frac{1}{x - 2} + 2$.
16. $m = 2, n = 3$

Lesson 9.3, pp. 537–539

1. a) $\{(0, -2), (1, -10), (2, 21), (3, 60)\}$
b) $\{(0, 12), (2, -20)\}$
c) $4x$
d) $2x^2$
e) $x^3 - 3x + 2$
f) $2^x\sqrt{x - 2}$
2. a) 1(c):

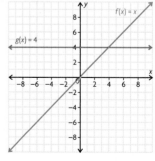

1(d):

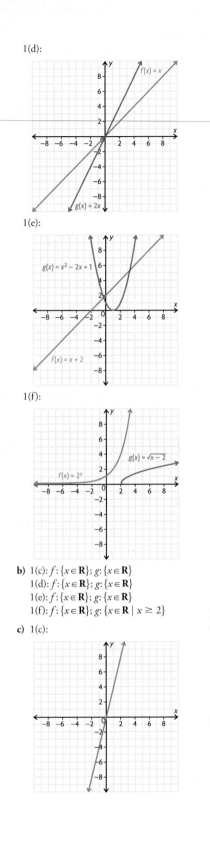

1(e):

1(f):

b) 1(c): $f: \{x \in \mathbf{R}\}$; $g: \{x \in \mathbf{R}\}$
1(d): $f: \{x \in \mathbf{R}\}$; $g: \{x \in \mathbf{R}\}$
1(e): $f: \{x \in \mathbf{R}\}$; $g: \{x \in \mathbf{R}\}$
1(f): $f: \{x \in \mathbf{R}\}$; $g: \{x \in \mathbf{R} \mid x \geq 2\}$

c) 1(c):

1(d):

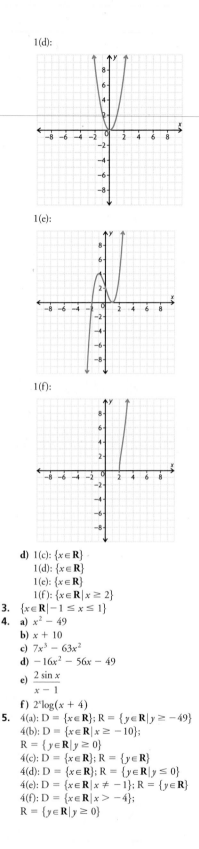

1(e):

1(f):

d) 1(c): $\{x \in \mathbf{R}\}$
1(d): $\{x \in \mathbf{R}\}$
1(e): $\{x \in \mathbf{R}\}$
1(f): $\{x \in \mathbf{R} \mid x \geq 2\}$

3. $\{x \in \mathbf{R} \mid -1 \leq x \leq 1\}$

4. **a)** $x^2 - 49$
b) $x + 10$
c) $7x^3 - 63x^2$
d) $-16x^2 - 56x - 49$
e) $\dfrac{2 \sin x}{x - 1}$
f) $2^x \log(x + 4)$

5. 4(a): $\mathrm{D} = \{x \in \mathbf{R}\}$; $\mathrm{R} = \{y \in \mathbf{R} \mid y \geq -49\}$
4(b): $\mathrm{D} = \{x \in \mathbf{R} \mid x \geq -10\}$;
$\mathrm{R} = \{y \in \mathbf{R} \mid y \geq 0\}$
4(c): $\mathrm{D} = \{x \in \mathbf{R}\}$; $\mathrm{R} = \{y \in \mathbf{R}\}$
4(d): $\mathrm{D} = \{x \in \mathbf{R}\}$; $\mathrm{R} = \{y \in \mathbf{R} \mid y \leq 0\}$
4(e): $\mathrm{D} = \{x \in \mathbf{R} \mid x \neq -1\}$; $\mathrm{R} = \{y \in \mathbf{R}\}$
4(f): $\mathrm{D} = \{x \in \mathbf{R} \mid x > -4\}$;
$\mathrm{R} = \{y \in \mathbf{R} \mid y \geq 0\}$

6. 4(a): The function is symmetric about the
line $x = 0$.
The function is increasing from 0 to ∞.
The function is decreasing from $-\infty$ to 0.
zeros at $x = -7, 7$
The minimum is at $x = 0$.
period: N/A
4(b): The function is not symmetric.
The function is increasing from -10 to ∞.
zero at $x = -10$
The minimum is at $x = -10$.
period: N/A
4(c): The function is not symmetric.
The function is increasing from $-\infty$ to 0
and from 6 to ∞.
zeros at $x = 0, 9$
The relative minimum is at $x = -6$. The
relative maximum is at $x = 0$.
period: N/A
4(d): The function is symmetric about the
line $x = -1.75$.
The function is increasing from $-\infty$ to
-1.75 and is decreasing from -1.75 to ∞.
zero at $x = -1.75$
The maximum is at $x = -1.75$.
period: N/A
4(e): The function is not symmetric.
The function is increasing from $-\infty$ to 0
and from 6 to ∞.
zeros at $x = 0, 9$
The relative minima are at $x = -4.5336$
and 4.4286. The relative maximum is at
$x = -1.1323$.
period: N/A
4(f): The function is not symmetric.
The function is increasing from -4 to ∞.
zeros: none
maximum/minimum: none
period: N/A

7.

8. **a)** $\left\{ x \in \mathbf{R} \,\middle|\, x \neq -2, 7, \dfrac{\pi}{2}, \text{ or } \dfrac{3\pi}{2} \right\}$
b) $\{x \in \mathbf{R} \mid x > 8\}$
c) $\{x \in \mathbf{R} \mid x \geq -81 \text{ and } x \neq 0, \pi, \text{ or } 2\pi\}$
d) $\{x \in \mathbf{R} \mid x \leq -1 \text{ or } x \geq 1,$
and $x \neq -3\}$

9. $(f \times p)(t)$ represents the total energy
consumption in a particular country at time t

10. **a)** $R(x) = (20\,000 - 750x)(25 + x)$ or
$R(x) = 500\,000 + 1250x - 750x^2$,
where x is the increase in the admission
fee in dollars

b) Yes, it's the product of the function $P(x) = 20\,000 - 750x$, which represents the number of daily visitors, and $F(x) = 25 + x$, which represents the admission fee.

c) $25.83

11. $m(t) = ((0.9)^t)(650 + 300t)$
The amount of contaminated material is at its greatest after about 7.3 s.

12. The statement is false. If $f(x)$ and $g(x)$ are odd functions, then their product will always be an even function. When you multiply a function that has an odd degree with another function that has an odd degree, you add the exponents, and when you add two odd numbers together, you get an even number.

13. $f(x) = 3x^2 + 2x + 5$ and $g(x) = 2x^2 - 4x - 2$

14. a) $(f \times g)(x) = \sqrt{-x}\,\log\,(x + 10)$
The domain is $\{x \in \mathbf{R} \mid -10 < x \leq 0\}$.

b) One strategy is to create a table of values for $f(x)$ and $g(x)$ and to multiply the corresponding y-values together. The resulting values could then be graphed. Another strategy is to graph $f(x)$ and $g(x)$ and to then create a graph for $(f \times g)(x)$ based on these two graphs. The first strategy is probably better than the second strategy, since the y-values for $f(x)$ and $g(x)$ will not be round numbers and will not be easily discernable from the graphs of $f(x)$ and $g(x)$.

c)

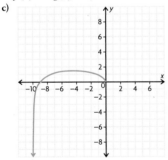

15. a) $f(x) \times \dfrac{1}{f(x)} = 1$

b) $\{x \in \mathbf{R} \mid x \neq -5 \text{ or } 5\}$

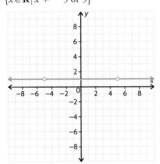

c) The range will always be 1. If f is of odd degree, there will always be at least one value that makes the product undefined and which is excluded from the domain. If f is of even degree, there may be no values that are excluded from the domain.

16. a) $f(x) = 2^x$
$g(x) = x^2 + 1$
$(f \times g)(x) = 2^x(x^2 + 1)$

b) $f(x) = x$
$g(x) = \sin\,(2\pi x)$
$(f \times g)(x) = x\sin\,(2\pi x)$

17. a) $f(x) = (2x + 9)$
$g(x) = (2x - 9)$

b) $f(x) = (2\,\sin x + 3)$
$g(x) = (4\,\sin^2 x - 6\,\sin x + 9)$

c) $f(x) = x^{\frac{1}{3}}$
$g(x) = (4x^5 - 3x^3 + 1)$

d) $f(x) = \dfrac{1}{2x + 1}$
$g(x) = 6x - 5$

Lesson 9.4, p. 542

1. a) $(f \div g)(x) = \dfrac{5}{x},\ x \neq 0$

b) $(f \div g)(x) = \dfrac{4x}{2x - 1},\ x \neq \dfrac{1}{2}$

c) $(f \div g)(x) = \dfrac{4x}{x^2 + 4}$

d) $(f \div g)(x) = \dfrac{(x + 2)\left(\sqrt{x - 2}\right)}{x - 2},\ x > 2$

e) $(f \div g)(x) = \dfrac{8}{1 + \left(\frac{1}{2}\right)^x}$

f) $(f \div g)(x) = \dfrac{x^2}{\log\,(x)},\ x > 0$

2. a) 1(a):

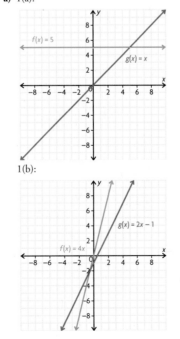

1(b):

1(c):

1(d):

1(e):

1(f):

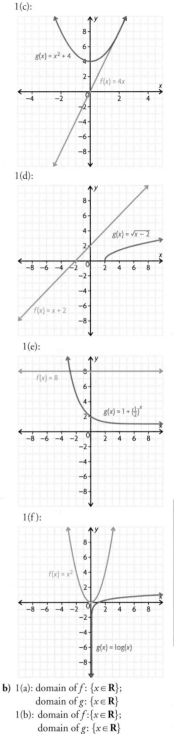

b) 1(a): domain of f: $\{x \in \mathbf{R}\}$;
domain of g: $\{x \in \mathbf{R}\}$
1(b): domain of f: $\{x \in \mathbf{R}\}$;
domain of g: $\{x \in \mathbf{R}\}$
1(c): domain of f: $\{x \in \mathbf{R}\}$;
domain of g: $\{x \in \mathbf{R}\}$
1(d): domain of f: $\{x \in \mathbf{R}\}$;
domain of g: $\{x \in \mathbf{R} \mid x \geq 2\}$
1(e): domain of f: $\{x \in \mathbf{R}\}$;
domain of g: $\{x \in \mathbf{R}\}$
1(f): domain of f: $\{x \in \mathbf{R}\}$;
domain of g: $\{x \in \mathbf{R} \mid x > 0\}$

c) 1(a):

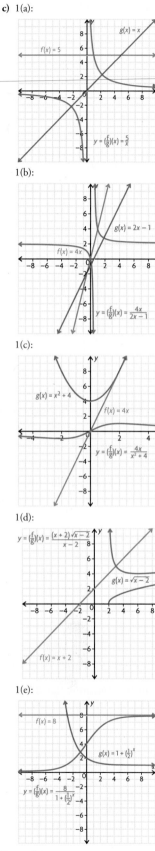

1(b):

1(c):

1(d):

1(e):

1(f):

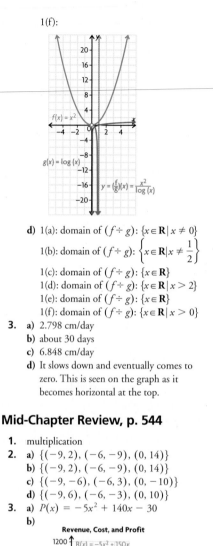

d) 1(a): domain of $(f \div g)$: $\{x \in \mathbf{R} \mid x \neq 0\}$

1(b): domain of $(f \div g)$: $\left\{x \in \mathbf{R} \mid x \neq \dfrac{1}{2}\right\}$

1(c): domain of $(f \div g)$: $\{x \in \mathbf{R}\}$

1(d): domain of $(f \div g)$: $\{x \in \mathbf{R} \mid x > 2\}$

1(e): domain of $(f \div g)$: $\{x \in \mathbf{R}\}$

1(f): domain of $(f \div g)$: $\{x \in \mathbf{R} \mid x > 0\}$

3. a) 2.798 cm/day

b) about 30 days

c) 6.848 cm/day

d) It slows down and eventually comes to zero. This is seen on the graph as it becomes horizontal at the top.

Mid-Chapter Review, p. 544

1. multiplication

2. a) $\{(-9, 2), (-6, -9), (0, 14)\}$

b) $\{(-9, 2), (-6, -9), (0, 14)\}$

c) $\{(-9, -6), (-6, 3), (0, -10)\}$

d) $\{(-9, 6), (-6, -3), (0, 10)\}$

3. a) $P(x) = -5x^2 + 140x - 30$

b)

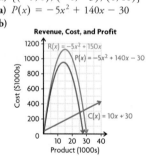

c) \$738 750

4. a) $R(h) = 24.39h$

b) $N(h) = 24.97h$

c) $W(h) = 24.78h$

d) $S(h) = 25.36h$

e) \$317

5. a) $(f \times g)(x) = x^2 + x + \dfrac{1}{4}$

$D = \{x \in \mathbf{R}\}$

b) $(f \times g)(x) = \sin(3x)(\sqrt{x - 10})$

$D = \{x \in \mathbf{R} \mid x \geq 10\}$

c) $(f \times g)(x) = \dfrac{22x^3}{x + 5}$

$D = \{x \in \mathbf{R} \mid x \neq -5\}$

d) $(f \times g)(x) = 8100x^2 - 1$

$D = \{x \in \mathbf{R}\}$

6. a) $R(h) = 90 \cos\left(\dfrac{\pi}{6}h\right) \sin\left(\dfrac{\pi}{6}h\right)$

$- 102 \sin\left(\dfrac{\pi}{6}h\right) - 210 \cos\left(\dfrac{\pi}{6}h\right) + 238$

b)

Average Revenue

c) about \$470.30

7. a) $(f \div g)(x) = \dfrac{80}{x}$

$D = \{x \in \mathbf{R} \mid x \neq 0\}$

b) $(f \div g)(x) = \dfrac{10x^2}{x^2 - 3}$

$D = \{x \in \mathbf{R} \mid x \neq \pm\sqrt{3}\}$

c) $(f \div g)(x) = \dfrac{x + 8}{\sqrt{x - 8}}$

$D = \{x \in \mathbf{R} \mid x > 8\}$

d) $(f \div g)(x) = \dfrac{7x^2}{\log x}$

$D = \{x \in \mathbf{R} \mid x > 0\}$

8. $\csc x, \sec x, \cot x$

Lesson 9.5, pp. 552–554

1. a) -1

b) -24

c) -129

d) $\dfrac{7}{16}$

e) 1

f) -8

2. a) 3

b) 5

c) 10

d) $(f \circ g)(0)$ is undefined.

e) 2

f) 4

3. a) 5

b) 5

c) 4

d) $(f \circ f)(2)$ is undefined.

4. a) $C(d(5)) = 36$

It costs \$36 to travel for 5 h.

b) $C(d(t))$ represents the relationship between the time driven and the cost of gasoline.

5. a) $f(g(x)) = 3x^2 - 6x + 3$
The domain is $\{x \in \mathbf{R}\}$.

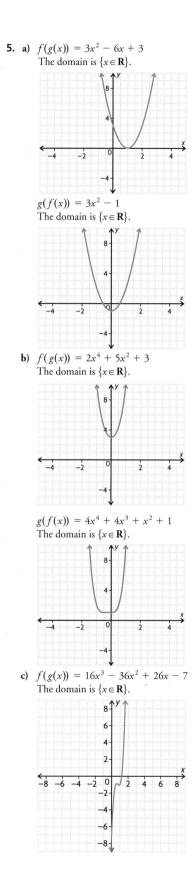

$g(f(x)) = 3x^2 - 1$
The domain is $\{x \in \mathbf{R}\}$.

b) $f(g(x)) = 2x^4 + 5x^2 + 3$
The domain is $\{x \in \mathbf{R}\}$.

$g(f(x)) = 4x^4 + 4x^3 + x^2 + 1$
The domain is $\{x \in \mathbf{R}\}$.

c) $f(g(x)) = 16x^3 - 36x^2 + 26x - 7$
The domain is $\{x \in \mathbf{R}\}$.

$g(f(x)) = 4x^3 - 6x^2 + 2x - 3$
The domain is $\{x \in \mathbf{R}\}$.

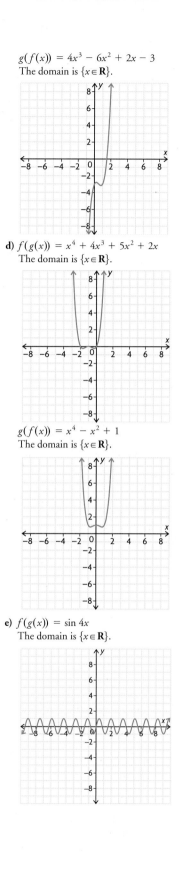

d) $f(g(x)) = x^4 + 4x^3 + 5x^2 + 2x$
The domain is $\{x \in \mathbf{R}\}$.

$g(f(x)) = x^4 - x^2 + 1$
The domain is $\{x \in \mathbf{R}\}$.

e) $f(g(x)) = \sin 4x$
The domain is $\{x \in \mathbf{R}\}$.

$g(f(x)) = 4 \sin x$
The domain is $\{x \in \mathbf{R}\}$.

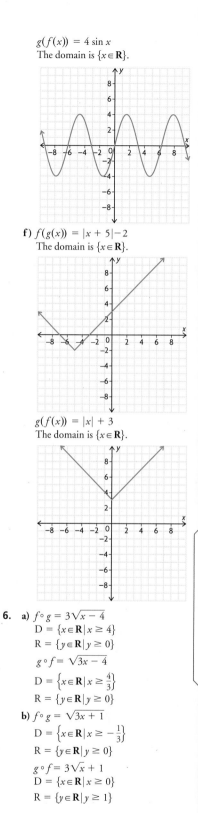

f) $f(g(x)) = |x + 5| - 2$
The domain is $\{x \in \mathbf{R}\}$.

$g(f(x)) = |x| + 3$
The domain is $\{x \in \mathbf{R}\}$.

6. a) $f \circ g = 3\sqrt{x - 4}$
$D = \{x \in \mathbf{R} \mid x \geq 4\}$
$R = \{y \in \mathbf{R} \mid y \geq 0\}$
$g \circ f = \sqrt{3x - 4}$
$D = \{x \in \mathbf{R} \mid x \geq \frac{4}{3}\}$
$R = \{y \in \mathbf{R} \mid y \geq 0\}$

b) $f \circ g = \sqrt{3x + 1}$
$D = \{x \in \mathbf{R} \mid x \geq -\frac{1}{3}\}$
$R = \{y \in \mathbf{R} \mid y \geq 0\}$
$g \circ f = 3\sqrt{x} + 1$
$D = \{x \in \mathbf{R} \mid x \geq 0\}$
$R = \{y \in \mathbf{R} \mid y \geq 1\}$

c) $f \circ g = \sqrt{4 - x^4}$
$D = \{x \in \mathbf{R} \mid -\sqrt{2} \le x \le \sqrt{2}\}$
$R = \{y \in \mathbf{R} \mid y \ge 0\}$
$g \circ f = 4 - x^2$
$D = \{x \in \mathbf{R} \mid -2 \le x \le 2\}$
$R = \{y \in \mathbf{R} \mid 0 < y < 2\}$

d) $f \circ g = 2\sqrt{x - 1}$
$D = \{x \in \mathbf{R} \mid x \ge 1\}$
$R = \{y \in \mathbf{R} \mid y \ge 1\}$
$g \circ f = \sqrt{2^x - 1}$
$D = \{x \in \mathbf{R} \mid x \ge 0\}$
$R = \{y \in \mathbf{R} \mid y \ge 0\}$

e) $f \circ g = x$
$D = \{x \in \mathbf{R} \mid x > 0\}$
$R = \{y \in \mathbf{R}\}$
$g \circ f = x$
$D = \{x \in \mathbf{R}\}$
$R = \{y \in \mathbf{R}\}$

f) $f \circ g = \sin(5^{2x} + 1)$
$D = \{x \in \mathbf{R}\}$
$R = \{y \in \mathbf{R} \mid -1 \le y \le 1\}$
$g \circ f = 5^{2 \sin x} + 1$
$D = \{x \in \mathbf{R}\}$
$R = \left\{y \in \mathbf{R} \mid \frac{26}{25} \le y \le 26\right\}$

7. a) Answers may vary. For example,
$f(x) = \sqrt{x}$ and $g(x) = x^2 + 6$
b) Answers may vary. For example,
$f(x) = x^6$ and $g(x) = 5x - 8$
c) Answers may vary. For example,
$f(x) = 2^x$ and $g(x) = 6x + 7$
d) Answers may vary. For example,
$f(x) = \frac{1}{x}$ and $g(x) = x^3 - 7x + 2$
e) Answers may vary. For example,
$f(x) = \sin^2 x$ and $g(x) = 10x + 5$
f) Answers may vary. For example,
$f(x) = \sqrt[3]{x}$ and $g(x) = (x + 4)^2$

8. a) $(f \circ g)(x) = 2x^2 - 1$
b)

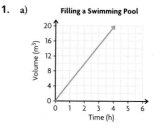

c) It is compressed by a factor of 2 and translated down 1 unit.

9. a) $f(g(x)) = 6x + 3$
The slope of $g(x)$ has been multiplied by 2, and the y-intercept of $g(x)$ has been vertically translated 1 unit up.
b) $g(f(x)) = 6x - 1$
The slope of $f(x)$ has been multiplied by 3.

10. $D(p) = 780 + 31.96p$
11. $f(g(x)) = 0.06x$
12. a) $d(s) = \sqrt{16 + s^2}$; $s(t) = 560t$
b) $d(s(t)) = \sqrt{16 + 313\,600t^2}$, where t is the time in hours and $d(s(t))$ is the distance in kilometres

13. $c(v(t)) = \left(\dfrac{40 + 3t + t^2}{500} - 0.1\right)^2 + 0.15$;
The car is running most economically 2 h into the trip.

14. Graph A(k); $f(x)$ is vertically compressed by a factor of 0.5 and reflected in the x-axis. Graph B(b); $f(x)$ is translated 3 units to the left.
Graph C(d); $f(x)$ is horizontally compressed by a factor of $\frac{1}{2}$.
Graph D(1); $f(x)$ is translated 4 units down. Graph E(g); $f(x)$ is translated 3 units up. Graph F(c); $f(x)$ is reflected in the y-axis.

15. Sum: $y = f + g$
$$f(x) = \frac{4}{x - 3}; g(x) = 1$$
Product: $y = f \times g$
$$f(x) = x - 3; g(x) = \frac{x + 1}{(x - 3)^2}$$
Quotient: $y = f \div g$
$$f(x) = 1 + x; g(x) = x - 3$$
Composition: $y = f \circ g$
$$f(x) = \frac{4}{x} + 1; g(x) = x - 3$$

16. a) $f(k) = 27k - 14$
b) $f(k) = 2\sqrt{9k - 16} - 5$

Lesson 9.6, pp. 560–562

1. a) i) $x = \dfrac{1}{2}, 2,$ or $\dfrac{7}{2}$
ii) $x = -1$ or 2
b) i) $\dfrac{1}{2} < x < 2$ or $x > \dfrac{7}{2}$
ii) $-1 < x < 2$
c) i) $x \le \dfrac{1}{2}; 2 \le x \le \dfrac{7}{2}$
ii) $x \le -1$ or $x \ge 2$
d) i) $\dfrac{1}{2} \le x \le 2$ or $x \ge \dfrac{7}{2}$
ii) $-1 \le x \le 2$

2. a) $x \doteq 0.8$
b) $x = 0$ and 3.5
c) $x \doteq -2.4$
d) $x \doteq 0.7$
3. $x = -1.3$ or 1.8
4. $f(x) < g(x)$: $1.3 < x < 1.6$
$f(x) = g(x)$: $x = 0$ or 1.3
$f(x) > g(x)$: $0 < x < 1.3$ or $1.6 < x < 3$

5. a) $x \doteq 2.5$
b) $x \doteq 2.2$
c) $x \doteq 1.8$
d) $x \doteq -2.1$
e) $x = 10$
f) $x = 1$ or 3

6. a) $x = -1.81$ or 0.48
b) $x = -1.38$ or 1.6
c) $x = -1.38$ or 1.30
d) $x = -0.8, 0,$ or 0.8
e) $x = 0.21$ or 0.74
f) $x = 0, 0.18, 0.38,$ or 1

7. $(0.7, -1.5)$
8. They will be about the same in 2012.
9. a) $x \in (-0.57, 1)$
b) $x \in [0, 0.58]$
c) $x \in (-\infty, 0)$
d) $x \in (0.17, 0.83)$
e) $x \in (0.35, 1.51)$
f) $x \in (0.1, 0.5)$

10. Answers may vary. For example,
$f(x) = x^3 + 5x^2 + 2x - 8$ and $g(x) = 0$.
11. Answers may vary. For example,
$f(x) = -x^2 + 25$ and $g(x) = -x + 5$.
12. $a \doteq 7, b \doteq 2$
13. Answers may vary. For example:

Perform the necessary algebraic operations to move all of the terms on the right side of the equation to the left side of the equation.

↓

Construct the function $f(x)$, such that $f(x)$ equals the left side of the equation.

↓

Graph the function $f(x)$.

↓

Determine the x-intercepts of the graph that fall within the interval provided, if applicable.

↓

The x-intercepts of the graph are the solutions to the equation.

14. $x = 0 \pm 2n$, $x = -0.67 \pm 2n$ or $x = 0.62 \pm 2n$, where $n \in$ I
15. $x \in (2n, 2n + 1)$, where $n \in$ I

Lesson 9.7, pp. 569–574

1. a)

Filling a Swimming Pool

b) $y = 6.25\pi\left(\dfrac{x}{4}\right)$

c) about 1.6 h

2. a) $y = \dfrac{6.25\pi}{64}(x-8)^2$

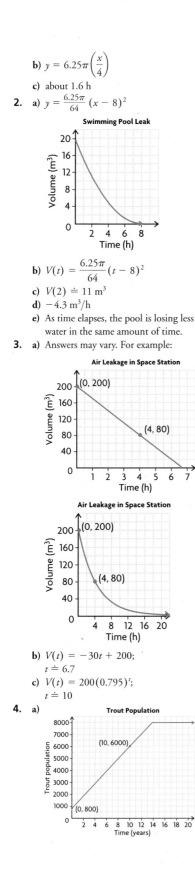

Swimming Pool Leak

b) $V(t) = \dfrac{6.25\pi}{64}(t-8)^2$

c) $V(2) \doteq 11 \text{ m}^3$

d) $-4.3 \text{ m}^3/\text{h}$

e) As time elapses, the pool is losing less water in the same amount of time.

3. a) Answers may vary. For example:

Air Leakage in Space Station

(0, 200)
(4, 80)

Air Leakage in Space Station

(0, 200)
(4, 80)

b) $V(t) = -30t + 200$; $t \doteq 6.7$

c) $V(t) = 200(0.795)^t$; $t \doteq 10$

4. a)

Trout Population

(10, 6000)
(0, 800)

b) $P(t) = \dfrac{8000}{1 + 9(0.719)^t}$

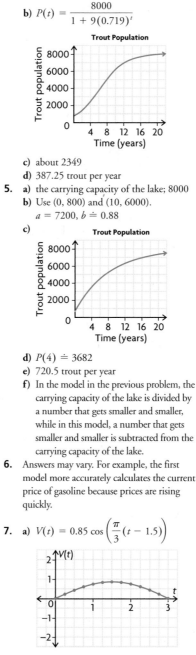

Trout Population

c) about 2349

d) 387.25 trout per year

5. a) the carrying capacity of the lake; 8000

b) Use (0, 800) and (10, 6000). $a = 7200$, $b \doteq 0.88$

c)

Trout Population

d) $P(4) \doteq 3682$

e) 720.5 trout per year

f) In the model in the previous problem, the carrying capacity of the lake is divided by a number that gets smaller and smaller, while in this model, a number that gets smaller and smaller is subtracted from the carrying capacity of the lake.

6. Answers may vary. For example, the first model more accurately calculates the current price of gasoline because prices are rising quickly.

7. a) $V(t) = 0.85\cos\left(\dfrac{\pi}{3}(t - 1.5)\right)$

$V(t)$ graph

b) The scatter plot and the graph are very close to being the same, but they are not exactly the same.

c) $V(6) = 0 \text{ L/s}$

d) From the graph, the rate of change appears to be at its smallest at $t = 1.5$ s.

e) It is the maximum of the function.

f) From the graph, the rate of change appears to be greatest at $t = 0$ s.

8. a)

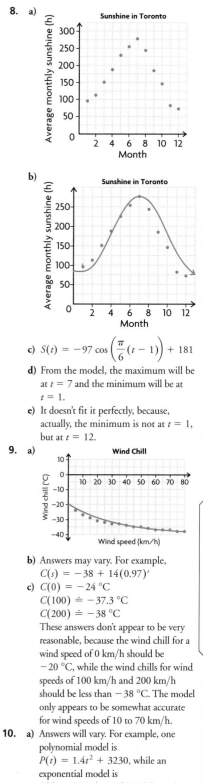

Sunshine in Toronto

b)

Sunshine in Toronto

c) $S(t) = -97\cos\left(\dfrac{\pi}{6}(t - 1)\right) + 181$

d) From the model, the maximum will be at $t = 7$ and the minimum will be at $t = 1$.

e) It doesn't fit it perfectly, because, actually, the minimum is not at $t = 1$, but at $t = 12$.

9. a)

Wind Chill

b) Answers may vary. For example, $C(s) = -38 + 14(0.97)^s$

c) $C(0) = -24\ ^\circ\text{C}$
$C(100) \doteq -37.3\ ^\circ\text{C}$
$C(200) \doteq -38\ ^\circ\text{C}$
These answers don't appear to be very reasonable, because the wind chill for a wind speed of 0 km/h should be $-20\ ^\circ\text{C}$, while the wind chills for wind speeds of 100 km/h and 200 km/h should be less than $-38\ ^\circ\text{C}$. The model only appears to be somewhat accurate for wind speeds of 10 to 70 km/h.

10. a) Answers will vary. For example, one polynomial model is $P(t) = 1.4t^2 + 3230$, while an exponential model is $P(t) = 3230(1.016)^t$. While neither model is perfect, it appears that the polynomial model fits the data better.

Answers

b) $P(155) = 1.4(155)^2 + 3230$
$\doteq 36\ 865$
$P(155) = 3230(1.016)^{155} \doteq 37\ 820$

c) A case could be made for either model. The polynomial model appears to fit the data better, but population growth is usually exponential.

d) According to the polynomial model, in 2000, the population was increasing at a rate of about 389 000 per year, while according to the exponential model, in 2000, the population was increasing at a rate of about 465 000 per year.

11. a) $P(t) = 3339.18(1.132\ 25)^t$
b) They were introduced around the year 1924.
c) rate of growth $\doteq$ 2641 rabbits per year
d) $P(65) \doteq 10\ 712\ 509.96$

12. a) $V(t) = 155.6 \sin\left(120\pi t + \frac{\pi}{2}\right)$
b) $V(t) = 155.6 \cos(120\pi t)$
c) The cosine function was easier to determine. The cosine function is at its maximum when the argument is 0, so no horizontal translation was necessary.

13. a) Answers will vary. For example, a linear model is $P(t) = -9t + 400$, a quadratic model is $P(t) = \frac{23}{90}(t - 30)^2 + 170$, and an exponential model is $P(t) = 400(0.972)^t$.

The exponential model fits the data far better than the other two models.

b) $P(t) = -9t + 400$
$P(60) = -140$ kPa
$P(t) = \frac{23}{90}(t - 30)^2 + 170$,
$P(60) = 400$ kPa
$P(t) = 400(0.972)^t$, $P(60) \doteq 73$ kPa

c) The exponential model gives the most realistic answer, because it fits the data the best. Also, the pressure must be less than 170 kPa, but it cannot be negative.

14. As a population procreates, the population becomes larger, and thus, more and more organisms exist that can procreate some more. In other words, the act of procreating enables even more procreating in the future.

15. a) linear, quadratic, or exponential
b) linear or quadratic
c) exponential

16. a) $T(n) = \frac{1}{6}n^3 + \frac{1}{2}n^2 + \frac{1}{3}n$
b) $47\ 850 = \frac{1}{6}n^3 + \frac{1}{2}n^2 + \frac{1}{3}n$
So, $n \doteq 64.975$. So, it is not a tetrahedral number because n must be an integer.

17. a) $P(t) = 30.75(1.008\ 418)^t$
b) In 2000, the growth rate of Canada was less than the growth rate of Ontario and Alberta.

Chapter Review, pp. 576–577

1. division
2. a) Shop 2
b) $S_{1+2} = t^3 + 1.6t^2 + 1200$
c) 1 473 600
d) The owner should close the first shop, because the sales are decreasing and will eventually reach zero.

3. a) $C(x) = 9.45x + 52\ 000$
b) $I(x) = 15.8x$
c) $P(x) = 6.35x - 52\ 000$

4. a) $12 \sin(7x)$
b) $9x^2$
c) $121x^2 - 49$
d) $2a^2 b^{3x}$

5. a) $C \times A = 42\ 750\ 000\ 000(1.01)^t + 3\ 000\ 000\ 000t(1.01)^t$
b)

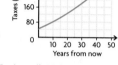

d) about \$156 402 200 032.31

6. a) $\dfrac{21}{x}$
b) $\dfrac{1}{2x + 9}$
c) $\dfrac{\sqrt{x + 15}}{x + 15}$
d) $\dfrac{x^3}{2 \log x}$

7. a) $\{x \in \mathbf{R} \mid x \neq 0\}$
b) $\left\{x \in \mathbf{R} \mid x \neq 4, x \neq -\dfrac{9}{2}\right\}$
c) $\{x \in \mathbf{R} \mid x > -15\}$
d) $\{x \in \mathbf{R} \mid x > 0\}$

8. a) Domain of $f(x)$: $\{x \in \mathbf{R} \mid x > -1\}$
Range of $f(x)$: $\{y \in \mathbf{R} \mid y > 0\}$
Domain of $g(x)$: $\{x \in \mathbf{R}\}$
Range of $g(x)$: $\{y \in \mathbf{R} \mid y \geq 3\}$
b) $f(g(x)) = \dfrac{1}{\sqrt{x^2 + 4}}$
c) $g(f(x)) = \dfrac{3x + 4}{x + 1}$
d) $f(g(0)) = \dfrac{1}{2}$
e) $g(f(0)) = 4$
f) For $f(g(x))$: $\{x \in \mathbf{R}\}$
For $g(f(x))$: $\{x \in \mathbf{R} \mid x > -1\}$

9. a) $x - 6$
b) $x - 9$
c) $x - 12$
d) $x - 3(1 + n)$

10. a) $A(r) = \pi r^2$
b) $r(C) = \dfrac{C}{2\pi}$
c) $A(r(C)) = \dfrac{C^2}{4\pi}$
d) $\dfrac{C^2}{4\pi} \doteq 1.03$ m

11. $f(x) < g(x)$: $-1.2 < x < 0$ or $x > 1.2$
$f(x) = g(x)$: $x = -1.2, 0,$ or 1.2
$f(x) > g(x)$: $x < -1.2$ or $0 < x < 1.2$

12. a) $x \doteq 4.0$
b) $x \doteq 2.0$
c) $x \doteq -0.8$
d) $x \doteq 0.7$

13. a) $P(t) = 600t - 1000$. The slope is the rate that the population is changing.
b) $P(t) = 617.6(1.26)^t$, 617.6 is the initial population and 1.26 represents the growth.

14. $P(t) = 2570.99(1.018)^t$

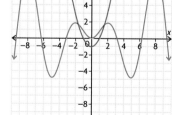

When $t = 13$, $P(t) = 3242$.
When $t = 23$, $P(t) = 3875$.
When $t = 90$, $P(t) = 12\ 806$.

Chapter Self-Test, p. 578

1. a) $A(r) = 4\pi r^2$
b) $r(V) = \sqrt[3]{\dfrac{3V}{4\pi}}$
c) $A(r(V)) = 4\pi\left(\dfrac{3V}{4\pi}\right)^{\frac{2}{3}}$
d) $4\pi\left(\dfrac{3(0.75)}{4\pi}\right)^{\frac{2}{3}} \doteq 4$ m^2

2.

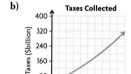

From the graph, the solution is $-1.62 \leq x \leq 1.62$.

3. Answers may vary. For example, $g(x) = x^7$ and $h(x) = 2x + 3$, $g(x) = (x + 3)^7$ and $h(x) = 2x$

4. a) $N(n) = 1n^3 + 8n^2 + 40n + 400$
b) $N(3) = 619$
5. $(f \times g)(x) = 30x^3 + 405x^2 + 714x - 4785$
6. a) There is a horizontal asymptote of $y = 275$ cm. This is the maximum height this species will reach.
b) when $t \doteq 21.2$ months
7. $x = 4.5$ or 4500 items
8.

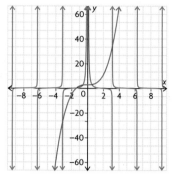

The solutions are $x = -3.1, -1.4, -0.6, 0.5$, or 3.2.

9. Division will turn it into a tangent function that is not sinusoidal.

Cumulative Review Chapters 7–9, pp. 580–583

1. (d)	**10.** (d)	**19.** (c)	**28.** (a)
2. (b)	**11.** (a)	**20.** (d)	**29.** (d)
3. (a)	**12.** (b)	**21.** (b)	**30.** (d)
4. (a)	**13.** (d)	**22.** (a)	**31.** (c)
5. (d)	**14.** (d)	**23.** (c)	**32.** (d)
6. (c)	**15.** (c)	**24.** (c)	**33.** (d)
7. (d)	**16.** (a)	**25.** (c)	**34.** (b)
8. (b)	**17.** (b)	**26.** (b)	
9. (c)	**18.** (b)	**27.** (a)	

35. $27°$ or $63°$
36. a) Answers may vary. For example,
Niagara: $P(x) = (414.8)(1.0044^x)$;
Waterloo: $P(x) = (418.3)(1.0117^x)$

b) Answers may vary. For example, Niagara: 159 years; Waterloo: 60 years
c) Answers may vary. For example, Waterloo is growing faster. In 2025, the instantaneous rate of change for the population in Waterloo is about 6800 people/year, compared to about 2000 people/year for Niagara.
37. $m(t) = 30\,000 - 100t$,

$$a(t) = \frac{T}{30\,000 - 100t} - 10,$$

$$v(t) = -\frac{\log\left(1 - \frac{t}{300}\right)}{\log 2.72} - gt;$$

at $t = 0$, $\frac{T}{30\,000} - 10$ must be greater than 0 m/s², so T must be greater than $300\,000$ kg $\times$ m/s² (or $300\,000$ N)

Index

Index

Index

Credits

This page constitutes an extension of the copyright page. We have made every effort to trace the ownership of all copyrighted material and to secure permission from copyright holders. In the event of any question arising as to the use of any material, we will be pleased to make the necessary corrections in future printings. Thanks are due to the following authors, publishers, and agents for permission to use the material indicated.

Chapter 1 Opener pages x–1: Matt Apps/Shutterstock; page 3: © iStockphoto/ Bill Grove; page 4: Jody Dingle/Shutterstock; page 63: Michael C. Gray/Shutterstock

Chapter 2 Opener pages 64–65: John Foxx/Stockbyte/Getty Images; page 67: Mark Atkins/Shutterstock; page 104: (top left) Hiroshi Ichikawa/Shutterstock, (middle left) © iStockphoto/Pali Rao, (middle right) © iStockphoto/TerrainScan

Chapter 3 Opener pages 120–121: Simon Tatham; page 144: Four Oaks/Shutterstock; page 187: Tiplyashin Anatoly/Shutterstock

Chapter 4 Opener pages 192–193: Philip Date/Shutterstock; page 195: © iStockphoto/ Jenni Morgan; page 196: Scott L. Williams/Shutterstock; page 200: Clara Natoli/ Shutterstock; page 219: Andy Lim/Shutterstock; page 223: © iStockphoto/Michal Rozanski; page 243: Chris Knights/Oxford Scientific/Jupiterimages

Chapter 5 Opener pages 244–245: Vankina/Shutterstock; page 247: © Tetra Images/ Corbis; page 278: Wave/First Light; page 311: Doug Strachan/Surrey School District

Chapter 6 Opener page 312: Joe Gough/Shutterstock, (inset) How Stuff Works; page 313: (top) Jiri Pavlik/Shutterstock, (middle) Dana Bartekoske/Shutterstock, (bottom) Dragan Trifunovic/Shutterstock; page 315: Lori Martin/Shutterstock; page 354: Taiga/Shutterstock; page 356: World Climate website; page 372: Tony Freeman/Photo Edit; page 379: World Climate website

Chapter 7 Opener page 384: (top) Armin Rose/Shutterstock, (bottom) Aaron Kohr/ Shutterstock; page 385: (top) Jerry Sharp/Shutterstock, (bottom) Maksym Gorpenyuk/ Shutterstock; page 387: Galina Barskaya/Shutterstock; page 422: Reproduced with the permission of the Canadian Hydrographic Service; page 429: With permission from Heriot-Watt University; page 442: (top) Danielle Phaneuf/Shutterstock, (bottom) Calculations are based on Hours of Daylight by Latitude found in MSN Encarta. Reprinted/modified with permission from Microsoft

Chapter 8 Opener pages 444–445: © Patrick Robert/Sygma/CORBIS; page 447: Khoroshunova Olga/Shutterstock; page 502: Hobbs, Frank and Nicole Stoops, U.S. Census Bureau, Census 2000 Special Reports, Series CENSR-4, Demographic Trends in the 20th Century, U.S. Government Printing Office, Washington, DC, 2002

Chapter 9 Opener pages 514–515: © iStockphoto/Jaimie D. Travis; page 517: © iStockphoto/Sergey Lavrentev; page 531: Mikael Damkier/Shutterstock; page 545: PhotoSky/Shutterstock; page 566: Source: Median Annual Price of Unleaded Gasoline in Toronto: 1981–2006, adapted from Statistics Canada CANSIM Database, Table 326-0009, V735062; page 572: Average Hours of Sunshine in Toronto, from Environment Canada Weather Office, © Her Majesty The Queen in Right of Canada, Environment Canada, (2007). Reproduced with the permission of the Minister of Public Works and Government Services Canada; Data figures calculated from the Wind Chill Calculator: Environment Canada, © Her Majesty The Queen in Right of Canada, Environment Canada, (2007). Reproduced with the permission of the Minister of Public Works and Government Services Canada; page 573: Source: Table: "Census of Population 1851–1861 to 2001–2006", adapted from the Statistics Canada website Population and growth components (1851–2001 Censuses) and Population and dwelling counts, for Canada, provinces and territories, 2006 and 2001 censuses—100% data

Chapters 7–9 Cumulative Review page 583: © Queen's Printer for Ontario, 2000. Reproduced with permission.

Appendix T pages 586–597: adapted with permission from Texas Instruments